TRUE MINT

MR. MINT'S PRICE & INVESTMENT GUIDE TO TRUE MINT BASEBALL CARDS

By
Alan "Mr. Mint" Rosen
with T.S. O'Connell

TRUE MINT

Published by

krause
publications

700 E. State Street • Iola, WI 54990-0001

Please call or write for our free catalog of sports publications. Our toll-free number to place an
order or obtain a free catalog is 800-258-0929 or please use our regular business telephone 715-445-
2214 for editorial comment and further information.

Library of Congress Catalog Number: 94-77496
ISBN: 0-87341-327-X
Printed in the United States of America

Table of Contents

Chapter 1

Mr. Mint - The Art of the (Baseball Card) Deal

When he walked into his first card show in Parsippany, N.J. in 1978, the man who would become the most famous baseball card dealer in the country didn't own a baseball card. As has happened to so many, the experience was a magical one.

There, on the dozen or so tables scattered around the room, were the color pasteboards of his youth, the stars of the game that loomed larger-than-life for many a youngster, and certainly no less so for Alan Rosen.

A fine Little League pitcher, he had appeared in the Little League World Series and on one heady day as a teen-ager had met, and posed for pictures with, virtually every member of one of the most famous teams in history. Though he could hardly know it at the time, it was a prophetic moment. Three decades later Alan Rosen, a.k.a. "Mr. Mint," would host the surviving members of the 1961 Yankees in a gala reunion/card show that would bring together names like Hector Lopez, Jim Coates, Yogi Berra and Mickey Mantle, hob-nobbing alongside Donald Trump, the ultimate deal maker, and Mr. Mint, the man who by then held a similar title in the world of baseball card collecting.

There was little in his background, save for that glorious moment in Williamsport, Pa., that would suggest that he would eventually so inextricably link his name to the National Pastime.

I got out of the Army in 1971, after being stationed in Italy. My first job was selling copy machines in New Jersey. That first job interview was quite unusual; the boss took his watch off and said, "Alan, I want you to sell me this watch."

So I went on and on, blabbing about the watch, and must have been good enough at it because I got the job. A couple of years later I was at the top of the division in sales, and they made me a supervisor. I was doing pretty well.

By 1974, I decided to try it on my own, which worked OK until 1977 when the plain paper copiers came along and I was sort of lost in the shuffle. I had gotten interested in antiques, buying and selling oak furniture and refinishing it part-time in the basement of my apartment in Hackensack, N.J. It was 1978, and I had the copy machine store and an antique store with my wife, Marnee, and my mother-in-law. And then I walked into that card show, and everything started to change.

I couldn't believe it, they were buying and selling my memories! I looked at a 1957 Topps Mantle and the resplendent 1959 Mantle card with its red background, and I was hooked. These were the cards that I remembered as a kid. People get hooked on baseball card collecting because it recaptures your past on cardboard. Here was an opportunity to go to a card show and relive your childhood through baseball cards.

My favorite card in the whole world is the 1953 Topps Mantle card, and I bought one at that first show, along with a 1978 Topps set. I quickly became a lunatic collector, and it wasn't long before a friend of mine gave me the nickname "Mr. Mint." Many people probably think that I got the name because I only buy and sell mint cards (which isn't necessarily true anyway), but I really got it when I was collecting and being pretty finicky about condition long before such a predilection would become in vogue.

There were plenty of mint cards available back then, and I would work all day at the copy machine business, then go out at night and buy baseball card collections. It was a natural evolution to become a dealer, as most serious collectors were often dealing in those days, if for no other reason than to enhance their own private collections.

And boy, did I ever enchance mine! Before I would sell even one card, I would bring them home and go through them, putting them in numerical order. Then, taking out my own personal collection, I would compare each card that I had bought with my own, card by card, for centering, corners, gloss, you name it. This was long before centering was much of an issue in the hobby.

But I was a lunatic collector in those days, I was a maniac. And that is how I got the name "Mr. Mint." Ian Donnis, a young collector whom I met early on at shows as I went around buying cards for my collection, noticed my preoccupation with finding mint specimens. He said, "Aw, you're always looking for mint cards...you're Mr. Mint." That's what he used to call me, and the name stuck and ultimately would become a vital factor in the promotion of my business.

I had been a coin collector, and virtually from the beginning of my card collecting I understood the importance of condition. I realized that when the time came to sell your cards, you get the most for your collection when it is in the best possible condition. That understanding served me well, when, in 1982, I decided to get out of the copy machine and antique businesses and become a full-time card dealer. That pristine collection that I had been working on for almost five years went on the selling block.

I sold my collection in the pages of Sports Collectors Digest. I had gem mint sets, from 1953 forward, and I got top dollar for the cards. Of course, top dollar in 1982 meant that I sold things like a gem mint 1956 Topps set, with both checklists, for $350. Today, you would likely need more than that just to get the two checklists.

Anyway, I took all the money and became a full-time dealer. I didn't forsee doing six million dollars in a year (that would come around 1990), but I did see a business where you could buy something for $500 and turn around and sell it for $800 and have people begging you to sell it to them.

A young Alan Rosen meets Mickey Mantle.

This was a splendid turn of events from my years selling copy machines, where I would go around knocking on doors and get them slammed in my face, 400 times a day. Such repeated rejection is unwelcome, to say the least, and now I was selling cards, which are so easy to sell that they just sell themselves.

Sometime in the mid-1980's, the personna of "Mr. Mint" achieved full-fledged, legendary status within the card collecting world, and often well beyond. He is easily the most recognizable figure in the hobby, having appeared on the front pages of almost three dozen major daily newspapers and from numerous forays into radio and television, including several appearances on Good Morning America and other network shows. When the hobby became trendy in the 80's, Mr. Mint was front and center, ready as much to help promote that new-found legitimacy as to capitalize on it.

More than any other individual in the hobby, he parlayed an intuitive sense for business with an almost shameless flair for self-promotion. What appears to have been largely a highly effective campaign to make his name a household word was often chided by contemporaries as self promotion for its own sake, ignoring the obvious reality that, as he grew ever more famous, his business grew right along with it. His fame expanded from the relatively narrow confines of the card collecting community; by the end of the decade he was something of a minor celebrity in his own right, recognized even outside the friendly cocoon of the card shows and conventions, and frequently pressed for autographs almost as eagerly as the baseball stars themselves.

Sports Illustrated and Sport Magazine both did substantial pieces that lovingly looked at baseball cards in general and Mr. Mint in particular, but perhaps nothing solidified his annointment as a mini-icon as much as his appearance in a couple of panels in a comic book a few years back. When Mr. Lodge's priceless baseball memorabilia turns up missing, Archie ventures to the Montvale, N.J. offices of "Mr. Mint" for help in tracing the merchandise.

Obviously a good move, because if the stuff was any good at all (and we all know Mr. Lodge would have nothing but the best) it would likely cross paths, sooner or later, with Alan Rosen.

Even before I sold my collection in 1982 and moved into dealing full-time, I had been buying advertisements in Sports Collectors Digest, often making outrageous, frequently nonsensical pronouncements, all designed to make my ad noticeable in an ocean of same that looked indistinguishable from one another. 'Sell me your cards or I'll jump out of a plane' or 'Sell me your cards or I'll shoot the dog,' that type of thing, and with each ad I would be pictured somewhere, ready to leap earthward from a speeding airplane, or menacing a terror-filled puppy with a sidearm.

Politically correct these were not, but I obviously never meant to offend anyone, though I apparently did on occasion. It all stemmed from a belief I had, apparently instinctive, since I never had any formal education beyond high school, that photo recognition is very important.

A guy walks into a show with his lifelong collection in tow and he sees me. 'That's the guy who advertised in *SCD*,' they say, and already I've got a leg up on the competition.

There are dealers who have advertised for decades, some of the most respected people in the entire hobby, but no one knows them.

Me, I pose for pictures with everyone; men, women, children, even dogs (see, I really was just kidding in that ad). People stop me in the street, they have stopped me on the freeway in Chicago, and they recognize me. That's a kick, I concede, but it's also good for business.

It was a calculated decision to pursue that, but I didn't know that it would work. I wanted to be recognized, I wanted to be set apart.

Most of the time, I just do things out of instinct. It's sort of like watching professional wrestling. The World Wrestling Federation is everywhere; good guys, bad guys, pro wrestling is very well promoted. And that's the way I like to promote myself.

I call attention to myself and my big finds and purchases because I want people to know that when they call me I actually do have the money to spend on their cards. Most dealers have money, but they don't have hundreds of thousands of dollars. I do. I spend at least $75,000 a week buying baseball cards. I turn them over quickly, and get my money back quickly, but I don't have any trepidation about spending that money.

But if I didn't put pictures in the *SCD* of people receiving money from Mr. Mint, no one would know about it. Why do I make up these crazy poems, and mix in all the hammy pictures? Because people read it, they turn to my ad because it's interesting, and most important, they remember it.

Bob Lemke, the vice president for sports at Krause Publications, which publishes *SCD, Sportscards Magazine* and a host of other magazines and books (including this one), always told me, 'Advertising doesn't cost, it pays.' And he's right.

Another key is that I continue to advertise. Other dealers run ads for a while, but I've been in there, every year, two or three pages and eight pages for my auctions. I average about $12,000 a month to *SCD*. When the bill comes in it's tough, and it hurts to pay it, but I can't stop, because I believe that that's the reason that I am here today.

The element of showmanship that I employ in my ads certainly comes into play as well at shows and conventions. At a show I make a big deal out of paying the customer. I take the hundred dollar bills and I lay them all over the table.

At the deal in Chicago for a cache of Wilson Franks cards in 1990, I had $20,000 in hundred dollar bills spread out over two tables. There must have been 50-75 people watching the whole thing with rapt attention. I was counting money as fast as I could, simply to make a show of it. Then I would count it again, this time very slowly, ostensibly to make sure that the amount is correct, but to me, it's showmanship.

But even with all the self-promotion and flair for the dramatic, I would still be in trouble without the basic understanding of how to buy and sell baseball cards. You can't do one without the other for very long, and it helps if you're good at doing both.

You can't retail everything that you buy. When I buy a collection with a wide variety of different components, I will sell specific things to other prominent dealers that I work with, and save others for my own retail customers or my auctions.

In 1989, I bought out Manny's Baseball Land, one of the most famous names in the collecting hobby pre-1981. A grand total of about 50,000 year-books. I kept some of the nicer publications for my auction and quickly wholesaled the rest.

And having those other dealers to work with is an important part of my success. It is impossible to overstate the importance of knowing where to place the goods once you have made a purchase, whether it be wholesale, retail or auctions.

Paul Lewicki, for one example, is amazing, which is why he goes with me on so many deals. He knows everything about 50's and 60's Topps and Bow-mans, and he doesn't have to look at a book. He knows what every card sells for, and, like me, he knows what his customers want and where he can move particular pieces.

Some dealers only want to buy certain things, and often only in pristine condition. When you're spending three or four million dollars a year, it's very difficult to wear two hats, to be both the buyer and the seller.

My retail outlet consists of an extensive list of collectors who I have known over the years, and I am constantly watching out for things on their lists, picking out the very best items.

When you buy a big collection, you've got old stuff, new stuff, autographs, statues, you name it; I have customers for all of that. I know in my head who buys what. When I make a purchase I label it in my head, knowing where it is going. I make very quick, snap decisions, but one of my strengths is that I can tell immediately whether or not it's a good collection.

But as my volume grew the need to quickly wholesale things grew with it, and my network of top-flight dealers is invaluable in that regard. One of the big differences is that for some of the dealers that I work with I will extend credit, and many other dealers, even the bigger ones, often can't afford to do that.

The secret is capitalization, the lack of same being the downfall of most of the defunct businesses in America. I can give some of those trusted dealers some time to pay, and that can make a world of difference in my ability to quickly move a large volume of material.

Of course, there are detractors to that philosophy. They say that I sell too cheap, but that gives me the ability to buy every day. I get a couple of dozen calls every day. I buy something for a buck (figuratively speaking), and sell it for a buck-forty. Another dealer might want to make three dollars on his buck, but, in many cases, before he gets his three dollars I have turned my money over several times and made much more.

If I can make 10 or 15 percent on my money I am content to do so. And that same view helps out when I am buying from a collector, because I can pay more because of my more modest expectations. I will buy a hoard or a collection and work on a smaller margin than another dealer, and that dif-ference can often be enough to determine who makes the initial purchase. I would rather spend $10,000 to make $1,000 than to let the deal get away and get nothing at all. That is especially true with really nice material; if it's great stuff I will work on 10 or 15 percent.

With the rare exception of the finds, I don't make more than 15-17 percent on most deals, and usually wind up around that figure for the year. I publish my tax returns in the pages of *SCD*, and I have never made more than 20 percent profit in any calendar year. That may sound like a very tight margin, but it is quite acceptable when your volume gets large enough.

When people call me about buying sets, I ask very pointed questions about them. Where did they buy them originally, and how long ago? Finding out that the cards came from someone like Bill Goodwin, or Larry Fritsch, or a number of other dealers who specialize in high grade material, can be a real thrill, because I immediately can picture the quality of the cards. People will also sometimes send me photographs and faxes, which can be a help be-cause it gives you an idea about the sets, but that would be about the extent of their usefulness.

I don't really think about how to dispose of a collection until I actually see it. We run four auctions a year, 200 lots each, so I need 800 near-mint or better lots every calendar year, and that can be tough to find sometimes. When I buy a major collection I will almost always take some items for the auction.

1953 Topps Mickey Mantle

Buying the cards from the public at shows is tricky as well, but I have a well-defined system, one that I seldom stray from. I never cheat people, I give them a fair price for their goods, and I don't give them a song and a dance. I just pay the price.

And I will take a shot on things from time to time, even though I don't buy new cards. So many dealers sit on their hands, waiting for someone to come to them to buy something or to sell something to them. And then they don't buy it unless they can steal it, and that slows down the wheels of business.

When somebody brings me a collection at a show, say a 1957 Topps set, for example, I will immediately put a retail price on it in my head. That's what I think I can reasonably get for the set at retail. I ask the customer to quote a price, and if I figure I can make 10 or 20 percent on their figure, I own it. I don't want to double or triple my money.

Naturally, having a good table location at card shows is important too, and I almost always have tables right up at the front of the room these days, but it wasn't always that way.

Early in 1983, I was doing Bruce Paynter's show in Chicago, and I walked in and introduced myself, 'Hi, I'm Mr. Mint, Alan Rosen.' He said that I should walk back until my nose hits the wall, that's your table, and he pointed to the back of the room.

I was really bummed out, because I thought I was a real big deal, since I had been advertising in *SCD* for a couple of years. Obviously, Mr. Paynter wasn't impressed.

But over the years as my reputation grew I asked promoters for better table locations. It's the same thing in the coin business, the guy in the back of the room has no shot at purchasing walk-in material. If I am in the front of the room and I have the first table, I have a big advantage..

I think I have earned the right to be there; I have gotten the hobby a lot of positive publicity. I also list my upcoming show calendar in my ads, and I think that can also help promoters with attendance. At the risk of sounding immodest, I think that when I list a show in my ads it probably brings in a few more table holders and customers than it might have otherwise.

I am also very loyal to specific promoters and shows. Many of these promoters take good care of me with a consistent, top table position and the rest, but I think they also appreciate my longevity and my loyalty. I am frequently pursued by other promoters to do what might be considered competing events, but I only do certain shows with promoters that I have known over the years.

I may be the most aggressive card dealer on earth, but I don't make it a habit to pursue collections. I have never done that. Other dealers will call some people contantly, but that's not my style. If you want to sell, fine. I pinpoint my advertising in Krause Publications; I don't find it effective to target the general public.

With tables at the front of the room for almost the last 10 years, I've had pretty good success. I can't recall ever losing anything major at a show, in terms of major material getting away. I've had some of the most prominent finds in the hobby in the past decade; two exceptions that wound up in someone else's hands that come to mind would be the Southern find of tobacco cards and the Canadian find of 1953 Topps.

Obviously, I've lost collections to other dealers at shows, but if it's something good, like a good find, a collector is going to have to give me his arm before I will let him walk away from my table. I don't let them walk away. I try my best to pay as much as I can, and I don't try to lowball anybody unless the stuff is in off condition or I simply don't want it.

With every collector who comes to my table at a show carrying a shoebox, or with almost every ring of the phone at my office in New Jersey, I am looking for that next call that describes a major find of interest to the hobby. Truth to tell, those calls haven't been coming too much in the last four years, but I remain an eternal optimist.

Oh, I still get major collections, the Mike Keasler Collection in my September 1994 auction would be a good example, but very few finds.

That has understandably put a strain on my business, because finds have historically been much more profitable, on a percentage basis and often in gross dollars, than simply acquiring someone's collection. I only make 10 percent on my auctions, and that is a major part of my total volume every year, perhaps greater than one-third.

Still, I remain hopeful that the next fellow coming slowly up to my table, or the next phone call, is going to be the big one. It keeps me going, keeps me alert. But most of the calls that I get now are false alarms.

Having said all that, I am still convinced that there is "find" type material out there, though perhaps not in the quantity and breathtaking magnitude of some of my earlier finds. That's one of the reasons why I give every interview that comes along, even when little kids come up to me with a microphone. I do a lot of school book reports and things; I talk to anyone.

Every single person who interviews me, I don't care if I am in the middle of a deal...the deal waits. The press comes first. Without press, we were nothing. When we started getting press about baseball cards, that's when the hobby took off. That's what we need again.

There have been a lot of negative articles lately, but we need positive articles. That's why I give every interview, not only for myself, but also for the hobby.

And maybe to help find that find.

What could I do that is more exciting than selling baseball cards for a living and rubbing elbows with most of the game's greatest players from decades past? I could pitch for the Yankees. Were that an option, we'd have known by now.

Most people have a job in life. There are not many people who, when they wake up in the morning, want to go to work. I am one of those people. I have never had a day in all the years I've been doing it that I said 'I am not going to work today.' I love the business.

Where else could a person of limited education make as much money, though I would stress that the income is not as compelling as the attendant fame. You walk into a show like the National last year in Chicago, and I signed 9,700 of those little wiffle balls. People ask to take your picture with their babies; it's an honor. It's an honor to be known as an expert in something.

I am a baseball card dealer. I don't keep any baseball cards. I like them. When I purchase a major find or a collection, say an autographed Ruth photo, that's pretty neat. I enjoy holding it and looking at it, then I take a picture of it and then I sell it.

I have a photo library of 25,000 to 30,000 photos; that's what I collect now. Looking at some of the major pieces and examining them for a while, that's a big kick, but 15 minutes after I look at it and enjoy it (and take a picture of it), I sell it, because it's a business.

I don't do anything else really well, but I do know how to buy and sell baseball cards better than anybody. I am very confident about that. I am doing this book because it's an honor to even have someone ask me to do a book. I am writing a book on baseball cards, and I want to write it even more than they want to publish it. It's just another step in the process of thinking that Alan Rosen is the main man about buying and selling older cards.

Maybe someday nobody will care about Mr. Mint, but for now, while they do, while that phone keeps ringing, I will keep going. Maybe the next call will be the big one.

Alan "Mr. Mint" Rosen

Chapter 2

If It Ain't (Mint),
It Ain't

**If you buy a perfect card, you
will never have to say you're
sorry the next morning.**

Alan Rosen

*There are baseball cards, and then there are baseball cards. A
true collector will embrace his cards and treasure them regardless of
condition, and that, of course, is laudable, and speaks to the highest
traditions of card collecting.*

*But even for the purest of hobbyists, the mint baseball card offers
a special attraction, and cynicism aside, it is an attraction that tran-
scends the mere acknowledgement that this tiny bit of cardboard is
worth a whole lot of money.*

*Certainly, that may be a factor for most, maybe even the biggest
factor, when a collector stares lovingly at a pristine example of, let's
say, a 1954 Topps Henry Aaron rookie card. But it says here that
money isn't the biggest reason that such cards draw our admiration
and delight.*

*No, if nostalgia is the fuel of the card collecting hobby, then mint
condition is a high octane additive, a boost, if you will, that shows
up from time to time to renew that original ardor and remind the collector what the hobby is all about.*

*For if we cherish our baseball cards because they allow us to re-
call, for a moment, our youth, then we celebrate the mint card because it truly manages to take us back in time.*

*Don't believe it? Look at a very good condition card from 1959, in
this case the Willie Mays card from the first series. With most of the
gloss gone from the card, and a heavily yellowed back, here then is
a card that shows what longtime collectors like to call "honest
wear."*

*The corners are worn, perhaps not actually rounded but clearly
showing the ravages of loads of attention from perhaps several*

youngsters, all of it loving but perhaps not all of it careful. A boy of nine may well have spread them out on the living room floor on Saturday afternoon, watching the game of the week with his father, while Dizzy Dean mangles the English language with his play by play. Ironically, a lesser light like Bobby Gene Smith might well wind up with a card in far better shape than Mays'. He is relegated to the bench at this home, while Mays plays every day, and his card is read and studied, and carefully examined in every detail. The result is that honest wear mentioned above. And that is not a bad thing.

But take that same Mays card, #50 from the 1959 Topps set, and put it in mint condition. And you will have, forgive the expression, a whole new ballgame. Here then is a card that not only recalls the days of your youth, but because of its incredible condition, figuratively takes you back in time. For when you hold a weathered and beaten 1959 Mays in your hand, you are constantly reminded that here is a 35-year-old card that, like all of us, shows the wear of almost four decades.

But a mint card comes to you in exactly the same shape as it did when it was printed. That, after all, is essentially the definition of mint. So when you hold a mint 1959 Mays in your hand, just for a fraction of a second, an indiscernible moment, it is 1959 once again.

And if that isn't enough of an attraction, there's always the money thing.

Most people in this business grade wrong. What does it mean, "mint?" It means new as manufactured. Maybe it is off-center, and maybe there are print lines, but it is still mint. What is needed is to understand the distinction between grading the card and describing it for sale purposes. There are factors, like off-centering and print dots, that exist but clearly fall within the description of "as manufactured."

People say that a severely off-center card can be graded no better than excellent. Nonsense. If you were blindfolded and I told you that I had in my hand an excellent 1952 Topps Mantle card, what would you envision? You might see slightly fuzzy corners, borders not pure white, perhaps a card that displayed a bit of honest wear. What you would not imagine is a gem mint, full gloss card with white borders and 80-20 centering.

Take the imaginary scenario one step further. You have just opened a mint pack of 1952 Topps high numbers, and the aforementioned Mantle card is among the bounty. All the cards in the pack except the Mantle are centered decently, but there's that 80-20 Mick. How can all the rest of the cards be mint, and the Mantle card from the same pack be excellent? They are all "as manufactured."

The answer is, of course, that the Mantle card is still mint, but it is off-center. It certainly will not command the same dollars as a similar-condition card with tolerable centering, but it is still mint. Our mythical card is clearly the same condition as the other cards in the pack, but it doesn't have the same characteristics as the others.

Another frequent mistake by both novices and even experienced collectors and dealers is either an overt or subconscious allowance for the age of the card. I had never actually seen a mint 1952 Mantle until my find. People would say when they saw a nice condition Mantle, "it's mint, for a 1952." And there's no such thing as that.

Age has nothing to do with condition. It doesn't matter if the card is 100 years old....mint means new as manufactured. There is no allowance for age. If it's mint, it's mint.....and if it ain't, it ain't.

And just as clearly, there is no allowance for how tough it might be to find specimens of the card at all, with the 1952 Topps high numbers an excellent example of that. That might make the card(s) scarce, but it does not permit any grading on a curve. That works for sixth period American History, but not in the hobby.

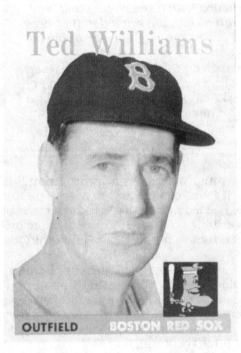

1958 Topps Ted Williams

People will make allowances in their heads for cards that they seldom, if ever, see in top grades, and that is understandable. But it doesn't make it accurate.

Do you know how many 1954 Aarons I've had where you would say, "Wow, look at this one!" Maybe one in 500, or one in 1,000. Look at the borders, and they are pure white. That's the way they came. Four sharp corners. Turn it over to the back, a bright green.

Mint is a special card, and I've always said it doesn't much matter what you pay for it now, because over the years it will always be worth more. That theory has never gone wrong in any case.

Okay, okay, maybe with the exception of the extraordinary high-end cards like the Wagner card that Wayne Gretzky and Bruce McNall bought several years ago at auction for $450,000. That card would only bring about $350,000 now.

But anything under $5,000, I have never seen a card go down. Certainly not the Hall of Famers. I know a dealer who has two gem mint Babe Ruth Goudeys; he has them marked at $20,000. It's only a $7,500 to $10,000 card, it's not a $20,000 card. So, I guess I should say that mint always sells as long as it's appropriately priced.

And even if they do go down slightly in a calendar year, if you've got a card that is mint and centered, someone will always pay more. There are always two or three guys who want that card.

Because of the relatively miniscule amount available, especially in the 50s and 60s, mint cards are sold within hours. It's amazing, they are always in demand. I vehemently disagree with price guides that show the price of older mint cards dropping; from 1968 and back I can get way in excess of guide for mint cards. In relation to any guide, there is no card in strict mint condition before 1975 that I would get less than book for.

Whatever sets I've had in strict mint, or matched sets or even presentation sets, I have always gotten 30-50 percent over the guide. And the buyers did not make a mistake, because there simply is not enough supply, in that condition, to meet the existing demand.

When you buy mint, when you buy quality, you can be assured that when it comes time to sell you will get the most for your card. Mint cards are liquid at whatever the number has to be. When it's perfect, we are not going to argue about the centering, gloss, etc. There's only one thing that we are going to argue about, and that's the price.

The best calls I get are when a collector says that he wants to sell his cards and that he bought them from me, or Paul Lewicki, or Bill Goodwin or some of the other top dealers. When they say they are mint, they are mint.

There is a special lure to mint cards. You show a guy a mint 1958 Mantle, or a 1955 Clemente, and he just stares at it, and a smile comes quickly to his face. He can't find anything wrong with it. The borders are white, it's perfectly centered, it's beautiful. There's no price that you can pay for something that stands so far above an ex-mt or vg card. Well, actually, there is a price, but it is often a hefty one, and you get the point.

The novice, and even experienced collector, often gets hurt by buying near-mint cards as mint. There is, now more than ever, a big difference between mint and near-mint.

1953 Bowman Stan Musial

Ex-mt used to be a very nice grade, but now you've got to sell that for 50 percent of the mint price, when it used to be 80 percent. That preoccupation with grading has helped raise the prices of older cards, and it becomes a self-perpetuating cycle, since people get even more picky about condition as prices increase.

The spread between very good and mint is huge now, but there comes a point when a collector will buy the off-condition card, paying 25 to 30 percent of the book price for ex-mt. And off-condition has become in vogue a bit because the price of mint condition has gotten so inaccessible to most hobbyists.

Given that, and the fact that finding mint condition cards can often be an iffy, frustrating prospect, is it even reasonable to suggest that collectors look for mint cards before 1970? Yup.

If they look hard enough and have patience, they will find them. Finding mint cards is difficult, but it is fun, and whether it is a complete set, a team set or a Mantle collection, you must be patient and not settle for lesser grades.

If you go to the best shows and follow the major dealers, the mint material is still available, but you have to go slowly. You can't work on just one set, because you will get antsy and discouraged. Many of the top collectors have want lists for several sets at any given time, so that if a particular show has nothing available from one year they can move to the next.

RANKING THE TOUGHEST SETS

Herewith a ranking of both Topps and Bowman major sets in terms of difficulty in finding mint cards to complete a set:

Topps - I hate to rank 1971, with the stark black borders that chip so easily and readily show even the slightest wear, as the toughest Topps set, but there it is. I have never owned one in strict mint condition. In a narrow sense 1952 Topps high numbers would be more difficult, but overall 1971 is atop the list, followed by 1952 and then 1953, because of the red and black panels at the bottom of the cards. Next would be 1962 with the wood grain borders and 1963 with the colored panels. After that would be 1958, a set where the paper seems to degenerate easily and is really tough to find in strict mint (over the years I have probably owned one or two sets that I would call 98 percent mint and two percent near-mint).

The remainder of the list would be, in order, 1954, 55, 56, 57, 59, 66, 67, 61 and 1960. The bottom half of the order would be 1964, 65, 69, 68, 70, 72, 75, 73 and 1974.

Bowman - The toughest Bowman set is easy; 1955, because of the brown borders. The next most difficult would be the 1953 color set, because of centering, followed by 1950 Bowman because of those pesky low numbers which are so hard to find in mint. After that, 1948, because of the color of the paper and despite the fact that it is not a large set and then 1949. I would probably put 1951 and 1952 in a tie, but I guess 1951 would be ahead of it because of the tendency to have print lines in the high number series. The easiest Bowman set, by far, to find in mint condition would be 1954.

For those left holding the cards, so to speak, the last 15 years or so have been radiant times. Of the prices of vintage cards from post-World War II, virtually all the price maturity came within that decade and one half. The 1980s were good times for a lot of people and a variety of businesses, but few experienced the kind of phenomenal growth that this hobby enjoyed. Folks from Wall Street to Main Street were touting baseball cards as an investment, and if they managed to do so only with a snicker and perhaps toungue-in-cheek in 1981, by 1991 nobody was laughing.

Collector's Notebook

RANKING OF TOPPS AND BOWMAN SETS FOR DIFFICULTY IN FINDING MINT CARDS TO COMPLETE A SET

TOPPS

1.	1971	13.	1967
2.	1952	14.	1961
3.	1953	15.	1960
4.	1962	16.	1964
5.	1963	17.	1965
6.	1958	18.	1969
7.	1954	19.	1968
8.	1955	20.	1970
9.	1956	21.	1972
10.	1957	22.	1975
11.	1959	23.	1973
12.	1966	24.	1974

BOWMAN

1.	1955	5.	1949
2.	1953	6.	1951
3.	1950	7.	1952
4.	1948	8.	1954

There is nothing on the face of the earth from 1952 that is worth more now, relative to what it was worth then, than baseball cards. Nothing.

That case of 1952 Topps from my find cost $26 in 1952. It's worth, in today's market, maybe $4.5 million. And there is nothing else that you could have purchased for $26 in 1952 that would be worth that much today. A 1969 Topps Super set was $20 that year. There is nothing else that you could have bought for $20 in 1969 that is worth $5,000 today. Baseball cards are it. And mint cards are at the head of the line.

But even having said that, I must dispel one more common misconception. A lot of people think that I only buy mint cards, but that's a fallacy. I buy all kinds of cards. I buy cards with bullet holes in them. Anything that I can make a living on. Remember, probably less than one percent of the cards out there are mint, and most of the cards from the '50s and '60s are very good to excellent.

A collector will come to me with an excellent to mint 1966 Topps set and say, "Gee, I didn't know that you bought anything except mint condition cards." Well, if I had to exist on mint cards, I would be broke and washing pots and pans at the Thorson House. But mint is still it. Mint is king.

Can I keep my nickname?

1955 Bowman Mickey Mantle

****

Chapter 3

Buyer Beware

Buying mint baseball cards is sort of like playing in a high-stakes poker game. Most importantly, the risk is substantial, but the potential payoff just as impressive. Having a well-defined and strictly-adhered-to game plan also helps.

And just like in a game of five-card stud in a smoke-filled room; the fellow with the most knowledge and understanding of the game wins more often than he loses. But even he must be wary of those fellows who might deal from the bottom of the deck or slip an extra ace up his sleeve.

That's pretty good advice for card collectors, too.

COUNTERFEITS

I bought a 1954 Topps set in Boston which was near-mint to mint. I paid $5,250 for it, but never took the cards out of the sleeves or the major stars from the holders. I quickly broke it up, sold some of the stars, then the commons to a dealer, and I am left with five or six of the key cards.

At which time I took the Aaron rookie out of its holder and said to myself, "Gee, it feels kind of funny." It's about half the thickness of a genuine Topps card, and I looked at the edge and it had three layers, like an Oreo cookie. That turned out to be a painful and expensive lesson.

Obviously, you must take the cards out of the holders to look at them.

There is an East Coast dealer who has taken to photocopying cards, and then, with a cereal box-type of cardboard, pastes the card front and back to it. That produces the Oreo effect. If you look at a real card either with the naked eye or under magnification, there is nothing but one cardboard piece on the edge. It can also help to compare the thickness with another card that you know to be genuine.

Another thing to watch for is the size, since copy machines don't always reproduce at exactly the same size as the original. The difference can be quite slight, but still perceptible, and examining specific words or letters on the card can be a help.

There are counterfeits in the 1951 Bowmans (Mantle, Mays and Williams), 1952 Bowmans (Mays and Mantle), 1953 Mantle and the Fleer #68 "Ted Signs" card, to name just a few. The *SCD* guide to counterfeit cards is a must. If you are going to buy modern cards, you must have that book.

(Editor's note: the *Sports Collectors Digest* Sportscard Counterfeit Detector book lists over 170 cards, with illustrations, that have been counterfeited, most of those from cards after 1969.)

Counterfeiting in the newer cards is a greater problem. Were someone to surface with several hundred (or, for that matter, a dozen) 1953 Topps Mantles in uniform mint condition, people would be suspicious. Actually, that's probably an understatement considering the card in question, but you get the idea. It is more reasonable to expect that anyone passing quantities of expensive cards would stick to the later issues.

I've seen very little counterfeiting in the years from 1948 to 1975. Like virtually any aspect of acquiring expensive cards, you need to know who you are dealing with, use common sense, and read this book. And my first book, Mr. Mint's Guide to Investing in Baseball Cards.

Not bad, plugging three books in two paragraphs.

TRIMMING

Trimming is one of the things that has been going on for a long time. It is the easiest way without going through a lot of restoration to improve the condition of a card. This is especially significant because of the huge dollar difference between an excellent card and a mint card, a gap that has grown considerably in the last decade.

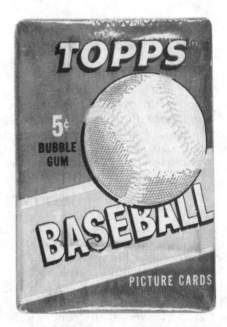

1955 Topps unopened pack

One pull of a lever on a paper cutter and you can turn an excellent card into a mint card just by improving the borders and sharpening the corners. It is worth somebody's time to slice off 1/16 of an inch top and bottom from a 1957 Mantle; instantly a $700 card jumps to $1,200 or more. Still, it should be relatively easy to detect, and these days people are very aware about trimmed cards. There are still a lot of trimmed cards out there, so vigilance is absolutely essential. I would never buy a set of cards without measuring the major stars.

I know of three dealers where virtually every single card in their cases had four sharp corners and blazing whiteness (presumably from bleaching), but most of those cards have been sold off and it isn't as much of an issue now.

In a related vein, you hear a lot of mumbling in the hobby about "tolerance," which is nothing more than suggesting some leeway is allowed in card size to account for factory cutting. That's another fallacy. I hate that word tolerance. If it ain't, it ain't. And if it doesn't measure, it ain't.

Now in my 1955 Bowman find there were many cards cut either long or short from the factory, and that's cool when you are there to see the cards come from an uncirculated source and you can attest to the fact that it was the factory, and not your Uncle Ned, that made those cards shorter than they are supposed to be.

But what about after you leave and you sell those cards? The next guy can tell the same story, but with every generation removed from the original owner the tale loses some of its impact.

My advice is that a Topps card should measure 2 1/2 X 3 1/2 inches. If you want to buy a card, any card, if you measure it with a ruler or another card, it has to measure up. If you don't have a ruler, find a common card, even a poor condition common card, from the same year and compare them. It's useful to talk about using a common in rough shape, because the mere description suggests that this is a card that has not been tampered with.

Remember, if you buy that card that is shorter than it is supposed to be you are stuck with it. If you want to sell it to me, I will measure it.

BLEACHING

White borders. Until the advent of the glitzy modern card, with its full-bleed photography and all the attendant hoopla, the white border was a mainstay of most baseball cards. Given the ravages of time, that whiteness would deteriorate, and the extent of the decline was dependent on a number of factors like handling, exposure to sunlight and the quality of the card stock itself.

But few things catch a collectors eye like a nice bright white border, and when it is found in an issue that collectors normally see with gray or even yellow borders, the attraction can be enormous.

Given that, it was inevitable that there would be some chicanery. In recent years a lot of guys were bleaching the Goudeys and Cracker Jacks. I looked at some cards on dealers' tables and the Cracker Jacks were whiter than my new underwear. It's stupid. A piece of paper can't stay white for 80 years. They are not supposed to be white; they should be an off-white. It (bleaching) fooled collectors a couple of years back, but now not that many people are bleaching cards. Hey, you can tell, you can even smell the bleach on the card!

The bleaching doesn't work with the Topps cards because they are coated. You can whiten it slightly with an eraser, but it takes the gloss off. There are guys with Topps cards from 1954 through 1957 with the white borders, and they will take a small eraser and just shave off a little tip of the corner, just a layer of the cardboard. It's white under there, so the card looks nicer. This can be easily spotted with a magnifying glass.....you check the corners and you can see that part of the card is missing.

It seems so simple and obvious, but there is much to be said for taking great care, and your time, while evaluating cards that you are going to purchase. Take it out of the holder; no one can be expected to buy an expensive card while it is slabbed in plastic. Make sure the lighting is good, and if it isn't, ask to move to somewhere where it is better.

Look at the corners, one at a time, then look at the gloss on the borders, to check for erasing. It will be dull where the eraser has been applied and the gloss removed.

Then turn to the back, and you must look at the back to ensure that there are no rips, tears, writing or stains, and that it is decently centered. The most important thing is to look at the tips of the corners on the backs. With white borders it is sometimes hard to see slight wear on the fronts, wear that might well show up on a colored back. Good examples of this would be the 1954 Topps with the blocks of green on the back, or the 1968 Topps with the gold backs. In that set it can be very difficult to tell about wear on the brown burlap front, but much easier to pick it up by turning over the card.

When I grade a card I base it about 70 percent to the front of the card, 30 percent to the back. If a bit of wear is on the back, I don't put as much stock in it as I would if it were on the front.

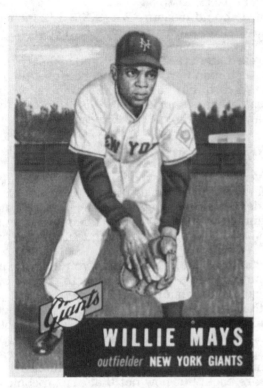

1953 Topps Willie Mays

One year at Willow Grove I bought a 1953 Topps set and paid several thousand dollars for the privilege, taking the Mantle and Mays out of the sheets for close examination. The dealer next to me wanted it, so I tacked on $750 and passed it along.

About an hour later the dealer comes back to my table with an ashen face and looking like someone just ran over his puppy. "We've got a problem," he said, but it turned out that I was the only one with a problem. Every one of the cards had a stamp on the back with the original owner's initials, and I had never looked at the back of the cards. I do now.

CENTERING

Ten years ago in the hobby centering wasn't much of an issue, though of course severely off-center cards were hardly acceptable except as fillers. But over the last decade, as prices increased the attention to centering went right along with it. And just like the vicious cycle with grading, hyper attention to centering helps to raise prices itself.

These days the centering of modern cards is much better, but people ought to bear in mind that when baseball cards were being made 30 or 40 years ago, they were produced very inexpensively, indeed, at a cost of a fraction of a cent per card. They were not designed as works of art or heirlooms; they were playthings for children designed to help sell bubble gum.

Once you start down that road of getting a bit too fixated, the results can be predictible. At an auction, I had a Jordan rookie that I described as gem mint, unimprovable, side to side, top to bottom. It was returned by the customer saying that the centering was 51-49! Now, this is a sickness.

At another auction I sold a Ryan rookie that was perfectly centered all around with razor sharp corners. The lady who bought it called and said that she had a problem with the card because it was centered 55-45 ON THE BACK. Now, I am ready to jump out of the window. That's the mentality.

It is very bad for the card business for people to automatically reject an otherwise swell card just because it has 55-45 centering. The way the market is now, you have to discount any centering that is worse than 55-45, which I do, and I describe all centering.

You can sell commons at 60-40, but for major stars it's a problem. Which brings me to that pet peeve that is mentioned elsewhere in the book. People come to me and say that any card worse than 60-40 is excellent at best. That is the stupidest thing. I don't know why it bugs me so much, but it is so wrong. It can't be excellent if it just came out of a pack; it's mint, it just doesn't sell for as much.

ROUGH CUT

Here then is an interesting story of a characteristic that was once largely devalued but is slowly becoming something of a positive. The cut most often shows up on mint Topps cards from 1953 to 1956 and early Bowmans. I think that it's the greatest thing, I love that little crooked edge and I think it is so authentic. Because with that cut, and the tiny flakes of paper, it gives the card a certain look, a look that virtually trumpets that this then is an uncirculated card.

For a rough cut is so delicate, so fragile, that it would rarely survive much, if any, handling. And it used to be that people didn't like it, but I think that they are coming around.

Most people don't, but I would attach a premium to it.

PRINT DOTS, LINES

The examples of these are endless, but the result is always the same; people don't like it and cards that otherwise might be considered fabulous face discounting it not outright derision.

And all for a little, tiny dot, or a "bubble", or some of those lines that seem to distract incessantly, like a old television set with the horizontal hold on the fritz.

Like grading and centering, the price boom of the 1980s brought new emphasis on even the smallest of flaws, and collectors must be aware of them even if they don't personally believe them important.

The simple answer is that the cards are hard to sell with substantial printing imperfections, even if the card is "as manufactured."

PLASTIC SHEETS

Once you've purchased those mint cards it's pretty important that you keep them that way. Make that vital. And some of those nine-pocket plastic sheets are not the ticket, since they bend on the two folds. When you turn the pages to look at the cards they bend and put stress on the corners; I am convinced of that. Top loaders are OK, they don't do that.

I like those collections where every single card is in a card saver. The semi-rigid ones work well; it is easy to put the cards in and take them out, and they protect the corners. I would tell people to only use top loading sheets, and only PVC free, or individual card savers for their sets.

And while we're on the topic, I want to point out something to people who put their

1954 Topps Henry Aaron rookie
(with the rough cut)

cards in the Lucite holders. Some of them are manufactured just a hair too thin, so that when you put the larger cards in (like Topps 1952-56) and screw them down, they can actually bow the card in the middle. Leave it in the holder for a couple of weeks and you will have a bowed card.

If you use one of the holders you should always use an oversized one. And for collectors buying cards, as mentioned elsewhere in this book, they should always ask dealers to remove the card from the screw down. I never buy a card without taking it out of there. Screw downs can hide a lot of problems, perhaps most notably a light, hairline crease that can only be spotted with the card tilted a certain angle to the light source, and then only outside the holder.

SLABBING

It ruined the coin business and it will ruin the card business. There is a lot of resistance to it in the hobby. And just like picayune centering and inflated grading, it breeds higher prices.

Collectors are frantically trying for eights, nines and tens....no one wants to hear that their card is a six or a seven. That is a nice card, an excellent to mint card, but they don't want to hear it. Using numbers to grade doesn't work. Even if you had a scale of one to 100, you give the card a 70 and you might as well burn it.

Produce a 1954 Aaron rookie graded a nine or a ten and people will go beserk. The price is thousands, but if you've got a near-mint to mint one, it's $1,200. It is such a growing spread that it doesn't make sense. A piece of cardboard can't be that perfect, and if it is, it sure shouldn't be $4,000 or $5,000 and another card only a hair less than that $1,200. It's crazy.

It just doesn't make sense for so many reasons. People like to touch their cards, they like to show them. If you put a set of cards in individual holders you would need a tractor trailer to carry it around. Not to mention, at $25 or $30 a card for the grading, a 1967 set would cost $1,500 just to grade every card.

Grading is in the eye of the beholder. If you are buying, the card is less; if you are selling, it is more. It's the way of the world. The grading of anything is subjective, and to have one person saying this is an eight, or this is a nine, is absurd.

UNOPENED PACKS

Obviously, there is a tremendous temptation to open the packs, take out the valuable cards, replace them with commons and reseal the package. Still, it's fairly easy for me to tell, but a lot of that comes with experience. I hold the pack on the edge and look at the corners of the wrapper where it has been folded. If the cards have been taken out there will be tiny little cracks on the edges, but again, it takes a lof of experience to tell this.

An unopened pack is like playing a slot machine, to continue our gambling metaphor. You can't win unless the stars are on top of the pack, and in the case of a cello pack you would pay dearly for that occurence.

Over the years I've had several significant finds in unopenend material, but I don't like to buy from other dealers. From my finds, some of the packs I would find Mantle right on top of the stack, so you know that the packs had not been tinkered with.

If a guy has a run of Topps sets and he has a pack and a wrapper at the front of the book, that's pretty cool, but why people open up unopened packs is beyond me. Come to think of it, why they even buy unopened packs is beyond me. You can't win. You certainly can't win if you open them, unless you hit an 18-1 shot, and if you've ever been to the racetrack, you know how many 18-1 shots come in.

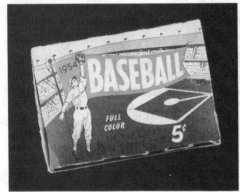

1954 Bowman unopened box

1953 Topps unopened box

1954 Topps unopened box

1958 Topps unopened box

1959 Topps unopened box

1960 Topps unopened box

1972 Topps unopened box

1973 Topps unopened box

Chapter 4

Every Collector's Fantasy (The True Life Adventures of Mr. Mint and the Most Famous Finds in the Hobby)

Before Alan Rosen knocked on the door of a once stately home in Quincy, Mass., the notion of finding a huge stash of mint 1952 Topps baseball cards was little more than a fantasy, albeit a fantasy that countless collectors indulged in with great regularity.

There had been "finds" before, and naturally since, but nothing to ever compare with this. On a balmy day in 1986, the card collecting hobby got an unexpected boost with the realization that the most outlandish daydream could actually come true.

Though naturally there can be no documentation of this, there must have been a considerable jolt on the seismic meter of activity in attics, basements, garages and abandoned warehouses all across the country following the announcement of this historic find. Previously people had rummaged through their personal archives searching for long forgotten treasures out of a sense of recapturing their youth, or perhaps simply making a few extra dollars. This historic find raised the stakes considerably.

By 1986 it was becoming widely understood that baseball cards were no longer simply the playthings of children, and that many of the oldest and most treasured were indeed valuable and, perhaps just as significantly, now quite liquid. Baseball cards were now a big business, both in terms of new cards being produced every day and the sale of vintage cards from yesterday.

But nobody was prepared for what Rosen found when that door was opened.

THE 1952 TOPPS FIND

A guy walks into a flea market booth in Boston and shows a card dealer, David Espinola, mint 1952 Topps cards of Mickey Mantle, Jackie Robinson and Roy Campanella. I will never forget the call. It was Saturday, and I had been at a show on Long Island, and no one was there so I had left early and was home watching the Wide World of Sports and waiting for my wife to come home.

The phone rings and David Espinola says that he has a guy standing in front of him with a gem mint 1952 Mantle, Robinson and Campanella. I told David that I had heard that story many times before, and that if I had a hair on my head for every time I heard about a mint 1952 Mantle I wouldn't be bald. I had never seen a mint Mantle. And he says, "Alan, I am telling you, these things look like they came out of the pack yesterday."

Now, I am the ultimate optimist, so when I heard that I really got excited. I asked a lot of questions: Does he have them in lucite? Does he have any more? David says that the guy claims to have one to three of all of the high numbers, from 311 to 407. I couldn't believe it and asked David if he had personally seen the cards. He said he hadn't, but the guy did have this hand-written list and the cards he did have looked like brand new. David said he would give the guy my phone number.

He didn't call me that night, and I was really angry about that because I couldn't sleep all night. He called me on Monday, saying that he had one to three of every card and asking how much I could pay. I told him 50 percent of book, and he said that was okay and we made arrangements for the following Saturday.

I don't think I slept an hour or two that next night. I went to bed thinking about mint cards. The guy calls me on Wednesday and says that he actually has three to five of every card, not just one to three. I didn't ask him at that point if he had any more than that; I don't know why I didn't, but perhaps I simply couldn't believe that there COULD be any more. I told him that with three to five of each I could pay between 35 and 40 percent of book. Okay.

The next day he calls me again, and now he says that he has five to 10 of each card, at which point I made a phone call to another dealer. I had $50,000 to my name at that time, and I borrowed another $50,000 from that dealer. I went to the dealer's house with my wife Marnee, who was pregnant at the time, and told him that we would be partners on the deal, but he didn't want any part of that. So I said that I would give him his money back within one week.

I drove to Quincy on Saturday, and I will never forget any of this as long as I live. It's this old, New England saltbox-type house, now in a disarrayed state, with kids running around, one in a diaper, another with no shirt. And the guy comes to the door with his yellow legal pad listing his cards and says, "Mr. Rosen, I have 35 to 50 of every card."

I had a tingling sensation in my body, like a racehorse that wants to run, or an explosion waiting to happen. I couldn't wait until I saw those cards....when he said 35 to 50 of every card I thought, God, this guy is trying to scam me or something.

I really don't know why he kept increasing the number of cards that way, but maybe he didn't want to scare me away with the quantity. We had come

A Gem Mint 1952 Topps Mantle
from the high number find

to an agreement on the percentage of book that I would pay based on a certain quantity, and now he was telling me he actually had five to seven times as many cards.

So, into the house I go, and he walks me into this beautiful room. The floor was made out of this giant sunburst of wood. The whole side of the dining room, which must have been 15 feet by 20 feet, was this elegant paneling on the lower half, with a leaded, stained-glass china closet almost the length of the room and a gorgeous, long mahogany table.

I sat down. The guy bends over this china closet and pulls out this big, silver tray (the house was filled with antiques) and comes at me with it, covered with cards piled high, 15 or 20 piles. I thought it was like he was serving me dinner. He puts the tray down, and I remember that the cards were piled so high that I couldn't see over the top.

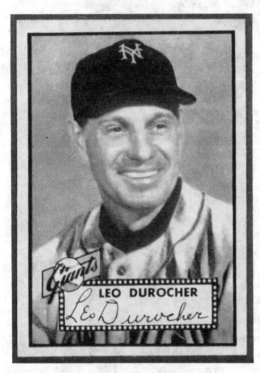

1952 Topps Leo Durocher
from the find

Now, what I want is to get to the Mantles, that's all that I thought about was Mantle. I want to see just how good this deal is going to be. I knew that the cards were mint, but I still could not believe that there were that many Mantles. So I stood halfway up and spun the tray around and I saw #309, and started thumbing through them, then #310, and there it was.

I looked and saw #311, and I picked up a stack, and then I picked up another stack, and they were still Mantles. I had 37 of them. I turned them over and they were bright blue with sparkling white borders, and they were gem mint, they were unbelievable. My hands were shaking there was so much adrenalin flowing through my body.

At this point there were so many cards, literally thousands of cards, that I told him that I could only pay 25 percent. We agreed on 25 percent for the superstars and 20 percent for the commons, both the mid-numbers and the high numbers. So I started to go through the cards. There was no deduction for off-centering, but he had already pulled some culls out, which I didn't know at the time, and those that were left were pretty decently centered within 70-30. Besides, in 1986 centering wasn't deemed as important as it is today, as long as the corners were sharp.

There were 5,500 cards in the whole find, including 4,100 high numbers and 1,400 mids and lows.

When we got done going through the high numbers, we started on the mid-numbers, with the Mays, Wynn and Lemon being extra, and all the rest were the same price. He also had cards from 81-151, some commons, and we had a deal.

We shook hands on the deal, and right after I shook his hand he kissed me on the lips and he thanked me. And after he kissed me he says, "I have the rest of the cards, the rest of the case actually, in the kitchen."

I remember picking up a stack of cards at that point and smelling them, thinking that all this could not be real, he must be scamming me somehow. I told him that he couldn't possibly have more of these, I simply couldn't use any more. I had already spent almost $90,000 and I didn't have that much left, and now he tells me he has the rest of the case in the kitchen!

Off I go into the kitchen, and there's the case. I drop my hand inside, and I start straightening the cards out, because I am a mint maniac, and I started putting all the heads the same way. I scooped some up, and started leafing through them real quick....Mantle, Mantle, Mathews, some were stuck together, they had been dropped in the case, but most were mint cards.

About then I started to get a little aggravated. He seemed like a nice enough guy, but maybe he was taking advantage of me. It's just too many cards. I asked him what he wanted for the rest of the case. And he said, "Mr. Rosen, you've been fair to me, I want $7,500 for the rest of the cards."

Hell, I had already come across three or four Mantles by then, and there was a whole bunch of cards in the box, so I said I'll do it. In all, I paid the man $95,000.

I took all the cards, wrapped them in kitchen toweling, took the case of cards with the loose cards all out to my van. I sat in the passenger seat and I went through that loose case, since I hadn't really even looked through it completely.

I found more Mantles, five or six Mathews, but some of the other cards were creased, some were stuck together. There was one stack of 40 or 50 high numbers that was stuck together and water damaged, and I never did get that apart.

I got home and stayed up the whole night and next day, sorting cards. I made 21 runs. The first 14 were mint, then they started to get little nicks and dings. The Johnny Rutherford cards were all mint, but there were only five that didn't have little paper wrinkles. I had 14 or 15 perfect runs except for him, and I had 18 complete runs from the mid-numbers to the high numbers. There were 37 or 38 runs of the mid-numbers 251-310.

I placed an advertisement in SCD trying to sell the Mantles for $3,500 each, perfectly centered gem mint cards, and I ran photos with the advertisement. I didn't sell any Mantles at that price. I was crushed. So, I started blowing them out, and most of them I sold to dealers for $2,000 each. The last 10 I sold to John Broggi of JKJ Sports Collectibles. He paid me $12,500 for 10 of them.

That was okay, I had more than doubled my money, but I had trouble selling the Mays cards, too. I was trying to sell those for $450 initially in the ad, but they eventually went for a lot less than that. I was selling the mid-numbers, which I paid $8 for, at $14 or $15, and the high numbers I sold at $25 each, and I was getting opposition at that price. The only ones I pulled out were Mathews, Campy, Robinson and Wilhelm, and I wound up having those for almost two months.

Before I sold any I talked to Tom Reid, a longtime hobby dealer from New Jersey. I remembered that he had found some mid-numbers in unopened packs, so I asked him what I should do. He told me that when people see the high numbers, when they actually see them, they are going to go up in value because of the incredible condition. And I called a couple of other dealer friends and asked them what I should do, should I hold on to the cards?

And they said, naw, you know how you are, Al, you buy and you sell and to hell with it. I should have listened to Tom Reid and kept them. Six months later the Mantles were selling for $8,000 to $10,000.

I sold a couple of runs to Paul Lewicki for $9,000, #'s 251-407. I am sitting there thinking, what a stupid move that was, 156 cards for $9,000. I wish I could go back in time. The 21 complete runs went pretty quickly.

I had one Mantle left, the best one. I had it on my desk. We had taken the money from the find and we wanted to remodel our home which we had bought a year earlier. There was a guy actually working on my bathroom one day when the phone rang. It was a California collector, and he wanted to know if I had any Mantles left with the seams on the baseball facing right (It was a double printed card). Sure enough, the seams faced right. He offered me $4,000 for it, and that was more than I had ever gotten for a Mantle. So I asked my wife if I should sell it. She said no, you've always wanted a Mantle, but meanwhile the guy is banging away in my bathroom, charging me thousands of dollars. I decided to sell it.

Ultimately, that collector sold the card himself, and it finally wound up in the hands of Jim Copeland. When his collection went up for auction at Sotheby's, I ended up being a losing bidder at $41,000 on the same card that I had sold for $4,000 two years before.

What's the story behind such an amazing find? The man's father had worked at a company called GRAYCO, which manufactured children's toys. The Topps cards had apparently been used in a promotion to help sell the children's products, five different items including a glove, ball and bat and a couple of combinations of those items. On the outside of each package the advertising said. "Hey kids, with every new GRAYCO product, get three shiny, new Topps baseball cards." It was the first year of coated cards.

According to prevailing legend, when Topps printed the final series in 1952 it was so late in the season that most of the product wound up being returned to the company. Topps apparently tried a number of arrangements to dispose of the extra cards, including linking them with other products as in this case, to putting them in vending machines at amusement parks. Ultimately, around 1960 or so, and this is the best kind of legend because, of course, it is fact, Sy Berger sailed out into the New York harbor on a barge loaded with the remaining cases and unceremoniously dumped them into the ocean.

****

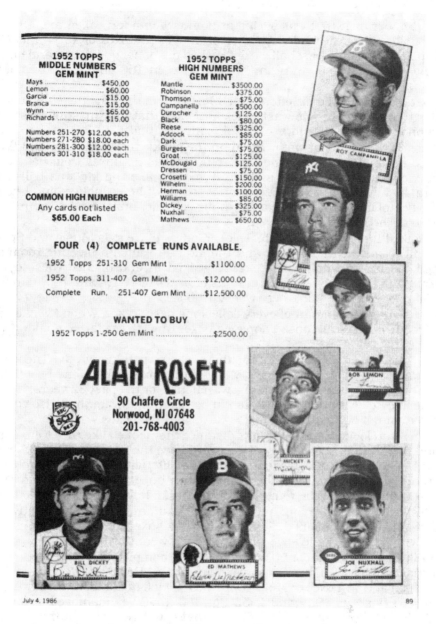

Mr. Mint's advertisement for the 1952 Topps cards from his find.
From the July 4, 1986 issue of Sports Collectors Digest

THE PARIS, TENN. FIND(S)

In October of 1987 I was sitting at home when a kid called me, 18 or 19 years old, saying he had a number of unopened boxes of 1954 and 1955 Topps and Bowman baseball cards. I asked my usual questions, and he said he had wrappers too, and that he had between 150 and 200 boxes of the cards.

I get those kind of calls often, and 99 percent of the time they are no good. I don't know why people waste their time like that, but most of those calls are phony, just fabrications of people's imaginations.

I asked the kid what was written on the packs and the boxes, and then I called up another dealer who had some packs and boxes from both years and we compared the information. It seemed like the kid was telling the truth, so I called him back. I flew on a couple of hours notice, and I had to take two planes and endure a two-hour car ride, but there I was, in Paris, Tenn. at the Holiday Inn.

I walked into that place with Dick DeCourcy of Georgia Music and Sports, whom we met at the airport, and the kid had rented a meeting room and lined the tables with these boxes. I walked in and opened these double doors, and there they were, hundreds of boxes of Topps and Bowman from 1954 and 1955. All told, there were 212 boxes.

The sight was right out of every collector's best dream. When I walked into the room and saw all those unopened boxes, my knees started shaking. And then panic set in.

As I got closer, I could see that there was something wrong. There were bugs crawling all over the place. Many of the boxes, which had been sitting on a dirt floor in the basement of a warehouse for the past 32 years, had become infested with bugs - silverfish to be exact. And water had also contributed to much of the damage to the cards and the boxes.

When you looked at them from a distance they looked like they were in nice condition, but as you got closer you could see the damage. We held in our hands packs of 1955 Bowman cards that literally had holes bored right through them as if they had been shot with a bullet. Many of the boxes were filled with bugs and the remnants of the cards. It was a shame.

Despite the massive amount of damage and destroyed cards, many mint cards and boxes remained. Some of the worst boxes we threw on a table and opened all the packs to save whatever cards were worth saving.

Still, there were almost 50 boxes that were completely undamaged, which included 24 boxes of five-cent wax packs of 1954 Bowman; 13 boxes of 1955 Bowman and 11 boxes of 1955 Topps wax packs. In addition, there were another 61 boxes of 1954 and 1955 Bowman that were damaged beyond repair, but still contained a lot of cards that could be saved. In the end, over 70 boxes of 1954 and 1955 Bowman and 1955 Topps had to be thrown away.

After we made the deal for the cards, they told us about another guy who had bought a quantity of 1955 Bowman boxes from the same warehouse and had opened them all up. We called that man late that night, and went over to his house. We were there so long that Dick DeCourcy fell asleep on the couch while we sorting 1955 Bowmans on the pool table.

There were 45 to 50 of every card in the set, except that we came up with only 319 stacks, instead of the 320 in the set. There was one stack missing, and I couldn't figure out why. Then the guy says, "Oh, I know what happened. The Chick King cards, we gave them to his parents."

And I said, well, you've got to get them back. There I was with 40 or 50 gem mint Bowman sets, missing Chick King. We contacted the parents, but they wouldn't give them back, so to this day there are probably three dozen people looking for mint Chick King cards for their Bowman sets.

The next morning, as we were preparing to leave, I decided to check my messages from home. I had gotten a call from a guy named Randy Scarborough, who also happened to live in Paris, wanting to know if I was interested in three cases of unopened football. Obviously, he didn't know that we were already in the area. An hour later, I was at his house.

Coming from the same warehouse, the football card boxes were damaged in the same fashion as the baseball, and once again box after box had to be thrown away. But still we wound up saving 39 boxes of one-cent wax packs of 1954 Bowman and 26 boxes of five-cent wax packs.

Scarborough also produced 15 heavily damaged boxes of 1960 Topps baseball, but due to the heavy water and bug damage, only a small number of cards were saved.

Imagine sitting at a table and opening 1960 Topps wax packs and getting dozens of Mantles, McCoveys, Aarons and Clementes, but having to throw them away because they were ruined. What a shame!

Some of the damaged cards from the Paris, Tenn. find. Over 70 boxes of 1954 and 1955 Bowman and 1955 Topps had to be thrown away, but almost 50 boxes remained.

Mr. Mint and Randy Scarborough with some of the unopened 1954 Bowman football in the Paris, Tenn. find.

Two months later I got another call from Paris, this time from a guy who had bought a station wagon that had two cases of 1960 Topps tattoos in the back. The guy had bought the car at an auction, and anything inside the car came with the winning bid.

Now, before I got my greedy little hands on them, Topps tattoos were very rare, and I hadn't known anybody who had had a complete set of them. They were in the Krause guide for thousands, but unfortunately I had 27,000 packs. In a recent auction a set sold for about $500. The same guy said that he had thrown thousands of 1954-55 Bowman wrappers and cards into the dump. After we fished those out, most of the cards had the same damage and few could be saved, but we were able to salvage all the wrappers, which is why 1954 and 1955 Bowman wrappers ain't worth nothing.

All in all, I spent about $125,000 in Paris, Tenn.

As you might expect, the history of the cards is interesting. A Paris candy wholesaler was the original owner of the boxes. He had passed away recently and the widow wanted to sell the building where the cards had been resting for three decades plus. It was filled with all kinds of stuff from the 1950s; bobby pins, cigarette lighters. She had the building emptied and the person who cleaned out the property was given the cards for an undisclosed amount. The cards were then sold to the kid who called me.

****

Above are some of the gem mint 1954 Bowman cards from the Paris, Tenn. find, and below two boxes that survived intact.

TED KOCH COLLECTION

This was the largest deal, in terms of dollars, that I was ever involved in. I used to set up next to Ted Koch at the Indianapolis show, and he called Bill Mastro and me at the same time when he wanted to sell his collection in 1989. I had always told Ted over the years that if he ever decided to sell out, I wanted to be the buyer.

Bill and I went to his house in Indianapolis, and when we got there I was flabbergasted at the size of his collection. He had been a dealer for many years, but he also had a very nice personal collection.

He had all the tobacco sets, Play Ball sets, a T-3 set, all the Topps and Bowmans, regionals, thousands of duplicates and triplicates and a lot of oddball sets. I was amazed when we walked into his house and we had to step over piles of cards; they were all over the floor.

We started with the tobacco sets, and when he handed me the Turkey Red set I couldn't believe it, it was so beautiful. Bill had gone over all the singles, W issues, V issues and N cards, plus the premiums.

I think that we were at about $390,000 or so, so we finally decided on an even $400,000 for the sets. Then the most incredible thing happened. Bill says, "I want to pay you $50,000 for the floor." And the floor was just this conglomeration of cards laid out all over the living room. There were thousands of cards. And that was it.

The whole deal was $452,000, and it was the largest deal that I had ever done.

Mr. Mint and Bill Mastro (left), with Ted Koch and his incredible collection.

1952 TOPPS SEATTLE FIND

I was at a show in Seattle in the winter of 1991 with Paul Lewicki, who had made the flight with me. Right before the show opened on Friday, a man walks in with hundreds of packs of 1952 Topps, unopened. The packs were in bricks of six, wrapped in a cellophane band that had the words "1952 Topps Baseball" on it.

All of the packs were low numbers, black backs, and he also had several hundred cards loose that came from packs that he opened before he found out that they were worth more unopened. There were five Pafkos in that group, plus three to five of all of the low numbers, 1-80.

They were beautiful, mint packs, but when you opened them up a lot of the cards still had little nicks or dings. Virtually all of the Billy Loes cards from this find had a little pull on the bottom right-hand corner, apparently from the gripper on the press.

The whole deal came to about $75,000.

The man wouldn't take my check, and I didn't have enough money to pay him in cash and still be able to conduct business at the show. I called my bank in New Jersey (three hours later in the Eastern Time Zone), which didn't give them much time to make a wire transfer. After many phone calls we finally got it done a few minutes before 5 p.m., Eastern time.

I remember I asked the man where he got the cards and whether he had any more, and he said that he had paid $50 for them at a garage sale. He also said that he didn't have any more, but I found out later that he lied. He sold several more to other dealers and consigned several low number boxes in an auction.

Seattle show promoters Terry Diener(left) and Bud Obermeyer help Mr. Mint display some of the unopened packs and gem mint cards from the Seattle find.

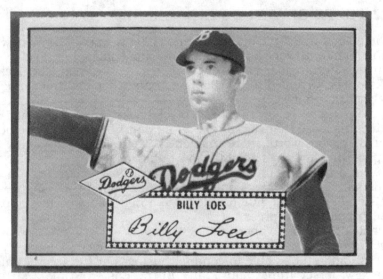

Pictured above is a 1952 Topps Billy Loes card from the find, and below a wrapper and Dom DiMaggio card.

Two of the rare number cards from the 1948 Leaf find.

1948 LEAF RARE NUMBERS FIND

This was the oldest unopened material of any volume that I've ever had. I got a call in 1989 from Orve Johansson, a friend of mine who has a store in Tampa/St. Pete. A guy walked into his store with a box of 1948 Leaf unopened packs (five-cent packs, six cards to a pack) and said he had three more where that came from.

Orve told me how much the guy wanted for the boxes, so I flew down there. I met the guy, and he also had some loose cards, all mint and and all rare numbers. That's all well and good, but I wanted to open one to see if they are damaged and also to ensure that they were rare numbers. The whole deal was $50,000 for the four boxes, but it would not have been nearly that much were they not the rare numbers.

Opening up those packs was incredible. I sat down at a card table in Orve's shop. I opened up the first pack very carefully, because I had never seen a wrapper from 1948 Leaf. Inside, the same size as the card, was the purplish-brown gum, stuck to the card. I turned the cards over and they were all one tight brick, and I couldn't get them apart. Then I took my thumbs and my two forefingers and just gave it a little crack, and they separated nice as can be, with no damage except for the back card, which had a big gum stain. Every pack that I opened, the back card was ruined by the gum.

I opened up the whole box, they were all rare numbers and I paid the guy the money. Then I opened up a second box while I was still there in the shop.

I got even splits, 288 cards and there were two and three of every card except for Paige. Two boxes, no Satchel Paige. That was a disappointment, because I wanted a Paige to put in my auction. I later sold the last two boxes to Jim Copeland, and he opened them up and got three Paiges. I know that Paige is a tough card to find; four boxes and just three Paiges.

With the boxes we also got some of the famous 1948 Leaf premiums, which were on the bottom with a notice to the retailer that said something like; "Dear Retailer; Give this premium to the last kid who buys a pack of 1948 Leaf."

HERB ROSS

Herb Ross was a dealer who had a store in South Jersey. The original name of the store was L & R Card Company, for Don Lepore, who was Herb's partner. We had gotten to know each other over the years at shows, and I had bought a lot of little things from him in the past.

I had been putting the details of my big deals on the pages of *SCD*, so when Herb decided in the summer of 1983 that he wanted to sell out, he called me. I brought my friend, Rick Starks, and a big truck, and we went to Herb's place.

He had been in the business 10 years before I got into it, and he had a lot of great stuff. All the insert sets, hundreds of singles of 1969 Supers, Deckle Edge, 1968 3-D, rare variations from 1958. He also had all these oddball test sets, Connie Mack All-Stars, coins, stamps, in some cases he had 10 and 20 of each player.

He had 700 checklists from 1956, and they were a dollar each. It was the same thing with the 1958 yellow letters; he had a couple of thousand of those, and they were just laying in roll boxes with the tops cut off. When I looked at Herb's collection, I realized why they were so scarce; he had them all.

There were stacks and stacks of hundreds of cards. We were there the whole day, and Herb spent the day pacing back and forth. We started at the front of the store with the showcases, and moved to the back of the room, putting a price on everything. We got up to $23,500, and right near the end he got a little emotional, because he had been in the business a long time. "Look, just make it $25,000 and take whatever else is there," he said finally.

Now, normally you jump at a deal like that, but in those days $25,000 was a lot of money for baseball cards. I remember looking up at the wall and seeing this 1968 Topps Action All-Star stickers box that was thumbtacked to the wall, and I had never seen that before. It had Mantle on it, plus he had the 1968 Topps discs, test cards, plaques and a lot of other things laying around in boxes. I turned to Rick and asked him, "What do you think, $1,500 for the rest?" and he said okay. Done deal.

We brought it all home, and we had about a week before Jack Farscht's show, the Freehold Classic, a show which I had been doing for years. We took it to my apartment in Hackensack, and the superintendent was a friend of mine, so he allowed us to use a room in the same building. We set it up like a supermarket, called a whole bunch of dealers and gave out flyers just as it if were a regular show, saying that on Tuesday we were going to have a sale of the Herb Ross material.

We had 35 dealers show up, and we spent all day and all night there, till 3 or 4 a.m. Linda and Aubrey Shoemake flew in from Houston, and rented a truck to drive everything they purchased home.

And we ran it just like a supermarket checkout. I walked around and helped anybody who needed it, Rick wrote up the invoices, and the superintendent, Fred Towers, checked to make sure that everybody had the correct merchandise and that nothing, uh, disappeared.

I also remember Aubrey's truck, taking cases of 1982s and 1981s, cut card cases, late in the evening (technically early in the morning), and Linda was on the back of the truck actually kicking and pushing the last couple of cases into the truck.

We had had 10 cases of the famous (infamous?) K-Mart sets from 1982, and they took the last five or six. I can still see Linda giving me a dirty look as she tried to cram them into the truck. She actually had to take her hand and push them in as she closed the door. That's how many cards they bought that day.

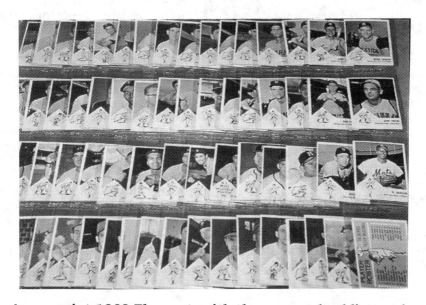

A near-mint 1963 Fleer set, with the scarce checklist card, from the Herb Ross buyout.

****

1932 US CARAMEL FIND

I got a call in 1990 from Paul Longo, a longtime Boston dealer, about a kid who had a find of 1932 U.S. Caramel cards. The kid who sold me the cards told me that his grandfather had worked for U.S. Caramel, and I believed him. He had hundreds of the cards, and he even had the presidents and non-sports.

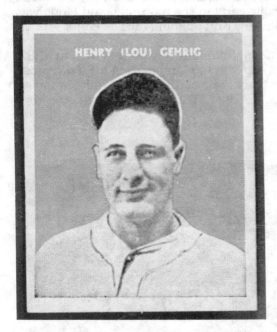

1932 U.S. Caramel of Lou Gehrig

I bought 15 or 20 of every baseball card that he had, but there was one card missing, the Hornsby. The kid didn't know why. I had eight or nine complete sets except for one card, plus hundreds of duplicates. I had seven or eight of both Ruth and Gehrig, all with pure white borders and the bright background colors. Like the cards from the 1952 Topps find, these cards are so distinctive that you can spot them when they turn up. They must have been taken from the factory without ever being put with any product.

It is amazing how fast these cards sold. I sold many of them to dealers and retail customers, including several of the superstars to Larry Berra, one of Yogi's sons.

The kid who had sold me the cards told me that that was all he had, but about a year later Longo called me and said the kid was buzzing around again. I went back up there and he sold me some more, with both deals coming to more than $100,000.

He claimed again that he was all out of cards, but I am still waiting for a call.

****

NEIL SAKOW AND MICKEY MANTLE

Neil Sakow is a very nice man who lives in Connecticut and has the world's greatest Howdy Doody collection and possibly the world's greatest Mickey Mantle collection as well. He recently published a book on Mantle memorabilia. He also provided me with one of the most extraordinary moments that I have ever experienced in the hobby, the kind of thing that makes this business so exciting and enduring.

My first deal with him was 1987. Paul Lewicki and I went up to his shop and we filled up a van with stuff. Uncut sheets, four or five complete Hartland statue sets, plus individual Hartlands in original boxes. Kahns sets, Wilson Franks, display pieces, original Topps presentation sets, 1968 3-Ds, just incredible material.

He is a hoarder. All the stuff that he accumulated in the 1950s, and people thought he was crazy for hanging on to such things, and it all turned out to be gold.

The first time we went to his store, then five years later I went to his house, this time with Bill Mastro. The collection at his home was beyond my wildest dreams. His "Mickey Mantle Room" was absolutely filled to the brim with drawers crammed with Mantle advertising pieces, wrappers, 1968 Topps test panels, empty wax boxes, anything with Mickey Mantle on it. He has met Mantle many times, and has a picture of himself with the Mick in his book. The room was like a shrine.

We would open a drawer and it would have 200 Mickey Mantle cards, all mint. Bowman and Topps cards from 1955, 1956, 1957 and 1958, Stahl-Meyers, one after another, literally thousands of pieces, and a lot of it I had never seen before.

1954 Red Heart Dog Food

He had many items from Mantle's Country Kitchen restaurant as well. We bought a number of sets from 1958 to 1968, along with a lot of Mantle cards. Several of the sets wound up in the Christie's auction.

Then, in 1994, I went up to his home again, plowing my way through six or eight inches of snow, and it was the most unbelievable feeling after I got there and found out what was about to take place.

He told me that he had sets from Larry Fritsch, all the Topps sets from 1960 to 1970, still in a box that had never been opened. I was dumbfounded, I couldn't believe it. He pulls out this huge carton, with heavy twine wrapped around it. He says, "Okay, here's the box, you open it, and you'll be the first person to see this stuff in 23 years."

The mailing label was still on it, addressed to him, and postmarked July or August, 1971.

I cut the cord, and my hand was shaking as I ripped open the paper. I opened the carton, and there were those blue vendor boxes on one side, and another larger box on the other side with little covers.

Turns out, the blue vendor boxes held the 1968-1970 sets, but the other sets were in a different, pre-vendor

1956 Topps Mickey Mantle

style box. The first one I touched was 1960 Topps, standing vertically in the box. All of the edges of the cards were pure white and squeezed in tight in the box with shreds of paper.

1962 Topps Managers' Dream

I took out a handful of 70 or 80 cards, and you had to squeeze them a bit to get them apart. There were some miscuts, but all the cards were mint, uncirculated. I went through all the sets, one at a time, and he had all the inserts, a 1964 Stand Up set, coins, the 1965 embossed set, stick-ons, rub-offs and posters. He had the whole decade of Topps issues, virtually everything that Topps made from 1960 to 1970.

I'll never forget reaching into that box, one set at a time, searching through the paper shreds for another box. It was just like Christmas, and it was the worst feeling in the world after I had found the 1970 set to fish around among the paper shreds and find nothing else. There was just one of every set.

There are some deals that you remember, and some that you forget, but cutting the cord on that box was something that will always stay with me.

****

BALTIMORE FIND OF TOBACCO CARDS

In 1988, a guy walks into Wayne Miller's show in Baltimore with this long box, filled with almost 750 gem mint T-206s. I probably will never see anything like that again. He walked right up to my table and said, "Mr. Rosen, I have just uncovered a find from a woman's house of about 1,500 tobacco cards. These are the T-206s, and I have the rest in the car."

That was more than enough for me. My show was over. I took a big cloth and a sheet and put it over my table. We spent the entire day in my hotel room. There was almost a complete set of Turkey Reds, gem mint T-205s and T-207s, Zeenuts and that box of T-206s.

T-206 from the Baltimore find

For the record, it did not include any Wagners, Planks or Magees, but he did have about 35 Cobbs, absolutely gem mint. I kept a couple for my auction, and the rest went very quickly. The deal took place on Friday, and by Sunday they were gone. Dealers just ate them up, and I was charging 80 or 90 percent of book after paying him 65 or 70 percent.

The cards were extraordinary, very distinctive, and I measured them and they were so large. I wanted to check, because you often find T-206s that have been trimmed. These had obviously never been monkeyed with. Out of the 750 or so T-206s, 90 percent were absolutely gem mint, with razor sharp corners, full gloss and still had the little paper shavings on the edges. Easily the best T-206s that I had ever seen.

Final total was in excess of $40,000 for the deal.

****

KANSAS CITY BOWMAN FIND

Longtime Kansas City promoters John Mehlin and James Cumpton called me about this incredible stash of thousands of gem mint early Bowman cards. It was 1985, and John Broggi and I flew out to Kansas City.

I still remember some of the amazing quantities. The heaviest concentration was 1951 and 1952, and I had 17 Ford rookies, 45 Mantle rookies and over 60 Mantles from 1952. They were absolutely gem mint, right out of packs, with bright white borders. They couldn't get any better. I spent about $125,000.

One box after another, they were all the same. There were dozens and dozens of 1952 Bowman Musials. When you run across some of the cards from this find you recognize them immediately; they are that distinctive, they are so white.

I put them out at Willow Grove a couple of weeks later, and I sold almost every card between two and three dealers and the public. Within a week all those gem mint cards were gone. You look back at a deal like that, and that's what makes this business fun. To sit there and look at thousands of gem mint Bowmans, it is amazing. Those Musials surface now and then with the bright white borders, but where did the rest go? I haven't seen a perfect 1951 Bowman set in a couple of years.

1952 Bowman Mantle

****

QUINCY, ILL. MINT SETS

A school principal from Quincy, Ill. had seen my ads in *SCD* and called me in 1991 about his collection. He said he was retiring and that he had complete sets from 1953 to 1957 and multiple sets after that. I asked him to send me one card, the same player, from every set so that I could check the condition. That's a good system, not foolproof but useful, and he sent me the Norm Siebern card from each set. They all were mint.

He took me down to his basement, and at first I was very disappointed. I had brought over $250,000 in cash, and the 1953 Topps set looked like it

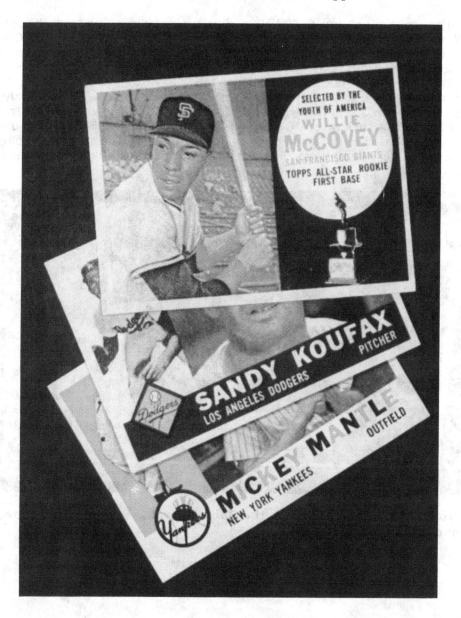

had fallen off a bridge somewhere (don't blame Norm Siebern, his first Topps card was 1958). But as the years kept going up, 54, 55, 56 and 57, the cards kept getting better and better, and by 1958 they were all mint. Just right out of packs.

The guy told me he just kept buying packs and packs. Everything was in sets, there was not one single loose card in the whole room, and the cards were not in sheets but rather in boxes in shelves all around the basement. He had two 1958s, four 1959s, six or seven 1960s, eight or 10 1961s and so on, and I think there were about 20 1969 Topps sets. He went right up to the 1980s, and had 20 or 30 sets from 1981 and the same number from 1982.

The deal, which came to $295,000, filled an entire van. I had to fly back to New Jersey, so rather than ship the cards UPS, I paid the guy $5,000 to drive the cards to my home. I waited at my office for four hours before he showed up with the van.

We had eight or nine guys, Joe Esposito, John Broggi, Paul Lewicki and a bunch of other dealers that helped me sort through the sets. We worked until about 4 a.m. I kept the best of set of each for my auction and sold the rest to the dealers, tacking on 10 or 15 percent. After spending $300,000 in one crack, I needed to get some of my money back. The dealers were flipping coins for the others; it was like a draft day. The whole thing was tremendously exciting.

Mint 1960 Topps cards from the Quincy purchase are pictured above and on the previous page.

****

An uncut sheet of the 1959 Fleer Ted Williams set, which includes the scarce "Ted Signs" card in the upper left corner.

DAN WELLS FLORIDA FIND

Dan Wells was a college professor, and I went down to Florida in 1984 with Linda and Aubrey Shoemake and met Mr. Wells. He had a garage that was filled with Post Cereal sets and thousands of Post Cereal uncut panels. He had Topps sets from 1959 to 1963, Fleer sets, literally hundreds of sets all told, and I would spend days at a time going through the cards. I made several trips to his home, spending a total of more than $100,000.

After the second or third trip, he started running out of sets, and we started to buy stars and high numbers. He had hundreds of Mantles, and on one occasion we bought 50 Topps Mantles from 1959, paying six bucks each.

On the fifth trip we bought the Post Cereal sets and singles panels, and filled five suitcases in the process. I had flown there with Tom Reid, and on the return flight there was a storm and the plane was shaking a bit, and Reid says, "I don't care about me, but don't let the suitcases go down."

We had about 1,000 uncut panels of 1963 Post Cereal. We made sets, and eventually we ran out of the rare numbers and we started cutting up the panels. I remember sitting with Reid for two days in my apartment, and I had a blister on my right hand from cutting the panels.

Topps contest winner

In May of 1992 I went to the home of Jack Glenn in New York City. He was the guy who won the Topps contest where the first prize was 40 years of Topps sets. I purchased his entire run of sets, including the 1952 Mantle, and paid him $34,000. Topps had billed the prize as being worth much more than that, but the cards were really only very good to excellent. I was proud of the fact that the guy who won the Topps sets wound up selling to Mr. Mint.

A LONG ISLAND INVESTOR

Rick Starks and I went out to this gentleman's house on Long Island. He had a penchant for unopened material, and he had over 250 wax boxes, almost a case of 1962 Topps First Series, nearly a case of 1960 Leaf with the marbles, plus boxes of 1961, 1963, 1968 and 1969, four or five 1970 high numbers, 1971 and 1972 wax and cellos. That deal came to $23,500, which was a lot in 1982.

I bought from him three different times starting in 1982, later buying cases from 1977-81 and early 80s traded cases. The last time I purchased many uncut sheets, plus he consigned a large number of other uncut sheets to the Christie's auction in October of 1992. He had a couple of sheets from virtually every year from the early 1950s on, including several 1969 Topps sheets with Mantle on them.

The gentleman is very sharp, a shrewd investor, and he knew which years to buy. Over the three trips, I spent more than $225,000.

A 1960 unopened Leaf box with the marbles

****

THE ROGER MARTH COLLECTION

This was the second largest deal that I ever had. Roger Marth was a partner in the Sports Collectors Store in LaGrange, Ill. He got out in the early 1970s, and his personal collection included some remarkable material. He called me in September of 1990 and we wound up handling almost three-quarters of his collection.

And he had everything. Tobacco cards, E cards, N cards, R cards, Topps, Bowman, Fleer, pictures, buttons, inserts. It took a 16-foot truck, driven by my assistant, Glenn Stuart, to get it all back to New Jersey. We purchased some of the collection and auctioned the rest. The total proceeds, cash and auction, exceeded $300,000.

Afterwards, Roger gave me a letter saying that he had received 15 to 20 percent more from the auction than he had anticipated.

Mr. Mint poses with noted collector Roger Marth and some of his staggering collection that brought over $300,000 at auction.

****

THE MIKE KEASLER COLLECTION

I auctioned off the collection of another famous Chicago-area collector in the fall of 1994. Mike Keasler, also a former partner in the Sports Collectors Store and a close friend of Roger Marth, decided in the spring of 1994 to part with his amazing collection that he had compiled over more than two decades.

He called me and I made several trips to Chicago, spending several days each trip, going through his collection and creating lots for my auction that September.

Keasler, a successful college basketball coach, was an old-time collector who had extraordinary self-control in selecting only the finest quality specimens. In chronicling some of his pieces, including many rare premium issues from the 1930s, it was not uncommon to find some cards missing, since he would never settle for less than top condition regardless of how difficult something might be to find.

He had, quite literally, thousands and thousands of autographed cards, including some very expensive ones, like his pair of 1939 and 1941 Play Ball DiMaggios. Keasler was collecting in the 1970s when it was not uncommon to send out cards, even very valuable ones, for signatures. He even sent out a 1951 Bowman Mantle rookie card, but alas, that one never made it back to the Keasler household.

It was easily one of the most impressive and developed collections that I've ever had the pleasure of handling. Included in his collection were thousands of cards that came directly from vending boxes, and you haven't lived until you've seen a 100-card run of middle-number 1952 Bowmans directly from vendors.

He had near-mint sets from Topps, Bowman and Fleer from 1954 forward, tobacco cards in super condition, 1939 Goudey premiums, Red Man Tobacco sets, 1934 Butterfinger premiums and on and on.

This book went to print prior to the auction, but we expected at least $300,000 to be realized from his lifelong collection. A number of his most treasured pieces were on display at the 1994 National Convention at my table and at the Krause Publications/*Sports Collectors Digest* booth.

Mike Keasler (left) shows some of his top condition cards from the 1950s and 1960s with the aid of the Mint Man.

****

SEATTLE PHOTO FIND

I bought the entire autographed photo collection of a priest in Seattle in 1991. A member of his parish told me about the priest and his collection when I was at a show in Seattle, and I went to the rectory where he lived to take a look at his holdings.

The priest had over 20 file cabinets filled with autographed photos. His collection was incredible and was filled with baseball players, movie stars, presidents, captains of industry and virtually any kind of famous person that you could think of. There were Cobbs, and there were a lot of scrub players that weren't worth much of anything, but there was very little duplication.

There were 27,000 autographed photos, and in addition to the photo, he also had a 3 x 5-inch card with information about when he sent the piece out and who he sent it to. He also had attached the envelopes that the photos were returned in, which was a wonderful bit of authentication for the autographs.

He had put all of it together before 1975; there was no postmark later than that year. It was the largest photo collection that I had ever seen. We actually never even counted all the pieces. We simply counted one drawer and multiplied by the total number of drawers.

The whole deal was $30,000. I saved a bunch of it for my auction and sold the rest to my customers and other dealers.

MANNY'S BASEBALL LAND

For many years, Manny's Baseball Land was a landmark directly across from Yankee Stadium in the Bronx, selling souvenirs, cards and memorabilia. It was also one of the first major mail-order companies, with ads running in countless sports publications in the 1960s and 1970s.

It was also known as the source for yearbooks and programs, and Manny's son Miles called me in 1989 about selling out the inventory of these. I went there with Joe Esposito, who is a publication expert, and my assistant, Glenn Stuart.

There were 50,000 yearbooks, basically never touched, still packed in the original shipping cartons. They ran primarily from 1962 to 1980, all teams. The deal wound up being $100,000.

I had no idea how heavy all those books would be. They were grouped 25 or 50 to a bundle. We hired six people, and all told it took nine of us 22 hours of nothing but lifting to load the truck and then unload all of it in a warehouse that Joe had rented for the deal.

We figured that if each book weighed just a half pound or so, we had lifted 25,000 pounds.

When you look back and think, Geez, 1968 Yankee yearbooks, 450 of them, what am I going to do with them? And you know what? They are gone, because they are mint and they sell. When our ad came out we were getting 20 to 40 calls a day for yearbooks. We had no idea about how much space would be needed either, and we ended up stacking books upon books. People would call asking for a specific book and we couldn't get to it because there were hundreds of books piled on top of it.

We sold runs of Yankee yearbooks, gem mint, from 1962 to 1980, at $3 and $4 per book. Now you can't buy them for $15 or $20 each. All we knew is that we had put out $100,000 and we needed to get our money back. You don't think about what they might be worth later on, not when you are buying that kind of quantity and you are getting calls for other deals every day.

Mr. Mint and his assistant, Glenn Stuart, front right, with Joe Esposito (back left) and Manny's son Miles, displaying some of the thousands of yearbooks in the buyout of Manny's Baseball Land.

****

THE $50,000 MANTLE

In June of 1991, Bill Dominic came into my office with a gem mint 1952 Mantle from my find. My wife Marnee just happened to be at the office at the time, and she understands the business because she does the books and thinks nothing of my spending hundreds of thousands of dollars on cards.

Bill wanted $45,000 for this Mantle, which was dead center and perfect. And Marnee kept giving me these subtle looks saying I shouldn't buy the card.

I wanted to pay $38,000, and he wouldn't sell it to me. This was on a Tuesday, right before my Father's Day show at Madison Square Garden.

After he left, Marnee said, "Don't you ever spend that kind of money on that card. Who's going to pay that much for it? You've already made enough money on those 1952s."

But the next day he came back, and I still really wanted that card. I knew I could get at least for $45,000 for it. We finally settled on $40,000. And my wife stormed out of the office, giving me that look where if looks could kill, I am a goner.

I put the card out on the table on Friday, the only card in my whole showcase. One card, gem mint, unimprovable - $55,000. About 11:30 a.m., a man and his young son came up and asked to see the card. I showed it to him, and he asked if he could see it out of the case.

Now, as I take the card out of the holder I am wondering if I should tell the guy that the price is $55,000, not $5,500 or $550. Sometimes a novice has no conception of what these things cost, and the decimal points get confusing. So I said something like, "It's an awful lot of money to spend on a very beautiful card."

He responded that he had been looking at a lot of cards in the $30,000 to $35,000 price range, and this one seemed to be the best in the bunch, but he felt it was overpriced.

I told him that you have to pay for the best. And he kept looking at the card, taking it around to better light, examining it and such.

Finally, he asked me how much did I have on it? I told him $55,000. He asked if I would take $50,000 for it right now? I thought he was pulling my leg, but actually that was only my wife, who was sitting next to me and kicking me under the table.

I said, "You have the cash here?" And he said, no, he had $10,000 now and would come to my office on Monday and pay the rest. I shook his hand and we had a deal.

I made $10,000, and to this day I still remind Marnee of it.

****

THE LILLIAN BROTHERS

Would you pay $200 to just take a peek inside this room?

I met the Lillian brothers, Sid and Harry, in 1986 at a show at Nassau Coliseum on Long Island, and over the years made eight or nine trips to their home, purchasing cards each time. That first year they invited me over, sat me down at a table and eventually came out with these cigar boxes filled with cards. And everything was mint.

They had Berk Ross sets, Red Hearts, literally hundreds of them, plus Topps and Bowman from the late 40s and early 50s. Nothing after 1955.

It was like going to a candy store. When the Lillians called, they would bring out a certain amount of cards each time, obviously to get a specific amount of money, and that would be it. It was the same routine every time, coffee and cake, chat for a while and then the boxes would come out. I never wanted it to end.

1951 Bowman Whitey Ford

One time, when I was going through a couple of 1951 Bowman sets that I had purchased, I found a Ford rookie with a crease on it. I showed it to them and they went into the other room and quickly returned with a mint one. And I was never allowed in that other room over all those years.

Every time I went there the wives were out shopping. The last time I went over the wives were out but returned unexpectedly. I was fumbling with some money. I told the ladies, "Your husbands tell me that they are all out of cards, and I have been here several times. I would like to know how much it would take for me to see the other room? I won't walk into the room, I'll just look through the doorway. I will pay $200 just to look through the doorway."

To this day, I have still never seen that room.

****

THE YANKEE LADY

One of the most interesting buys that I ever made was from "The Yankee Lady," Barbara Grossman. She was hell-bent on getting every card of every Yankee, every photo or print, every button.

And she had everything; meat cards, regionals, Topps, Bowmans, all the T cards, bats, balls, autographed books, pictures and artwork, she had three rooms filled with the stuff. She had singles of everything, no duplication. She had Stahl-Meyers of Mantle and the extremely rare 1961 Topps dice game, which I had sold her many years earlier. A good 30 to 40 percent of the items I had never seen before.

She lived in an apartment in Queens, and she and her husband wanted to buy a house after having their first child, plus I think she got a little burned out after all that collecting. It took three vans to get all of the stuff out of her apartment, and I took everything that wasn't nailed down. It was the summer of 1988, and four or five of us were at her apartment for three days doing that deal.

She is a great lady and she had a wonderful collection.

The whole deal was about $75,000 and it took me nearly six months to sell all of it.

**Mr. Mint has the cards, etc., and the Yankee Lady,
Barbara Grossman, has the cash.**

****

THE WAYNE MILLER DEAL

A T-206 from the tobacco find

In 1982 I was still in the copy machine business, and I used to run advertisements in the local papers to buy baseball cards. I would buy the collections in the evenings, and this man called me and I went to Oradell, N.J. to look at his collection.

He had a wonderful collection of tobacco cards, over 1,000 in all. He had several packages of M-116 Sporting Life cards, team sets, Giants, Philadelphia, Detroit with Cobb and one other one. These were still in the original packages. He had over 100 Turkey Reds and hundreds of T-205s and T-206s.

I paid $12,500, and that was a lot of money back then. I sold the cards to Wayne Miller, and that's how I bought my very first new car. Which is why this is the only deal named after the person I sold the cards to, rather than who I bought them from.

Can you imagine what those cards are worth now? Probably $250,000, maybe more. There were no rarities in the group, but all of the cards were near-mint or better.

****

Many years later, in 1989, I did run across a couple of the tobacco rarities. I got a call from a lady in Brooklyn, probably prompted by the article about me in *Sports Illustrated*, about some tobacco cards that she had. Paul Lewicki and I went to her house, and she had three T-206 Planks, a Magee and a few Cobbs. The whole deal was for $23,000, and I sold the cards to several collectors.

****

WILSON FRANKS FIND

At the Bruce Paynter Chicago show in 1990, a guy walked right past Bill Mastro's table, and Bill asked him if he had anything to sell, but got no response. The guy walked five feet over to my table and said, "Mr. Rosen, are you buying today?" It's exciting....I get the ultimate rush. That is what makes my job so special, when I am a show and expecting somebody to walk in. I am the ultimate optimist....I think every new deal is *THE* deal.

The man had a lunch box with him, so I said, "What's in that box that I can't live another day without?" He told me that he had some gem mint Wilson Franks cards, and I couldn't believe it. He had 290 of them, with 12 or 13 different players and 15 to 25 of each card, but he didn't have the Williams. There was some off-centering, but no product stains. And they were mint, so mint that I had to squeeze them with my thumb and forefinger to get them apart.

I spread them all out over my table, wanting to put a little show on since there were 75 to 100 people watching. I paid the man $27,000. I kept looking over at Bill Mastro's table and he had kind of a sour look on his face.

This was the first time I had ever seen mint Wilson Franks cards. I bought those cards in the afternoon, just as I was eating lunch, and by 4 p.m. they were gone, with the exception of a few that I kept for my auction. They were so distinctive, they were stiff. Just unbelievable cards.

**1954 Wilson Franks
Roy Campanella**

****

A BASEMENT ON STATEN ISLAND

When I started advertising in 1982 I was doing a lot of bragging about buying all these collections. A major Staten Island dealer came up to me at a show in Brooklyn in 1983. "Oh, you're that Mr. Mint guy. I want you over at my place on Wednesday with $50,000 in cash," said the dealer. He added that he didn't really think that I could do it, but gave me his address anyway.

On Wednesday, I picked up Rick Starks and we headed out to Staten Island. We put up $25,000 each.

The dealer had a basement full of cards, and every one was in numerical order. We went straight up and down each row, taking only stars and not bothering with any commons.

At that time, I can remember buying Rose rookies for $8 each, and 1964 Roses for $3 or $4 each. I took bricks of nothing but Pete Rose, hundreds of 1970 Roses, and we were taking to 50 to 100 cards of whatever players we wanted. We also got a couple of hundred Brett and Yount rookies. And all of these cards were directly from vending boxes.

We walked out of there with only three cartons, and we had spent $37,000. Those cards are probably worth $250,000 to $300,000 now.

A TRIP TO POTTSTOWN, PA.

I bought a wonderful collection in 1992 after a long car ride to Pottstown, Pa. This young guy was getting married and decided to sell out, and he had collected everything. Record albums, guns, comic books, cars, baseball and football cards, you name it. There were boxes and boxes of football cards, including 3,000 or 4,000 tall boys from 1965 Topps (no Namaths; he must have pulled them).

They were all mint cards, and we could barely fit it all in the truck. I paid him $75,000 for the cards.

During the same trip, I had also arranged for a deal of 1941 Play Balls. I had seen the cards before at a show and knew that the guy had probably the best Play Balls I had ever run across, including four or five Williams.

After closing the earlier deal in Pottstown, I drove to this guy's house and didn't get there until about 11 p.m. After I sat down I started taking the cards out of the holders and pricing them. And the guy says, "What's the invoice for?" I told him that I came here to buy the cards.

He said, "No, I thought you were coming here to look at them." Uh huh. "What the hell would I want to look at them for? I had already seen them before," I said with some enthusiasm.

And the guy got upset, and I was not exactly in the mood for too much either. It had been a long drive and I already had spent a pile of money and had a van full of cards. But I really wanted those Play Balls.

I walked out of there scratching my head. Maybe he changed his mind just as I was totaling everything up.

****

VIRGINIA MINT

There was a man in Virginia who had the best mint cards I had ever seen, and considering all the mint cards that have passed my way, that is saying a lot. His collection was primarily from 1954 through 1957, and I spent over $200,000 from 1987 to 1992, making several trips during that span.

He had literally hundreds of 1957s. All of his cards were so mint that they were stiff as a board, and shiny. Going to his house was one of those genuine thrills that keep me going in this business. None of his cards were in plastic sheets. They were all standing up in boxes with towels over the top.

Any time I was in the Baltimore/Washington D.C. area I

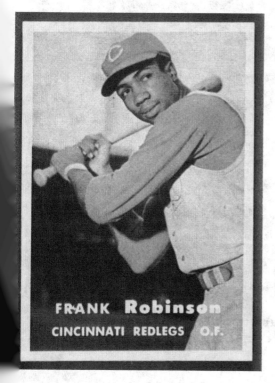

> **Above, a gem mint 1957 Topps Mantle, and at left, a matching 1957 Topps Frank Robinson, his rookie card**

would call him and ask if I could stop at his house. Sometimes he would say yes, and sometimes no.

Through the same time period he consigned several items in my auctions, many of which sold for double and triple book.

****

A TRIP TO MONTANA

In the summer of 1989, Joe Esposito of B & E Sports Collectibles and I flew to White Sulphur Springs, Mont. to buy a collection from Bill Sheanan. After the flight we still had another four or five hours of driving. I was amazed that as we drove through this flat area, you could look at the mountains in the distance and they were snow-capped. I had never seen snow-capped mountains.

And I couldn't find Bill's house. He lived in the middle of nowhere.

He had told me to stop at the general store and ask for directions to his house. I guess I didn't realize how many houses were in the community. In the town, the bank and the bar were in the same building, with the bank on one side and the bar on the other. There was also a taxidermist, and a McDonalds, and they even delivered. The McDonalds delivered stuff right to our door!

Anyway, Joe and I got to the house, and there was an outhouse in the back. He had a very nice family, and his wife made cookies for us while we looked at the cards.

When Mr. Mint arrived in Montana in 1989, he had the cash and Bill Sheanan (right) had the cards. A couple of days later the situation was reversed.

And what cards they were! He had beautiful near-mint to mint sets, all the Bowmans and Topps, and there were thousands of duplicates. The bad news is that he had sent out a lot of the cards to be autographed. We were there for hours, and the deal was about $45,000. It cost about $1,000 in UPS charges to get all of the albums shipped back to New Jersey.

He had all the catalogs and had purchased quality sets down through the years from many of the old-time dealers. It was one of the nicest card collections I had ever seen. His 1954 Topps set had borders that were as white as snow, but the Williams card was autographed and bent. It was otherwise a mint card, but it had obviously been damaged in the mail.

If those cards weren't autographed, the deal probably would have been a couple of hundred thousand dollars for the cards. Some of the sets were more than 60 percent autographed, and Joe ended up buying a lot of those.

I remember buying complete Topps and Bowman sets from 1953 to 1957 from Barry Halper. Almost all of the cards were autographed except for Clemente, Campanella and a few commons. The sets were in excellent to mint condition, and it turns out that I couldn't get 50 percent of book at auction.

The only cards that are really good autographed are deceased Hall of Famers. A collector of cards doesn't want to pay for the autographs, and a collector of autographs doesn't want to pay for the cards.

NORTH TO ALASKA

I had never been to Alaska before, and it was a real thrill to travel to James Soucek's house near Anchorage. It took two flights and over three hours of driving to get there.

He was originally from Montana, and had been a lifelong card collector. He worked for the phone company for about half of the year, and trained sled dogs, which he kept alongside his trailer, the rest of the time.

He had all the Topps, Bowman, and non-sport cards. All I know is, my UPS bill for that one came to $2,600, which was for 17 cartons of cards. I also paid him $58,000.

In the morning at his place, I looked out the window and there was a moose standing 100 yards from the door. I don't know exactly how tall it was, but it was bigger than the trailer.

The next day he took me to where the Iditarod sled dog race was held, and we saw Mt. McKinley and some glaciers. When we started out it was so beautiful and around 30 degrees, but as we got closer to the mountain it was snowing so hard that you couldn't see anything. In one of my famous ads in *SCD* I ran a picture of myself standing in front of that mountain.

Apparently, Mr. Mint will go anywhere to buy your cards.

****

PRESS PINS IN A COFFEE CAN

A man called me in 1988 saying he had a significant find of Baltimore Sun Babe Ruth cards, plus T-205s and "press buttons," as he called them.

I went to his home and we started going through the various pieces. I bought several of the Baltimore Sun Babe Ruth cards (and later sold them for $5,000 each), and afterwards we went through all the tobacco cards. At this point he told his wife to "get the can," and in she came with this rusty Maxwell House coffee can.

He dug his hand in, and the first pin out was the 1911 Philadelphia A's, and it was mint, with the silk ribbon and the gold imprint. The ribbon had the tiny beads along the edges, and the gold was bright and vivid. I had seen 1911 pins before, but they were always raggedy, and this one was unbelievable. He started pulling out the others, 1912, 1913, 1914 and so on, and they were all brand new, mint, and had apparently never been worn or used.

He told me that his grandfather was a reporter with the Baltimore Sun. I bought it all for about $38,000, and I sold a lot of them to Jim Copeland. Bill Mastro has many of them now, having picked them up after they didn't sell at the Sotheby's auction.

BABE RUTH BONANZA

Speaking of autographs, a man walked into the Strongsville show (Cleveland) in 1989 with several Babe Ruth checks. He told me that his father had been one of the Babe's accountants, and I believed him.

He was at the show all day, going around to different dealers, showing the checks, signed balls and autographed books. Thank God he chose me. I paid him $50,000.

After the show, Paul Lewicki and I drove to the man's home in Crestline, Ohio, meeting at the Crestline Diner. He had over 100 personal checks, some even made out to Claire, Ruth's wife, and a couple made out to the IRS. On the checks made out to Claire, it looked like the same signature, front and back.

For all those who had concerns about stories that Claire actually signed a lot of Babe Ruth autographs, that news can't be encouraging. I couldn't tell the difference between the two signatures.

****

"UP AGAINST THE CAR"

In the summer of 1989 I went with Paul Lewicki down to Bill Huggins' store, The House of Cards, in Wheaton, Md. I was there to purchase a collection of baseball and football cards, which I did.

But the collection hadn't been nearly as extensive, or expensive, as I had expected, and I think I still had about $155,000 in cash with me. Paul and I marched into Bill's store to try to sell the football cards to him, and he did buy quite a few of them. At some point we decided to take a break for lunch. Naturally I took my briefcase, still loaded with cash, with me as we went a couple of doors down to a delicatessen for some sandwiches to go.

We returned to his shop, and normally, when I am carrying a lot of money with me, I keep my foot against my briefcase so that I know if someone moves it. Instinctively I put my leg out, and no briefcase. I had left it at the delicatessen.

I ran next door and there's the lady. She has the briefcase open and she's looking at it, and at the same time she's on the phone.

She hangs up and tells me, "Sir, I founda you briefcase, and I scared you have a lotsa money." I thanked her profusely. My heart was pounding. Again, I thanked her and tried to give her a reward, but she wouldn't take it. We went back to the store, finished our lunch and later our business with Bill, and headed back to our car.

As we walked down the street, we were surrounded suddenly by policemen. "Up against the car," one of them said. There were five officers, and they had me spread-eagled while they searched me. They had Paul's hands behind his back, and he was getting a little obnoxious asking them why we had been stopped.

They said that they had gotten a tip that I had been in the baseball card store, and that I had a lot of money. That's apparently illegal in Wheaton, Md. I told them that it was none of their business if I had that much money in my briefcase. After they found out that I wasn't a drug dealer, one of the sergeants came over to me and apologized. We were just happy to get the hell out of there.

Also, it taught me a lesson. I never leave my briefcase at delicatessens anymore.

****

A MOUNTAIN OF UNOPENED PACKS

In 1982, I purchased 15 or 20 cases of 1975 rack packs, 24 packs to a box, six boxes to a case, from a man in South Jersey. I paid him over $10,000, and I brought the whole thing to a show at the Hotel Penta across from Madison Square Garden in New York. That pile of unopened packs created quite a stir.

I was literally on the floor for hours during the show, cracking open cases and selling boxes to dealers. They were not allowed to search any of the boxes, and after they bought the boxes they were putting them out and selling them immediately to the public.

As they sold the packs and boxes, they would come back for more. It was getting pretty crazy; we were betting on whether or not there was a Yount or a Brett rookie on top of any of the packs. If there was not, I would give the dealer a $100 rebate.

We were selling the packs for $5, and $20 for those with Brett and Yount showing. In those days, people were incredulous that I would have the nerve to charge $20 for a Brett or a Yount rookie.

Unopened rack pack of 1975 Topps

Paul and I were at Jack Petruzelli's Anaheim show over Labor Day of 1993 when a guy strolls in with eight or 10 of every 1966 high number, and a few 1964s and 1965s.

He said that his mother had owned a miniature golf course in the 1960s, and had had vending machines with baseball cards. He walked right over to my table and said, "I read about you in *Sports Illustrated*. Here I am. Make me rich."

So I did. I spent over $20,000 on those high numbers.

****

AND A TRIP TO CANADA

I have avoided trips to our neighbors to the north just because of this particular incident. In July of 1987, a Canadian dealer I know as Jimmy V called me and said there was a good collection just across the border in St. Catherines.

I flew to Buffalo with Paul, rented a car and crossed the border into Canada. They asked me if I had anything to declare, and I said no, though I did have $55,000 in cash with me.

We drove to his house and bought his collection, which was sets from the early 1950s in binders. We put all the binders into a large box, and neatly placed that on the back seat, along with the invoice stating that I had paid $43,000 for these cards.

When Paul and I get back to the border, the inspector asked me again if I have anything to declare. I told him that I had bought some baseball cards, and that other than that, I had spent the day with a friend.

He politely asked me to pull the car over, looked in the back seat and saw the cards. Unfortunately, he also saw the invoice, which I had stupidly left with it. But I wasn't trying to hide anything.

I told the inspector that all of the cards were printed in the United States, so therefore there was no duty on them. He didn't seem to agree with that assessment.

He was pretty nice, except for holding me up for half an hour. I still contend to this day that since the cards weren't printed in Canada, there should not be a duty on them. He told me that I had a choice; take the cards back to Canada or pay a duty, which would have been over $3,000. I wasn't about to do that.

Back we went to Canada, called Jimmy V and later met him at his house. Jimmy V explained our situation to a couple of friends of his, so they put the bag of cards into their car, told Paul and I to get a 10-minute head start, and back we go to the border.

Of course, I get the same inspector at the border. He asked me if I was trying it again, and I said, no, I was having the cards sent to me.

And he has me pull over once again. At this point, I start to get a little obnoxious, pointing out that I am an American citizen and demanding my rights as such. He countered that I would be under arrest if I failed to pull over, and I conceded that point.

The inspector takes out his flashlight and tells me to open the trunk, and I make a few more pointed comments, but he just kept on searching for those cards.

About that time, I turn around and see that the other car, the one with the cards in it, was coming up to the booth. And I said to myself, "If they catch these guys, I am going to jail and I will never see my wife again."

But they get through without a hitch, and as I hear them speed off, my inspector gives me a stern warning and lets me go. I was never so happy as when we passed the falls and I saw that sign saying "Entering the United States."

****

AND THREE THAT GOT AWAY

Paul, Glenn Stuart and I flew to Chicago one time, and then had to drive another three hours to Indiana to look at this collection. I should preface this by saying that I don't like smoking, and I certainly don't like it in a confined room when I am trying to look at baseball cards.

Anway, we get to this house, and I sat down at this long table to look at the cards, and immediately there are two elderly women sitting on either side of me, smoking incessantly.

They were there for security reasons, we were told. The man selling the cards didn't want to sit down at the table with me, he didn't want to hear any discusscions, he simply wanted to hear how much money I was going to pay for his collection.

He wanted $321,000 for his cards, but he wouldn't give me a breakdown explaining how he had arrived at that figure. I needed to know how he was grading and pricing the older sets. It took a couple of hours to go through all of the older sets, and I told him that I wanted to see where we stood before I spent a lot more time on the deal. His answer; "The whole deal is cut in stone."

Meanwhile, Paul gets up to go to the bathroom, and I told the guy that if his price was cut in stone, I still needed to see how he had graded and priced the sets from 1952 to 1959.

"Nope, it's cut in stone," was all he would say.

By the time Paul gets out of the bathroom, it was all over and we were on our way out the door. I had certified checks for $321,000 in my pocket, and the guy would not tell me how he had priced the older cards.

The bottom line is that it probably wasn't a good deal. A year and one half later he sold out to another dealer for a lot less money than he would've gotten from me.

****

I went down to Florida with Aubrey and Linda Shoemake to the home of a sergeant in the Air Force. He had also called Howards Sports Collectibles, and this was the first time I had ever done this kind of arrangement with both of us offering bids for the cards.

I was delayed for three hours coming in, and the two guys from Howards had been there quite some time going through the cards when I got there. The guy wanted sealed bids from both of us, and it took me about four hours to go through it all, and we waited some more for Howards to finish.

When he opened the bids they had beat me by $100 on a total bid of about $24,000. I didn't mind all that much, since I still had a couple of other deals working in Florida on that trip. And the guy was very nice. After it was all over, he handed me about $1,000 worth of Goudeys and Play Balls for my air fare, which I thought was pretty classy.

Still, I hate losing collections.

****

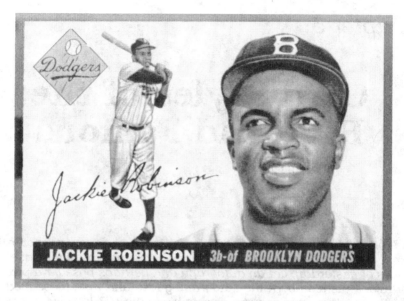

1955 Topps Jackie Robinson

Another time, John Broggi and I went up the Thruway to Albany for a deal with a guy who had gem mint Topps cards from 1955 and 1956.

John was going through the single cards and pricing them, and I was pricing the sets. We came to a price; the single cards were, I think, $8,500, and the whole deal around $15,000.

And the guy says, "Absolutely not. The set price is okay, but the singles price is much too low. I don't want to sell them."

So I said, "Okay, can I buy the sets?"

And he said no, adding that now he wanted both of us to leave his house immediately. And he threw us out.

We had almost a four hour drive back, and I asked Broggi what had he done in coming up with the price for the singles? "You must have been off in your price," I told him.

But he said, no, he had priced them at 50 or 60 percent of the guide. It was just one that got away.

Still, we mourn missing all those mint 1956s. Not that we would have made a lot of money, but it was simply disappointing to have cards that nice elude our grasp.

****

Chapter 5

Card Styles of the Rich and Famous

It probably started out innocently enough. Some show promoter figured maybe collectors would like to mingle with some of the baseball stars of yesterday, get an autograph and perhaps pose for a picture or two. Thus was born the autograph guest, and from those modest mythical beginnings sometime probably in the 1970s, a big business has developed.

To be whimsical, call the autograph game a subset of the card collecting business, but whatever you call it it is a multimillion dollar enterprise that, happily, provides a lot of money to retired ballplayers. Given that many of them played when financial rewards were only a fraction of modern times, that is reason enough to applaud, but there is much more.

Despite its current trappings that seem to reduce the autograph experience to the warmth and intimacy of a flu shot on the first day of boot camp, it still offers the average fan something unique and often treasured. A chance to meet, however briefly, some of the heroes of their youth.

In the last 15 years, fans from every corner of the country have had the chance to meet some of the game's brightest lights, and if the cynical want to sneer at the value of the autograph, it would seem impossible to dismiss the impact of the moment itself for so many.

Such moments remain treasured long after the autograph or the baseball card have been sold. For Alan Rosen, a baseball fan as a young man and a card collector, with the traditional interruptions, his emergence as America's most widely known baseball card dealer has provided him with literally hundreds of those moments.

He seems to treasure them with the same zeal as the lone collector who finally shakes hands with his favorite player after a 25-year wait. Perhaps Mr. Mint was destined for this role; as a teen-ager he had met and been photographed with his own favorite player, Mickey Mantle, along with several other members of one of the most famous teams in history, the 1961 New York Yankees.

If the Yankees gave Rosen a special moment in 1961, he handsomely returned the favor a full 30 years later. With a little help from a friend named Trump.

I had collected cards from 1959 to 1962, so this was the period of baseball that I cherished more than any other, and it was a thrill to put together the reunion show for one of the best teams ever. I ran that show with Bill Hongach of Capital Cards, and we got 32 members of the 1961 team to come to Trump Castle for the show.

It was like a happening. It was really neat, especially with all the signed bats, and balls, and the lithographs by Ron Lewis, who did the 500 Home Run print. Hector Lopez, Bob Cerv, Earl Torgeson, Jim Coates. To have all the **1961 Yankees** together at one time was amazing.

I had dinner with Johnny Blanchard, Bill Stafford and Ralph Terry. Bob Turley, a millionaire now, had his private pilot bring him to the show. Al Downing, whom I had met almost a year earlier, was there, and Bobby Richardson, the extraordinary second baseman, who hugged me and apologized profusely because he was four hours late because of his son's graduation from college that same day.

It was a tremendous paycheck for all of the players, with each one getting $7,000 for doing the show, except for Mantle, Berra and Ford, who got considerably more. We paid the airfares. We paid for most of it, but Donald Trump gave us a lot, too. He paid for the drinks and meals. We had buffets, roast beef, shrimp, everything was on the house. He gave us the rooms, threw a fantastic disco party.

Alan Rosen warms the bench with (left to right), Art Ditmar, Tony Kubek and Darrell Johnson.

Some 30 years after this picture was taken, Alan Rosen and Donald Trump teamed up to help celebrate Yogi's 65th birthday.

It was also a surprise 65th birthday party for Yogi, and Trump came down with this giant cake and we all sang happy birthday. On the Saturday morning before the show we had a photo shoot, and Trump spent three hours taking team-style pictures with the players.

It was great. Marnee and I had lunch with Trump, and he led us around by the hand at the casinos and escorted us around the Taj Mahal. He is a baseball fan, a Ted Williams fan. He was nice to all the players and their wives, and talked baseball with everybody.

We laid out $725,000 for that show, and wound up making $10,000. Like dopes, we held it on Mother's Day, and wound up not making any money. We had a lock of about $650,000 in pre-ordered autographed stuff from the show, so we weren't really at risk, but we thought we would make more.

I thought the single autographs would sell well, but it wound up being the team stuff. People were buying the super tickets for all 32 guys. We also had a lot of sales following the show from the remaining stock.

It if sounds like regrets, it isn't. To this day the players tell me that it was the greatest show that they have ever been at. I didn't make a lot of money, but it was a great weekend.

****

Speaking of Yankees, I guess I have always had a link there ever since those posed pictures with the team when I was a teenager. Last year (1993) I bought the collection from the estate of **Del Webb**, one of the owners of the Yankees during their heyday of pennants and world championships from 1947 to 1964.

Webb's second wife called me from California about purchasing his memorabilia, which included all those American League Championship or World Series rings. She had been negotiating with other major dealers as well, and I finally got a chance in the summer to look at the stuff.

I was in California for Jack Petruzelli's Anaheim show, and I drove to her home in Beverly Hills. From the intercom, Mrs. Webb told me to pull into the garage. I couldn't believe that all of that valuable memorabilia was in the garage, but she said, "Oh, yes, it's carpeted."

Indeed, it was carpeted, and it proved a cozy atmosphere for the Rolls Royce. Mrs. Webb comes in, dressed to kill, points to the corner and comes out with this leather box with D.E.W. initials on it.

Inside were the 15 rings, and he had never worn them. They were gorgeous. They were bright gold and they looked like they had been made yesterday afternoon.

I opened up some of the other boxes, and there were 15 or 20 balls autographed by all the members of the 1956 Yankees, still in the original box with the same tissue paper.

There were hundreds of press pins, including specially made 14-karat versions for the wives, black bats, team pictures, silver trays and service trays elaborately engraved to team members and dignitaries, pendants, pocket watches and belt buckles. Literally hundreds of pieces, and many were one of a kind items.

We started negotiating. And she said, "I'll tell you what, you're going to be in town for a while, call me tomorrow. I want to think about it."

I was upset, because I really wanted to buy the stuff. And I was ready to buy it; I had offered her $155,000 for the whole pile, at which point she said she wanted to think about it. It's kind of tough to negotiate with someone

World Series rings from the estate of former Yankee owner Del Webb.

who lives in a $3 million house and drives a $200,000 car.

I left, and I was really bummed out. I called her the next day and she's talking about anything EXCEPT the deal, and then she says, "You know, Mr. Rosen, I was thinking about it and I'd like to get $165,000. That would be much fairer." We agreed on $160,000.

I went back to Beverly Hills with Ron Oser and an executive with Superior Galleries. She counted out the money that I handed her and gave it to the butler.

We took the collection back to Superior. They took some of the stuff, I sold the 1961 ring and a couple of the others, broke up the press pin collection and put the baseballs in my auction.

****

That same year, I went to the home of Hall of Famer **Lou Boudreau**, a teammate of Dale Mitchell's and the MVP on that 1948 Cleveland squad, and purchased a large quantity of autographed baseballs. I also bought a beautiful Joe DiMaggio jersey which DiMaggio had given Boudreau, and it even included a photo of the Yankee Clipper giving it to him.

I bought several uniforms and autographed bats and even his silver bat that he was awarded for winning the 1944 batting title. It wasn't engraved, because he had won the championship on the final day of the season, beating out Bobby Doerr of Boston by two points.

But he wouldn't sell me his World Series ring from 1948, nor would he part with his MVP trophy from that same year. The entire deal was almost $100,000.

****

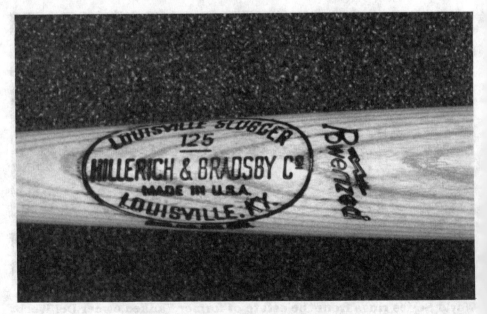

An autographed Lou Boudreau bat

Dale Mitchell wasn't a Yankee, having spent virtually his whole career with the Indians, but to his eternal chagrin he is remembered almost solely for his role in a game against the Yankees.

In February of 1992 I got a call from Dale Mitchell Jr., the son of the former Cleveland outfielder who wound up as the answer to a trivia question after taking a disputed called third strike for the final out of Don Larsen's perfect game in the 1956 World Series.

I met the son in Pennsylvania, and we discussed the purchase of his father's memorabilia. His father had died in 1987 at the age of 65.

I purchased his father's World Series ring from 1948 and several uniforms. I also bought a highly unusual, game-used couch, a bat couch (this was nothing designed by Batman or Robin, it was a couch made of bats). This was in Washington, D.C., so we tied it to the roof of my car and drove home to New Jersey in the pouring rain with this bat couch on top. The whole deal was about $15,000.

He was a real nice guy, and we got to talking about baseball players and personalities. I've dealt with literally hundreds of ballplayers and their families over the years, and he told me something that was really sad.

His father had been a helluva ballplayer, with a .312 lifetime average and had been one of the toughest hitters in baseball to strike out. In seven full seasons and parts of four others, the most times he ever struck out in any one season was 21.

Towards the end of his life, his father got so aggravated by people asking him about that one stupid strikeout. Here he was, a lifetime .300 hitter, and every time he was interviewed it wasn't for his accomplishments on the field, it was for that strikeout. His son told me that, to the day his father died, it bothered him greatly. He wanted to be known as a good ballplayer, not for one strikeout.

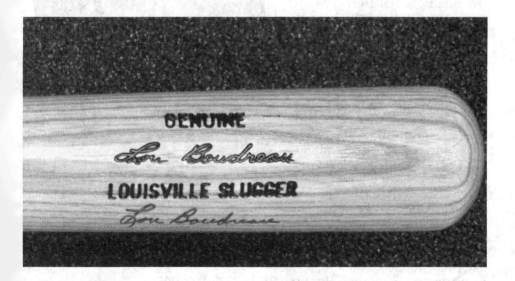

1956 Topps Dale Mitchell

He was so bitter about it, in fact, that in the last two years he wouldn't give any interviews at all. And he still maintained to the end that the called third strike was a bad call, and also that the home plate umpire, Babe Pinelli, had agreed with him that he had blown the call. He was haunted by it.

****

I met Leslie Wagner-Blair, a granddaughter of **Honus Wagner**, at the Pittsburgh show at Robert Morris College in 1991. It was truly exciting to meet a relative of Wagner's, who in his time was the greatest star in baseball. I became friendly with the family, and I've been to the home where he was born and where he grew up.

Of course, I asked her about the T-206 legend, or at least the most oft-repeated one, that Wagner had that card pulled from production because he didn't approve of tobacco. She said that the story was not accurate. While he did have a dislike for tobacco, his main concern was children. Honus

Above, and on the following page, are two of the loving cups from the estate of Honus Wagner.

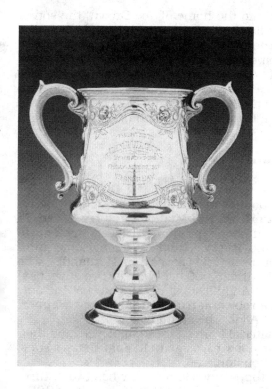

had a soft spot for kids and baseball, and he was heavily involved in a number of kids' baseball leagues, leagues that bore his name, and he was commissioner of several of them.

Anyway, he didn't want his face or name used in a situation that might prompt children to smoke or even buy tobacco products. That explanation is also confirmed by a couple of old newspaper articles of the period.

One year later I was working with Christie's Auction, and she gave me several items from his estate for the auction. Wagner is a genuine American icon, and when you get memorabilia directly from the source it sells for two or three times what it might otherwise. We also had a letter to go with each of the items.

The list included his 1907 batting championship medal, several of the loving cups that he won for excellence on the field, advertising pieces, bats, all told about 30 or 40 lots.

The batting medal brought $75,000 from Bruce McNall of Honus Wagner card fame, and the game-used bat brought $10,000. A gold and silver-plated safety razor with his initials, with original blade, brought $1,000 for a used razor in a velvet box. Noted collector Bill Mastro also bought several of the auction items.

****

As I mentioned before, I had met **Al Downing** even before the 30th reunion show, and the circumstances were somewhat unusual. I ran across his World Series ring in a pawn shop, and paid $4,500 for it.

Curious about how it had come to such a lowly fate, and wondering whether Downing himself still wanted the piece, I tracked him down in September of 1990 and asked him to tell me the story.

He said that he had lost the ring many years ago after leaving it in a hotel room on a road trip. I told him that I would gladly sell to him for the same amount that I paid. "It's your ring," I told him.

And he shocked me, because he didn't have any interest in it at all. To me, you would have to cut my finger off to get that ring.

I ultimately sold it for $7,500.

****

In 1989, I flew to out to California to the home of Joe Brown, the son of **Joe E. Brown**, the famous vaudeville comedian. He had, at that time, the largest collection of press pins in the world, with all the phantoms, all the all-stars and all the World Series pins.

I went to his beautiful home, and he had all these pins on this giant coffee table, under glass, with notes on each one giving the year. I paid him $225,000 for the collection, and promptly sold it for $275,000 to one of the more famous collectors around, Jim Copeland, who had made the trip with me.

****

The list of players that we have bought memorabilia from is lengthy indeed, including names like **Steve Carlton, Bill Madlock** and **Irv Noren**. In 1992, Mead Chasky, an agent to a number of prominent players, took me to the homes of **Keith Hernandez** and **Rusty Staub**. I bought some autographed baseballs, photos and a couple of Gold Gloves from Hernandez, who was moving to California. I spent about $25,000 between the two guys, paying $5,000 each for the Gold Gloves. And baseball players are not the only athletes we've dealt with; I bought a robe and trunks from **Chuck Wepner**, "The Bayonne Bleeder," who fought Ali for the championship.

While I have purchased a lot of material from various ballplayers and their families, I have also sold them quite a few cards as well. **Yogi Berra's** sons, Larry and Tim Berra, are both good customers.

Larry is an advanced collector, a Topps guy. He probably has two or three sets from 1953-55, four or five 1956 sets and eight or 10 sets from 1957, plus he has a ton of star cards. He might have eight or nine Koufax rookies. I sold him the Ruth, Gehrig and Cobb from the U.S. Caramel find for $1,500. He put all three in my auction later on and got $8,600.

Tim Berra is a mint freak. The card must be gem mint, unimprovable, shot out of a cannon. If the BACK of the card is not 50/50 centering, he's out.

Reggie Jackson not only is a friend of mine but a collector who buys Mantle, Ruth and Gehrig, and his own rookie cards. I have sold him well over 250 of his own rookie cards. At one time he had a plan to offer a signed version of his rookie card for each of his home runs, but a devastating fire at his home may have torpedoed that notion. A real nice guy, but sometimes he wants to pay with autographs, and that won't work.

Gary Carter is one of the famous ballplayers who is widely known to be a card collector as well. I helped him finish his 1953 Topps set with the Mantle and the Mays. Another nice guy, and just like Reggie, he wanted to pay me in autographs, but I wouldn't go for it.

I also sell cards to **Tom Harmer**, the famous harness driver, who trained horses for years for George Steinbrenner and currently trains for Cubs pitcher Dan Plesac. He is another advanced collector, with gem mint, unimprovable Topps sets from 1964 and up, and numerous star cards, all gem mint and centered.

Royals shortstop **Greg Gagne** walks around at shows in a t-shirt and jeans, talking to dealers and having a good time, piecing together a 1971 Topps set. I asked him, "What the hell are you doing piecing together a set that you could afford to buy all at once?" And he told me that he would never buy a set all at once, that it was much more fun and exciting putting it together a little bit at a time.

I thought that was pretty neat.

****

Joe Garagiola and his wife Audrey are good friends. He came to the Christie's sale, and sat with me through the whole auction. **Pete Rose** has become a pretty good friend. He's getting out of a cab in Detroit at a show and I'm pulling in. "Hey, Mint Man, how's it going?" he says.

Monte Irvin, Willie Mays, Mickey Mantle, Nolan Ryan, Whitey Ford, Stan Musial, Richie Ashburn. I could probably name 500 ballplayers that I've met over the years, and, unbelievably, many who remember my name.

Plus, I met **Howdy Doody** and **Buffalo Bob**.

And if you don't know who they are, that only means that you're younger than the Mint Man.

****

Chapter 6

Around the Corner

It is hard to comprehend all that has taken place in the card collecting hobby in the years since Fleer and Donruss broke Topps' monopoly back in 1981.

A small hobby for arrested adolescents was then on the verge of probably the greatest sustained period of growth that any hobby had ever experienced. The only thing that even remotely makes sense about the period is the day-to-day context of growth; without it the increase in the number of new cards and of new card sets would seem too farfetched.

If you had told someone 10 years ago that by 1994 there would six or more major companies producing cards in all four major sports, and that each company was producing four or five sets per sport, in some cases, you would have likely had your sanity seriously questioned. It is only now that we are starting to feel some of the strain from that wild expansion.

These days new card sales are terrible, and people selling cards from 1981 to present are going out of business right and left. All because of the state of the economy and the incredible number of new cards that are produced every year.

I will sell about three million dollars in old cards this year, down from a high of nearly twice that much four years ago, and I know other dealers who sell old cards whose numbers are also down, and in some cases, substantially. And the number of tables at shows and attendance in many cases has been going down for a couple of years. The avalanche of newer cards is primarily responsible for this.

I don't necessarily think that that means that the state of the hobby is bad.

There's nothing inherently wrong with getting smaller. The truth is, we (the hobby) don't know what size we are supposed to be. From 1988-90 you could have sold almost anything, the growth and expansion was so unbelievable.

I was even within one week or so of going public back then. We had the papers prepared and everything, but at the last minute I decided against it, not wanting to answer to a board of directors. And ever since then my business has contracted, for the reasons mentioned above.

That aforementioned avalanche of new material puts a crimp in the sales of old and new cards alike. It all has a synergistic effect; a collector goes to a show and gets soured seeing all the new material around. He looks at a price guide and sees the prices going down, sees sets selling for less than he paid for them. Before you know it, the new card business is struggling.

The card companies have, in many cases, adjusted their total print runs, even to the point of hinting that this or that item is scarce or rare. Huh? Rare is roast beef and hair. There is nothing made currently that is rare, and if it is, it is a contrived rarity like an insert card.

The major dealers selling older material, like Kit Young, or Bill Goepner from San Diego Sports Collectibles, and the other longtime players, are still in the hobby and still making money. Still, many dealers don't even do some of the major conventions anymore, like Willow Grove, and many others are cutting back in a variety of ways, but I think it can all be attributed to the economy and the bashing that we took from all those new cards. There is simply too much for a person to collect, and only so much money to go around for hobby purposes.

What puts additional pressure on my own business is the absence of genuine "finds" in recent years. As I check my records, virtually all of the significant finds, as opposed to simply purchasing a known collection, occured before 1991. There has been very little in the past three or four years, a couple of small ones like the 1932 U.S. Caramels, but not much else.

That's hard on my business, since the profit margin on finds can be a lot greater than routine purchases and sales and my auctions, all of which are run on tighter margins.

I do a bit on the Home Shopping Network every year with Bill Roller, a big baseball fan and a walking encyclopedia about the game. We've done it every year for the past eight or nine years, taping 10 or 15 five-minute segments or maybe a half-hour, and then the network plays them through the rest of the year while they are selling sports memorabilia.

And with all those people watching those segments, all of that exposure over several years and literally hours of interviews, nothing has ever turned up in the way of finds as a result of those appearances.

Oh, we would get a lot of calls every time another segment would air, even hundreds of calls over the years, but not one good one. Nobody in this business has gotten more publicity than Alan Rosen. So many people know about me, know who I am and about my previous finds and deals, and look how little has turned up in the last four or five years.

But even having said that, I still believe that there may be something out there. The next phone call could be the one. One case of cards could change a person's life.

Down the road I still see positive signs for the vintage card business. For one thing, the new millenium holds great promise for values of cards from this century. I think that once the economy improves and/or the year 2000 arrives, cards from 1952 to 1975 will show another significant jump, especially the cards from the 1960s and 1970s.

For right now, the prices of those cards are just about right, accurately reflecting current market conditions, but they will rise in the next five or six years.

Many people may not have enough money for a 1952 Topps set, or even a 1952 Topps Mantle, but the star cards from the 1960s that are a couple of hundred dollars will jump in the year 2000. Call it a pyschological effect if you will, but being in another century will change the way people think about those cards. They obviously won't be that much older than they are right now, but they will SEEM much older.

But when those heady days come, Mr. Mint probably won't have any inventory to speak of. I haven't got much right now. There's no hobby that I know of that has ever been on such a roll as this one. It was an 11-year fling from 1979 to 1990, and I always wondered when it was going to stop. That sense of anticipation played into my decision about not keeping any inventory. I was always skeptical about how long the swell ride would last.

When the music stops, I want to be sitting down, meaning I want to have money and not inventory.

And if that sounds gloomy, it shouldn't. It's simply the way my business works. Baseball cards are here to stay. There will always be a market for people to buy and sell their heroes on cardboard. It's nostalgia, just like Rock 'n Roll. And Rock 'n Roll will never go away, just like baseball cards.

1960 Topps Mickey Mantle

****

1948 Babe Ruth Story

The Philadelphia Gum Co., in 1948, created a card set about the movie "The Babe Ruth Story", which starred William Bendix and Claire Trevor. The set, whose American Card Catalog designation is R421, contains 28 black and white, numbered cards which measure 2" by 2-1/2". The Babe Ruth Story set was originally intended to consist of sixteen cards. Twelve additional cards (#'s 17-28) were added when Ruth died before the release of the film. The card backs include an offer for an autographed photo of William Bendix, starring as the Babe, for five Swell Bubble Gum wrappers and five cents.

Mr. Mint Says - This is an extremely undervalued set. I've had no more than three sets since I've been in the hobby.

It sells very well when not discolored (gray or brown). It looks like 1948 Bowman in size and black and white format, and from the fact that it never really seems to come with bright white stock. It is frequently seen off-center and dark gray.

The high numbers are much tougher, but a lot of them seem to come with sharp corners, though. I can't recall any problem with print lines with this issue.

If there were more of these around there would be more interest from collectors because they are neat cards. They are largely unavailable, however, and I haven't seen any at a show in years.

		MT
Complete Set:		2000.00
Common Player (1-16):		20.00
Common Player (17-28):		60.00
1	"The Babe Ruth Story" In The Making	100.00
2	Bat Boy Becomes the Babe... William Bendix	100.00
3	Claire Hodgson...Claire Trevor	100.00
4	Babe Ruth and Claire Hodgson	100.00
5	Brother Matthias...Charles Bickford	100.00
6	Phil Conrad...Sam Levene	100.00
7	Night Club Singer...Gertrude Niesen	100.00
8	Baseball's Famous Deal...Jack Dunn (William Frawley)	100.00
9	Mr. & Mrs. Babe Ruth	100.00
10	Babe Ruth, Claire Ruth, and Brother Matthias	20.00
11	Babe Ruth and Miller Huggins (Fred Lightner)	20.00
12	Babe Ruth At Bed Of Ill Boy Johnny Sylvester (Gregory Marshall)	20.00
13	Sylvester Family Listening To Game	20.00
14	"When A Feller Needs a Friend" (With Dog At Police Station)	20.00
15	Dramatic Home Run	20.00
16	The Homer That Set the Record (#60)	20.00
17	"The Slap That Started Baseball's Famous Career"	60.00
18	The Babe Plays Santa Claus	60.00
19	Meeting Of Owner And Manager	60.00
20	"Broken Window Paid Off"	60.00
21	Babe In A Crowd Of Autograph Collectors	60.00
22	Charley Grimm And William Bendix	60.00
23	Ted Lyons And William Bendix	75.00
24	Lefty Gomez, William Bendix, And Bucky Harris	75.00
25	Babe Ruth and William Bendix	150.00
26	Babe Ruth And William Bendix	150.00
27	Babe Ruth And Claire Trevor	150.00
28	William Bendix, Babe Ruth, And Claire Trevor	150.00

No. 1
"THE BABE RUTH STORY"
IN THE MAKING

Babe Ruth gives William Bendix some fine pointers in the art of hitting home runs.

Bendix enacts the part of the Bambino in the film's glorification of Ruth's dramatic life, an Allied Artists picture produced by Roy Del Ruth.

As bat boy for the Yankees Ruth was Bendix's idol years ago. Little did he think that more than 20 years later he would be selected to play the Sultan of Swat in the motion picture "The Babe Ruth Story".

Send us 5 Swell Bubble Gum wrappers and 5c for a large autographed picture of William Bendix, starring as Babe Ruth.

SWELL BUBBLE GUM
Philadelphia Chewing Gum Corporation
Havertown, Pa.

1948 Bowman

Bowman Gum Co.'s premiere set was produced in 1948, making it one of the first major issues of the post-war period. Forty-eight black and white cards comprise the set, with each card measuring 2-1/16" by 2-1/2" in size. The card backs, printed in black ink on grey stock, include the card number and the player's name, team, position, and a short biography. Twelve cards (#'s 7, 8, 13, 16, 20, 22, 24, 26, 29, 30 and 34) were printed in short supply when they were removed from the 36-card printing sheet to make room for the set's high numbers (#'s 37-48). These 24 cards command a higher price than the remaining cards in the set.

Mr. Mint Says - I seldom find this set in mint condition. This was Bowman's first try at producing baseball cards, and it shows. The photography is black and white and the design and production are relatively crude. The card stock is soft; most of the cards that you find at shows are gray or off-white. The cards sell great when the borders are truly white, but you rarely find it. Centering is not particularly bad with this set; the princrpal condition problem is with the borders.

The 12 short print cards seem to be on everyone's want list; I don't think that the higher numbers are that much more difficult to find than the lower ones.

The main cards are the Musial, Spahn, Rizzuto, Berra and other Hall of Famers, and the Berra, being his rookie card, is really tough to get in top condition.

Though I have never had any major finds or purchases, I did buy eight mint sets from the Lillian brothers in New York. I have never seen an unopened pack.

The set is not that popular, though collectors who focus on Bowmans usually collect all of them. At only 48 cards, it is pretty easy to collect.

		MT
Complete Set (48):		4800.
Common Player (1-36):		25.00
Common Player (37-48):		30.00
1	Bob Elliott	150.00
2	Ewell Blackwell	30.00
3	Ralph Kiner	200.00
4	Johnny Mize	135.00
5	Bob Feller	300.00
6	Yogi Berra	750.00
7	Pete Reiser	75.00
8	Phil Rizzuto	350.00
9	Walker Cooper	25.00
10	Buddy Rosar	25.00
11	Johnny Lindell	30.00
12	Johnny Sain	30.00
13	Willard Marshall	75.00
14	Allie Reynolds	50.00
15	Eddie Joost	25.00
16	Jack Lohrke	75.00
17	Enos Slaughter	125.00
18	Warren Spahn	400.00
19	Tommy Henrich	30.00
20	Buddy Kerr	75.00
21	Ferris Fain	25.00
22	Floyd (Bill) Bevens	75.00
23	Larry Jansen	25.00
24	Emil (Dutch) Leonard	35.00
25	Barney McCoskey (McCosky)	25.00
26	Frank Shea	75.00
27	Sid Gordon	25.00
28	Emil Verban	25.00
29	Joe Page	80.00
30	Whitey Lockman	75.00
31	Bill McCahan	25.00
32	Bill Rigney	25.00
33	Billy Johnson	30.00
34	Sheldon Jones	75.00
35	Snuffy Stirnweiss	30.00
36	Stan Musial	1100.00
37	Clint Hartung	30.00
38	Red Schoendienst	200.00
39	Augie Galan	30.00
40	Marty Marion	70.00
41	Rex Barney	30.00
42	Ray Poat	30.00
43	Bruce Edwards	30.00
44	Johnny Wyrostek	30.00
45	Hank Sauer	30.00
46	Herman Wehmeier	30.00
47	Bobby Thomson	75.00
48	Dave Koslo	75.00

1949 Bowman

In 1949, Bowman increased the size of its issue to 240 numbered cards. The cards, which measure 2-1/16" by 2-1/2", are black and white photos overprinted with various pastel colors. Beginning with card #109 in the set, Bowman inserted the players' names on the card fronts. Twelve cards (#'s 4, 78, 83, 85, 88, 98, 109, 124, 127, 132 and 143), which were produced in the first four series of printings, were reprinted in the seventh series with either a card front or back modification. These variations are noted in the checklist that follows. Card #'s 1-3 and 5-73 can be found with either white or grey backs. The complete set of value in the following checklist does not include the higher priced variation cards.

The many (96) high numbers now pose a real problem for collectors because of the high cost. Spending almost $10,000 for a high number series with only three Hall of Famers can scare away someone from even starting. When they were $10 or $15 each that was okay, but now at $75 or so it discourages collectors. In addition to being expensive, the high numbers are very tough to find. Probably 90 percent of the 1949 Bowmans that you see on the market are low numbers.

Jackie Robinson, Berra and Campanella are very tough cards to find, and along with Musial, are the main cards in the set. Paige, Snider and Ashburn in mint condition are undervalued, and the name on front/back variations are difficult to find and expensive when you do.

		MT
Complete Set (240):		20000.
Common Player (1-36):		18.50
Common Player (37-73):		22.00
Common Player (74-144):		18.50
Common Player (145-240):		80.00
1	Vernon Bickford	150.00
2	"Whitey" Lockman	18.50
3	Bob Porterfield	22.00
4a	Jerry Priddy (no name on front)	18.50
4b	Jerry Priddy (name on front)	50.00
5	Hank Sauer	18.50
6	Phil Cavarretta	20.00
7	Joe Dobson	18.50
8	Murry Dickson	18.50
9	Ferris Fain	22.00
10	Ted Gray	18.50
11	Lou Boudreau (FC)	75.00
12	Cass Michaels	18.50
13	Bob Chesnes	18.50
14	*Curt Simmons*	30.00
15	*Ned Garver*	21.00
16	Al Kozar	18.50
17	Earl Torgeson	18.50
18	Bobby Thomson	30.00
19	*Bobby Brown*	40.00
20	Gene Hermanski	20.00
21	Frank Baumholtz	18.50
22	Harry "P-Nuts" Lowrey	18.50
23	Bobby Doerr (FC)	100.00
24	Stan Musial	1000.00
25	Carl Scheib	18.50
26	George Kell (FC)	75.00
27	Bob Feller	225.00
28	Don Kolloway	18.50
29	Ralph Kiner	100.00
30	Andy Seminick	18.50
31	Dick Kokos	18.50
32	Eddie Yost	18.50
33	Warren Spahn	250.00
34	Dave Koslo	18.50
35	*Vic Raschi*	22.00
36	Pee Wee Reese (FC)	300.00
37	John Wyrostek	22.00
38	Emil Verban	22.00

Mr. Mint Says - This was the company's first effort at making a decent size set, and though it included more Hall of Famers than the first year, it was still too large a set for such a small percentage of major stars. This was Bowman's first try at color, and it was pretty crude, with a lot of the cards out of registration. That produces what I call "googey eyes" in the colorized black and white photos. These cards seem to have been printed on a thick, soft paper, that, like 1948, is seldom found pure white.

#	Player	Price	#	Player	Price
39	Bill Goodman	22.00	107	Eddie Lake	18.50
40	"Red" Munger	22.00	108	Ken Heintzelman	18.50
41	Lou Brissie	22.00	109a	Ed Fitz Gerald (script name on back)	18.50
42	"Hoot" Evers	22.00	109b	Ed Fitz Gerald (printed name on back)	75.00
43	Dale Mitchell	22.00	110	*Early Wynn*	100.00
44	Dave Philley	22.00	111	Red Schoendienst	75.00
45	Wally Westlake	22.00	112	Sam Chapman	18.50
46	*Robin Roberts*	325.00	113	Ray Lamanno	18.50
47	Johnny Sain	24.00	114	Allie Reynolds	25.00
48	Willard Marshall	22.00	115	Emil "Dutch" Leonard	18.50
49	Frank Shea	24.00	116	Joe Hatten	22.00
50	Jackie Robinson (FC)	1250.00	117	Walker Cooper	18.50
51	Herman Wehmeier	22.00	118	Sam Mele	18.50
52	Johnny Schmitz	22.00	119	Floyd Baker	18.50
53	Jack Kramer	22.00	120	Cliff Fannin	18.50
54	Marty Marion	25.00	121	Mark Christman	18.50
55	Eddie Joost	22.00	122	George Vico	18.50
56	Pat Mullin	22.00	123	Johnny Blatnick	18.50
57	Gene Bearden	22.00	124a	Danny Murtaugh (script name on back)	18.50
58	Bob Elliott	22.00	124b	Danny Murtaugh (printed name on back)	75.00
59	Jack Lohrke	22.00	125	Ken Keltner	21.00
60	Yogi Berra	500.00	126a	Al Brazle (script name on back)	18.50
61	Rex Barney	24.00	126b	Al Brazle (printed name on back)	75.00
62	Grady Hatton	22.00	127a	Henry Majeski (script name on back)	18.50
63	Andy Pafko	22.00	127b	Henry Majeski (printed name on back)	75.00
64	Dom DiMaggio (FC)	30.00	128	Johnny Vander Meer	21.00
65	Enos Slaughter	75.00	129	Billy Johnson	24.00
66	Elmer Valo	22.00	130	Harry "The Hat" Walker	21.00
67	Alvin Dark	24.00	131	Paul Lehner	18.50
68	Sheldon Jones	22.00	132a	Al Evans (script name on back)	18.50
69	Tommy Henrich	25.00	132b	Al Evans (printed name on back)	40.00
70	*Carl Furillo*	75.00	133	Aaron Robinson	18.50
71	Vern Stephens	22.00	134	Hank Borowy	18.50
72	Tommy Holmes	22.00	135	Stan Rojek	18.50
73	Billy Cox	24.00	136	Hank Edwards	18.50
74	Tom McBride	18.50	137	Ted Wilks	18.50
75	Eddie Mayo	18.50	138	"Buddy" Rosar	18.50
76	Bill Nicholson	18.50	139	Hank "Bow-Wow" Arft	18.50
77	Ernie Bonham	18.50	140	Ray Scarborough	18.50
78a	Sam Zoldak (no name on front)	18.50	141	"Tony" Lupien	18.50
78b	Sam Zoldak (name on front)	75.00	142	Eddie Waitkus	18.50
79	Ron Northey	18.50	143a	Bob Dillinger (script name on back)	18.50
80	Bill McCahan	18.50	143b	Bob Dillinger (printed name on back)	75.00
81	Virgil "Red" Stallcup	18.50	144	Mickey Haefner	18.50
82	Joe Page	24.00	145	"Blix" Donnelly	80.00
83a	Bob Scheffing (no name on front)	18.50	146	Mike McCormick	85.00
83b	Bob Scheffing (name on front)	75.00	147	Elmer Singleton	80.00
84	*Roy Campanella*	1000.00	148	Bob Swift	80.00
85a	Johnny Mize (no name on front)	65.00	149	Roy Partee	90.00
85b	Johnny Mize (name on front)	175.00	150	Allie Clark	80.00
86	Johnny Pesky	18.50	151	Mickey Harris	80.00
87	Randy Gumpert	18.50	152	Clarence Maddern	80.00
88a	Bill Salkeld (no name on front)	18.50	153	Phil Masi	80.00
88b	Bill Salkeld (name on front)	75.00	154	Clint Hartung	80.00
89	Mizell Platt	18.50	155	Mickey Guerra	80.00
90	Gil Coan	18.50	156	Al Zarilla	80.00
91	Dick Wakefield	18.50	157	Walt Masterson	80.00
92	Willie Jones	18.50	158	Harry Brecheen	80.00
93	Ed Stevens	18.50	159	Glen Moulder	80.00
94	*Mickey Vernon*	21.00	160	Jim Blackburn	80.00
95	Howie Pollett	18.50	161	"Jocko" Thompson	80.00
96	Taft Wright	18.50	162	*Preacher Roe*	135.00
97	Danny Litwhiler	18.50	163	Clyde McCullough	80.00
98a	Phil Rizzuto (no name on front)	150.00	164	*Vic Wertz*	80.00
98b	Phil Rizzuto (name on front)	225.00	165	"Snuffy" Stirnweiss	90.00
99	Frank Gustine	18.50	166	Mike Tresh	80.00
100	*Gil Hodges*	150.00	167	Boris "Babe" Martin	80.00
101	Sid Gordon	21.00	168	Doyle Lade	80.00
102	Stan Spence	18.50	169	Jeff Heath	80.00
103	Joe Tipton	18.50	170	Bill Rigney	80.00
104	Ed Stanky	21.00	171	Dick Fowler	80.00
105	Bill Kennedy	18.50	172	Eddie Pellagrini	80.00
106	Jake Early	18.50	173	Eddie Stewart	80.00

174	*Terry Moore*	90.00
175	Luke Appling (FC)	125.00
176	Ken Raffensberger	80.00
177	Stan Lopata	80.00
178	Tommy Brown	85.00
179	Hugh Casey	85.00
180	Connie Berry	80.00
181	Gus Niarhos	90.00
182	Hal Peck	80.00
183	Lou Stringer	80.00
184	Bob Chipman	80.00
185	Pete Reiser	85.00
186	"Buddy" Kerr	80.00
187	Phil Marchildon	80.00
188	Karl Drews	80.00
189	Earl Wooten	80.00
190	*Jim Hearn*	80.00
191	Joe Haynes	80.00
192	Harry Gumbert	80.00
193	Ken Trinkle	80.00
194	Ralph Branca	95.00
195	Eddie Bockman	80.00
196	Fred Hutchinson (FC)	80.00
197	Johnny Lindell	90.00
198	Steve Gromek	80.00
199	"Tex" Hughson	80.00
200	Jess Dobernic	80.00
201	Sibby Sisti	80.00
202	Larry Jansen	80.00
203	Barney McCosky	80.00
204	Bob Savage	80.00
205	Dick Sisler	80.00
206	Bruce Edwards	85.00
207	Johnny Hopp	80.00
208	"Dizzy" Trout	80.00
209	Charlie Keller	90.00
210	Joe Gordon	80.00
211	Dave "Boo" Ferris	80.00
212	Ralph Hamner	80.00
213	Charles "Red" Barrett	80.00
214	*Richie Ashburn*	750.00
215	Kirby Higbe	80.00
216	"Schoolboy" Rowe	85.00
217	Marino Pieretti	80.00
218	Dick Kryhoski	90.00
219	Virgil "Fire" Trucks (FC)	85.00
220	Johnny McCarthy	80.00
221	Bob Muncrief	80.00
222	Alex Kellner	80.00
223	Bob Hofman	80.00
224	*Satchel Paige* (FC)	1750.00
225	*Gerry Coleman*	100.00
226	Duke Snider	1500.00
227	Fritz Ostermueller	80.00
228	Jackie Mayo	80.00
229	Ed Lopat	150.00
230	Augie Galan	80.00
231	Earl Johnson	80.00
232	George McQuinn	90.00
233	Larry Doby (FC)	250.00
234	"Rip" Sewell	80.00
235	Jim Russell	80.00
236	Fred Sanford	90.00
237	Monte Kennedy	80.00
238	*Bob Lemon*	250.00
239	Frank McCormick	80.00
240	Norm "Babe" Young (Photo actually Bobby Young)	175.00

AUGIE GALAN

LEROY "Satchell" PAIGE

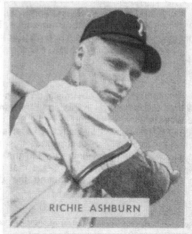

RICHIE ASHBURN

1950 Bowman

The quality of the 1950 Bowman issue showed a marked improvement over the company's previous efforts. The cards are beautiful color art reproductions of actual photographs and measure 2-1/16" by 2-1/2" in size. The card backs include the same type of information as found in the previous year's issue but are designed in a horizontal format. Cards found in the first two series of the set (#'s 1-72) are the scarcest in the issue. The backs of the final 72 cards in the set (#'s 181-252) can be found with or without the copyright line at the bottom of the card, the "without" version being the less common.

Mr. Mint Says - This was an improvement over earlier Bowman issues. The availability of these cards is much greater than the first two years, and after card #72 they can be found in mint condition.

Bowman put most of the Hall of Famers in the first series (1-72), obviously on purpose. The first and last cards in this set, Mel Parnell and Billy DeMars, are tough to find in top condition, as they are in virtually all older sets. Centering can be a problem with this set, especially in the high numbers, and there is frequently an aggravating print line that runs across the player's face, making the card almost impossible to sell.

		MT
Complete Set (252):		14000.
Common Player (1-72):		75.00
Common Player (73-252):		25.00

1	Mel Parnell	300.00
2	Vern Stephens	75.00
3	Dom DiMaggio	100.00
4	Gus Zernial	75.00
5	Bob Kuzava	75.00
6	Bob Feller	325.00
7	Jim Hegan	75.00
8	George Kell	125.00
9	Vic Wertz	75.00
10	Tommy Henrich	85.00
11	Phil Rizzuto	250.00
12	Joe Page	75.00
13	Ferris Fain	75.00
14	Alex Kellner	75.00
15	Al Kozar	75.00
16	*Roy Sievers*	75.00
17	Sid Hudson	75.00
18	Eddie Robinson	75.00
19	Warren Spahn	325.00
20	Bob Elliott	75.00
21	Pee Wee Reese	325.00
22	Jackie Robinson	1000.00
23	*Don Newcombe*	175.00
24	Johnny Schmitz	75.00
25	Hank Sauer	75.00
26	Grady Hatton	75.00
27	Herman Wehmeier	75.00
28	Bobby Thomson	100.00
29	Ed Stanky	75.00
30	Eddie Waitkus	75.00
31	*Del Ennis*	75.00
32	Robin Roberts	200.00
33	Ralph Kiner	175.00
34	Murry Dickson	75.00
35	Enos Slaughter	125.00
36	Eddie Kazak	75.00
37	Luke Appling	125.00
38	Bill Wight	75.00
39	Larry Doby	85.00
40	Bob Lemon	125.00
41	"Hoot" Evers	75.00
42	Art Houtteman	75.00
43	Bobby Doerr	125.00
44	Joe Dobson	75.00
45	Al Zarilla	75.00
46	Yogi Berra	750.00
47	Jerry Coleman	75.00
48	Lou Brissie	75.00
49	Elmer Valo	75.00
50	Dick Kokos	75.00
51	Ned Garver	75.00
52	Sam Mele	75.00
53	Clyde Vollmer	75.00
54	Gil Coan	75.00
55	"Buddy" Kerr	75.00
56	*Del Crandell* (Crandall)	80.00
57	Vernon Bickford	75.00
58	Carl Furillo	100.00
59	Ralph Branca	75.00
60	Andy Pafko	75.00
61	Bob Rush	75.00
62	Ted Kluszewski (FC)	100.00
63	Ewell Blackwell	75.00
64	Alvin Dark	75.00
65	Dave Koslo	75.00
66	Larry Jansen	75.00
67	Willie Jones	75.00
68	Curt Simmons	75.00

69	Wally Westlake	75.00		142	*Sherman Lollar*	25.00
70	Bob Chesnes	75.00		143	Eddie Stewart	20.00
71	Red Schoendienst	125.00		144	Al Evans	20.00
72	Howie Pollet	75.00		145	Jack Graham	20.00
73	Willard Marshall	20.00		146	Floyd Baker	20.00
74	*Johnny Antonelli*	20.00		147	*Mike Garcia*	30.00
75	Roy Campanella	450.00		148	Early Wynn	75.00
76	Rex Barney	20.00		149	Bob Swift	20.00
77	Duke Snider	425.00		150	George Vico	20.00
78	Mickey Owen	20.00		151	Fred Hutchinson	20.00
79	Johnny Vander Meer	20.00		152	Ellis Kinder	20.00
80	Howard Fox	20.00		153	Walt Masterson	20.00
81	Ron Northey	20.00		154	Gus Niarhos	25.00
82	"Whitey" Lockman	20.00		155	Frank "Spec" Shea	25.00
83	Sheldon Jones	20.00		156	Fred Sanford	25.00
84	Richie Ashburn	125.00		157	Mike Guerra	25.00
85	Ken Heintzelman	20.00		158	Paul Lehner	20.00
86	Stan Rojek	20.00		159	Joe Tipton	20.00
87	Bill Werle	20.00		160	Mickey Harris	20.00
88	Marty Marion	20.00		161	Sherry Robertson	20.00
89	George Munger	20.00		162	Eddie Yost	20.00
90	Harry Brecheen	20.00		163	Earl Torgeson	20.00
91	Cass Michaels	20.00		164	Sibby Sisti	20.00
92	Hank Majeski	20.00		165	Bruce Edwards	20.00
93	Gene Bearden	20.00		166	Joe Hatten	20.00
94	Lou Boudreau	75.00		167	Preacher Roe	55.00
95	Aaron Robinson	20.00		168	Bob Scheffing	20.00
96	Virgil "Fire" Trucks	20.00		169	Hank Edwards	20.00
97	Maurice McDermott	20.00		170	Emil Leonard	20.00
98	Ted Williams (FC)	1250.00		171	Harry Gumbert	20.00
99	Billy Goodman	20.00		172	Harry Lowrey	20.00
100	Vic Raschi	25.00		173	Lloyd Merriman	20.00
101	Bobby Brown	30.00		174	*Henry Thompson*	20.00
102	Billy Johnson	25.00		175	Monte Kennedy	20.00
103	Eddie Joost	20.00		176	"Blix" Donnelly	20.00
104	Sam Chapman	20.00		177	Hank Borowy	20.00
105	Bob Dillinger	20.00		178	Eddy Fitz Gerald	20.00
106	Cliff Fannin	20.00		179	Charles Diering	20.00
107	Sam Dente	20.00		180	Harry "The Hat" Walker	20.00
108	Ray Scarborough	20.00		181	Marino Pieretti	20.00
109	Sid Gordon	22.00		182	Sam Zoldak	20.00
110	Tommy Holmes	20.00		183	Mickey Haefner	20.00
111	Walker Cooper	20.00		184	Randy Gumpert	20.00
112	Gil Hodges	100.00		185	Howie Judson	20.00
113	Gene Hermanski	20.00		186	Ken Keltner	20.00
114	*Wayne Terwilliger*	20.00		187	Lou Stringer	20.00
115	Roy Smalley	20.00		188	Earl Johnson	20.00
116	Virgil "Red" Stallcup	20.00		189	Owen Friend	20.00
117	Bill Rigney	20.00		190	Ken Wood	20.00
118	Clint Hartung	20.00		191	Dick Starr	20.00
119	Dick Sisler	20.00		192	Bob Chipman	20.00
120	Jocko Thompson	20.00		193	Pete Reiser	20.00
121	Andy Seminick	20.00		194	Billy Cox	20.00
122	Johnny Hopp	20.00		195	Phil Cavarretta	20.00
123	Dino Restelli	20.00		196	Doyle Lade	20.00
124	Clyde McCullough	20.00		197	Johnny Wyrostek	20.00
125	Del Rice	20.00		198	Danny Litwhiler	20.00
126	Al Brazle	20.00		199	Jack Kramer	20.00
127	Dave Philley	20.00		200	Kirby Higbe	20.00
128	Phil Masi	20.00		201	Pete Castiglione	20.00
129	Joe Gordon	20.00		202	Cliff Chambers	20.00
130	Dale Mitchell	20.00		203	Danny Murtaugh	20.00
131	Steve Gromek	20.00		204	Granny Hamner	20.00
132	Mickey Vernon	20.00		205	Mike Goliat	20.00
133	Don Kolloway	20.00		206	Stan Lopata	20.00
134	"Dizzy" Trout	20.00		207	Max Lanier	20.00
135	Pat Mullin	20.00		208	Jim Hearn	20.00
136	"Buddy" Rosar	20.00		209	Johnny Lindell	20.00
137	Johnny Pesky	20.00		210	Ted Gray	20.00
138	Allie Reynolds	60.00		211	Charlie Keller	20.00
139	Johnny Mize	75.00		212	Gerry Priddy	20.00
140	Pete Suder	20.00		213	Carl Scheib	20.00
141	Joe Coleman	20.00		214	Dick Fowler	20.00

215	Ed Lopat	30.00
216	Bob Porterfield	20.00
217	Casey Stengel (FC)	200.00
218	Cliff Mapes	20.00
219	*Hank Bauer*	85.00
220	Leo Durocher (FC)	65.00
221	Don Mueller	20.00
222	Bobby Morgan	20.00
223	Jimmy Russell	20.00
224	Jack Banta	20.00
225	Eddie Sawyer	20.00
226	*Jim Konstanty*	20.00
227	Bob Miller	20.00
228	Bill Nicholson	20.00
229	Frank Frisch	75.00
230	Bill Serena	20.00
231	Preston Ward	20.00
232	*Al Rosen*	60.00
233	Allie Clark	20.00
234	*Bobby Shantz*	30.00
235	Harold Gilbert	20.00
236	Bob Cain	20.00
237	Bill Salkeld	20.00
238	Nippy Jones	20.00
239	Bill Howerton	20.00
240	Eddie Lake	20.00
241	Neil Berry	20.00
242	Dick Kryhoski	20.00
243	Johnny Groth	20.00
244	Dale Coogan	20.00
245	Al Papai	20.00
246	*Walt Dropo*	25.00
247	*Irv Noren*	20.00
248	*Sam Jethroe*	20.00
249	"Snuffy" Stirnweiss	20.00
250	Ray Coleman	20.00
251	Les Moss	20.00
252	Billy DeMars	100.00

1951 Bowman

In 1951, Bowman increased the number of cards in its set for the third consecutive year when it issued 324 cards. The cards are, like 1950, color art reproductions of actual photographs but now measured 2-1/16" by 3-1/8" in size. The player's name is situated in a small, black box on the card front. Several of the card fronts are enlargements of the 1950 version. The high-numbered series of the set (#'s 253-324), which includes the rookie cards of Mantle and Mays, are the scarcest of the issue.

There are 72 high numbers in the set which are scarce but not overly so; they are not as expensive as the 1949s, so collectors still feel like the set is obtainable. Off-center cards can be a problem, especially in the high number run; the Mantle rookie card often is found off-center, as is the Bill Dickey card in the high series.

The Ford card can be a bear because it is his rookie card and also the first card in the set. It is also a good illustration of the dramatic difference between grades, with an enormous swing between the mint price and the price of an off-condition specimen.

The Mantle and Mays rookie cards have helped to make this a very collectable and popular set, especially on the East Coast. It also helps that there are only about two dozen cards over $100.

Over the years I have purchased ten times as many 1951 sets as 1949, and the years 1951-53 are much more popular with collectors than the earlier issues. There were eight or ten sets in the Bowman find, and I have never seen any unopened material.

TED WILLIAMS

Mr. Mint Says - This was the first set with major rookie cards (Mantle, Mays and Ford), with beautiful artwork and a size (2-1/16" by 3-1/8" inches) that was becoming more popular and inching up towards the standard style of the modern card. Once again this is a very large set (324 cards) with a low percentage of major stars, and the three rookie cards often comprise 40 or 50 percent of the total value of the set. Because of the wonderful artwork and brilliant white borders, it sells far better than the previous two Bowman issues.

		MT
Complete Set (324):		32000.
Common Player (1-36):		25.00
Common Player (37-252):		18.00
Common Player (253-324):		75.00
1	*Whitey Ford*	2000.00
2	Yogi Berra	500.00
3	Robin Roberts	100.00
4	Del Ennis	25.00
5	Dale Mitchell	25.00
6	Don Newcombe	40.00
7	Gil Hodges	100.00
8	Paul Lehner	25.00
9	Sam Chapman	25.00
10	Red Schoendienst	90.00
11	"Red" Munger	25.00
12	Hank Majeski	25.00
13	Ed Stanky	30.00
14	Alvin Dark	30.00
15	Johnny Pesky	25.00
16	Maurice McDermott	25.00
17	Pete Castiglione	25.00
18	Gil Coan	25.00
19	Sid Gordon	25.00
20	Del Crandall	25.00
21	"Snuffy" Stirnweiss	25.00
22	Hank Sauer	25.00
23	"Hoot" Evers	25.00
24	Ewell Blackwell	25.00
25	Vic Raschi	35.00
26	Phil Rizzuto	150.00
27	Jim Konstanty	25.00
28	Eddie Waitkus	25.00
29	Allie Clark	25.00

30	Bob Feller	175.00
31	Roy Campanella	375.00
32	Duke Snider	375.00
33	Bob Hooper	25.00
34	Marty Marion	28.00
35	Al Zarilla	25.00
36	Joe Dobson	25.00
37	Whitey Lockman	18.00
38	Al Evans	18.00
39	Ray Scarborough	18.00
40	*Gus Bell*	22.00
41	Eddie Yost	18.00
42	Vern Bickford	18.00
43	Billy DeMars	18.00
44	Roy Smalley	18.00
45	Art Houtteman	18.00
46	George Kell	75.00
47	Grady Hatton	18.00
48	Ken Raffensberger	18.00
49	Jerry Coleman	22.00
50	Johnny Mize	75.00
51	Andy Seminick	18.00
52	Dick Sisler	18.00
53	Bob Lemon	75.00
54	*Ray Boone*	22.00
55	Gene Hermanski	20.00
56	Ralph Branca	35.00
57	Alex Kellner	18.00
58	Enos Slaughter	75.00
59	Randy Gumpert	18.00
60	"Chico" Carrasquel	18.00
61	Jim Hearn	18.00
62	Lou Boudreau	75.00
63	Bob Dillinger	18.00
64	Bill Werle	18.00
65	Mickey Vernon	20.00
66	Bob Elliott	18.00
67	Roy Sievers	18.00
68	Dick Kokos	18.00
69	Johnny Schmitz	18.00
70	Ron Northey	18.00
71	Jerry Priddy	18.00
72	Lloyd Merriman	18.00
73	Tommy Byrne	18.00
74	Billy Johnson	18.00
75	Russ Meyer	18.00
76	Stan Lopata	18.00
77	Mike Goliat	18.00
78	Early Wynn	75.00
79	Jim Hegan	18.00
80	Pee Wee Reese	225.00
81	Carl Furillo	45.00
82	Joe Tipton	18.00
83	Carl Scheib	18.00
84	Barney McCosky	18.00
85	Eddie Kazak	18.00
86	Harry Brecheen	18.00
87	Floyd Baker	18.00
88	Eddie Robinson	18.00
89	Henry Thompson	18.00
90	Dave Koslo	18.00
91	Clyde Vollmer	18.00
92	Vern Stephens	18.00
93	Danny O'Connell	18.00
94	Clyde McCullough	18.00
95	Sherry Robertson	18.00
96	Sandy Consuegra	18.00
97	Bob Kuzava	18.00
98	Willard Marshall	18.00
99	Earl Torgeson	18.00
100	Sherman Lollar	18.00
101	Owen Friend	18.00
102	Emil "Dutch" Leonard	18.00
103	Andy Pafko	18.00
104	Virgil "Fire" Trucks	18.00
105	Don Kolloway	18.00
106	Pat Mullin	18.00
107	Johnny Wyrostek	18.00
108	Virgil Stallcup	18.00
109	Allie Reynolds	30.00
110	Bobby Brown	35.00
111	Curt Simmons	18.00
112	Willie Jones	18.00
113	Bill "Swish" Nicholson	18.00
114	Sam Zoldak	18.00
115	Steve Gromek	18.00
116	Bruce Edwards	18.00
117	Eddie Miksis	18.00
118	Preacher Roe	30.00
119	Eddie Joost	18.00
120	Joe Coleman	18.00
121	Gerry Staley	18.00
122	*Joe Garagiola*	150.00
123	Howie Judson	18.00
124	Gus Niarhos	18.00
125	Bill Rigney	18.00
126	Bobby Thomson	35.00
127	*Sal Maglie*	45.00
128	Ellis Kinder	18.00
129	Matt Batts	18.00
130	Tom Saffell	18.00
131	Cliff Chambers	18.00
132	Cass Michaels	18.00
133	Sam Dente	18.00
134	Warren Spahn	175.00
135	Walker Cooper	18.00
136	Ray Coleman	18.00
137	Dick Starr	18.00
138	Phil Cavarretta	18.00
139	Doyle Lade	18.00
140	Eddie Lake	18.00
141	Fred Hutchinson	18.00
142	Aaron Robinson	18.00
143	Ted Kluszewski	50.00
144	Herman Wehmeier	18.00
145	Fred Sanford	18.00
146	Johnny Hopp	18.00
147	Ken Heintzelman	18.00
148	Granny Hamner	18.00
149	"Bubba" Church	18.00
150	Mike Garcia	18.00
151	Larry Doby	25.00
152	Cal Abrams	20.00
153	Rex Barney	20.00
154	Pete Suder	18.00
155	Lou Brissie	18.00
156	Del Rice	18.00
157	Al Brazle	18.00
158	Chuck Diering	18.00
159	Eddie Stewart	18.00
160	Phil Masi	18.00
161	Wes Westrum	18.00
162	Larry Jansen	18.00
163	Monte Kennedy	18.00
164	Bill Wight	18.00
165	Ted Williams	1000.00
166	Stan Rojek	18.00
167	Murry Dickson	18.00
168	Sam Mele	18.00
169	Sid Hudson	18.00
170	Sibby Sisti	18.00
171	Buddy Kerr	18.00
172	Ned Garver	18.00
173	Hank Arft	18.00
174	Mickey Owen	18.00
175	Wayne Terwilliger	18.00
176	Vic Wertz	18.00
177	Charlie Keller	18.00

178	Ted Gray	18.00		252	"Dixie" Howell	18.00
179	Danny Litwhiler	18.00		253	*Mickey Mantle*	12500.00
180	Howie Fox	18.00		254	*Jackie Jensen*	125.00
181	Casey Stengel	140.00		255	Milo Candini	75.00
182	Tom Ferrick	18.00		256	Ken Silvestri	75.00
183	Hank Bauer	35.00		257	Birdie Tebbetts	75.00
184	Eddie Sawyer	18.00		258	*Luke Easter*	75.00
185	Jimmy Bloodworth	18.00		259	Charlie Dressen	80.00
186	Richie Ashburn	85.00		260	*Carl Erskine*	110.00
187	Al Rosen	25.00		261	Wally Moses	75.00
188	*Roberto Avila*	18.00		262	Gus Zernial	75.00
189	Erv Palica	18.00		263	Howie Pollet	75.00
190	Joe Hatten	18.00		264	Don Richmond	75.00
191	Billy Hitchcock	18.00		265	*Steve Bilko*	75.00
192	Hank Wyse	18.00		266	Harry Dorish	75.00
193	Ted Wilks	18.00		267	Ken Holcombe	75.00
194	Harry "Peanuts" Lowrey	18.00		268	Don Mueller	75.00
195	Paul Richards	35.00		269	Ray Noble	75.00
196	*Bill Pierce*	25.00		270	Willard Nixon	75.00
197	Bob Cain	18.00		271	Tommy Wright	75.00
198	*Monte Irvin*	125.00		272	Billy Meyer	75.00
199	Sheldon Jones	18.00		273	Danny Murtaugh	75.00
200	Jack Kramer	18.00		274	George Metkovich	75.00
201	Steve O'Neill	18.00		275	Bucky Harris	100.00
202	Mike Guerra	18.00		276	Frank Quinn	75.00
203	*Vernon Law*	25.00		277	Roy Hartsfield	75.00
204	Vic Lombardi	18.00		278	Norman Roy	75.00
205	Mickey Grasso	18.00		279	Jim Delsing	75.00
206	Connie Marrero	18.00		280	Frank Overmire	75.00
207	Billy Southworth	18.00		281	Al Widmar	75.00
208	"Blix" Donnelly	18.00		282	Frank Frisch	115.00
209	Ken Wood	18.00		283	Walt Dubiel	75.00
210	Les Moss	18.00		284	Gene Bearden	75.00
211	Hal Jeffcoat	18.00		285	Johnny Lipon	75.00
212	Bob Rush	18.00		286	Bob Usher	75.00
213	Neil Berry	18.00		287	Jim Blackburn	75.00
214	Bob Swift	18.00		288	Bobby Adams	75.00
215	Kent Peterson	18.00		289	Cliff Mapes	75.00
216	Connie Ryan	18.00		290	Bill Dickey (FC)	225.00
217	Joe Page	22.00		291	Tommy Henrich	80.00
218	Ed Lopat	22.00		292	Eddie Pellagrini	75.00
219	*Gene Woodling*	50.00		293	Ken Johnson	75.00
220	Bob Miller	18.00		294	Jocko Thompson	75.00
221	Dick Whitman	18.00		295	Al Lopez	115.00
222	Thurman Tucker	18.00		296	Bob Kennedy	75.00
223	Johnny Vander Meer	18.00		297	Dave Philley	75.00
224	Billy Cox	20.00		298	Joe Astroth	75.00
225	*Dan Bankhead*	18.00		299	Clyde King	75.00
226	Jimmy Dykes	18.00		300	Hal Rice	75.00
227	Bobby Shantz	18.00		301	Tommy Glaviano	75.00
228	*Cloyd Boyer*	18.00		302	Jim Busby	75.00
229	Bill Howerton	18.00		303	Marv Rotblatt	75.00
230	Max Lanier	18.00		304	Allen Gettel	75.00
231	Luis Aloma	18.00		305	*Willie Mays*	4500.00
232	*Nellie Fox*	150.00		306	*Jim Piersall*	125.00
233	Leo Durocher	60.00		307	Walt Masterson	75.00
234	Clint Hartung	18.00		308	Ted Beard	75.00
235	Jack Lohrke	18.00		309	Mel Queen	75.00
236	"Buddy" Rosar	18.00		310	Erv Dusak	75.00
237	Billy Goodman	18.00		311	Mickey Harris	75.00
238	Pete Reiser	18.00		312	*Gene Mauch*	80.00
239	Bill MacDonald	18.00		313	Ray Mueller	75.00
240	Joe Haynes	18.00		314	Johnny Sain	80.00
241	Irv Noren	18.00		315	Zack Taylor	75.00
242	Sam Jethroe	18.00		316	Duane Pillette	75.00
243	Johnny Antonelli	18.00		317	*Smoky Burgess*	90.00
244	Cliff Fannin	18.00		318	Warren Hacker	75.00
245	John Berardino	30.00		319	Red Rolfe	75.00
246	Bill Serena	18.00		320	Hal White	75.00
247	Bob Ramazotti	18.00		321	Earl Johnson	75.00
248	*Johnny Klippstein*	18.00		322	Luke Sewell	75.00
249	Johnny Groth	18.00		323	*Joe Adcock*	125.00
250	Hank Borowy	18.00		324	Johnny Pramesa	150.00
251	Willard Ramsdell	18.00				

1952 Bowman

Bowman reverted back to a 252-card set in 1952, but retained the card size (2-1/16" x 3-1/8") employed the preceding year. The cards, which are color art reproductions of actual photographs, feature a facsimile autograph on the fronts.

Mr. Mint Says - The size of the set decreased a bit, with only 11 cards valued in excess of $100, but the absence of the high dollar rookie cards makes it less in demand than 1951.

The cards are just as tough to find as other early Bowmans. There are a significant number of low number 51s with color differences; one shiny and one dull, similar to the 1956 Topps football set. There is not normally any premium attached to either version, though the dull variations are relatively unattractive.

Mantle and Mays are popular, pricey cards, and the #1 Berra card is also tough. Print lines tend to be much less of a problem in 1952 than in earlier years.

I did make a major purchase of these in the Kansas City Bowman find, and also bought six or eight sets from the Lillian brothers. At one time I had almost a full box of 1952 unopened

high number packs that I purchased from a Canadian dealer, but I sold them without opening so much as one pack. Though tough, these can be found in mint condition by the persistent collector.

		MT
Complete Set (252):		12000.
Common Player (1-36):		22.00
Common Player (37-216):		20.00
Common Player (217-252):		35.00
1	Yogi Berra	800.00
2	Bobby Thomson	30.00
3	Fred Hutchinson	22.00
4	Robin Roberts	75.00
5	*Minnie Minoso*	90.00
6	Virgil "Red" Stallcup	22.00
7	Mike Garcia	22.00
8	Pee Wee Reese	125.00
9	Vern Stephens	22.00
10	Bob Hooper	22.00
11	Ralph Kiner	65.00
12	Max Surkont	22.00
13	Cliff Mapes	22.00
14	Cliff Chambers	22.00
15	Sam Mele	22.00
16	Omar Lown	22.00
17	Ed Lopat	26.00
18	Don Mueller	22.00
19	Bob Cain	22.00
20	Willie Jones	22.00
21	Nellie Fox	45.00
22	Willard Ramsdell	22.00
23	Bob Lemon	65.00
24	Carl Furillo	35.00
25	Maurice McDermott	22.00
26	Eddie Joost	22.00
27	Joe Garagiola	80.00
28	Roy Hartsfield	22.00
29	Ned Garver	22.00
30	Red Schoendienst	75.00
31	Eddie Yost	22.00
32	Eddie Miksis	22.00
33	*Gil McDougald*	90.00
34	Al Dark	26.00
35	Granny Hamner	22.00
36	Cass Michaels	22.00
37	Vic Raschi	26.00
38	Whitey Lockman	20.00
39	Vic Wertz	20.00
40	"Bubba" Church	20.00
41	"Chico" Carrasquel	20.00
42	Johnny Wyrostek	20.00
43	Bob Feller	200.00
44	Roy Campanella	325.00
45	Johnny Pesky	20.00
46	Carl Scheib	20.00
47	Pete Castiglione	20.00
48	Vernon Bickford	20.00
49	Jim Hearn	20.00
50	Gerry Staley	20.00
51	Gil Coan	20.00
52	Phil Rizzuto	115.00
53	Richie Ashburn	75.00
54	Billy Pierce	22.00
55	Ken Raffensberger	20.00
56	Clyde King	20.00

57	Clyde Vollmer	20.00
58	Hank Majeski	20.00
59	Murry Dickson	20.00
60	Sid Gordon	20.00
61	Tommy Byrne	20.00
62	Joe Presko	20.00
63	Irv Noren	20.00
64	Roy Smalley	20.00
65	Hank Bauer	30.00
66	Sal Maglie	25.00
67	Johnny Groth	20.00
68	Jim Busby	20.00
69	Joe Adcock	22.00
70	Carl Erskine	26.00
71	Vernon Law	20.00
72	Earl Torgeson	20.00
73	Jerry Coleman	26.00
74	Wes Westrum	20.00
75	George Kell	65.00
76	Del Ennis	20.00
77	Eddie Robinson	20.00
78	Lloyd Merriman	20.00
79	Lou Brissie	20.00
80	Gil Hodges	100.00
81	Billy Goodman	20.00
82	Gus Zernial	20.00
83	Howie Pollet	20.00
84	Sam Jethroe	20.00
85	Marty Marion	20.00
86	Cal Abrams	20.00
87	Mickey Vernon	20.00
88	Bruce Edwards	20.00
89	Billy Hitchcock	20.00
90	Larry Jansen	20.00
91	Don Kolloway	20.00
92	Eddie Waitkus	20.00
93	Paul Richards	20.00
94	Luke Sewell	20.00
95	Luke Easter	20.00
96	Ralph Branca	26.00
97	Willard Marshall	20.00
98	Jimmy Dykes	20.00
99	Clyde McCullough	20.00
100	Sibby Sisti	20.00
101	Mickey Mantle	3500.00
102	Peanuts Lowrey	20.00
103	Joe Haynes	20.00
104	Hal Jeffcoat	20.00
105	Bobby Brown	35.00
106	Randy Gumpert	20.00
107	Del Rice	20.00
108	George Metkovich	20.00
109	Tom Morgan	26.00
110	Max Lanier	20.00
111	"Hoot" Evers	20.00
112	"Smoky" Burgess	20.00
113	Al Zarilla	20.00
114	Frank Hiller	20.00
115	Larry Doby	35.00
116	Duke Snider	300.00
117	Bill Wight	20.00
118	Ray Murray	20.00
119	Bill Howerton	20.00
120	Chet Nichols	20.00
121	Al Corwin	20.00
122	Billy Johnson	20.00
123	Sid Hudson	20.00
124	Birdie Tebbetts	20.00
125	Howie Fox	20.00
126	Phil Cavarretta	20.00
127	Dick Sisler	20.00
128	Don Newcombe	30.00
129	Gus Niarhos	20.00
130	Allie Clark	20.00
131	Bob Swift	20.00
132	Dave Cole	20.00
133	Dick Kryhoski	20.00
134	Al Brazle	20.00
135	Mickey Harris	20.00
136	Gene Hermanski	20.00
137	Stan Rojek	20.00
138	Ted Wilks	20.00
139	Jerry Priddy	20.00
140	Ray Scarborough	20.00
141	Hank Edwards	20.00
142	Early Wynn	60.00
143	Sandy Consuegra	20.00
144	Joe Hatten	20.00
145	Johnny Mize	60.00
146	Leo Durocher	50.00
147	Marlin Stuart	20.00
148	Ken Heintzelman	20.00
149	Howie Judson	20.00
150	Herman Wehmeier	20.00
151	Al Rosen	22.00
152	Billy Cox	22.00
153	Fred Hatfield	20.00
154	Ferris Fain	20.00
155	Billy Meyer	20.00
156	Warren Spahn	140.00
157	Jim Delsing	20.00
158	Bucky Harris	50.00
159	Dutch Leonard	20.00
160	Eddie Stanky	22.00
161	Jackie Jensen	30.00
162	Monte Irvin	60.00
163	Johnny Lipon	20.00
164	Connie Ryan	20.00
165	Saul Rogovin	20.00
166	Bobby Adams	20.00
167	Bob Avila	20.00
168	Preacher Roe	30.00
169	Walt Dropo	20.00
170	Joe Astroth	20.00
171	Mel Queen	20.00
172	Ebba St. Claire	20.00
173	Gene Bearden	20.00
174	Mickey Grasso	20.00
175	Ransom Jackson	20.00
176	Harry Brecheen	20.00
177	Gene Woodling	20.00
178	Dave Williams	20.00
179	Pete Suder	20.00
180	Eddie Fitz Gerald	20.00
181	Joe Collins	26.00
182	Dave Koslo	20.00
183	Pat Mullin	20.00
184	Curt Simmons	20.00
185	Eddie Stewart	20.00
186	Frank Smith	20.00
187	Jim Hegan	20.00
188	Charlie Dressen	26.00
189	Jim Piersall	26.00
190	Dick Fowler	20.00
191	*Bob Friend*	20.00
192	John Cusick	20.00
193	Bobby Young	20.00
194	Bob Porterfield	20.00
195	Frank Baumholtz	20.00
196	Stan Musial	650.00
197	*Charlie Silvera*	20.00
198	Chuck Diering	20.00
199	Ted Gray	20.00
200	Ken Silvestri	20.00
201	Ray Coleman	20.00
202	Harry Perkowski	20.00

203	Steve Gromek	20.00
204	Andy Pafko	20.00
205	Walt Masterson	20.00
206	Elmer Valo	20.00
207	George Strickland	20.00
208	Walker Cooper	20.00
209	Dick Littlefield	20.00
210	Archie Wilson	20.00
211	Paul Minner	20.00
212	Solly Hemus	20.00
213	Monte Kennedy	20.00
214	Ray Boone	20.00
215	Sheldon Jones	20.00
216	Matt Batts	20.00
217	Casey Stengel	200.00
218	Willie Mays	1700.00
219	Neil Berry	35.00
220	Russ Meyer	35.00
221	Lou Kretlow	35.00
222	"Dixie" Howell	35.00
223	*Harry Simpson*	35.00
224	Johnny Schmitz	35.00
225	Del Wilber	35.00
226	Alex Kellner	35.00
227	Clyde Sukeforth	35.00
228	Bob Chipman	35.00
229	Hank Arft	35.00
230	Frank Shea	35.00
231	*Dee Fondy*	35.00
232	Enos Slaughter	115.00
233	Bob Kuzava	35.00
234	Fred Fitzsimmons	35.00
235	Steve Souchock	35.00
236	Tommy Brown	35.00
237	Sherman Lollar	35.00
238	*Roy McMillan*	35.00
239	Dale Mitchell	35.00
240	*Billy Loes*	35.00
241	Mel Parnell	35.00
242	Everett Kell	35.00
243	"Red" Munger	35.00
244	*Lew Burdette*	80.00
245	George Schmees	35.00
246	Jerry Snyder	35.00
247	John Pramesa	35.00
248	Bill Werle	35.00
249	Henry Thompson	35.00
250	Ike Delock	35.00
251	Jack Lohrke	35.00
252	Frank Crosetti	200.00

1953 Bowman Color

The first set of current major league players featuring actual color photographs, the 160-card 1953 Bowman Color set remains one of the most popular issues of the postwar era. The set is greatly appreciated for its uncluttered look; card fronts that contain no names, teams or facsimile autographs. Bowman increased the size of their cards to a 2-1/2" by 3-3/4" in order to better compete with Topps' larger format. Bowman copied an idea from the 1952 Topps set and developed card backs that gave player career and previous-year statistics. The high-numbered cards (#s 113-160) are the scarcest of the set, with (#s 113-128) being exceptionally difficult to find.

Mr. Mint Says - This is one of the most popular card sets ever produced, and with good reason. Pure photos, no graphic devices on the front, beautiful color. This was the first real use of photography and it would be a lot of years before anybody did it better.

The set has wonderful cards of Hall of Famers like Mantle, Campy, Reese, Ford and Snider, along with the best Musial card ever made. The set also marks the first appearance of several multiple player cards, like Berra,

Bauer and Mantle or Martin and Rizzuto, which are extremely popular with collectors.

The high number series from 113-128 is super tough. Often I will buy a collection and it will be beautiful, but those numbers invariably have just little touches of wear. In the high series (129-160) off-center cards become a problem, and there are a lot of roller marks and print lines. It is virtually impossible to find a Ford, Berra or Snider perfectly centered.

In the Kansas City Bowman deal, there were about 3,700 cards from 1953 Bowman, with about 20 to 30 of every card. Through the years, I can't recall any unopened material.

The set is much harder to find in mint condition than 1951 and 1952, and the attractive photos gives the set a significant edge in demand over both the earlier and later issues.

		MT
Complete Set (160):		17500.
Common Player (1-112):		40.00
Common Player (113-128):		75.00
Common Player (129-160):		50.00
1	Davey Williams	100.00
2	Vic Wertz	40.00
3	Sam Jethroe	40.00
4	Art Houtteman	40.00
5	Sid Gordon	40.00
6	Joe Ginsberg	40.00
7	Harry Chiti	40.00
8	Al Rosen	40.00
9	Phil Rizzuto	165.00
10	Richie Ashburn	125.00
11	Bobby Shantz	45.00
12	Carl Erskine	45.00
13	Gus Zernial	40.00
14	Billy Loes	45.00
15	Jim Busby	40.00
16	Bob Friend	40.00
17	Gerry Staley	40.00
18	Nellie Fox	100.00
19	Al Dark	40.00
20	Don Lenhardt	40.00
21	Joe Garagiola	100.00
22	Bob Porterfield	40.00
23	Herman Wehmeier	40.00
24	Jackie Jensen	55.00
25	"Hoot" Evers	40.00
26	Roy McMillan	40.00
27	Vic Raschi	50.00
28	"Smoky" Burgess	40.00
29	Roberto Avila	40.00
30	Phil Cavarretta	40.00
31	Jimmy Dykes	40.00
32	Stan Musial	850.00
33	Pee Wee Reese	750.00
34	Gil Coan	40.00
35	Maury McDermott	40.00
36	Minnie Minoso	55.00
37	Jim Wilson	40.00
38	Harry Byrd	40.00

#	Player	Value		#	Player	Value
39	Paul Richards	40.00		112	Toby Atwell	40.00
40	Larry Doby	55.00		113	Karl Drews	75.00
41	Sammy White	40.00		114	Bob Feller	500.00
42	Tommy Brown	40.00		115	Cloyd Boyer	75.00
43	Mike Garcia	40.00		116	Eddie Yost	75.00
44	Hank Bauer, Yogi Berra, Mickey Mantle	700.00		117	Duke Snider	1000.00
45	Walt Dropo	40.00		118	Billy Martin(FC)	500.00
46	Roy Campanella	400.00		119	Dale Mitchell	75.00
47	Ned Garver	40.00		120	Marlin Stuart	75.00
48	Hank Sauer	40.00		121	Yogi Berra	900.00
49	Eddie Stanky	40.00		122	Bill Serena	75.00
50	Lou Kretlow	40.00		123	Johnny Lipon	75.00
51	Monte Irvin	80.00		124	Charlie Dressen	75.00
52	Marty Marion	45.00		125	Fred Hatfield	75.00
53	Del Rice	40.00		126	Al Corwin	75.00
54	"Chico" Carrasquel	40.00		127	Dick Kryhoski	75.00
55	Leo Durocher	55.00		128	"Whitey" Lockman	75.00
56	Bob Cain	40.00		129	Russ Meyer	50.00
57	Lou Boudreau	80.00		130	Cass Michaels	50.00
58	Willard Marshall	45.00		131	Connie Ryan	50.00
59	Mickey Mantle	3500.00		132	Fred Hutchinson	50.00
60	Granny Hamner	40.00		133	Willie Jones	50.00
61	George Kell	80.00		134	Johnny Pesky	50.00
62	Ted Kluszewski	55.00		135	Bobby Morgan	50.00
63	Gil McDougald	55.00		136	Jim Brideweser	50.00
64	Curt Simmons	40.00		137	Sam Dente	50.00
65	Robin Roberts	90.00		138	"Bubba" Church	50.00
66	Mel Parnell	40.00		139	Pete Runnels	50.00
67	Mel Clark	40.00		140	Alpha Brazle	50.00
68	Allie Reynolds	55.00		141	Frank "Spec" Shea	50.00
69	Charlie Grimm	40.00		142	Larry Miggins	50.00
70	Clint Courtney	40.00		143	Al Lopez(FC)	75.00
71	Paul Minner	40.00		144	Warren Hacker	50.00
72	Ted Gray	40.00		145	George Shuba	50.00
73	Billy Pierce	40.00		146	Early Wynn	200.00
74	Don Mueller	40.00		147	Clem Koshorek	50.00
75	Saul Rogovin	40.00		148	Billy Goodman	50.00
76	Jim Hearn	40.00		149	Al Corwin	50.00
77	Mickey Grasso	40.00		150	Carl Scheib	50.00
78	Carl Furillo	55.00		151	Joe Adcock	50.00
79	Ray Boone	40.00		152	Clyde Vollmer	50.00
80	Ralph Kiner	100.00		153	Whitey Ford	750.00
81	Enos Slaughter	90.00		154	Omar "Turk" Lown	50.00
82	Joe Astroth	40.00		155	Allie Clark	50.00
83	Jack Daniels	40.00		156	Max Surkont	50.00
84	Hank Bauer	55.00		157	Sherman Lollar	50.00
85	Solly Hemus	40.00		158	Howard Fox	50.00
86	Harry Simpson	40.00		159	Mickey Vernon (Photo actually Floyd Baker)	50.00
87	Harry Perkowski	40.00		160	Cal Abrams	150.00
88	Joe Dobson	40.00				
89	Sandalio Consuegra	40.00				
90	Joe Nuxhall	40.00				
91	Steve Souchock	40.00				
92	Gil Hodges	165.00				
93	Billy Martin, Phil Rizzuto	325.00				
94	Bob Addis	40.00				
95	Wally Moses	40.00				
96	Sal Maglie	40.00				
97	Eddie Mathews(FC)	275.00				
98	Hector Rodriquez	40.00				
99	Warren Spahn	300.00				
100	Bill Wight	40.00				
101	Red Schoendienst	90.00				
102	Jim Hegan	40.00				
103	Del Ennis	40.00				
104	Luke Easter	40.00				
105	Eddie Joost	40.00				
106	Ken Raffensberger	40.00				
107	Alex Kellner	40.00				
108	Bobby Adams	40.00				
109	Ken Wood	40.00				
110	Bob Rush	40.00				
111	Jim Dyck	40.00				

1953 Bowman Black & White

The 1953 Bowman Black and White set is similar in all respects to the 1953 Bowman Color set, except that it lacks color. Purportedly, high costs in producing the color series forced Bowman to issue the set in black and white. Sixty-four cards, which measure 2-1/2" by 3-3/4", comprise the set.

Mr. Mint Says - This is a terribly undervalued set, but unfortunately without much collector interest. To me, this set is ten times rarer than the color issue, but with very little corresponding demand. It remains an excellent example of why collectors must understand the importance of demand, as well as scarcity, in determining prices.

It is extremely difficult to find a nicely focused set centered and with four sharp corners; I have probably only run across three sets that I would call great and I have never seen a perfect one.

There are not as many print lines as in the color issue, but there are a lot of centering problems. The Stengel card, they key card in the set, is always very hard to find with good centering.

		MT
Complete Set (64):		3800.
Common Player:		50.00
1	Gus Bell	250.00
2	Willard Nixon	50.00
3	Bill Rigney	50.00
4	Pat Mullin	50.00
5	Dee Fondy	50.00
6	Ray Murray	50.00
7	Andy Seminick	50.00
8	Pete Suder	50.00
9	Walt Masterson	50.00
10	Dick Sisler	50.00
11	Dick Gernert	50.00
12	Randy Jackson	50.00
13	Joe Tipton	50.00
14	Bill Nicholson	50.00
15	Johnny Mize	200.00
16	Stu Miller	50.00
17	Virgil Trucks	50.00
18	Billy Hoeft	50.00
19	Paul LaPalme	50.00
20	Eddie Robinson	50.00
21	Clarence "Bud" Podbielan	50.00
22	Matt Batts	50.00
23	Wilmer Mizell	50.00
24	Del Wilber	50.00
25	Johnny Sain	100.00
26	Preacher Roe	100.00
27	Bob Lemon	200.00
28	Hoyt Wilhelm(FC)	200.00
29	Sid Hudson	50.00
30	Walker Cooper	50.00
31	Gene Woodling	75.00
32	Rocky Bridges	50.00
33	Bob Kuzava	50.00
34	Ebba St. Clair (St. Claire)	50.00
35	Johnny Wyrostek	50.00
36	Jim Piersall	75.00
37	Hal Jeffcoat	50.00
38	Dave Cole	50.00
39	Casey Stengel	575.00
40	Larry Jansen	50.00
41	Bob Ramazotti	50.00
42	Howie Judson	50.00
43	Hal Bevan	50.00
44	Jim Delsing	50.00
45	Irv Noren	50.00
46	Bucky Harris	75.00
47	Jack Lohrke	50.00
48	Steve Ridzik	50.00
49	Floyd Baker	50.00
50	Emil "Dutch" Leonard	50.00
51	Lew Burdette	50.00
52	Ralph Branca	55.00
53	Morris Martin	50.00
54	Bill Miller	50.00
55	Don Johnson	50.00
56	Roy Smalley	50.00
57	Andy Pafko	50.00
58	Jim Konstanty	50.00
59	Duane Pillette	50.00
60	Billy Cox	50.00
61	Tom Gorman	50.00
62	Keith Thomas	50.00
63	Steve Gromek	50.00
64	Andy Hansen	100.00

1954 Bowman

Bowman's 1954 set consists of 224 full-color cards that measure 2-1/2" by 3-3/4". It is believed that contractual problems caused the pulling of card #66 (Ted Williams) from the set, creating one of the most sought-after scarcities of the postwar era. The Williams card was replaced by Jim Piersall (who is also #210) in subsequent print runs. The set contains over 40 variations, most involving statistical errors on the card backs that were corrected. On most cards neither variation carries a premium value as both varieties appear to have been printed in equal amounts. The complete set price that follows does not include all variations or #66 Williams.

Mr. Mint Says - This is another set with very little popularity, no major rookie cards or high numbers. The photos often seem blurry and out of register. The backgrounds of the cards have a pastel quality. No real problems with print lines and, as a rule, not much off-centering.

The Mantle card is popular with collectors, but finding one with sharp focus and excellent centering can be difficult. The Williams card is overpriced and not as rare as most people think. When prices rose on that card some dealers were asking $6,000 to $10,000 in mint, but I think now that the most you can get is $4,000 or maybe $5,000.

It is like the Honus Wagner (T-206) card; it has the mystique. I know a lot of cards that are rarer than that. I think that there are more Wagners than Planks, and I think that the Williams card is in the same ballpark; overpriced relative to scarcity.

I did purchase between 50-75 unopened boxes in the Paris, Tenn. find, and I think that there are a lot more 54s available than the previous five years.

		MT
Complete Set (224):		6000.
Common Player (1-112):		10.00
Common Player (113-224):		13.00
1	Phil Rizzuto	250.00
2	Jack Jensen	15.00
3	Marion Fricano	10.00
4	Bob Hooper	10.00
5	Billy Hunter	10.00
6	.Nellie Fox	50.00
7	Walter Dropo	10.00
8	Jim Busby	10.00
9	Dave Williams	10.00
10	Carl Erskine	15.00
11	Sid Gordon	10.00
12a	Roy McMillan (551/1290 At Bat)	10.00
12b	Roy McMillan (557/1296 At Bat)	10.00
13	Paul Minner	10.00
14	Gerald Staley	10.00
15	Richie Ashburn	50.00
16	Jim Wilson	10.00
17	Tom Gorman	10.00
18	"Hoot" Evers	10.00
19	Bobby Shantz	10.00
20	Artie Houtteman	10.00
21	Vic Wertz	10.00
22a	Sam Mele (213/1661 Putouts)	10.00
22b	Sam Mele (217/1665 Putouts)	10.00
23	*Harvey Kuenn*	50.00
24	Bob Porterfield	10.00
25a	Wes Westrum (1.000/.987 Field Avg.)	10.00
25b	Wes Westrum (.982/.986 Field Avg.)	10.00
26a	Billy Cox (1.000/.960 Field Avg.)	15.00
26b	Billy Cox (.972/.960 Field Avg.)	15.00
27	Dick Cole	10.00
28a	Jim Greengrass (Birthplace Addison, N.J.)	10.00
28b	Jim Greengrass (Birthplace Addison, N.Y.)	10.00
29	Johnny Klippstein	10.00
30	Del Rice	10.00
31	"Smoky" Burgess	10.00
32	Del Crandall	10.00
33a	Vic Raschi (no trade line)	15.00
33b	Vic Raschi (traded line)	40.00
34	Sammy White	10.00
35a	Eddie Joost (quiz answer is 8)	10.00
35b	Eddie Joost (quiz answer is 33)	10.00
36	George Strickland	10.00
37	Dick Kokos	10.00
38a	Minnie Minoso (.895/.961 Field Avg.)	10.00
38b	Minnie Minoso (.963/.963 Field Avg.)	10.00
39	Ned Garver	10.00

#	Player	Price		#	Player	Price
40	Gil Coan	10.00		99a	Peter Suder (.985/.974 Field Avg.)	10.00
41a	Alvin Dark (.986/.960 Field Avg.)	10.00		99b	Peter Suder (.978/.974 Field Avg.)	10.00
41b	Alvin Dark (.968/.960 Field Avg.)	10.00		100	Mike Garcia	10.00
42	Billy Loes	10.00		101	*Don Larsen*	60.00
43a	Bob Friend (20 shutouts in quiz question)	10.00		102	Bill Pierce	10.00
43b	Bob Friend (16 shutouts in quiz question)	10.00		103a	Stephen Souchock (144/1192 Putouts)	9.00
44	Harry Perkowski	10.00		103b	Stephen Souchock (147/1195 Putouts)	9.00
45	Ralph Kiner	50.00		104	Frank Spec Shea	9.00
46	"Rip" Repulski	10.00		105a	Sal Maglie (quiz answer is 8)	10.00
47a	Granny Hamner (.970/.953 Field Avg.)	10.00		105b	Sal Maglie (quiz answer is 1904)	10.00
47b	Granny Hamner (.953/.951 Field Avg.)	10.00		106	Clem Labine	12.00
48	Jack Dittmer	10.00		107	Paul LaPalme	9.00
49	Harry Byrd	10.00		108	Bobby Adams	9.00
50	George Kell	40.00		109	Roy Smalley	9.00
51	Alex Kellner	10.00		110	Red Schoendienst	50.00
52	Joe Ginsberg	10.00		111	Murry Dickson	10.00
53a	Don Lenhardt (.969/.984 Field Avg.)	10.00		112	Andy Pafko	10.00
53b	Don Lenhardt (.966/.983 Field Avg.)	10.00		113	Allie Reynolds	20.00
54	"Chico" Carrasquel	10.00		114	Willard Nixon	13.00
55	Jim Delsing	10.00		115	Don Bollweg	13.00
56	Maurice McDermott	10.00		116	Luke Easter	13.00
57	Hoyt Wilhelm	50.00		117	Dick Kryhoski	13.00
58	Pee Wee Reese	85.00		118	Bob Boyd	13.00
59	Bob Schultz	10.00		119	Fred Hatfield	13.00
60	Fred Baczewski	10.00		120	Mel Hoderlein	13.00
61a	Eddie Miksis (.954/.962 Field Avg.)	10.00		121	Ray Katt	13.00
61b	Eddie Miksis (.954/.961 Field Avg.)	10.00		122	Carl Furillo	25.00
62	Enos Slaughter	50.00		123	Toby Atwell	13.00
63	Earl Torgeson	10.00		124a	Gus Bell (15/27 Errors)	13.00
64	Eddie Mathews	80.00		124b	Gus Bell (11/26 Errors)	13.00
65	Mickey Mantle	1450.00		125	Warren Hacker	13.00
66a	Ted Williams	6000.00		126	Cliff Chambers	13.00
66b	Jimmy Piersall	150.00		127	Del Ennis	13.00
67a	Carl Scheib (.306 Pct. with two lines under bio)	10.00		128	Ebba St. Claire	13.00
67b	Carl Scheib (.306 Pct. with one line under bio)	10.00		129	Hank Bauer	25.00
67c	Carl Scheib (.300 Pct.)	10.00		130	Milt Bolling	13.00
68	Bob Avila	10.00		131	Joe Astroth	13.00
69	Clinton Courtney	10.00		132	Bob Feller	150.00
70	Willard Marshall	10.00		133	Duane Pillette	13.00
71	Ted Gray	10.00		134	Luis Aloma	13.00
72	Ed Yost	10.00		135	Johnny Pesky	13.00
73	Don Mueller	10.00		136	Clyde Vollmer	13.00
74	Jim Gilliam (FC)	20.00		137	Al Corwin	13.00
75	Max Surkont	10.00		138a	Gil Hodges (.993/.991 Field Avg.)	85.00
76	Joe Nuxhall	10.00		138b	Gil Hodges (.992/.991 Field Avg.)	70.00
77	Bob Rush	10.00		139a	Preston Ward (.961/.992 Field Avg.)	13.00
78	Sal Yvars	10.00		139b	Preston Ward (.990/.992 Field Avg.)	13.00
79	Curt Simmons	10.00		140a	Saul Rogovin (7-12 Won/Lost with 2 Strikeouts)	13.00
80a	Johnny Logan (106 Runs)	10.00		140b	Saul Rogovin (7-12 Won/Lost with 62 Strikeouts)	13.00
80b	Johnny Logan (100 Runs)	10.00		140c	Saul Rogovin (8-12 Won/Lost)	13.00
81a	Jerry Coleman (1.000/.975 Field Avg.)	18.00		141	Joe Garagiola	50.00
81b	Jerry Coleman (.952/.975 Field Avg.)	18.00		142	Al Brazle	13.00
82a	Bill Goodman (.965/.986 Field Avg.)	10.00		143	Willie Jones	13.00
82b	Bill Goodman (.972/.985 Field Avg.)	10.00		144	*Ernie Johnson*	13.00
83	Ray Murray	10.00		145a	Billy Martin (.985/.983 Field Avg.)	50.00
84	Larry Doby	15.00		145b	Billy Martin (.983/.982 Field Avg.)	60.00
85a	Jim Dyck (.926/.956 Field Avg.)	10.00		146	Dick Gernert	13.00
85b	Jim Dyck (.947/.960 Field Avg.)	10.00		147	Joe DeMaestri	13.00
86	Harry Dorish	10.00		148	Dale Mitchell	13.00
87	Don Lund	10.00		149	Bob Young	13.00
88	Tommy Umphlett	10.00		150	Cass Michaels	13.00
89	Willie Mays	550.00		151	Pat Mullin	13.00
90	Roy Campanella	225.00		152	Mickey Vernon	13.00
91	Cal Abrams	10.00		153a	"Whitey" Lockman (100/331 Assists)	13.00
92	Ken Raffensberger	10.00		153b	"Whitey" Lockman (102/333 Assists)	13.00
93a	Bill Serena (.983/.966 Field Avg.)	10.00		154	Don Newcombe	30.00
93b	Bill Serena (.977/.966 Field Avg.)	10.00		155	*Frank J. Thomas*	13.00
94a	Solly Hemus (476/1343 Assists)	10.00		156a	Rocky Bridges (320/467 Assists)	13.00
94b	Solly Hemus (477/1343 Assists)	10.00		156b	Rocky Bridges (328/475 Assists)	13.00
95	Robin Roberts	50.00		157	Omar Lown	13.00
96	Joe Adcock	10.00		158	Stu Miller	13.00
97	Gil McDougald	20.00		159	John Lindell	13.00
98	Ellis Kinder	10.00		160	Danny O'Connell	13.00

161	Yogi Berra	250.00
162	Ted Lepcio	13.00
163a	Dave Philley (152 Games, no traded line)	40.00
163b	Dave Philley (152 Games, traded line)	30.00
163c	Dave Philley (157 Games, traded line)	13.00
164	Early Wynn	60.00
165	Johnny Groth	13.00
166	Sandy Consuegra	13.00
167	Bill Hoeft	13.00
168	Edward Fitz Gerald	13.00
169	Larry Jansen	13.00
170	Duke Snider	250.00
171	Carlos Bernier	13.00
172	Andy Seminick	13.00
173	Dee Fondy	13.00
174a	Pete Castiglione (.966/.959 Field Avg.)	13.00
174b	Pete Castiglione (.970/.959 Field Avg.)	13.00
175	Mel Clark	13.00
176	Vernon Bickford	13.00
177	Whitey Ford	135.00
178	Del Wilber	13.00
179a	Morris Martin (44 ERA)	13.00
179b	Morris Martin (4.44 ERA)	13.00
180	Joe Tipton	13.00
181	Les Moss	13.00
182	Sherman Lollar	13.00
183	Matt Batts	13.00
184	Mickey Grasso	13.00
185a	*Daryl Spencer* (.941/.944 Field Avg.)	13.00
185b	*Daryl Spencer* (.933/.936 Field Avg.)	13.00
186	Russ Meyer	13.00
187	Vern Law	13.00
188	Frank Smith	13.00
189	Ransom Jackson	13.00
190	Joe Presko	13.00
191	Karl Drews	13.00
192	Lew Burdette	13.00
193	Eddie Robinson	13.00
194	Sid Hudson	13.00
195	Bob Cain	13.00
196	Bob Lemon	45.00
197	Lou Kretlow	13.00
198	Virgil Trucks	13.00
199	Steve Gromek	13.00
200	Connie Marrero	13.00
201	Bob Thomson	25.00
202	George Shuba	13.00
203	Vic Janowicz	13.00
204	Jack Collum	13.00
205	Hal Jeffcoat	13.00
206	Steve Bilko	13.00
207	Stan Lopata	13.00
208	Johnny Antonelli	13.00
209	Gene Woodling (photo reversed)	13.00
210	Jimmy Piersall	13.00
211	Jim Robertson	13.00
212a	Owen Friend (.964/.957 Field Avg.)	13.00
212b	Owen Friend (.967/.958 Field Avg.)	13.00
213	Dick Littlefield	13.00
214	Ferris Fain	13.00
215	Johnny Bucha	13.00
216a	Jerry Snyder (.988/.988 Field Avg.)	13.00
216b	Jerry Snyder (.968/.968 Field Avg.)	13.00
217a	Henry Thompson (.956/.951 Field Avg.)	13.00
217b	Henry Thompson (.958/.952 Field Avg.)	13.00
218	Preacher Roe	13.00
219	Hal Rice	13.00
220	Hobie Landrith	13.00
221	Frank Baumholtz	13.00
222	Memo Luna	13.00
223	Steve Ridzik	13.00
224	Billy Bruton	50.00

1955 Bowman

Bowman produced its final baseball card set in 1955, a popular issue which has player photographs placed inside a television set design. The set consists of 320 cards that measure 2-1/2" by 3-3/4" in size. High-numbered cards (#s 225-320) appear to have replaced certain low-numbered cards on the press sheets and are somewhat scarcer. The high series includes 31 umpire cards.

Mr. Mint Says - This was my favorite set when I was a kid. With the little brown TVs, the player looks like he's peering out at you from your television. These are beautiful cards when found in top condition, but like 1962 or 1971 Topps, the colored borders readily show any wear at all.

In the Paris, Tenn. find there were over 150 boxes and, in the second of three purchases, over 50 gem mint 1955 Bowman sets. After that there was a lot of availability of this set in mint condition, but it is hard to find six years later. In that find there were many cards cut short from the factory; they were sold with that description.

It is hard to find four sharp corners with the brown undisturbed throughout the set, but even more so in the dark brown series two and three compared with the lighter borders in the first series (1-96). Now it is virtually impossible to piece together a mint 1955 Bowman set.

		MT
Complete Set (320):		6600.
Common Player (1-96):		8.00
Common Player (97-224):		6.00
Common Player (225-320):		17.00

1	Hoyt Wilhelm	125.00
2	Al Dark	10.00
3	Joe Coleman	8.00
4	Eddie Waitkus	8.00
5	Jim Robertson	8.00
6	Pete Suder	8.00
7	Gene Baker	8.00
8	Warren Hacker	8.00

9	Gil McDougald	18.00
10	Phil Rizzuto	50.00
11	Billy Bruton	8.00
12	Andy Pafko	8.00
13	Clyde Vollmer	8.00
14	Gus Keriazakos	8.00
15	*Frank Sullivan*	8.00
16	Jim Piersall	10.00
17	Del Ennis	8.00
18	Stan Lopata	8.00
19	Bobby Avila	8.00
20	Al Smith	8.00
21	Don Hoak (FC)	8.00
22	Roy Campanella	135.00
23	Al Kaline (FC)	145.00
24	Al Aber	8.00
25	Minnie Minoso	15.00
26	Virgil Trucks	8.00
27	Preston Ward	8.00
28	Dick Cole	8.00
29	Red Schoendienst	30.00
30	Bill Sarni	8.00
31	Johnny Temple	8.00
32	Wally Post	8.00
33	Nellie Fox	35.00
34	Clint Courtney	8.00
35	Bill Tuttle	8.00
36	Wayne Belardi	8.00
37	Pee Wee Reese	100.00
38	Early Wynn	40.00
39	Bob Darnell	12.00
40	Vic Wertz	7.00
41	Mel Clark	7.00
42	Bob Greenwood	7.00
43	Bob Buhl	7.00
44	Danny O'Connell	7.00
45	Tom Umphlett	7.00
46	Mickey Vernon	7.00
47	Sammy White	8.00
48a	Milt Bolling (Frank Bolling back)	15.00
48b	Milt Bolling (Milt Bolling back)	20.00
49	Jim Greengrass	8.00
50	Hobie Landrith	8.00
51	Elvin Tappe	8.00
52	Hal Rice	8.00
53	Alex Kellner	8.00
54	Don Bollweg	8.00
55	Cal Abrams	8.00
56	Billy Cox	8.00
57	Bob Friend	8.00
58	Frank J. Thomas	8.00
59	Whitey Ford	95.00
60	Enos Slaughter	40.00
61	Paul LaPalme	8.00
62	Royce Lint	8.00
63	Irv Noren	8.00
64	Curt Simmons	8.00
65	*Don Zimmer*	25.00
66	George Shuba	8.00
67	Don Larsen	20.00
68	*Elston Howard*	75.00
69	Bill Hunter	8.00
70	Lew Burdette	8.00
71	Dave Jolly	8.00
72	Chet Nichols	8.00
73	Eddie Yost	8.00
74	Jerry Snyder	8.00
75	Brooks Lawrence	8.00
76	Tom Poholsky	8.00

77	Jim McDonald	8.00	148	Bob Chakales	6.00
78	Gil Coan	8.00	149	Cloyd Boyer	6.00
79	Willie Miranda	8.00	150	Bill Klaus	6.00
80	Lou Limmer	8.00	151	Jim Brideweser	6.00
81	Bob Morgan	8.00	152	Johnny Klippstein	6.00
82	Lee Walls	8.00	153	Eddie Robinson	6.00
83	Max Surkont	8.00	154	*Frank Lary*	6.00
84	George Freese	8.00	155	Gerry Staley	6.00
85	Cass Michaels	8.00	156	Jim Hughes	6.00
86	Ted Gray	8.00	157a	Ernie Johnson	
87	Randy Jackson	8.00		[Don Johnson (Orioles) picture on front]	10.00
88	Steve Bilko	8.00	157b	Ernie Johnson	
89	Lou Boudreau	40.00		[Ernie Johnson (Braves) picture on front]	20.00
90	Art Ditmar	8.00	158	Gil Hodges	60.00
91	Dick Marlowe	8.00	159	Harry Byrd	6.00
92	George Zuverink	8.00	160	Bill Skowron (FC)	20.00
93	Andy Seminick	8.00	161	Matt Batts	6.00
94	Hank Thompson	8.00	162	Charlie Maxwell (FC)	6.00
95	Sal Maglie	8.00	163	Sid Gordon	6.00
96	Ray Narleski	8.00	164	Toby Atwell	6.00
97	John Podres (FC)	15.00	165	Maurice McDermott	6.00
98	Jim Gilliam	15.00	166	Jim Busby	6.00
99	Jerry Coleman	15.00	167	Bob Grim	6.00
100	Tom Morgan	15.00	168	Yogi Berra	120.00
101a	Don Johnson (Ernie Johnson (Braves) on front)	10.00	169	Carl Furillo	20.00
101b	Don Johnson (Don Johnson (Orioles) on front)	15.00	170	Carl Erskine	12.00
102	Bobby Thomson	10.00	171	Robin Roberts	40.00
103	Eddie Mathews	85.00	172	Willie Jones	6.00
104	Bob Porterfield	6.00	173	"Chico" Carrasquel	6.00
105	Johnny Schmitz	6.00	174	Sherman Lollar	6.00
106	Del Rice	6.00	175	Wilmer Shantz	6.00
107	Solly Hemus	6.00	176	Joe DeMaestri	6.00
108	Lou Kretlow	6.00	177	Willard Nixon	6.00
109	Vern Stephens	6.00	178	Tom Brewer	6.00
110	Bob Miller	6.00	179	Hank Aaron	325.00
111	Steve Ridzik	6.00	180	Johnny Logan	6.00
112	Granny Hamner	6.00	181	Eddie Miksis	6.00
113	Bob Hall	6.00	182	Bob Rush	6.00
114	Vic Janowicz	6.00	183	Ray Katt	6.00
115	Roger Bowman	6.00	184	Willie Mays	325.00
116	Sandy Consuegra	6.00	185	Vic Raschi	6.00
117	Johnny Groth	6.00	186	Alex Grammas	6.00
118	Bobby Adams	6.00	187	Fred Hatfield	6.00
119	Joe Astroth	6.00	188	Ned Garver	6.00
120	Ed Burtschy	6.00	189	Jack Collum	6.00
121	Rufus Crawford	6.00	190	Fred Baczewski	6.00
122	Al Corwin	6.00	191	Bob Lemon	40.00
123	Marv Grissom	6.00	192	George Strickland	6.00
124	Johnny Antonelli	6.00	193	Howie Judson	6.00
125	Paul Giel	6.00	194	Joe Nuxhall	6.00
126	Billy Goodman	6.00	195a	Erv Palica (no traded line)	10.00
127	Hank Majeski	6.00	195b	Erv Palica (traded line)	20.00
128	Mike Garcia	6.00	196	Russ Meyer	6.00
129	Hal Naragon	6.00	197	Ralph Kiner	
130	Richie Ashburn	30.00	198	Dave Pope	6.00
131	Willard Marshall	6.00	199	Vernon Law	6.00
132a	Harvey Kueen (misspelled last name)	10.00	200	Dick Littlefield	6.00
132b	Harvey Kuenn (corrected)	40.00	201	Allie Reynolds	15.00
133	Charles King	6.00	202	Mickey Mantle	1000.00
134	Bob Feller	85.00	203	Steve Gromek	6.00
135	Lloyd Merriman	6.00	204a	Frank Bolling (Milt Bolling back)	10.00
136	Rocky Bridges	6.00	204b	Frank Bolling (Frank Bolling back)	18.00
137	Bob Talbot	6.00	205	"Rip" Repulski	6.00
138	Davey Williams	6.00	206	Ralph Beard	6.00
139	Billy & Bobby Shantz	25.00	207	Frank Shea	6.00
140	Bobby Shantz	10.00	208	Ed Fitz Gerald	6.00
141	Wes Westrum	6.00	209	"Smoky" Burgess	6.00
142	Rudy Regalado	6.00	210	Earl Torgeson	6.00
143	Don Newcombe	15.00	211	John "Sonny" Dixon	6.00
144	Art Houtteman	6.00	212	Jack Dittmer	6.00
145	Bob Nieman	6.00	213	George Kell	35.00
146	Don Liddle	6.00	214	Billy Pierce	6.00
147	Sam Mele	6.00	215	Bob Kuzava	6.00
			216	Preacher Roe	6.00

217	Del Crandall	6.00
218	Joe Adcock	6.00
219	"Whitey" Lockman	6.00
220	Jim Hearn	6.00
221	Hector "Skinny" Brown	6.00
222	Russ Kemmerer	6.00
223	Hal Jeffcoat	6.00
224	Dee Fondy	6.00
225	Paul Richards	17.00
226	W.F. McKinley (umpire)	25.00
227	Frank Baumholtz	17.00
228	John M. Phillips	17.00
229	Jim Brosnan	17.00
230	Al Brazle	17.00
231	Jim Konstanty	17.00
232	Birdie Tebbetts	17.00
233	Bill Serena	17.00
234	Dick Bartell	17.00
235	J.A. Paparella (umpire)	25.00
236	Murry Dickson	17.00
237	Johnny Wyrostek	17.00
238	Eddie Stanky	17.00
239	Edwin A. Rommel (umpire)	25.00
240	Billy Loes	20.00
241	John Pesky	17.00
242	Ernie Banks (FC)	600.00
243	Gus Bell	17.00
244	Duane Pillette	17.00
245	Bill Miller	17.00
246	Hank Bauer	30.00
247	Dutch Leonard	17.00
248	Harry Dorish	17.00
249	Billy Gardner	17.00
250	Larry Napp (umpire)	25.00
251	Stan Jok	17.00
252	Roy Smalley	17.00
253	Jim Wilson	17.00
254	Bennett Flowers	17.00
255	Pete Runnels	17.00
256	Owen Friend	17.00
257	Tom Alston	17.00
258	John W. Stevens (umpire)	25.00
259	*Don Mossi*	17.00
260	Edwin H. Hurley (umpire)	25.00
261	Walt Moryn	17.00
262	Jim Lemon	17.00
263	Eddie Joost	17.00
264	Bill Henry	17.00
265	Al Barlick (umpire)	80.00
266	Mike Fornieles	17.00
267	George Honochick (umpire)	65.00
268	Roy Lee Hawes	17.00
269	Joe Amalfitano	17.00
270	Chico Fernandez	17.00
271	Bob Hooper	17.00
272	John Flaherty (umpire)	25.00
273	"Bubba" Church	17.00
274	Jim Delsing	17.00
275	William T. Grieve (umpire)	25.00
276	Ike Delock	17.00
277	Ed Runge (umpire)	25.00
278	*Charles Neal*	17.00
279	Hank Soar (umpire)	25.00
280	Clyde McCullough	17.00
281	Charles Berry (umpire)	25.00
282	Phil Cavarretta	17.00
283	Nestor Chylak (umpire)	25.00
284	William A. Jackowski (umpire)	25.00
285	Walt Dropo	17.00
286	Frank Secory (umpire)	25.00
287	Ron Mrozinski	17.00
288	Dick Smith	17.00
289	Art Gore (umpire)	25.00
290	Hershell Freeman	17.00
291	Frank Dascoli (umpire)	25.00
292	Marv Blaylock	17.00
293	Thomas D. Gorman (umpire)	25.00
294	Wally Moses	17.00
295	Lee Ballanfant (umpire)	25.00
296	*Bill Virdon*	17.00
297	"Dusty" Boggess (umpire)	25.00
298	Charlie Grimm	17.00
299	Lonnie Warneke (umpire)	25.00
300	Tommy Byrne	17.00
301	William Engeln (umpire)	25.00
302	*Frank Malzone*	17.00
303	Jocko Conlan (umpire)	100.00
304	Harry Chiti	17.00
305	Frank Umont (umpire)	25.00
306	Bob Cerv	17.00
307	"Babe" Pinelli (umpire)	25.00
308	Al Lopez	45.00
309	Hal Dixon (umpire)	25.00
310	Ken Lehman	17.00
311	Larry Goetz (umpire)	25.00
312	Bill Wight	17.00
313	Augie Donatelli (umpire)	25.00
314	Dale Mitchell	17.00
315	Cal Hubbard (umpire)	100.00
316	Marion Fricano	17.00
317	Bill Summers (umpire)	25.00
318	Sid Hudson	17.00
319	Al Schroll	17.00
320	George Susce, Jr.	100.00

1914 Cracker Jack

The 1914 Cracker Jack set, whose ACC designation is E145-1, is one of the most popular of the "E" card sets and features baseball stars from the American, National and Federal leagues. The cards, which measure 2-1/4" by 3" and are printed on thin stock, were found in boxes of Cracker Jack. The 1914 issue consists of 144 cards with tinted color photographs on a red background. The numbered backs feature a short biography plus an advertisement. The advertising on the low-numbered cards in the set indicate that 10 million cards were issued, while the high-numbered cards boast that 15 million were printed.

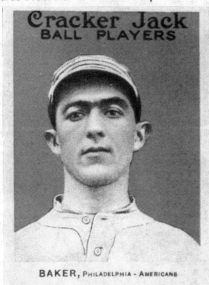

BAKER, PHILADELPHIA - AMERICANS

Mr. Mint Says - This is essentially impossible to obtain as a matched set because it wasn't issued that way.

I believe that near-mint prices are already over what you can get for a mint copy, but I do think you could sell a few mint matched sets in the $80,000 to $100,000 range.

		MT
Complete Set (144):		80000.00
Common Player:		200.00
1	Otto Knabe	750.00
2	Home Run Baker	900.00
3	Joe Tinker	700.00
4	Larry Doyle	200.00
5	Ward Miller	200.00
6	Eddie Plank	1000.00
7	Eddie Collins	650.00
8	Rube Oldring	200.00

9	Artie Hoffman (Hofman)	200.00
10	Stuffy McInnis	200.00
11	George Stovall	200.00
12	Connie Mack	700.00
13	Art Wilson	200.00
14	Sam Crawford	400.00
15	Reb Russell	200.00
16	Howie Camnitz	200.00
17a	Roger Bresnahan (no number on back)	600.00
17b	Roger Bresnahan (number on back)	600.00
18	Johnny Evers	550.00
19	Chief Bender	600.00
20	Cy Falkenberg	200.00
21	Heinie Zimmerman	200.00
22	Smoky Joe Wood	200.00
23	Charles Comiskey	600.00
24	George Mullen (Mullin)	200.00
25	Mike Simon	200.00
26	Jim Scott	200.00
27	Bill Carrigan	200.00
28	Jack Barry	200.00
29	Vean Gregg	200.00
30	Ty Cobb	6500.00
31	Heinie Wagner	200.00
32	Mordecai Brown	500.00
33	Amos Strunk	200.00
34	Ira Thomas	200.00
35	Harry Hooper	550.00
36	Ed Walsh	600.00
37	Grover C. Alexander	800.00
38	Red Dooin	200.00
39	Chick Gandil	200.00
40	Jimmy Austin	200.00
41	Tommy Leach	200.00
42	Al Bridwell	200.00
43	Rube Marquard	550.00
44	Jeff Tesreau	200.00
45	Fred Luderus	200.00
46	Bob Groom	200.00
47	Josh Devore	200.00
48	Harry Lord	375.00
49	Dots Miller	200.00
50	John Hummell (Hummel)	200.00
51	Nap Rucker	200.00
52	Zach Wheat	550.00
53	Otto Miller	200.00
54	Marty O'Toole	200.00
55	Dick Hoblitzel (Hoblitzell)	200.00
56	Clyde Milan	200.00
57	Walter Johnson	2500.00
58	Wally Schang	200.00
59	Doc Gessler	200.00
60	Rollie Zeider	500.00
61	Ray Schalk	500.00
62	Jay Cashion	500.00
63	Babe Adams	200.00
64	Jimmy Archer	200.00
65	Tris Speaker	1000.00
66	Nap Lajoie	1250.00
67	Doc Crandall	200.00
68	Honus Wagner	3000.00
69	John McGraw	900.00
70	Fred Clarke	450.00
71	Chief Meyers	200.00
72	Joe Boehling	200.00
73	Max Carey	400.00
74	Frank Owens	200.00
75	Miller Huggins	500.00
76	Claude Hendrix	200.00

77	Hughie Jennings	550.00
78	Fred Merkle	200.00
79	Ping Bodie	200.00
80	Ed Reulbach	200.00
81	Jim Delehanty (Delahanty)	200.00
82	Gavvy Cravath	200.00
83	Russ Ford	200.00
84	Elmer Knetzer	200.00
85	Buck Herzog	200.00
86	Burt Shotten	200.00
87	Hick Cady	200.00
88	Christy Mathewson	2400.00
89	Larry Cheney	200.00
90	Frank Smith	200.00
91	Roger Peckinpaugh	200.00
92	Al Demaree	200.00
93	Del Pratt	600.00
94	Eddie Cicotte	275.00
95	Ray Keating	200.00
96	Beals Becker	200.00
97	Rube Benton	200.00
98	Frank Laporte (LaPorte)	200.00
99	Frank Chance	1900.00
100	Tom Seaton	200.00
101	Wildfire Schulte	200.00
102	Ray Fisher	200.00
103	Shoeless Joe Jackson	12000.00
104	Vic Saier	200.00
105	Jimmy Lavender	200.00
106	Joe Birmingham	200.00
107	Tom Downey	200.00
108	Sherry Magee	200.00
109	Fred Blanding	200.00
110	Bob Bescher	200.00
111	Nixey Callahan	600.00
112	Jeff Sweeney	200.00
113	George Suggs	200.00
114	George Moriarity (Moriarty)	200.00
115	Ad Brennan	200.00
116	Rollie Zeider	200.00
117	Ted Easterly	200.00
118	Ed Konetchy	200.00
119	George Perring	200.00
120	Mickey Doolan	200.00
121	Hub Perdue	200.00
122	Donie Bush	200.00
123	Slim Sallee	200.00
124	Earle Moore (Earl)	200.00
125	Bert Niehoff	200.00
126	Walter Blair	200.00
127	Butch Schmidt	200.00
128	Steve Evans	200.00
129	Ray Caldwell	200.00
130	Ivy Wingo	200.00
131	George Baumgardner	200.00
132	Les Nunamaker	200.00
133	Branch Rickey	600.00
134	Armando Marsans	200.00
135	Bill Killifer (Killefer)	200.00
136	Rabbit Maranville	450.00
137	Bill Rariden	200.00
138	Hank Gowdy	200.00
139	Rebel Oakes	200.00
140	Danny Murphy	200.00
141	Cy Barger	200.00
142	Gene Packard	200.00
143	Jake Daubert	200.00
144	Jimmy Walsh	500.00

COBB, Detroit - Americans

WAGNER, Pittsburgh - Nationals

1915 Cracker Jack

The 1915 Cracker Jack set (E145-2) is a reissue of the 1914 edition with some card additions and deletions, team designation changes, and new poses. A total of 176 cards comprise the set. The deletions involve card #'s 48, 60, 62, 99 and 111. Cards can be distinguished as either 1914 or 1915 by the backs. The advertising on the backs of the 1914 cards call the set complete at 144 pictures, while the 1915 version notes 176 pictures. A complete set and an album were available from the company.

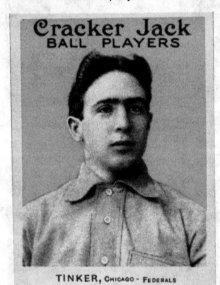

Mr. Mint Says - In the second year the company sold this as a complete set, so they tend to be found in uniformly better condition than the previous year. I believe a perfect set in the current market wouldn't bring over $60,000.

Collectors also need to be aware that Cracker Jack cards have been the recipient of a lot of bleaching of the borders. The cards are 80 years old and it is unreasonable to expect that the borders would be underwear white.

Cracker Jack cards also appear from time to time in dealer's showcases as genuine when the cards are, in fact, reprinted versions, but these should be easily discernible, with surface gloss (on the reprinted versions) one hint.

		MT
	Complete Set (176):	60000.
	Common Player: (1-144):	125.00
	Common Player: (145-176):	175.00
1	Otto Knabe	600.00
2	Home Run Baker	750.00
3	Joe Tinker	600.00
4	Larry Doyle	125.00
5	Ward Miller	125.00
6	Eddie Plank	750.00
7	Eddie Collins	550.00
8	Rube Oldring	125.00
9	Artie Hoffman (Hofman)	125.00
10	Stuffy McInnis	125.00
11	George Stovall	125.00
12	Connie Mack	500.00
13	Art Wilson	125.00
14	Sam Crawford	450.00
15	Reb Russell	125.00
16	Howie Camnitz	125.00
17	Roger Bresnahan	500.00
18	Johnny Evers	500.00
19	Chief Bender	400.00
20	Cy Falkenberg	125.00
21	Heinie Zimmerman	125.00
22	Smoky Joe Wood	125.00
23	Charles Comiskey	500.00
24	George Mullen (Mullin)	125.00
25	Mike Simon	125.00
26	Jim Scott	125.00
27	Bill Carrigan	125.00
28	Jack Barry	125.00
29	Vean Gregg	125.00
30	Ty Cobb	5000.00
31	Heinie Wagner	125.00
32	Mordecai Brown	450.00
33	Amos Strunk	125.00
34	Ira Thomas	125.00
35	Harry Hooper	450.00
36	Ed Walsh	450.00
37	Grover C. Alexander	700.00
38	Red Dooin	125.00
39	Chick Gandil	125.00
40	Jimmy Austin	125.00
41	Tommy Leach	125.00
42	Al Bridwell	125.00
43	Rube Marquard	500.00
44	Jeff Tesreau	125.00
45	Fred Luderus	125.00
46	Bob Groom	125.00
47	Josh Devore	125.00
48	Steve O'Neill	125.00
49	Dots Miller	125.00
50	John Hummell (Hummel)	125.00
51	Nap Rucker	125.00
52	Zach Wheat	500.00
53	Otto Miller	125.00
54	Marty O'Toole	125.00
55	Dick Hoblitzel (Hoblitzell)	125.00
56	Clyde Milan	125.00
57	Walter Johnson	1800.00
58	Wally Schang	125.00
59	Doc Gessler	125.00
60	Oscar Dugey	125.00
61	Ray Schalk	400.00
62	Willie Mitchell	125.00
63	Babe Adams	125.00
64	Jimmy Archer	125.00

65	Tris Speaker	950.00		121	Hub Perdue	125.00
66	Nap Lajoie	1000.00		122	Donie Bush	125.00
67	Doc Crandall	125.00		123	Slim Sallee	125.00
68	Honus Wagner	2250.00		124	Earle Moore (Earl)	125.00
69	John McGraw	750.00		125	Bert Niehoff	125.00
70	Fred Clarke	400.00		126	Walter Blair	125.00
71	Chief Meyers	125.00		127	Butch Schmidt	125.00
72	Joe Boehling	125.00		128	Steve Evans	125.00
73	Max Carey	375.00		129	Ray Caldwell	125.00
74	Frank Owens	125.00		130	Ivy Wingo	125.00
75	Miller Huggins	450.00		131	George Baumgardner	125.00
76	Claude Hendrix	125.00		132	Les Nunamaker	125.00
77	Hughie Jennings	450.00		133	Branch Rickey	500.00
78	Fred Merkle	125.00		134	Armando Marsans	125.00
79	Ping Bodie	125.00		135	Bill Killifer (Killefer)	125.00
80	Ed Reulbach	125.00		136	Rabbit Maranville	400.00
81	Jim Delehanty (Delahanty)	125.00		137	Bill Rariden	125.00
82	Gavvy Cravath	125.00		138	Hank Gowdy	125.00
83	Russ Ford	125.00		139	Rebel Oakes	125.00
84	Elmer Knetzer	125.00		140	Danny Murphy	125.00
85	Buck Herzog	125.00		141	Cy Barger	125.00
86	Burt Shotten	125.00		142	Gene Packard	125.00
87	Hick Cady	125.00		143	Jake Daubert	125.00
88	Christy Mathewson	1500.00		144	Jimmy Walsh	125.00
89	Larry Cheney	125.00		145	Ted Cather	175.00
90	Frank Smith	125.00		146	Lefty Tyler	175.00
91	Roger Peckinpaugh	125.00		147	Lee Magee	175.00
92	Al Demaree	125.00		148	Owen Wilson	175.00
93	Del Pratt	125.00		149	Hal Janvrin	175.00
94	Eddie Cicotte	125.00		150	Doc Johnston	175.00
95	Ray Keating	125.00		151	Possum Whitted	175.00
96	Beals Becker	125.00		152	George McQuillen (McQuillan)	175.00
97	Rube Benton	125.00		153	Bill James	175.00
98	Frank Laporte (LaPorte)	125.00		154	Dick Rudolph	175.00
99	Hal Chase	450.00		155	Joe Connolly	175.00
100	Tom Seaton	125.00		156	Jean Dubuc	175.00
101	Wildfire Schulte	125.00		157	George Kaiserling	175.00
102	Ray Fisher	125.00		158	Fritz Maisel	175.00
103	Shoeless Joe Jackson	7000.00		159	Heinie Groh	175.00
104	Vic Saier	125.00		160	Benny Kauff	175.00
105	Jimmy Lavender	125.00		161	Edd Rousch (Roush)	400.00
106	Joe Birmingham	125.00		162	George Stallings	175.00
107	Tom Downey	125.00		163	Bert Whaling	175.00
108	Sherry Magee	125.00		164	Bob Shawkey	175.00
109	Fred Blanding	125.00		165	Eddie Murphy	175.00
110	Bob Bescher	125.00		166	Bullet Joe Bush	200.00
111	Herbie Moran	125.00		167	Clark Griffith	550.00
112	Jeff Sweeney	125.00		168	Vin Campbell	175.00
113	George Suggs	125.00		169	Ray Collins	175.00
114	George Moriarity (Moriarty)	125.00		170	Hans Lobert	175.00
115	Ad Brennan	125.00		171	Earl Hamilton	175.00
116	Rollie Zeider	125.00		172	Erskine Mayer	175.00
117	Ted Easterly	125.00		173	Tilly Walker	175.00
118	Ed Konetchy	125.00		174	Bobby Veach	175.00
119	George Perring	125.00		175	Joe Benz	350.00
120	Mickey Doolan	125.00		176	Hippo Vaughn	500.00

1933 DeLong

The DeLong Gum Company of Boston, Mass. was among the first to sell baseball cards with gum. It issued a set of 24 cards in 1933, the same year the Goudey Gum Co. issued its premiere set, making both companies pioneers in the field. The DeLong cards measure 2" by 3" and feature black and white player photos on a color background. The photos show the players in various action poses and positions them in the middle of a miniature stadium setting so that they appear to be giant in size. Most of the cards in the set are vertically designed, but a few are horizontal. The backs of the cards, written by Austen Lake, editor of the Boston Transcript, contain a series of sports tips to help youngsters become better ballplayers. Lake later wrote the tips that appeared on the backs of the Diamond Stars cards issued by National Chicle from 1934-1936. The ACC designation for this set is R333. The checklist below gives the players' names exactly as they appear on the fronts of the cards.

more popular because the idea of putting it together is not so intimidating to collectors.

The cards are over 60 years old, so it, understandably, is difficult to find them in mint condition.

In 1988, I met a woman in Boston who, according to folklore, dug a substantial number (the story is a couple of thousand) out of a dumpster. Over a period of years I bought hundreds of cards from her, as she would apparently call me as she needed money.

All of the cards I bought were mint, brand new like they were printed yesterday, and with bright yellow borders. She had no Gehrigs, and only 12 different out of the 24; Simmons, Terry, Traynor, Maranville, Gomez, Klein and Grove, and numbers 1, 9, 10, 17 and 18.

		MT
Complete Set (24):		13500.
Common Player:		250.00
1	"Marty" McManus	250.00
2	Al Simmons	350.00
3	Oscar Melillo	250.00
4	William (Bill) Terry	500.00
5	Charlie Gehringer	500.00
6	Gordon (Mickey) Cochrane	500.00
7	Lou Gehrig	4500.00
8	Hazen S. (Kiki) Cuyler	400.00
9	Bill Urbanski	250.00
10	Frank J. (Lefty) O'Doul	250.00
11	Freddie Lindstrom	300.00
12	Harold (Pie) Traynor	400.00
13	"Rabbit" Maranville	400.00
14	Vernon "Lefty" Gomez	400.00
15	Riggs Stephenson	250.00
16	Lon Warneke	250.00
17	Pepper Martin	250.00
18	Jimmy Dykes	250.00
19	Chick Hafey	400.00
20	Joe Vosmik	250.00
21	Jimmy Foxx	750.00
22	Charles (Chuck) Klein	400.00
23	Robert (Lefty) Grove	600.00
24	"Goose" Goslin	400.00

HAROLD (PIE) TRAYNOR
PITTSBURGH PIRATES

Mr. Mint Says - This set is popular in that it is a small, compact set (24 cards) that is obtainable. Any attractive set that is printed with a small number of cards becomes a little

ROBERT (LEFTY) GROVE, PHILADELPHIA ATHLETICS

1934 - 36 Diamond Stars

Issued from 1934 through 1936, the Diamond Stars set (ACC designation R327) consists of 108 cards. Produced by National Chicle, the numbered cards measure 2-3/8" by 2-7/8" and are color art reproductions of actual photographs. The year of issue can be determined by the player's statistics found on the reverse of the card. The backs feature either a player biography or a baseball playing tip. Some cards can be found with either green or blue printing on the backs. Artwork for 12 cards that were never issued was uncovered several years ago and a set featuring those cards was subsequently made available to the collecting public. The complete set price does not include the higher priced variations.

Mr. Mint Says - To me, these are just as pretty as 1933 Goudeys, but you tell a guy you've got mint Diamond Stars and he looks at you like you said Strawberry rookie cards instead. I think the main complaint about the set is that there are no Ruths or Gehrigs, and no DiMaggio.

The last section of high numbers, 97-108, are simply impossible to find. In most of the major collections that I have purchased, those numbers are always missing. I have purchased many sets over the years, but probably only three or four with the scarce series. I have also had a few wrappers from time to time, but have never seen an unopened pack.

They seem to have been made on a harder stock and tend to hold up better than

Goudeys. Invariably they are found in better condition than Goudeys from the same period. There were occasionally print lines, especially in the high numbers.

		MT
Complete Set:		22500.
Common Player: (1-31):		90.00
Common Player: (32-72):		70.00
Common Player: (73-84):		75.00
Common Player: (85-96):		125.00
Common Player: (97-108):		450.00

1a	"Lefty" Grove (1934 green back)	1300.00
1b	"Lefty" Grove (1935 green back)	1300.00
2a	Al Simmons (1934 green back)	200.00
2b	Al Simmons (1935 green back)	200.00
2c	Al Simmons (1936 blue back)	225.00
3a	"Rabbit" Maranville (1934 green back)	100.00
3b	"Rabbit" Maranville (1935 green back)	100.00
4a	"Buddy" Myer (1934 green back)	90.00
4b	"Buddy" Myer (1935 green back)	90.00
4c	"Buddy" Myer (1936 blue back)	90.00
5a	Tom Bridges (1934 green back)	90.00
5b	Tom Bridges (1935 green back)	90.00
5c	Tom Bridges (1936 blue back)	90.00
6a	Max Bishop (1934 green back)	90.00
6b	Max Bishop (1935 green back)	90.00
7a	Lew Fonseca (1934 green back)	90.00
7b	Lew Fonseca (1935 green back)	90.00
8a	Joe Vosmik (1934 green back)	90.00
8b	Joe Vosmik (1935 green back)	90.00
8c	Joe Vosmik (1936 blue back)	90.00
9a	"Mickey" Cochrane (1934 green back)	225.00
9b	"Mickey" Cochrane (1935 green back)	225.00
9c	"Mickey" Cochrane (1936 blue back)	225.00
10a	Roy Mahaffey (1934 green back)	90.00
10b	Roy Mahaffey (1935 green back)	90.00
10c	Roy Mahaffey (1936 blue back)	90.00
11a	Bill Dickey (1934 green back)	275.00
11b	Bill Dickey (1935 green back)	275.00
12a	"Dixie" Walker (1934 green back)	90.00
12b	"Dixie" Walker (1935 green back)	90.00
12c	"Dixie" Walker (1936 blue back)	90.00
13a	George Blaeholder (1934 green back)	90.00
13b	George Blaeholder (1935 green back)	90.00
14a	Bill Terry (1934 green back)	110.00
14b	Bill Terry (1935 green back)	110.00
15a	Dick Bartell (1934 green back)	90.00
15b	Dick Bartell (1935 green back)	90.00
16a	Lloyd Waner (1934 green back)	125.00
16b	Lloyd Waner (1935 green back)	125.00
16c	Lloyd Waner (1936 blue back)	125.00
17a	Frankie Frisch (1934 green back)	110.00
17b	Frankie Frisch (1935 green back)	110.00
18a	"Chick" Hafey (1934 green back)	100.00
18b	"Chick" Hafey (1935 green back)	100.00
19a	Van Mungo (1934 green back)	90.00
19b	Van Mungo (1935 green back)	90.00
20a	"Shanty" Hogan (1934 green back)	90.00
20b	"Shanty" Hogan (1935 green back)	90.00
21a	Johnny Vergez (1934 green back)	90.00
21b	Johnny Vergez (1935 green back)	90.00
22a	Jimmy Wilson (1934 green back)	90.00
22b	Jimmy Wilson (1935 green back)	90.00
22c	Jimmy Wilson (1936 blue back)	90.00
23a	Bill Hallahan (1934 green back)	90.00
23b	Bill Hallahan (1935 green back)	90.00

24a	"Sparky" Adams (1934 green back)	90.00
24b	"Sparky" Adams (1935 green back)	90.00
25	Walter Berger	100.00
26a	"Pepper" Martin (1935 green back)	100.00
26b	"Pepper" Martin (1936 blue back)	100.00
27	"Pie" Traynor	225.00
28	"Al" Lopez	225.00
29	Robert Rolfe	90.00
30a	"Heinie" Manush (1935 green back)	125.00
30b	"Heinie" Manush (1936 blue back)	150.00
31a	"Kiki" Cuyler (1935 green back)	125.00
31b	"Kiki" Cuyler (1936 blue back)	125.00
32	Sam Rice	125.00
33	"Schoolboy" Rowe	90.00
34	Stanley Hack	90.00
35	Earle Averill	125.00
36a	Earnie Lombardi	200.00
36b	Ernie Lombardi	150.00
37	"Billie" Urbanski	70.00
38	Ben Chapman	90.00
39	Carl Hubbell	110.00
40	"Blondy" Ryan	70.00
41	Harvey Hendrick	70.00
42	Jimmy Dykes	90.00
43	Ted Lyons	100.00
44	Rogers Hornsby	350.00
45	"Jo Jo" White	70.00
46	"Red" Lucas	70.00
47	Cliff Bolton	70.00
48	"Rick" Ferrell	125.00
49	"Buck" Jordan	70.00
50	"Mel" Ott	275.00
51	John Whitehead	70.00
52	George Stainback	70.00
53	Oscar Melillo	70.00
54a	"Hank" Greenburg	400.00
54b	"Hank" Greenberg	250.00
55	Tony Cuccinello	70.00
56	"Gus" Suhr	70.00
57	"Cy" Blanton	70.00
58	Glenn Myatt	70.00
59	Jim Bottomley	125.00
60	Charley "Red" Ruffing	100.00
61	"Billie" Werber	70.00
62	Fred M. Frankhouse	70.00
63	"Stonewall" Jackson	125.00
64	Jimmie Foxx	350.00
65	"Zeke" Bonura	70.00
66	"Ducky" Medwick	100.00
67	Marvin Owen	70.00
68	"Sam" Leslie	70.00
69	Earl Grace	70.00
70	"Hal" Trosky	70.00
71	"Ossie" Bluege	70.00
72	"Tony" Piet	70.00
73a	"Fritz" Ostermueller (1935 green back)	75.00
73b	"Fritz" Ostermueller (1935 blue back)	75.00
73c	"Fritz" Ostermueller (1936 blue back)	75.00
74a	Tony Lazzeri (1935 green back)	125.00
74b	Tony Lazzeri (1935 blue back)	125.00
74c	Tony Lazzeri (1936 blue back)	125.00
75a	Irving Burns (1935 green back)	75.00
75b	Irving Burns (1935 blue back)	75.00
75c	Irving Burns (1936 blue back)	75.00
76a	Bill Rogell (1935 green back)	75.00
76b	Bill Rogell (1935 blue back)	75.00
76c	Bill Rogell (1936 blue back)	75.00
77a	Charlie Gehringer (1935 green back)	150.00
77b	Charlie Gehringer (1935 blue back)	150.00
77c	Charlie Gehringer (1936 blue back)	150.00
78a	Joe Kuhel (1935 green back)	75.00
78b	Joe Kuhel (1935 blue back)	75.00
78c	Joe Kuhel (1936 blue back)	75.00

79a	Willis Hudlin (1935 green back)	75.00
79b	Willis Hudlin (1935 blue back)	75.00
79c	Willis Hudlin (1936 blue back)	75.00
80a	Louis Chiozza (1935 green back)	75.00
80b	Louis Chiozza (1935 blue back)	75.00
80c	Louis Chiozza (1936 blue back)	75.00
81a	Bill DeLancey (1935 green back)	75.00
81b	Bill DeLancey (1935 blue back)	75.00
81c	Bill DeLancey (1936 blue back)	75.00
82a	John Babich (1935 green back)	100.00
82b	John Babich (1935 blue back)	100.00
82c	John Babich (1936 blue back)	100.00
83a	Paul Waner (1935 green back)	200.00
83b	Paul Waner (1935 blue back)	200.00
83c	Paul Waner (1936 blue back)	200.00
84a	Sam Byrd (1935 green back)	75.00
84b	Sam Byrd (1935 blue back)	75.00
84c	Sam Byrd (1936 blue back)	75.00
85	Julius Solters	125.00
86	Frank Crosetti	200.00
87	Steve O'Neil (O'Neill)	125.00
88	Geo. Selkirk	100.00
89	Joe Stripp	125.00
90	Ray Hayworth	125.00
91	Bucky Harris	150.00
92	Ethan Allen	125.00
93	Alvin Crowder	125.00
94	Wes Ferrell	125.00
95	Luke Appling	275.00
96	Lew Riggs	125.00
97	"Al" Lopez	650.00
98	"Schoolboy" Rowe	450.00
99	"Pie" Traynor	800.00
100	Earle Averill (Earl)	650.00
101	Dick Bartell	450.00
102	Van Mungo	450.00
103	Bill Dickey	950.00
104	Robert Rolfe	450.00
105	"Ernie" Lombardi	650.00
106	"Red" Lucas	450.00
107	Stanley Hack	450.00
108	Walter Berger	450.00

1941 Double Play

Issued by Gum, Inc., this set includes 75 numbered cards (two consecutive numbers per card) featuring 150 baseball players. The cards, which are blank-backed and measure 2-1/2" by 3-1/8", contain sepia-tone photos of two players. Action and portrait poses are found in the set, with card designs on either a vertical or horizontal format. The last fifty cards are the scarcest of the set. Cards cut to form two single cards have little value.

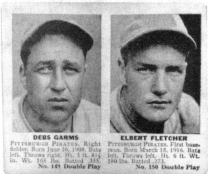

DEBS GARMS — PITTSBURGH PIRATES. Right fielder. Born June 26, 1908. Bats left. Throws right. Ht. 5 ft. 8½ in. Wt. 165 lbs. Batted .355. No. 149 Double Play

ELBERT FLETCHER — PITTSBURGH PIRATES. First baseman. Born March 18, 1916. Bats left. Throws left. Ht. 6 ft. Wt. 180 lbs. Batted .273. No. 150 Double Play

Mr. Mint Says - This is a scarce set and seldom seen complete. Most people don't piece them together anymore because they can't find them. Individually, the major Hall of Famers sell quite well.

The cards usually hold up well and are much easier to find in mint condition than the Goudeys of the same era. The corners maintain nicely but the white borders often get dirty.

I don't put much stock in the idea of the high numbers (101-150) being worth more than the low numbers. Some of the harder to find cards are in that series, but I don't think that they are worth 50 or 60 percent more.

		MT
Complete Set:		8700.
Common Player: (1-100):		45.00
Common Player: (101-150):		50.00

1	Larry French	
2	Vance Page	100.00
3	Billy Herman	
4	Stanley Hack	60.00
5	Linus Frey	
6	John Vander Meer	55.00
7	Paul Derringer	
8	Bucky Walters	45.00
9	Frank McCormick	
10	Bill Werber	45.00
11	Jimmy Ripple	
12	Ernie Lombardi	80.00
13	Alex Kampouris	
14	John Wyatt	45.00
15	Mickey Owen	
16	Paul Waner	80.00
17	Harry Lavagetto	
18	Harold Reiser	55.00
19	Jimmy Wasdell	
20	Dolph Camilli	55.00
21	Dixie Walker	
22	Ducky Medwick	80.00
23	Harold Reese	
24	Kirby Higbe	350.00
25	Harry Danning	
26	Cliff Melton	45.00
27	Harry Gumbert	
28	Burgess Whitehead	45.00
29	Joe Orengo	
30	Joe Moore	45.00
31	Mel Ott	
32	Babe Young	150.00
33	Lee Handley	
34	Arky Vaughan	80.00
35	Bob Klinger	
36	Stanley Brown	45.00
37	Terry Moore	
38	Gus Mancuso	45.00
39	Johnny Mize	
40	Enos Slaughter	150.00
41	John Cooney	
42	Sibby Sisti	45.00
43	Max West	
44	Carvel Rowell	45.00
45	Dan Litwhiler	
46	Merrill May	45.00
47	Frank Hayes	
48	Al Brancato	45.00
49	Bob Johnson	
50	Bill Nagel	45.00
51	Buck Newsom	
52	Hank Greenberg	150.00
53	Barney McCosky	
54	Charley Gehringer	150.00
55	Pinky Higgins	
56	Dick Bartell	45.00
57	Ted Williams	
58	Jim Tabor	850.00
59	Joe Cronin	
60	Jimmy Foxx	250.00
61	Lefty Gomez	
62	Phil Rizzuto	350.00
63	Joe DiMaggio	
64	Charley Keller	1000.00
65	Red Rolfe	
66	Bill Dickey	200.00
67	Joe Gordon	
68	Red Ruffing	100.00
69	Mike Tresh	
70	Luke Appling	80.00
71	Moose Solters	
72	John Rigney	45.00
73	Buddy Meyer	
74	Ben Chapman	45.00
75	Cecil Travis	
76	George Case	45.00
77	Joe Krakauskas	
78	Bob Feller	200.00
79	Ken Keltner	
80	Hal Trosky	45.00
81	Ted Williams	
82	Joe Cronin	850.00

83	Joe Gordon	
84	Charley Keller	75.00
85	Hank Greenberg	
86	Red Ruffing	150.00
87	Hal Trosky	
88	George Case	45.00
89	Mel Ott	
90	Burgess Whitehead	150.00
91	Harry Danning	
92	Harry Gumbert	45.00
93	Babe Young	
94	Cliff Melton	45.00
95	Jimmy Ripple	
96	Bucky Walters	45.00
97	Stanley Hack	
98	Bob Klinger	45.00
99	Johnny Mize	
100	Dan Litwhiler	75.00
101	Dominic Dallessandro	
102	Augie Galan	50.00
103	Bill Lee	
104	Phil Cavarretta	50.00
105	Lefty Grove	
106	Bobby Doerr	200.00
107	Frank Pytlak	
108	Dom DiMaggio	75.00
109	Gerald Priddy	
110	John Murphy	75.00
111	Tommy Henrich	
112	Marius Russo	90.00
113	Frank Crosetti	
114	John Sturm	90.00
115	Ival Goodman	
116	Myron McCormick	50.00
117	Eddie Joost	
118	Ernest Koy	50.00
119	Lloyd Waner	
120	Henry Majeski	90.00
121	Buddy Hassett	
122	Eugene Moore	50.00
123	Nick Etten	
124	John Rizzo	50.00
125	Sam Chapman	
126	Wally Moses	50.00
127	John Babich	
128	Richard Siebert	50.00
129	Nelson Potter	
130	Benny McCoy	50.00
131	Clarence Campbell	
132	Louis Boudreau	90.00
133	Rolly Hemsley	
134	Mel Harder	50.00
135	Gerald Walker	
136	Joe Heving	50.00
137	John Rucker	
138	Ace Adams	50.00
139	Morris Arnovich	
140	Carl Hubbell	175.00
141	Lew Riggs	
142	Leo Durocher	90.00
143	Fred Fitzsimmons	
144	Joe Vosmik	50.00
145	Frank Crespi	
146	Jim Brown	50.00
147	Don Heffner	
148	Harland Clift (Harlond)	50.00
149	Debs Garms	
150	Elbert Fletcher	100.00

HANK GREENBERG
DETROIT TIGERS. Left fielder. Born Jan. 1, 1911. Bats and throws right. Height 6 feet 4 inches. Weight 210 lbs. Batted .340.
No. 85 Double Play

RED RUFFING
NEW YORK YANKEES. Pitcher. Born May 4, 1904. Bats right. Throws right. Height 6 feet. Weight 200 lbs. Won 15. Lost 12.
No. 86 Double Play

HAL TROSKY
CLEVELAND INDIANS. First baseman. Born Nov. 11, 1912. Bats left. Throws right. Ht. 6 ft. 2 in. Wt. 205 lbs. Batted .295.
No. 87 Double Play

GEORGE CASE
WASHINGTON SENATORS. Right fielder. Born Nov. 11, 1915. Bats and throws right. Height 6 feet. Weight 185 lbs. Batted .293.
No. 88 Double Play

1959 Fleer Ted Williams

This 80-card 1959 Fleer set tells of the life of baseball great Ted Williams, from his childhood years up to 1958. The full-color cards measure 2-1/2" by 3-1/2" in size and make use of both horizontal and vertical formats. The card backs, all designed horizontally, contain a continuing biography of Williams. Card #68 was withdrawn from the set early in production and is scarce. Counterfeit cards of #68 have been produced and can be distinguished by a cross-hatch pattern which appears over the photo on the card fronts.

Jan. 23, 1959 — Ted Signs For 1959

Mr. Mint Says - Fleer's first foray into baseball cards is a very nice set, and one that I seldom see in rough condition.

I had a nice find in Clifton, N.J. in 1987 where a gentleman sold me two cases, with 12 boxes to a case. The story is that #68 was not issued in gum packs; there were no #68s in the packs that he sold me. One year later he sold me two more cases at the Willow Grove, Pa., with the same result.

In the past there have been a lot of counterfeit #68s going around, but they should be discernible from an odd pattern in the printing dots.

		MT
Complete Set:		1300.
Common Card:		6.50

1	The Early Years	30.00
2	Ted's Idol - Babe Ruth	40.00
3	Practice Makes Perfect	6.50
4	1934 - Ted Learns The Fine Points	6.50
5	Ted's Fame Spreads - 1935-36	6.50
6	Ted Turns Professional	6.50
7	1936 - From Mound To Plate	6.50
8	1937 - First Full Season	6.50
9	1937 - First Step To The Majors	6.50
10	1938 - Gunning As A Pastime	6.50
11	1938 - First Spring Training	6.50
12	1939 - Burning Up The Minors	6.50
13	1939 - Ted Shows He Will Stay	6.50
14	Outstanding Rookie of 1939	6.50
15	1940 - Williams Licks Sophomore Jinx	6.50
16	1941 - Williams' Greatest Year	6.50
17	1941 - How Ted Hit .400	6.50
18	1941 - All-Star Hero	6.50
19	1942 - Ted Wins Triple Crown	6.50
20	1942 - On To Naval Training	6.50
21	1943 - Honors For Williams	6.50
22	1944 - Ted Solos	6.50
23	1944 - Williams Wins His Wings	6.50
24	1945 - Sharpshooter	6.50
25	1945 - Ted Is Discharged	6.50
26	1946 - Off To A Flying Start	6.50
27	July 9, 1946 - One Man Show	6.50
28	July 14, 1946 - The Williams Shift	6.50
29	July 21, 1946, Ted Hits For The Cycle	6.50
30	1946 - Beating The Williams Shift	6.50
31	Oct. 1946 - Sox Lose The Series	6.50
32	1946 - Most Valuable Player	6.50
33	1947 - Another Triple Crown For Ted	6.50
34	1947 - Ted Sets Runs-Scored Record	6.50
35	1948 - The Sox Miss The Pennant	6.50
36	1948 - Banner Year For Ted	6.50
37	1949 - Sox Miss Out Again	6.50
38	1949 - Power Rampage	6.50
39	1950 - Great Start	6.50
40	July 11, 1950 - Ted Crashes Into Wall	6.50
41	1950 - Ted Recovers	6.50
42	1951 - Williams Slowed By Injury	6.50
43	1951 - Leads Outfielders In Double Plays	6.50
44	1952 - Back To The Marines	6.50
45	1952 - Farewell To Baseball?	6.50
46	1952 - Ready For Combat	6.50
47	1953 - Ted Crash Lands Jet	6.50
48	July 14, 1953 - Ted Returns	6.50
49	1953 - Smash Return	6.50
50	March 1954 - Spring Injury	6.50
51	May 16, 1954 - Ted Is Patched Up	6.50
52	1954 - Ted's Comeback	6.50
53	1954 - Ted's Comeback Is A Sucess	6.50
54	Dec. 1954, Fisherman Ted Hooks a Big One	6.50
55	1955 - Ted Decides Retirement Is "No Go"	6.50
56	1955 - 2,000th Major League Hit	6.50
57	400th Homer	6.50
58	1957 - Williams Hits .388	6.50
59	1957 - Hot September For Ted	6.50
60	1957 - More Records For Ted	6.50
61	1957 - Outfielder Ted	6.50
62	1958 - 6th Batting Title For Ted	6.50
63	Ted's All-Star Record	6.50
64	1958 - Daughter And Famous Daddy	6.50
65	August 30, 1958	6.50
66	1958 - Powerhouse	6.50
67	Two Famous Fishermen (with Sam Snead)	6.50
68	Jan. 23, 1959 - Ted Signs For 1959	6.50
69	A Future Ted Williams?	850.00
70	Ted Williams & Jim Thorpe	6.50
71	Ted's Hitting Fundamentals #1	25.00
72	Ted's Hitting Fundamentals #2	6.50
73	Ted's Hitting Fundamentals #3	6.50
74	Here's How!	6.50
75	Williams' Value To Red Sox (with Babe Ruth, Eddie Collins)	20.00
76	Ted's Remarkable "On Base" Record	6.50
77	Ted Relaxes	6.50
78	Honors For Williams	
79	Where Ted Stands	6.50
80	Ted's Goals For 1959	15.00

1960 Fleer

The 1960 Fleer Baseball Greats set consists of 78 cards of the game's top players from the past, plus a card of Ted Williams, who was in his final major league season. The cards are standard size (2-1/2" by 3-1/2") and feature color photos inside blue, green, red or yellow borders. The card backs carry a short player biography plus career hitting or pitching statistics. Unissued cards with a Pepper Martin back (#80), but with another player pictured on the front are in existence.

RABBIT MARANVILLE

Mr. Mint Says - This is a set featuring the old-time players, and there is not much interest in single cards with the exception of the major Hall of Famers. Williams, Ruth, Cobb, and Gehrig sell well individually, but there are not many people piecing together sets.

Centering problems plague the issue, and a lot of the cards come with different finishes on the background color, shiny and dull. They are unattractive with the dull finish.

In the past I've had unopened packs, but they have now disappeared. The cards were also reportedly sold in penny vending machines.

		MT
Complete Set (79):		550.00
Common Player:		3.00
1	Nap Lajoie	10.00
2	Christy Mathewson	10.00
3	Babe Ruth	125.00

4	Carl Hubbell	3.00
5	Grover Cleveland Alexander	5.00
6	Walter Johnson	10.00
7	Chief Bender	3.00
8	Roger Bresnahan	3.00
9	Mordecai Brown	3.00
10	Tris Speaker	3.00
11	Arky Vaughan	3.00
12	Zack Wheat	3.00
13	George Sisler	3.00
14	Connie Mack	4.00
15	Clark Griffith	3.00
16	Lou Boudreau	3.00
17	Ernie Lombardi	3.00
18	Heinie Manush	3.00
19	Marty Marion	3.00
20	Eddie Collins	3.00
21	Rabbit Maranville	3.00
22	Joe Medwick	3.00
23	Ed Barrow	3.00
24	Mickey Cochrane	3.00
25	Jimmy Collins	3.00
26	Bob Feller	7.00
27	Luke Appling	3.00
28	Lou Gehrig	
29	Gabby Hartnett	3.00
30	Chuck Klein	3.00
31	Tony Lazzeri	3.00
32	Al Simmons	3.00
33	Wilbert Robinson	3.00
34	Sam Rice	3.00
35	Herb Pennock	3.00
36	Mel Ott	3.00
37	Lefty O'Doul	3.00
38	Johnny Mize	3.00
39	Bing Miller	3.00
40	Joe Tinker	3.00
41	Frank Baker	3.00
42	Ty Cobb	65.00
43	Paul Derringer	3.00
44	Cap Anson	3.00
45	Jim Bottomley	3.00
46	Eddie Plank	3.00
47	Cy Young	5.00
48	Hack Wilson	3.00
49	Ed Walsh	3.00
50	Frank Chance	3.00
51	Dazzy Vance	3.00
52	Bill Terry	3.00
53	Jimmy Foxx	4.00
54	Lefty Gomez	3.00
55	Branch Rickey	3.00
56	Ray Schalk	3.00
57	Johnny Evers	3.00
58	Charlie Gehringer	3.00
59	Burleigh Grimes	3.00
60	Lefty Grove	3.00
61	Rube Waddell	3.00
62	Honus Wagner	10.00
63	Red Ruffing	3.00
64	Judge Landis	3.00
65	Harry Heilmann	3.00
66	John McGraw	3.00
67	Hughie Jennings	3.00
68	Hal Newhouser	3.00
69	Waite Hoyt	3.00
70	Bobo Newsom	3.00
71	Earl Averill	3.00
72	Ted Williams	75.00
73	Warren Giles	3.00
74	Ford Frick	3.00
75	Ki Ki Cuyler	3.00
76	Paul Waner	3.00
77	Pie Traynor	3.00
78	Lloyd Waner	3.00
79	Ralph Kiner	3.00

1961 - 62 Fleer

Over a two-year period, Fleer issued another set utilizing the Baseball Greats theme. The 154-card set was issued in two series and features a color player portrait against a color background. The player's name is located in a pennant set at the bottom of the card. The card backs feature orange and black on white stock and contain player biographical and statistical information. The cards measure 2-1/2" by 3-1/2" in size. The second series cards (#'s 89-154) were issued in 1962.

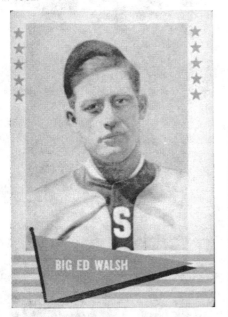

Mr. Mint Says - Another set featuring retired players, this is similar to 1960 Fleer in that it sells well as a set without much interest in single cards. The high numbers (89-154) are a little tougher, and the Williams and Wagner cards from that series are popular.

Unlike 1960, this set didn't have much of a problem with centering or print lines, and the card stock also seems to hold up better than the previous year.

		MT
Complete Set (154):		1250.
Common Player (1-88):		4.00
Common Player (89-154):		10.00

1	Checklist (Frank Baker, Ty Cobb, Zach Wheat)	75.00
2	G.C. Alexander	6.00
3	Nick Altrock	4.00
4	Cap Anson	4.00
5	Earl Averill	4.00
6	Home Run Baker	4.00
7	Dave Bancroft	4.00
8	Chief Bender	4.00
9	Jim Bottomley	4.00
10	Roger Bresnahan	4.00
11	Mordecai Brown	4.00
12	Max Carey	4.00
13	Jack Chesbro	4.00
14	Ty Cobb	75.00
15	Mickey Cochrane	4.00
16	Eddie Collins	4.00
17	Earle Combs	4.00
18	Charles Comiskey	4.00
19	Ki Ki Cuyler	4.00
20	Paul Derringer	4.00
21	Howard Ehmke	4.00
22	Billy Evans	4.00
23	Johnny Evers	4.00
24	Red Faber	4.00
25	Bob Feller	6.00
26	Wes Ferrell	4.00
27	Lew Fonseca	6.00
28	Jimmy Foxx	6.00
29	Ford Frick	4.00
30	Frankie Frisch	6.00
31	Lou Gehrig	100.00
32	Charlie Gehringer	4.00
33	Warren Giles	4.00
34	Lefty Gomez	4.00
35	Goose Goslin	4.00
36	Clark Griffith	4.00
37	Burleigh Grimes	4.00
38	Lefty Grove	4.00
39	Chick Hafey	4.00
40	Jesse Haines	4.00
41	Gabby Hartnett	4.00
42	Harry Heilmann	4.00
43	Rogers Hornsby	4.00
44	Waite Hoyt	4.00
45	Carl Hubbell	4.00
46	Miller Huggins	4.00
47	Hughie Jennings	4.00
48	Ban Johnson	4.00
49	Walter Johnson	49.00
50	Ralph Kiner	4.00
51	Chuck Klein	4.00
52	Johnny Kling	4.00
53	Judge Landis	4.00
54	Tony Lazzeri	4.00
55	Ernie Lombardi	4.00
56	Dolf Luque	4.00
57	Heinie Manush	4.00
58	Marty Marion	4.00
59	Christy Mathewson	10.00
60	John McGraw	4.00
61	Joe Medwick	4.00
62	Bing Miller	4.00
63	Johnny Mize	4.00
64	Johnny Mostil	4.00
65	Art Nehf	4.00
66	Hal Newhouser	4.00
67	Bobo Newsom	4.00
68	Mel Ott	4.00
69	Allie Reynolds	4.00
70	Sam Rice	4.00
71	Eppa Rixey	4.00
72	Edd Roush	4.00

73	Schoolboy Rowe	4.00
74	Red Ruffing	4.00
75	Babe Ruth	125.00
76	Joe Sewell	4.00
77	Al Simmons	4.00
78	George Sisler	4.00
79	Tris Speaker	4.00
80	Fred Toney	4.00
81	Dazzy Vance	4.00
82	Jim Vaughn	4.00
83	Big Ed Walsh	4.00
84	Lloyd Waner	4.00
85	Paul Waner	4.00
86	Zach Wheat	4.00
87	Hack Wilson	4.00
88	Jimmy Wilson	4.00
89	Checklist (George Sisler, Pie Traynor)	35.00
90	Babe Adams	10.00
91	Dale Alexander	10.00
92	Jim Bagby	10.00
93	Ossie Bluege	10.00
94	Lou Boudreau	10.00
95	Tommy Bridges	10.00
96	Donnie Bush (Donie)	10.00
97	Dolph Camilli	10.00
98	Frank Chance	10.00
99	Jimmy Collins	10.00
100	Stanley Coveleskie (Coveleski)	10.00
101	Hughie Critz	10.00
102	General Crowder	10.00
103	Joe Dugan	10.00
104	Bibb Falk	10.00
105	Rick Ferrell	10.00
106	Art Fletcher	10.00
107	Dennis Galehouse	10.00
108	Chick Galloway	10.00
109	Mule Haas	10.00
110	Stan Hack	10.00
111	Bump Hadley	10.00
112	Billy Hamilton	10.00
113	Joe Hauser	10.00
114	Babe Herman	10.00
115	Travis Jackson	10.00
116	Eddie Joost	10.00
117	Addie Joss	10.00
118	Joe Judge	10.00
119	Joe Kuhel	10.00
120	Nap Lajoie	10.00
121	Dutch Leonard	10.00
122	Ted Lyons	10.00
123	Connie Mack	10.00
124	Rabbit Maranville	10.00
125	Fred Marberry	10.00
126	Iron Man McGinnity	10.00
127	Oscar Melillo	10.00
128	Ray Mueller	10.00
129	Kid Nichols	10.00
130	Lefty O'Doul	10.00
131	Bob O'Farrell	10.00
132	Roger Peckinpaugh	10.00
133	Herb Pennock	10.00
134	George Pipgras	10.00
135	Eddie Plank	10.00
136	Ray Schalk	10.00
137	Hal Schumacher	10.00
138	Luke Sewell	10.00
139	Bob Shawkey	10.00
140	Riggs Stephenson	10.00
141	Billy Sullivan	10.00
142	Bill Terry	10.00
143	Joe Tinker	10.00
144	Pie Traynor	10.00
145	George Uhle	10.00

146	Hal Troskey (Trosky)	10.00
147	Arky Vaughan	10.00
148	Johnny Vander Meer	10.00
149	Rube Waddell	10.00
150	Honus Wagner	50.00
151	Dixie Walker	10.00
152	Ted Williams	85.00
153	Cy Young	12.00
154	Ross Young (Youngs)	12.00

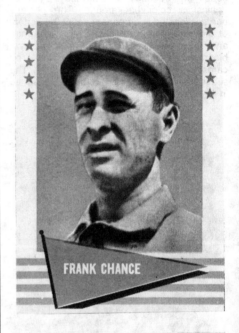

FRANK CHANCE

JOE HAUSER

1963 Fleer

A lawsuit by Topps stopped Fleer's 1963 set at one series of 66 cards. Issued with a cookie rather than gum, the set features color photos of current players. The card backs include statistical information for 1962 and career plus a brief player biography. The cards, which measure 2-1/2" by 3-1/2", are numbered 1-66. An unnumbered checklist was issued with the set and is included in the complete set price in the checklist that follows. The checklist and #46 Adcock are scarce.

Mr. Mint Says - This is easily the most popular of the Fleer sets. Star cards like Clemente, Koufax, Yaz, Mays and Brooks Robinson sell well, but I think the Adcock card is overrated.

It is extremely difficult to find the checklist centered, mint and unmarked; I can count on two hands the number of specimens that I've had meeting that criteria.

There are very few problems with print lines with this set, but centering can be a hassle.

		MT
Complete Set (67):		2000.
Common Player:		10.00
1	Steve Barber	30.00
2	Ron Hansen	10.00
3	Milt Pappas	10.00
4	Brooks Robinson	75.00
5	Willie Mays	200.00
6	Lou Clinton	10.00
7	Bill Monbouquette	10.00
8	Carl Yastrzemski	125.00
9	Ray Herbert	10.00
10	Jim Landis	10.00
11	Dick Donovan	10.00
12	Tito Francona	10.00
13	Jerry Kindall	10.00
14	Frank Lary	10.00
15	Dick Howser	15.00
16	Jerry Lumpe	10.00
17	Norm Siebern	10.00
18	Don Lee	10.00

19	Albie Pearson	10.00
20	Bob Rodgers	10.00
21	Leon Wagner	10.00
22	Jim Kaat	15.00
23	Vic Power	10.00
24	Rich Rollins	10.00
25	Bobby Richardson	15.00
26	Ralph Terry	15.00
27	Tom Cheney	12.50
28	Chuck Cottier	10.00
29	Jimmy Piersall	10.00
30	Dave Stenhouse	10.00
31	Glen Hobbie	10.00
32	Ron Santo	20.00
33	Gene Freese	10.00
34	Vada Pinson	15.00
35	Bob Purkey	10.00
36	Joe Amalfitano	10.00
37	Bob Aspromonte	10.00
38	Dick Farrell	10.00
39	Al Spangler	10.00
40	Tommy Davis	10.00
41	Don Drysdale	40.00
42	Sandy Koufax	200.00
43	Maury Wills	50.00
44	Frank Bolling	10.00
45	Warren Spahn	75.00
46	Joe Adcock	175.00
47	Roger Craig	10.00
48	Al Jackson	10.00
49	Rod Kanehl	10.00
50	Ruben Amaro	10.00
51	John Callison	10.00
52	Clay Dalrymple	10.00
53	Don Demeter	10.00
54	Art Mahaffey	10.00
55	"Smoky" Burgess	10.00
56	Roberto Clemente	225.00
57	Elroy Face	10.00
58	Vernon Law	10.00
59	Bill Mazeroski	20.00
60	Ken Boyer	20.00
61	Bob Gibson	75.00
62	Gene Oliver	10.00
63	Bill White	15.00
64	Orlando Cepeda	20.00
65	Jimmy Davenport	10.00
66	Billy O'Dell	10.00
----	Checklist	600.00

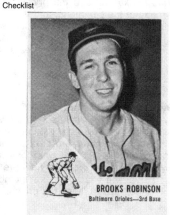

BROOKS ROBINSON
Baltimore Orioles—3rd Base

1933 Goudey

Goudey Gum Co.'s first baseball card issue was their 240-card effort in 1933. The cards are color art reproductions of either portrait or action photos. The numbered cards measure 2-3/8" by 2-7/8" in size and carry a short player biography on the reverse. Card #106 (Napoleon Lajoie) is listed in the set though it was not actually issued until 1934. The card is very scarce and is unique in that it carries a 1934 design obverse and a 1933 reverse. The ACC designation for the set is R319.

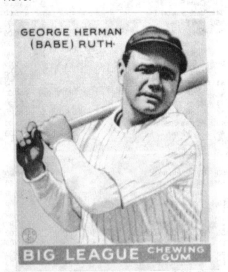

GEORGE HERMAN (BABE) RUTH

BIG LEAGUE CHEWING GUM

Mr. Mint Says - This is the classic set of the 1930s. It used to be that when a collector was finished with Topps and Bowman, he would move to the Goudeys. Now, if you look in the books and see the prices, especially of many of the commons, and then dozens of Hall of Famers, it scares people away. Some of the most advanced collectors have been piecing together sets for years and years.

Printed on a much softer card stock, the corners are often found with considerable wear. Get four sharp corners on '33 Goudeys and they sell instantly. Numbers 1-40 are very tough; every set I've ever had, whatever the condition, the low numbers are always worse. I have never seen a set that was consistent throughout, and I have probably had over 50 partial sets over the years. The low numbers should be priced at five times the price of the rest.

The set contains all the stars of the days, including four Ruths and two Gehrigs. The Bengough card is overrated.

Commons are hard to sell at the moment, for the same reason as in the case of tobacco cards. The Hall of Famers are actively sought. The Lajoie is very scarce, but I don't think that it is rare. It's worth $40,000 or $50,000 if you had a really nice white one.

I have had the letter that was sent to collectors with the Lajoie card. It said something to the effect of, "Dear Collector, thanks for sending in for the Lajoie card, sorry we accidentally forgot to print it last year." And it came with a paper clip, and that's why a lot of the Lajoie cards have a paper clip mark on them on the top of the card. I've seen it on three or four different cards.

I think that if there are 30 or 40 Wagners around, there might be 50 or 60 Lajoies. I've have had more of the former than the latter.

		MT
Complete Set:		99999.
Common Player (1-40):		150.00
Common Player (41-44):		80.00
Common Player (45-52):		150.00
Common Player (53-240):		65.00
1	Benny Bengough	3500.00
2	Arthur (Dazzy) Vance	500.00
3	Hugh Critz	150.00
4	Henry "Heinie" Schuble	150.00
5	Floyd (Babe) Herman	200.00
6a	Jimmy Dykes (age is 26 in bio)	200.00
6b	Jimmy Dykes (age is 36 in bio)	200.00
7	Ted Lyons	300.00
8	Roy Johnson	150.00
9	Dave Harris	150.00
10	Glenn Myatt	150.00
11	Billy Rogell	150.00
12	George Pipgras	150.00
13	Lafayette Thompson	150.00
14	Henry Johnson	150.00
15	Victor Sorrell	150.00
16	George Blaeholder	150.00
17	Watson Clark	150.00
18	Herold (Muddy) Ruel	150.00
19	Bill Dickey	550.00
20	Bill Terry	450.00
21	Phil Collins	150.00
22	Harold (Pie) Traynor	425.00
23	Hazen (Ki-Ki) Cuyler	375.00
24	Horace Ford	150.00
25	Paul Waner	300.00
26	Chalmer Cissell	130.00
27	George Connally	150.00
28	Dick Bartell	130.00
29	Jimmy Foxx	750.00
30	Frank Hogan	150.00
31	Tony Lazzeri	450.00
32	John (Bud) Clancy	130.00

No.	Name	Price
33	Ralph Kress	150.00
34	Bob O'Farrell	150.00
35	Al Simmons	600.00
36	Tommy Thevenow	150.00
37	Jimmy Wilson	150.00
38	Fred Brickell	150.00
39	Mark Koenig	150.00
40	Taylor Douthit	150.00
41	Gus Mancuso	80.00
42	Eddie Collins	275.00
43	Lew Fonseca	90.00
44	Jim Bottomley	275.00
45	Larry Benton	150.00
46	Ethan Allen	150.00
47	Henry "Heinie" Manush	375.00
48	Marty McManus	150.00
49	Frank Frisch	425.00
50	Ed Brandt	130.00
51	Charlie Grimm	150.00
52	Andy Cohen	130.00
53	George Herman (Babe) Ruth	8500.00
54	Ray Kremer	65.00
55	Perce (Pat) Malone	65.00
56	Charlie Ruffing	220.00
57	Earl Clark	65.00
58	Frank (Lefty) O'Doul	90.00
59	Edmund (Bing) Miller	65.00
60	Waite Hoyt	175.00
61	Max Bishop	65.00
62	"Pepper" Martin	100.00
63	Joe Cronin	240.00
64	Burleigh Grimes	200.00
65	Milton Gaston	65.00
66	George Grantham	65.00
67	Guy Bush	65.00
68	Horace Lisenbee	65.00
69	Randy Moore	65.00
70	Floyd (Pete) Scott	65.00
71	Robert J. Burke	65.00
72	Owen Carroll	65.00
73	Jesse Haines	175.00
74	Eppa Rixey	175.00
75	Willie Kamm	65.00
76	Gordon (Mickey) Cochrane	220.00
77	Adam Comorosky	65.00
78	Jack Quinn	65.00
79	Urban (Red) Faber	175.00
80	Clyde Manion	65.00
81	Sam Jones	75.00
82	Dibrell Williams	65.00
83	Pete Jablonowski	130.00
84	Glenn Spencer	65.00
85	John Henry "Heinie" Sand	65.00
86	Phil Todt	65.00
87	Frank O'Rourke	65.00
88	Russell Rollings	65.00
89	Tris Speaker	400.00
90	Jess Petty	65.00
91	Tom Zachary	65.00
92	Lou Gehrig	6000.00
93	John Welch	65.00
94	Bill Walker	65.00
95	Alvin Crowder	65.00
96	Willis Hudlin	65.00
97	Joe Morrissey	65.00
98	Walter Berger	65.00
99	Tony Cuccinello	65.00
100	George Uhle	90.00
101	Richard Coffman	65.00
102	Travis C. Jackson	175.00
103	Earl Combs (Earle)	175.00
104	Fred Marberry	65.00
105	Bernie Friberg	65.00
106	Napoleon (Larry) Lajoie	50000.00
107	Henry (Heinie) Manush	175.00
108	Joe Kuhel	65.00
109	Joe Cronin	175.00
110	Leon "Goose" Goslin	175.00
111	Monte Weaver	65.00
112	Fred Schulte	65.00
113	Oswald Bluege	65.00
114	Luke Sewell	65.00
115	Cliff Heathcote	65.00
116	Eddie Morgan	65.00
117	Walter (Rabbit) Maranville	175.00
118	Valentine J. (Val) Picinich	65.00
119	Rogers Hornsby	450.00
120	Carl Reynolds	65.00
121	Walter Stewart	65.00
122	Alvin Crowder	65.00
123	Jack Russell	65.00
124	Earl Whitehill	65.00
125	Bill Terry	260.00
126	Joe Moore	65.00
127	Melvin Ott	300.00
128	Charles (Chuck) Klein	200.00
129	Harold Schumacher	90.00
130	Fred Fitzsimmons	65.00
131	Fred Frankhouse	65.00
132	Jim Elliott	65.00
133	Fred Lindstrom	175.00
134	Edgar (Sam) Rice	175.00
135	Elwood (Woody) English	65.00
136	Flint Rhem	65.00
137	Fred (Red) Lucas	65.00
138	Herb Pennock	175.00
139	Ben Cantwell	65.00
140	Irving (Bump) Hadley	65.00
141	Ray Benge	65.00
142	Paul Richards	100.00
143	Glenn Wright	75.00
144	George Herman (Babe) Ruth	6500.00
145	George Walberg	65.00
146	Walter Stewart	65.00
147	Leo Durocher	200.00
148	Eddie Farrell	65.00
149	George Herman (Babe) Ruth	7500.00
150	Ray Kolp	65.00
151	D'Arcy (Jake) Flowers	65.00
152	James (Zack) Taylor	65.00
153	Charles (Buddy) Myer	65.00
154	Jimmy Foxx	400.00
155	Joe Judge	65.00
156	Danny Macfayden (MacFayden)	90.00
157	Sam Byrd	90.00
158	Morris (Moe) Berg	130.00
159	Oswald Bluege	65.00
160	Lou Gehrig	6000.00
161	Al Spohrer	65.00
162	Leo Mangum	65.00
163	Luke Sewell	65.00
164	Lloyd Waner	175.00
165	Joe Sewell	175.00
166	Sam West	65.00
167a	Jack Russell (name on two lines)	65.00
167b	Jack Russell (name on one line)	65.00
168a	Leon (Goose) Goslin (name on one line)	175.00
168b	Leon (Goose) Goslin (name on two lines)	65.00
169	Al Thomas	65.00
170	Harry McCurdy	65.00
171	Charley Jamieson	65.00
172	Billy Hargrave	65.00
173	Roscoe Holm	65.00
174	Warren (Curley) Ogden	65.00
175	Dan Howley	65.00
176	John Ogden	65.00

177	Walter French	65.00
178	Jackie Warner	65.00
179	Fred Leach	65.00
180	Eddie Moore	65.00
181	George Herman (Babe) Ruth	7500.00
182	Andy High	65.00
183	George Walberg	65.00
184	Charley Berry	65.00
185	Bob Smith	65.00
186	John Schulte	65.00
187	Henry (Heinie) Manush	175.00
188	Rogers Hornsby	450.00
189	Joe Cronin	175.00
190	Fred Schulte	65.00
191	Ben Chapman	100.00
192	Walter Brown	100.00
193	Lynford Lary	90.00
194	Earl Averill	175.00
195	Evar Swanson	65.00
196	Leroy Mahaffey	65.00
197	Richard (Rick) Ferrell	175.00
198	Irving (Jack) Burns	65.00
199	Tom Bridges	70.00
200	Bill Hallahan	65.00
201	Ernie Orsatti	65.00
202	Charles Leo (Gabby) Hartnett	175.00
203	Lonnie Warneke	65.00
204	Jackson Riggs Stephenson	100.00
205	Henry (Heinie) Meine	65.00
206	Gus Suhr	65.00
207	Melvin Ott	350.00
208	Byrne (Bernie) James	65.00
209	Adolfo Luque	65.00
210	Virgil Davis	65.00
211	Lewis (Hack) Wilson	300.00
212	Billy Urbanski	65.00
213	Earl Adams	65.00
214	John Kerr	65.00
215	Russell Van Atta	90.00
216	Vernon Gomez	350.00
217	Frank Crosetti	175.00
218	Wesley Ferrell	90.00
219	George (Mule) Haas	65.00
220	Robert (Lefty) Grove	450.00
221	Dale Alexander	65.00
222	Charley Gehringer	300.00
223	Jerome (Dizzy) Dean	700.00
224	Frank Demaree	65.00
225	Bill Jurges	65.00
226	Charley Root	90.00
227	Bill Herman	175.00
228	Tony Piet	65.00
229	Floyd Vaughan	175.00
230	Carl Hubbell	260.00
231	Joe Moore	65.00
232	Frank (Lefty) O'Doul	90.00
233	Johnny Vergez	65.00
234	Carl Hubbell	260.00
235	Fred Fitzsimmons	65.00
236	George Davis	65.00
237	Gus Mancuso	65.00
238	Hugh Critz	65.00
239	Leroy Parmelee	90.00
240	Harold Schumacher	350.00

1934 Goudey

The 1934 Goudey set contains 96 cards (2-3/8" by 2-7/8") that feature color art reproductions of actual photographs. The card fronts have two different designs; one featuring a small head-shot photo of Lou Gehrig with the words "Lou Gehrig says..." inside a blue band, while the other design carries a "Chuck Klein says..." and also has his photo. The card backs contain a short player biography that appears to have been written by Gehrig or Klein. The ACC designation for the set is R320.

Mr. Mint Says - This set is not as popular as 1933, but is still extremely difficult to obtain in top grade. At only 96 cards, it is a little more realistic for most collectors to pursue than the earlier set. The high numbers, 73-96, are especially difficult in mint.

There are two Gehrigs, and I think that they are equally scarce and popular. The Foxx card is always hard to get, as are all of the Hall of Famers.

Possibly printed on a better card stock than 1933, the cards are a little easier to obtain than the first year and normally in sharper condition.

		MT
Complete Set:		28200.
Common Player (1-48):		70.00
Common Player (49-72):		85.00
Common Player (73-96):		350.00

1	Jimmy Foxx	1500.00
2	Gordon (Mickey) Cochrane	250.00
3	Charlie Grimm	70.00
4	Elwood (Woody) English	70.00
5	Ed Brandt	70.00
6	Jerome (Dizzy) Dean	600.00
7	Leo Durocher	200.00
8	Tony Piet	70.00
9	Ben Chapman	85.00
10	Charles (Chuck) Klein	200.00
11	Paul Waner	200.00
12	Carl Hubbell	250.00
13	Frank Frisch	200.00
14	Willie Kamm	70.00
15	Alvin Crowder	70.00
16	Joe Kuhel	70.00
17	Hugh Critz	70.00
18	Henry (Heinie) Manush	200.00
19	Robert (Lefty) Grove	350.00
20	Frank Hogan	70.00
21	Bill Terry	250.00
22	Floyd Vaughan	200.00
23	Charley Gehringer	110.00
24	Ray Benge	70.00
25	Roger Cramer	70.00
26	Gerald Walker	70.00
27	Luke Appling	200.00
28	Ed. Coleman	70.00
29	Larry French	70.00
30	Julius Solters	70.00
31	Baxter Jordan	70.00
32	John (Blondy) Ryan	70.00
33	Frank (Don) Hurst	70.00
34	Charles (Chick) Hafey	200.00
35	Ernie Lombardi	200.00
36	Walter (Huck) Betts	70.00
37	Lou Gehrig	4000.00
38	Oral Hildebrand	70.00
39	Fred Walker	70.00
40	John Stone	70.00
41	George Earnshaw	70.00
42	John Allen	85.00
43	Dick Porter	70.00
44	Tom Bridges	55.00
45	Oscar Melillo	70.00
46	Joe Stripp	70.00
47	John Frederick	70.00
48	James (Tex) Carleton	70.00
49	Sam Leslie	85.00
50	Walter Beck	85.00
51	Jim (Rip) Collins	85.00
52	Herman Bell	85.00
53	George Watkins	85.00
54	Wesley Schulmerich	85.00
55	Ed Holley	85.00
56	Mark Koenig	85.00
57	Bill Swift	85.00
58	Earl Grace	85.00
59	Joe Mowry	85.00
60	Lynn Nelson	85.00
61	Lou Gehrig	4000.00
62	Henry Greenberg	350.00
63	Minter Hayes	85.00
64	Frank Grube	85.00
65	Cliff Bolton	85.00
66	Mel Harder	85.00
67	Bob Weiland	85.00
68	Bob Johnson	85.00
69	John Marcum	85.00
70	Ervin (Pete) Fox	85.00
71	Lyle Tinning	85.00

72	Arndt Jorgens	45.00		85	Adam Comorosky	350.00
73	Ed Wells	350.00		86	Lloyd Johnson	350.00
74	Bob Boken	350.00		87	George Darrow	350.00
75	Bill Werber	350.00		88	Homer Peel	350.00
76	Hal Trosky	350.00		89	Linus Frey	350.00
77	Joe Vosmik	350.00		90	Hazen (Ki-Ki) Cuyler	750.00
78	Frank (Pinkey) Higgins	350.00		91	Dolph Camilli	350.00
79	Eddie Durham	350.00		92	Steve Larkin	350.00
80	Marty McManus	350.00		93	Fred Ostermueller	350.00
81	Bob Brown	350.00		94	Robert A. (Red) Rolfe	450.00
82	Bill Hallahan	350.00		95	Myril Hoag	350.00
83	Jim Mooney	350.00		96	Jim DeShong	600.00
84	Paul Derringer	350.00				

1935 Goudey

The 1935 Goudey set features four players from the same team on one card. Thirty-six card fronts make up the set with numerous front/back combinations existing. The card backs form nine different puzzles: 1) Tigers Team, 2) Chuck Klein, 3) Frankie Frisch, 4) Mickey Cochrane, 5) Joe Cronin, 6) Jimmy Foxx, 7) Al Simmons, 8) Indians Team, and 9) Senators Team. The cards, which measure 2-3/8" x 2-7/8", have an ACC designation of R321.

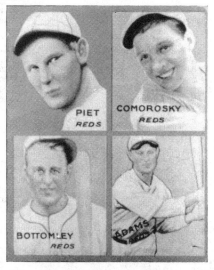

Mr. Mint Says - Most collectors just put together the 36 fronts, but there are some who collect the numerous front/back combinations. The set is appealing because it is colorful, small and relatively inexpensive compared to 33s and 34s. There are a lot of Hall of Famers for such a small set, and there is a lot of interest in all of the cards, especially the Ruth.

It is very desirable, especially in full mint with nice blue and red borders intact and no chips or dings, but the cards are hard to find in that condition.

	MT
Complete Set (36):	9500.
Common Player:	100.00

(1)	Sparky Adams, Jim Bottomley, Adam Comorosky, Tony Piet	125.00
(2)	Ethan Allen, Fred Brickell, Bubber Jonnard, Hack Wilson	125.00
(3)	Johnny Allen, Jimmie Deshong (DeShong), Red Rolfe, Dixie Walker	100.00
(4)	Luke Appling, Jimmie Dykes, George Earnshaw, Luke Sewell	125.00
(5)	Earl Averill, Oral Hildebrand, Willie Kamm, Hal Trosky	125.00
(6)	Dick Bartell, Hughie Critz, Gus Mancuso, Mel Ott	100.00
(7)	Ray Benge, Fred Fitzsimmons, Mark Koenig, Tom Zachary	100.00
(8)	Larry Benton, Ben Cantwell, Flint Rhem, Al Spohrer	100.00
(9)	Charlie Berry, Bobby Burke, Red Kress, Dazzy Vance	125.00
(10)	Max Bishop, Bill Cissell, Joe Cronin, Carl Reynolds	125.00
(11)	George Blaeholder, Dick Coffman, Oscar Melillo, Sammy West	100.00
(12)	Cy Blanton, Babe Herman, Tom Padden, Gus Suhr	100.00
(13)	Zeke Bonura, Mule Haas, Jackie Hayes, Ted Lyons	125.00
(14)	Jim Bottomley, Adam Comorosky, Willis Hudlin, Glenn Myatt	125.00
(15)	Ed Brandt, Fred Frankhouse, Shanty Hogan, Gene Moore	100.00
(16)	Ed Brandt, Rabbit Maranville, Marty McManus, Babe Ruth	2500.00
(17)	Tommy Bridges, Mickey Cochrane, Charlie Gehringer, Billy Rogell	250.00
(18)	Jack Burns, Frank Grube, Rollie Hemsley, Bob Weiland	100.00
(19)	Guy Bush, Waite Hoyt, Lloyd Waner, Paul Waner	225.00
(20)	Sammy Byrd, Danny MacFayden, Pepper Martin, Bob O'Farrell	100.00
(21)	Gilly Campbell, Ival Goodman, Alex Kampouris, Billy Meyers (Myers)	100.00
(22)	Tex Carleton, Dizzy Dean, Frankie Frisch, Ernie Orsatti	450.00
(23)	Watty Clark, Lonny Frey, Sam Leslie, Joe Stripp	100.00
(24)	Mickey Cochrane, Willie Kamm, Muddy Ruel, Al Simmons	200.00
(25)	Ed Coleman, Doc Cramer, Bob Johnson, Johnny Marcum	100.00
(26)	General Crowder, Goose Goslin, Firpo Marberry, Heinie Schuble	125.00
(27)	Kiki Cuyler, Woody English, Burleigh Grimes, Chuck Klein	100.00
(28)	Bill Dickey, Tony Lazzeri, Pat Malone, Red Ruffing	325.00
(29)	Rick Ferrell, Wes Ferrell, Fritz Ostermueller, Bill Werber	125.00
(30)	Pete Fox, Hank Greenberg, Schoolboy Rowe, Gee Walker	225.00
(31)	Jimmie Foxx, Pinky Higgins, Roy Mahaffey, Dib Williams	325.00
(32)	Bump Hadley, Lyn Lary, Heinie Manush, Monte Weaver	125.00
(33)	Mel Harder, Bill Knickerbocker, Lefty Stewart, Joe Vosmik	100.00
(34)	Travis Jackson, Gus Mancuso, Hal Schumacher, Bill Terry	225.00
(35)	Joe Kuhel, Buddy Meyer (Myer), John Stone, Earl Whitehill	100.00
(36)	Red Lucas, Tommy Thevenow, Pie Traynor, Glenn Wright	125.00

1936 Goudey

The 1936 Goudey set consists of 25 black and white cards, each measuring 2-3/8" x 2-7/8". A facsimile autograph is positioned on the card fronts. The card backs contain a brief player biography and were to be used by collectors to play a baseball game. Different game situations (out, single, double, etc.) are given on each card. Numerous front/back exist in the set. The ACC designation for the set is R322.

Mr. Mint Says - This is a black and white set and is not very popular. The backs of the cards are used for a baseball game, but the cards themselves are essentially ugly.

Over the years, I've probably bought more 1936 Goudey sets than 36s; despite the disclaimer it is still very difficult to find mint centered cards.

		MT
Complete Set:		3000.
Common Player:		75.00
(1)	Walter Berger	75.00
(2)	Henry Bonura	75.00
(3)	Stan Bordagaray	75.00
(4)	Bill Brubaker	75.00
(5)	Dolph Camilli	75.00
(6)	Clydell Castleman	75.00
(7)	"Mickey" Cochrane	250.00
(8)	Joe Coscarart	75.00
(9)	Frank Crosetti	125.00
(10)	"Kiki" Cuyler	175.00
(11)	Paul Derringer	75.00
(12)	Jimmy Dykes	75.00
(13)	"Rick" Ferrell	175.00
(14)	"Lefty" Gomez	325.00
(15)	Hank Greenberg	325.00
(16)	"Bucky" Harris	175.00
(17)	"Rolly" Hemsley	75.00
(18)	Frank Higgins	75.00
(19)	Oral Hildebrand	75.00
(20)	"Chuck" Klein	200.00
(21)	"Pepper" Martin	75.00
(22)	"Buck" Newsom	75.00
(23)	Joe Vosmik	75.00
(24)	Paul Waner	200.00
(25)	Bill Werber	75.00

1948 Leaf

The first color baseball cards of the post-World War II era were the 98-card, 2-3/8" by 2-7/8", set produced by Chicago's Leaf Gum Company in 1948-1949. The color was crude, probably helping to make the set less popular than the Bowman issues of the same era. One of the toughest postwar sets to complete, exactly half of the Leaf issue - 49 of the cards - are significantly harder to find than the other 49. Probably intended to confound bubble gum buyers of the day, the set is skip-numbered between 1-168. Card backs contain offers of felt pennants, an album for the cards or 5-1/2" by 7-1/2" premium photos of Hall of Famers.

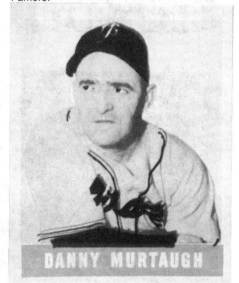

DANNY MURTAUGH

Mr. Mint Says - This is probably the ugliest postwar set ever made. Color registration was a major problem with this set, along with the crude color work. This is an extremely demanding 98-card set.

The 49 short prints are very tough to find in mint condition with good registration and centering. In fact, all of the short prints were wretchedly done, with print lines, off centers and the registration problem.

The Paige card just might be the toughest postwar card. In a small find in Tampa, Fla. I had four unopened boxes, opened three (432 cards) and got exactly one Paige. In all my years in the hobby, I have only purchased four complete sets. I bought a set at the Sotheby's auction for $20,000 and broke it up.

		MT
Complete Set (98):		35000.
Common Player:		25.00
Common Short-print:		350.00
1	Joe DiMaggio	2500.00
3	Babe Ruth	3000.00
4	*Stan Musial*	650.00
5	Virgil Trucks	400.00
8	*Satchel Paige*	3500.00
10	Paul Trout	25.00
11	*Phil Rizzuto*	300.00
13	Casimer Michaels	350.00
14	Billy Johnson	30.00
17	Frank Overmire	25.00
19	John Wyrostek	350.00
20	*Hank Sauer*	350.00
22	Al Evans	25.00
26	Sam Chapman	25.00
27	Mickey Harris	25.00
28	*Jim Hegan*	30.00
29	*Elmer Valo*	30.00
30	*Bill Goodman*	350.00
31	Lou Brissie	25.00
32	*Warren Spahn*	400.00
33	Harry Lowrey	300.00
36	Al Zarilla	350.00
38	*Ted Kluszewski*	125.00
39	*Ewell Blackwell*	25.00
42	Kent Peterson	25.00
43	Eddie Stevens	350.00
45	Ken Keltner	350.00
46	Johnny Mize	100.00
47	George Vico	25.00
48	Johnny Schmitz	350.00
49	*Del Ennis*	40.00
50	Dick Wakefield	25.00
51	*Alvin Dark*	400.00
53	John Vandermeer	40.00
54	Bobby Adams	350.00
55	Tommy Henrich	400.00
56	*Larry Jensen*	30.00
57	Bob McCall	25.00
59	Luke Appling	80.00
61	Jake Early	25.00
62	Eddie Joost	300.00
63	Barney McCosky	350.00
65	Bob Elliot (Elliott)	25.00
66	Orval Grove	350.00
68	Ed Miller	350.00
70	Honus Wagner	350.00
72	Hank Edwards	25.00
73	Pat Seerey	25.00
75	Dom DiMaggio	650.00
76	Ted Williams	1000.00
77	Roy Smalley	25.00
78	Walter Evers	350.00
79	*Jackie Robinson*	950.00
81	George Kurowski	350.00
82	Johnny Lindell	25.00
83	Bobby Doerr	100.00
84	Sid Hudson	25.00
85	*Dave Philley*	350.00
86	Ralph Weigel	25.00
88	Frank Gustine	350.00
91	*Ralph Kiner*	200.00
93	Bob Feller	1500.00
95	George Stirnweiss	25.00
97	*Martin Marion*	50.00

98	*Hal Newhouser*	600.00
102a	Gene Hermansk (incorrect spelling)	500.00
102b	Gene Hermanski (correct spelling)	25.00
104	Edward Stewart	350.00
106	Lou Boudreau	100.00
108	Matthew Batts	350.00
111	Gerald Priddy	25.00
113	Emil Leonard	350.00
117	Joe Gordon	25.00
120	*George Kell*	650.00
121	*John Pesky*	350.00
123	Clifford Fannin	350.00
125	*Andy Pafko*	30.00
127	Enos Slaughter	1000.00
128	Warren Rosar	25.00
129	Kirby Higbe	350.00
131	Sid Gordon	350.00
133	Tommy Holmes	350.00
136a	Cliff Aberson (full sleeve)	25.00
136b	Cliff Aberson (short sleeve)	25.00
137	Harry Walker	350.00
138	*Larry Doby*	500.00
139	Johnny Hopp	25.00
142	*Danny Murtaugh*	500.00
143	Dick Sisler	350.00
144	Bob Dillinger	350.00
146	Harold Reiser	350.00
149	Henry Majeski	350.00
153	Floyd Baker	350.00
158	*Harry Brecheen*	350.00
159	Mizell Platt	25.00
160	Bob Scheffing	350.00
161	*Vernon Stephens*	350.00
163	*Freddy Hutchinson*	350.00
165	*Dale Mitchell*	350.00
168	Phil Cavaretta	350.00

BABE RUTH

TED WILLIAMS.

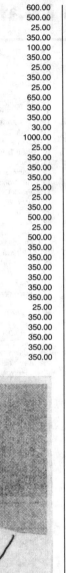

LEROY PAIGE

1960 Leaf

While known to the hobby as "Leaf" cards, this set of 144 cards carries the copyright of Sports Novelties Inc., Chicago. The 2-1/2" by 3-1/2" cards feature black and white player portrait photos, with background airbrushed away. Cards were sold in 5¢ wax packs with a marble, rather than a piece of bubble gum. The second half of the set, cards #73-144, are very scarce and make the set a real challenge for the collector. Card #25, Jim Grant, is found in two versions, with his own picture (black cap) and with a photo of Brooks Lawrence (white cap). Eight cards (#'s 1, 12, 17, 23, 35, 58, 61 and 72) exist with close-up photos that are much rarer than the normal cap to chest photos. It is believed the scarce "face only" cards are proof cards prepared by Leaf as only a handful are known to exist.

LUIS APARICIO
SHORTSTOP—CHICAGO WHITE SOX

Mr. Mint Says - This set has always excited me. These cards were issued with marbles, and most 1960 Leaf cards that are offered for sale are in pretty nice shape. There are not many top players in the set, the main ones being Aparicio, Snider and Brooks Robinson.

The Hal Smith variation is very tough, as is the "Smith Brothers" card, probably the hardest one in the set. Low numbers are available in mint, and the high numbers are significantly tougher than the lows. It is not easy to sell singles of the low numbers, but the highs sell well. A lot of people have low number runs looking for the high numbers. The complete set also sells well, and brings $1,400 to $1,800 for a mint set at auction.

		MT
Complete Set (145):		1600.
Common Player (1-72):		4.00
Common Player (73-145):		15.00

1	Luis Aparicio	40.00
2	Woody Held	4.00
3	Frank Lary	4.00
4	Camilo Pascual	4.00
5	Frank Herrera	4.00
6	Felipe Alou	9.00
7	Bennie Daniels	4.00
8	Roger Craig	7.00
9	Eddie Kasko	4.00
10	Bob Grim	4.00
11	Jim Busby	4.00
12	Ken Boyer	8.00
13	Bob Boyd	4.00
14	Sam Jones	4.00
15	Larry Jackson	4.00
16	Roy Face	6.00
17	Walt Moryn	4.00
18	Jim Gilliam	6.00
19	Don Newcombe	4.00
20	Glen Hobbie	4.00
21	Pedro Ramos	4.00
22	Ryne Duren	5.00
23	Joe Jay	4.00
24	Lou Berberet	4.00
25a	Jim Grant	
	(white cap, photo actually Brooks Lawrence)	14.00
25b	Jim Grant (dark cap, correct photo)	75.00
26	Tom Borland	4.00
27	Brooks Robinson	50.00
28	Jerry Adair	4.00
29	Ron Jackson	4.00
30	George Strickland	4.00
31	Rocky Bridges	4.00
32	Bill Tuttle	4.00
33	Ken Hunt	4.00
34	Hal Griggs	4.00
35	Jim Coates	4.00
36	Brooks Lawrence	4.00
37	Duke Snider	75.00
38	Al Spangler	4.00
39	Jim Owens	4.00
40	Bill Virdon	4.00
41	Ernie Broglio	4.00
42	Andre Rodgers	4.00
43	Julio Becquer	4.00
44	Tony Taylor	4.00
45	Jerry Lynch	4.00
46	Clete Boyer	4.00
47	Jerry Lumpe	4.00
48	Charlie Maxwell	4.00
49	Jim Perry	4.00
50	Danny McDevitt	4.00
51	Juan Pizarro	4.00
52	*Dallas Green*	9.00
53	Bob Friend	4.00
54	Jack Sanford	4.00
55	Jim Rivera	4.00

56	Ted Wills	4.00
57	Milt Pappas	4.00
58a	Hal Smith (team & position on back)	4.00
58b	Hal Smith (team blackened out on back)	50.00
58c	Hal Smith (team missing on back)	50.00
59	Bob Avila	4.00
60	Clem Labine	4.00
61	Vic Rehm	4.00
62	John Gabler	4.00
63	John Tsitouris	4.00
64	Dave Sisler	4.00
65	Vic Power	4.00
66	Earl Battey	4.00
67	Bob Purkey	4.00
68	Moe Drabowsky	4.00
69	Hoyt Wilhelm	18.00
70	Humberto Robinson	4.00
71	Whitey Herzog	8.00
72	Dick Donovan	4.00
73	Gordon Jones	15.00
74	Joe Hicks	15.00
75	*Ray Culp*	18.00
76	Dick Drott	15.00
77	Bob Duliba	15.00
78	Art Ditmar	18.00
79	Steve Korcheck	15.00
80	Henry Mason	15.00
81	Harry Simpson	15.00
82	Gene Green	15.00
83	Bob Shaw	15.00
84	Howard Reed	15.00
85	Dick Stigman	15.00
86	Rip Repulski	15.00
87	Seth Morehead	15.00
88	Camilo Carreon	15.00
89	John Blanchard	18.00
90	Billy Hoeft	15.00
91	Fred Hopke	15.00
92	Joe Martin	15.00
93	Wally Shannon	15.00
94	Baseball's Two Hal Smiths (Hal Smith, 15.Smith)	40.00
95	Al Schroll	15.00
96	John Kucks	15.00
97	Tom Morgan	15.00
98	Willie Jones	15.00
99	Marshall Renfroe	15.00
100	Willie Tasby	15.00
101	Irv Noren	15.00
102	Russ Snyder	15.00
103	Bob Turley	20.00
104	Jim Woods	15.00
105	Ronnie Kline	15.00
106	Steve Bilko	15.00
107	Elmer Valo	15.00
108	Tom McAvoy	15.00
109	Stan Williams	15.00
110	Earl Averill	15.00
111	Lee Walls	15.00
112	Paul Richards	18.00
113	Ed Sadowski	15.00
114	Stover McIlwain	18.00
115	Chuck Tanner (photo actually Ken Kuhn)	20.00

116	Lou Klimchock	15.00
117	Neil Chrisley	15.00
118	15. Callison	20.00
119	Hal Smith	15.00
120	Carl Sawatski	15.00
121	Frank Leja	15.00
122	Earl Torgeson	15.00
123	Art Schult	15.00
124	Jim Brosnan	18.00
125	Sparky Anderson	80.00
126	Joe Pignatano	15.00
127	Rocky Nelson	15.00
128	Orlando Cepeda	60.00
129	Daryl Spencer	15.00
130	Ralph Lumenti	15.00
131	Sam Taylor	15.00
132	Harry Brecheen	15.00
133	Johnny Groth	15.00
134	Wayne Terwilliger	15.00
135	Kent Hadley	15.00
136	Faye Throneberry	15.00
137	Jack Meyer	15.00
138	*Chuck Cottier*	15.00
139	Joe DeMaestri	15.00
140	Gene Freese	15.00
141	15. Flood	35.00
142	Gino Cimoli	15.00
143	Clay Dalrymple	15.00
144	15. Bunning	80.00

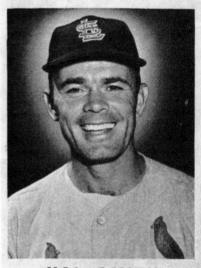

HAL SMITH
CATCHER — ST. LOUIS CARDINALS

1937 O-Pee-Chee

Kind of a combination of 1934 Goudeys and 1934-36 Batter Ups, the '37 OPC "Baseball Stars" set features black-and-white action photos against a stylized ballpark. About halfway up the 2-5/8" x 2-15/16" cards, the background was die-cut to allow it to be folded back to create a stand-up card. Backs are printed in English and French. The 40 cards in "Series A" are all American Leaguers, leading to speculation that a Series B of National League players was to have been issued at a later date. The set carries the American Card Catalog designation of V300.

There are only 40 cards in the set, and the DiMaggio is the key. The price for a matched set could probably reach as high as $15,000.

Some years ago a couple of sets of these surfaced when somebody ran across a couple of unopened boxes, and the only problem was that there were large gum stains on the card backs.

		MT
Complete Set (40):		12500.
Common Player:		100.00
101	John Lewis	100.00
102	"Jack" Hayes	100.00
103	Earl Averill	250.00
104	Harland Clift (Harlond)	100.00
105	"Beau" Bell	100.00
106	Jimmy Foxx (Jimmie)	800.00
107	Hank Greenberg	750.00
108	George Selkirk	100.00
109	Wally Moses	100.00
110	"Gerry" Walker	100.00
111	"Goose" Goslin	250.00
112	Charlie Gehringer	500.00
113	Hal Trosky	100.00
114	"Buddy" Myer	100.00
115	Luke Appling	250.00
116	"Zeke" Bonura	100.00
117	Tony Lazzeri	250.00
118	Joe DiMaggio	4000.00
119	Bill Dickey	600.00
120	Bob Feller	800.00
121	Harry Kelley	100.00
122	Johnny Allen	100.00
123	Bob Johnson	150.00
124	Joe Cronin	250.00
125	"Rip" Radcliff	100.00
126	Cecil Travis	100.00
127	Joe Kuhel	100.00
128	Odell Hale	100.00
129	Sam West	100.00
130	Ben Chapman	100.00
131	Monte Pearson	100.00
132	"Rick" Ferrell	250.00
133	Tommy Bridges	100.00
134	"Schoolboy" Rowe	125.00
135	Vernon Kennedy	100.00
136	"Red" Ruffing	250.00
137	"Lefty" Grove	400.00
138	Wes Farrell	100.00
139	"Buck" Newsom	100.00
140	Rogers Hornsby	800.00

JOE DI MAGGIO
Centre field, New York Yankees

Mr. Mint Says - This is a real nice set that kind of looks like the 1964 Topps Stand-Ups except that they are black and white. These are real pretty cards, but there are not a lot of them around so the demand is limited.

1939 Play Ball

With the issuance of this card set by Gum Incorporated, a new era of baseball cards was born. Although the cards are black and white, the full-frame, actual photos on the card fronts are of better quality than previously seen, and the 2-1/2" by 3-1/8" size was larger and more popular than the smaller tobacco and caramel cards of the early 20th Century. Card backs featured player names and extensive biographies. There are 162 cards in the set, including superstars Joe DiMaggio and Ted Williams. Card number 126 was never issued. The complete set price does not include all back variations found in the low-numbered series. Most of the cards between numbers 2-115 can be found with the player name on back either in all capital letters, or in both upper and lower case letters. The latter are worth a premium of about 10% over the former.

Mr. Mint Says - This was the first year of their entry into the card business. The cards are black and white, but still pretty neat. In the last couple of years this set seems to have fallen out of favor with collectors.

The high numbers are much more difficult to locate than the lows, and just as tough as any other high number series in the 1930s. Still, I think because they are black and white they are not as popular as color cards.

I don't think anyone cares about the error on the back of the DiMaggio card, or the upper

and lower case names on the commons. Few people collect that way. There are no horribly expensive cards in the set except the DiMaggio and the Williams rookie, and no major stars in the high number series.

I have bought many of them over the years and they sell well as a set, but they carry the stigma of being a black and white offering. There are problems with print lines and centering; the DiMaggio card is very hard to find centered.

		MT
Complete Set:		18000.
Common Player (1-115):		20.00
Common Player (116-162):		150.00
1	Alvin Jacob Powell	200.00
2a	Lee Theo Grissom (name in upper case letters)	25.00
2b	Lee Theo Grissom (name in upper and lower case)	35.00
3a	Charles Herbert Ruffing (name in upper case letters)	125.00
3b	Charles Herbert Ruffing (name in upper and lower case)	135.00
4a	Eldon LeRoy Auker (name in upper case letters)	20.00
4b	Eldon LeRoy Auker (name in upper and lower case)	22.00
5a	James Luther Sewell (name in upper case letters)	22.00
5b	James Luther Sewell (name in upper and lower case)	24.00
6a	Leo Ernest Durocher (name in upper case letters)	100.00
6b	Leo Ernest Durocher (name in upper and lower case)	125.00
7a	Robert Pershing Doerr (name in upper case letters)	100.00
7b	Robert Pershing Doerr (name in upper and lower case)	100.00
8	Henry Pippen	20.00
9a	James Tobin (name in upper case letters)	20.00
9b	James Tobin (name in upper and lower case)	22.00
10	James Brooklyn DeShong	20.00
11	John Costa Rizzo	20.00
12	Hershel Ray Martin (Herschel)	20.00
13a	Luke Daniel Hamlin (name in upper case letters)	20.00
13b	Luke Daniel Hamlin (name in upper and lower case)	22.00
14a	James R. Tabor ("...Tabor batted .295,...")	20.00
14b	James R. Tabor ("...Tabor batted 295,...")	22.00
15a	Paul Derringer (name in upper case letters)	22.00
15b	Paul Derringer (name in upper and lower case)	24.00
16	John Peacock	20.00
17	Emerson Dickman	20.00
18a	Harry Danning (name in upper case letters)	20.00
18b	Harry Danning (name in upper and lower case)	22.00
19	Paul Dean	35.00
20	Joseph Heving	20.00
21a	Emil Leonard (name in upper case letters)	20.00
21b	Emil Leonard (name in upper and lower case)	22.00
22a	William Henry Walters (name in upper case letters)	22.00
22b	William Henry Walters (name in upper and lower case)	24.00
23	Burgess U. Whitehead	20.00
24a	Richard S. Coffman (S. Richard) ("...Senators the same year.")	20.00
24b	Richard S. Coffman (S. Richard) (("...Browns the same year.")	35.00
25a	George Alexander Selkirk (name in upper caseletters)	35.00

25b	George Alexander Selkirk (name in upper and lower case)	40.00
26a	Joseph Paul DiMaggio ("...206 hits in 1938 games...")	2500.00
26b	Joseph Paul DiMaggio ("...206 hits in 138 games...")	2500.00
27a	Fred Ray Ostermueller (name in upper case letters)	20.00
27b	Fred Ray Ostermueller (name in upper and lower case)	22.00
28	Sylvester Johnson	20.00
29a	John Francis Wilson (name in upper case letters)	20.00
29b	John Francis Wilson (name in upper and lower case)	22.00
30a	William Malcolm Dickey (name in upper case letters)	200.00
30b	William Malcolm Dickey (name in upper and lower case)	225.00
31a	Samuel West (name in upper case letters)	20.00
31b	Samuel West (name in upper and lower case)	22.00
32	Robert I. Seeds	20.00
33	Del Howard Young (name actually Del Edward)	20.00
34a	Frank Joseph Demaree (Joseph Franklin) (name in upper case letters)	20.00
34b	Frank Joseph Demaree (Joseph Franklin) (name in upper and lower case)	22.00
35a	William Frederick Jurges (name in upper case letters)	22.00
35b	William Frederick Jurges (name in upper and lower case)	24.00
36a	Frank Andrew McCormick (name in upper case letters)	20.00
36b	Frank Andrew McCormick (name in upper and lower case)	22.00
37	Virgil Lawrence Davis	20.00
38a	William Harrison Myers (name in upper case letters)	20.00
38b	William Harrison Myers (name in upper and lower case)	22.00
39a	Richard Benjamin Ferrell (name in upper case letters)	100.00
39b	Richard Benjamin Ferrell (name in upper and lower case)	125.00
40	James Charles Bagby Jr.	20.00
41a	Lonnie Warneke ("...the earned run department...")	20.00
41b	Lonnie Warneke ("...the earned-run department...")	22.00
42	Arndt Jorgens	24.00
43	Melo Almada	20.00
44	Donald Henry Heffner	20.00
45a	Merrill May (name in upper case letters)	20.00
45b	Merrill May (name in upper and lower case)	22.00
46a	Morris Arnovich (name in upper case letters)	20.00
46b	Morris Arnovich (name in upper and lower case)	22.00
47a	John Kelly Lewis, Jr. (name in upper case letters)	20.00
47b	John Kelly Lewis, Jr. (name in upper and lower case)	22.00
48a	Vernon Gomez (name in upper case letters)	200.00
48b	Vernon Gomez (name in upper and lower case)	225.00
49	Edward Miller	20.00
50a	Charles Len Gehringer (name actually Charles Leonard) (name in upper case letters)	200.00
50b	Charles Len Gehringer (name actually Charles Leonard) (name in upper & lower case)	225.00
51a	Melvin Thomas Ott (name in upper case)	200.00
51b	Melvin Thomas Ott (name in upper and lower case)	225.00
52a	Thomas D. Henrich (name in upper case letters)	40.00
52b	Thomas D. Henrich (name in upper and lower case)	45.00
53a	Carl Owen Hubbell (name in upper case letters)	200.00
53b	Carl Owen Hubbell (name in upper and lower case)	225.00
54a	Harry Edward Gumbert (name in upper case letters)	20.00
54b	Harry Edward Gumbert (name in upper and lower case)	22.00
55a	Floyd E. Vaughan (Joseph Floyd) (name in upper case letters)	125.00
55b	Floyd E. Vaughan (Joseph Floyd) (name in upper and lower case)	125.00
56a	Henry Greenberg (name in upper case letters)	150.00
56b	Henry Greenberg (name in upper and lower case)	160.00
57a	John A. Hassett (name in upper case letters)	20.00
57b	John A. Hassett (name in upper and lower case)	22.00
58	Louis Peo Chiozza	20.00
59	Kendall Chase	20.00
60a	Lynwood Thomas Rowe (name in upper case letters)	22.00
60b	Lynwood Thomas Rowe (name in upper and lower case)	24.00
61a	Anthony F. Cuccinello (name in upper case letters)	20.00
61b	Anthony F. Cuccinello (name in upper and lower case)	22.00
62	Thomas Carey	20.00
63	Emmett Mueller	20.00
64a	Wallace Moses, Jr. (name in upper case letters)	20.00
64b	Wallace Moses, Jr. (name in upper and lower case)	22.00
65a	Harry Francis Craft (name in upper case letters)	20.00
65b	Harry Francis Craft (name in upper and lower case)	22.00
66	James A. Ripple	20.00
67	Edwin Joost	20.00
68	Fred Singleton	20.00
69	Elbert Preston Fletcher (Elburt)	20.00
70	Fred Maloy Frankhouse (Meloy)	20.00
71a	Marcellus Monte Pearson (name actually Montgomery Marcellus) (name in upper case)	24.00
71b	Marcellus Monte Pearson (name actually Montgomery Marcellus) (name in upper & lower)	35.00
72a	Debs Garms (Born: Bango, Tex.)	20.00
72b	Debs Garms (Born: Bangs, Tex.)	25.00
73a	Harold H. Schumacher (Born: Dolgville, N.Y.)	22.00
73b	Harold H. Schumacher (Born: Dolgeville, N.Y.)	40.00
74a	Harry A. Lavagetto (name in upper case letters)	24.00
74b	Harry A. Lavagetto (name in upper and lower case)	15.00
75a	Stanley Bordagaray (name in upper case letters)	20.00
75b	Stanley Bordagaray (name in upper and lower case)	22.00
76	Goodwin George Rosen	20.00
77	Lewis Sidney Riggs	20.00
78a	Julius Joseph Solters (name in upper case letters)	20.00
78b	Julius Joseph Solters (name in upper and lower case)	22.00
79a	Joseph Gregg Moore (given name is Joe) (Weight: 174 lbs.)	20.00
79b	Joseph Gregg Moore (given name is Joe) (Weight: 175 lbs.)	25.00
80a	Irwin Fox (Ervin) (Weight: 165 lbs.)	20.00
80b	Irwin Fox (Ervin) (Weight: 157 lbs.)	25.00
81a	Ellsworth Dahlgren (name in upper case letters)	24.00
81b	Ellsworth Dahlgren (name in upper and lower case)	35.00
82a	Charles Herbert Klein (name in upper case letters)	165.00
82b	Charles Herbert Klein (name in upper and lower case)	175.00
83a	August Richard Suhr (name in upper case letters)	20.00
83b	August Richard Suhr (name in upper and lower case)	22.00
84	Lamar Newsome	20.00
85	John Walter Cooney	20.00
86a	Adolph Camilli (Adolf) ("...start of the 1928 season,...")	22.00
86b	Adolph Camilli (Adolf) ("...start of the 1938 season,...")	35.00
87	Milburn G. Shoffner (middle initial actually J.)	20.00
88	Charles Keller	50.00
89a	Lloyd James Waner (name in upper case letters)	125.00
89b	Lloyd James Waner (name in upper and lower case)	135.00
90a	Robert H. Klinger (name in upper case letters)	20.00
90b	Robert H. Klinger (name in upper and lower case)	22.00
91a	John H. Knott (name in upper case letters)	20.00
91b	John H. Knott (name in upper and lower case)	22.00
92a	Ted Williams (name in upper case letters)	2500.00
92b	Ted Williams (name in upper and lower case)	2500.00
93	Charles M. Gelbert	20.00
94	Henry E. Manush	125.00
95a	Whitlow Wyatt (name in upper case letters)	22.00
95b	Whitlow Wyatt (name in upper and lower case)	24.00
96a	Ernest Gordon Phelps (name in upper case letters)	22.00
96b	Ernest Gordon Phelps (name in upper and lower case)	24.00

97a	Robert Lee Johnson (name in upper case letters)	20.00
97b	Robert Lee Johnson (name in upper and lower case)	22.00
98	Arthur Carter Whitney	20.00
99a	Walter Anton Berger (name in upper case letters)	22.00
99b	Walter Anton Berger (name in upper and lower case)	24.00
100a	Charles Solomon Myer (name in upper case letters)	20.00
100b	Charles Solomon Myer (name in upper and lowe case)	22.00
101a	Roger M. Cramer ("...the Martinburg Club...")	20.00
101b	Roger M. Cramer ("...the Martinsburg Club...")	25.00
102a	Lemuel Floyd Young (name in upper case letters)	20.00
102b	Lemuel Floyd Young (name in upper and lower case	22.00
103	Morris Berg	22.00
104a	Thomas Davis Bridges ("...280 games, winning 283,...")	22.00
104b	Thomas Davis Bridges ("...280 games, winning 133,...")	35.00
105a	Donald Eric McNair (name in upper case letters)	20.00
105b	Donald Eric McNair (name in upper and lower case)	22.00
106	Albert Stark	20.00
107	Joseph Franklin Vosmik	20.00
108a	Frank Witman Hayes (name in upper case letters)	20.00
108b	Frank Witman Hayes (name in upper and lower case)	22.00
109a	Myril Hoag (name in upper case letters)	20.00
109b	Myril Hoag (name in upper and lower case)	22.00
110	Fred L. Fitzsimmons	22.00
111a	Van Lingle Mungo (name in upper case letters)	35.00
111b	Van Lingle Mungo (name in upper and lower case)	40.00
112a	Paul Glee Waner ("...Waner, the older...")	125.00
112b	Paul Glee Waner ("...Waner, the elder...")	150.00
113	Al Schacht	25.00
114a	Cecil Howell Travis (name in upper case letters)	20.00
114b	Cecil Howell Travis (name in upper and lower case)	22.00
115a	Ralph Kress (name in upper case letters)	20.00
115b	Ralph Kress (name in upper and lower case)	22.00
116	Eugene A. Desautels	175.00
117	Wayne Ambler	175.00
118	Lynn Nelson	175.00
119	Willard McKee Hershberger	175.00
120	Harold Benton Warstler (middle name actually Burton)	175.00
121	William J. Posedel	175.00
122	George Hartley McQuinn	175.00
123	Ray T. Davis	175.00
124	Walter George Brown	175.00
125	Clifford George Melton	175.00
126	Not Issued	
127	Gilbert Herman Brack	175.00
128	Joseph Emil Bowman	175.00
129	William Swift	175.00
130	Wilbur Lee Brubaker	175.00
131	Morton Cecil Cooper	175.00
132	James Roberson Brown	175.00
133	Lynn Myers	175.00
134	Forrest Pressnell	175.00
135	Arnold Malcolm Owen	175.00
136	Roy Chester Bell	175.00
137	Peter William Appleton	175.00

138	George Washington Case Jr.	175.00
139	Vitautas C. Tamulis	175.00
140	Raymond Hall Hayworth	175.00
141	Peter Coscarart	175.00
142	Ira Kendall Hutchinson	175.00
143	Howard Earl Averill	500.00
144	Henry J. Bonura	175.00
145	Hugh Noyes Mulcahy	175.00
146	Thomas Sunkel	175.00
147	George D. Coffman	175.00
148	William Trotter	175.00
149	Max Edward West	175.00
150	James Elton Walkup	175.00
151	Hugh Thomas Casey	175.00
152	Roy Weatherly	175.00
153	Paul H. Trout	175.00
154	John W. Hudson	175.00
155	James Paul Outlaw (middle name actually Paulus)	175.00
156	Raymond Berres	175.00
157	Donald Willard Padgett (middle name actually Wilson)	175.00
158	Luther Baxter Thomas	175.00
159	Russell E. Evans	175.00
160	Eugene Moore Jr.	175.00
161	Linus Reinhard Frey	175.00
162	Lloyd Albert Moore	350.00

1940 Play Ball

Following the success of their initial effort in 1939, Gum Incorporated issued a bigger and better set in 1940. The 240 black and white cards are once again in the 2-1/2" x 3-1/8" size, but the photos on the card fronts are enclosed by a frame which listed the player's name. Card backs again offer extensive biographies. Backs are also dated. A number of old-timers were issued along with the current day's players, and many Hall of Famers are included. The final 60 cards of the set are more difficult to obtain.

"CASEY" STENGEL

Mr. Mint Says - These seem to have degenerated over the last 50 plus years much more than the 1939 cards. The paper became extremely brown. Pure white ones are extremely scarce.

The Williams, DiMaggio and Joe Jackson cards sell easily in top grades, and the #1 DiMaggio card could actually be virtually any price you name; I have never seen a gem mint one. It is one of the toughest cards in the hobby to obtain in mint condition.

It is harder to find mint cards from 1940 than the previous year, but the 1939 high numbers remain much more difficult. In 1940, there were very few print lines, but many off-center cards, including a bunch in the high series.

		MT
Complete Set:		25000.
Common Player (1-120):		22.00
Common Player (121-180):		25.00
Common Player (181-240):		80.00

1	Joe DiMaggio	3000.00
2	"Art" Jorgens	25.00
3	"Babe" Dahlgren	25.00
4	"Tommy" Henrich	35.00
5	"Monte" Pearson	25.00
6	"Lefty" Gomez	300.00
7	"Bill" Dickey	300.00
8	"Twinkletoes" Selkirk	25.00
9	"Charley" Keller	35.00
10	"Red" Ruffing	75.00
11	"Jake" Powell	35.00
12	"Johnny" Schulte	25.00
13	"Jack" Knott	22.00
14	"Rabbit" McNair	22.00
15	George Case	22.00
16	Cecil Travis	22.00
17	"Buddy" Myer	22.00
18	"Charley" Gelbert	22.00
19	"Ken" Chase	22.00
20	"Buddy" Lewis	22.00
21	"Rick" Ferrell	65.00
22	"Sammy" West	22.00
23	"Dutch" Leonard	22.00
24	Frank "Blimp" Hayes	22.00
25	"Cherokee" Bob Johnson	22.00
26	"Wally" Moses	22.00
27	"Ted" Williams	2500.00
28	"Gene" Desautels	22.00
29	"Doc" Cramer	22.00
30	"Moe" Berg	25.00
31	"Jack" Wilson	22.00
32	"Jim" Bagby	22.00
33	"Fritz" Ostermueller	22.00
34	John Peacock	22.00
35	"Joe" Heving	22.00
36	"Jim" Tabor	22.00
37	Emerson Dickman	22.00
38	"Bobby" Doerr	125.00
39	"Tom" Carey	22.00
40	"Hank" Greenberg	350.00
41	"Charley" Gehringer	200.00
42	"Bud" Thomas	22.00
43	Pete Fox	22.00
44	"Dizzy" Trout	25.00
45	"Red" Kress	22.00
46	Earl Averill	150.00
47	"Old Os" Vitt	22.00
48	"Luke" Sewell	25.00
49	"Stormy Weather" Weatherly	22.00
50	"Hal" Trosky	22.00
51	"Don" Heffner	22.00
52	Myril Hoag	22.00
53	"Mac" McQuinn	22.00
54	"Bill" Trotter	22.00
55	"Slick" Coffman	22.00
56	"Eddie" Miller	22.00
57	Max West	22.00
58	"Bill" Posedel	22.00
59	"Rabbit" Warstler	22.00
60	John Cooney	22.00
61	"Tony" Cuccinello	22.00
62	"Buddy" Hassett	22.00
63	"Pete" Cascarart	22.00
64	"Van" Mungo	30.00
65	"Fitz" Fitzsimmons	25.00
66	"Babe" Phelps	25.00
67	"Whit" Wyatt	25.00
68	"Dolph" Camilli	25.00
69	"Cookie" Lavagetto	25.00
70	"Hot Potato" Hamlin	22.00

71	"Mel" Almada	22.00	144	"Joe" Vosmik	25.00
72	"Chuck" Dressen	25.00	145	"Vito" Tamulis	25.00
73	"Bucky" Walters	25.00	146	"Tot" Pressnell	25.00
74	"Duke" Derringer	25.00	147	"Johnny" Hudson	25.00
75	"Buck" McCormick	22.00	148	"Hugh" Casey	25.00
76	"Lonny" Frey	22.00	149	"Pinky" Shoffner	25.00
77	"Bill" Hershberger	22.00	150	"Whitey" Moore	25.00
78	"Lew" Riggs	22.00	151	Edwin Joost	25.00
79	"Wildfire" Craft	22.00	152	"Jimmy" Wilson	25.00
80	"Bill" Myers	22.00	153	"Bill" McKechnie	100.00
81	"Wally" Berger	25.00	154	"Jumbo" Brown	25.00
82	"Hank" Gowdy	22.00	155	"Ray" Hayworth	25.00
83	"Clif" Melton (Cliff)	22.00	156	"Daffy" Dean	30.00
84	"Jo-Jo" Moore	22.00	157	"Lou" Chiozza	25.00
85	"Hal" Schumacher	25.00	158	"Stonewall" Jackson	100.00
86	Harry Gumbert	22.00	159	"Pancho" Snyder	25.00
87	Carl Hubbell	300.00	160	"Hans" Lobert	25.00
88	"Mel" Ott	300.00	161	"Debs" Garms	25.00
89	"Bill" Jurges	25.00	162	"Joe" Bowman	25.00
90	Frank Demaree	22.00	163	"Spud" Davis	25.00
91	Bob "Suitcase" Seeds	22.00	164	"Ray" Berres	25.00
92	"Whitey" Whitehead	22.00	165	"Bob" Klinger	25.00
93	Harry "The Horse" Danning	22.00	166	"Bill" Brubaker	25.00
94	"Gus" Suhr	22.00	167	"Frankie" Frisch	200.00
95	"Mul" Mulcahy	22.00	168	"Honus" Wagner	400.00
96	"Heinie" Mueller	22.00	169	"Gabby" Street	25.00
97	"Morry" Arnovich	22.00	170	"Tris" Speaker	375.00
98	"Pinky" May	22.00	171	Harry Heilmann	200.00
99	"Syl" Johnson	22.00	172	"Chief" Bender	200.00
100	"Hersh" Martin	22.00	173	"Larry" Lajoie	375.00
101	"Del" Young	22.00	174	"Johnny" Evers	200.00
102	"Chuck" Klein	200.00	175	"Christy" Mathewson	350.00
103	"Elbie" Fletcher	22.00	176	"Heinie" Manush	200.00
104	"Big Poison" Waner	200.00	177	Frank "Homerun" Baker	200.00
105	"Little Poison" Waner	200.00	178	Max Carey	200.00
106	"Pep" Young	22.00	179	George Sisler	200.00
107	"Arky" Vaughan	125.00	180	"Mickey" Cochrane	200.00
108	"Johnny" Rizzo	22.00	181	"Spud" Chandler	80.00
109	"Don" Padgett	22.00	182	"Knick" Knickerbocker	80.00
110	"Tom" Sunkel	22.00	183	Marvin Breuer	80.00
111	"Mickey" Owen	22.00	184	"Mule" Haas	80.00
112	"Jimmy" Brown	22.00	185	"Joe" Kuhel	80.00
113	"Mort" Cooper	22.00	186	Taft Wright	80.00
114	"Lon" Warneke	22.00	187	"Jimmy" Dykes	80.00
115	"Mike" Gonzales (Gonzalez)	22.00	188	"Joe" Krakauskas	80.00
116	"Al" Schacht	25.00	189	"Jim" Bloodworth	80.00
117	"Dolly" Stark	22.00	190	"Charley" Berry	80.00
118	"Schoolboy" Hoyt	125.00	191	John Babich	80.00
119	"Ol Pete" Alexander	225.00	192	"Dick" Siebert	80.00
120	Walter "Big Train" Johnson	400.00	193	"Chubby" Dean	80.00
121	Atley Donald	25.00	194	"Sam" Chapman	80.00
122	"Sandy" Sundra	25.00	195	"Dee" Miles	80.00
123	"Hildy" Hildebrand	25.00	196	"Nonny" Nonnenkamp	80.00
124	"Colonel" Combs	165.00	197	"Lou" Finney	80.00
125	"Art" Fletcher	25.00	198	"Denny" Galehouse	80.00
126	"Jake" Solters	25.00	199	"Pinky" Higgins	80.00
127	"Muddy" Ruel	25.00	200	"Soupy" Campbell	80.00
128	"Pete" Appleton	25.00	201	Barney McCosky	80.00
129	"Bucky" Harris	100.00	202	"Al" Milnar	80.00
130	"Deerfoot" Milan	25.00	203	"Bad News" Hale	80.00
131	"Zeke" Bonura	25.00	204	Harry Eisenstat	80.00
132	Connie Mack	300.00	205	"Rollie" Hemsley	80.00
133	"Jimmie" Foxx	350.00	206	"Chet" Laabs	80.00
134	"Joe" Cronin	175.00	207	"Gus" Mancuso	80.00
135	"Line Drive" Nelson	25.00	208	Lee Gamble	80.00
136	"Cotton" Pippen	25.00	209	"Hy" Vandenberg	80.00
137	"Bing" Miller	25.00	210	"Bill" Lohrman	80.00
138	"Beau" Bell	25.00	211	"Pop" Joiner	80.00
139	Elden Auker (Eldon)	25.00	212	"Babe" Young	80.00
140	"Dick" Coffman	25.00	213	John Rucker	80.00
141	"Casey" Stengel	250.00	214	"Ken" O'Dea	80.00
142	"Highpockets" Kelly	125.00	215	"Johnnie" McCarthy	80.00
143	"Gene" Moore	25.00	216	"Joe" Marty	80.00

217	Walter Beck	80.00
218	"Wally" Millies	80.00
219	"Russ" Bauers	80.00
220	Mace Brown	80.00
221	Lee Handley	80.00
222	"Max" Butcher	80.00
223	Hugh "Ee-Yah" Jennings	225.00
224	"Pie" Traynor	300.00
225	"Shoeless Joe" Jackson	3500.00
226	Harry Hooper	200.00
227	"Pop" Haines	200.00
228	"Charley" Grimm	80.00
229	"Buck" Herzog	80.00
230	"Red" Faber	175.00
231	"Dolf" Luque	80.00
232	"Goose" Goslin	175.00
233	"Moose" Earnshaw	80.00
234	Frank "Husk" Chance	250.00
235	John J. McGraw	300.00
236	"Sunny Jim" Bottomley	175.00
237	"Wee Willie" Keeler	250.00
238	"Poosh 'Em Up Tony" Lazzeri	125.00
239	George Uhle	80.00
240	"Bill" Atwood	250.00

1941 Play Ball

While the card backs are quite similar to the black and white cards Gum Incorporated issued in 1940, the card fronts in the 1941 set are printed in color. Many of the card photos, however, are just color versions of the player's 1940 card. The cards are still in the 2-1/2" by 3-1/8" size, but only 72 cards are included in the set. Joe DiMaggio and Ted Williams continue to be the key players in the set, while card numbers 49-72 are rarer than the lower-numbered cards. The cards were printed in sheets, and can still be found that way, or in paper strips, lacking the cardboard backing.

"DUKE" DERRINGER

Mr. Mint Says - The most popular of the Play Ball sets because of the fantastic pastel colors and also because of the size. There are only 72 cards, most of which are stars or Hall of Famers. The most popular set of the 40s, it can easily fetch $20,000 in mint condition.

Availability in mint is few and far between however, and tougher than either 1939 or 1940. I think the card stock was much softer and broke down a lot, and corner wear showed up easily. There are many off-center cards and print lines, and many of the DiMaggio cards that I have seen have had print lines.

		MT
Complete Set (72):		19250.
Common Player (1-48):		75.00
Common Player (49-72):		100.00

1	"Eddie" Miller	300.00
2	Max West	75.00
3	"Bucky" Walters	75.00
4	"Duke" Derringer	100.00
5	"Buck" McCormick	75.00
6	Carl Hubbell	350.00
7	"The Horse" Danning	75.00
8	"Mel" Ott	400.00
9	"Pinky" May	75.00
10	"Arky" Vaughan	100.00
11	Debs Garms	75.00
12	"Jimmy" Brown	75.00
13	"Jimmie" Foxx	525.00
14	"Ted" Williams	2750.00
15	"Joe" Cronin	200.00
16	"Hal" Trosky	75.00
17	"Stormy" Weatherly	75.00
18	"Hank" Greenberg	500.00
19	"Charley" Gehringer	300.00
20	"Red" Ruffing	200.00
21	"Charlie" Keller	100.00
22	"Indian Bob" Johnson	75.00
23	"Mac" McQuinn	75.00
24	"Dutch" Leonard	75.00
25	"Gene" Moore	75.00
26	Harry "Gunboat" Gumbert	75.00
27	"Babe" Young	75.00
28	"Joe" Marty	75.00
29	"Jack" Wilson	75.00
30	"Lou" Finney	75.00
31	"Joe" Kuhel	75.00
32	Taft Wright	75.00
33	"Happy" Milnar	75.00
34	"Rollie" Hemsley	75.00
35	"Pinky" Higgins	75.00
36	Barney McCosky	75.00
37	"Soupy" Campbell	75.00
38	Atley Donald	100.00
39	"Tommy" Henrich	100.00
40	"Johnny" Babich	75.00
41	Frank "Blimp" Hayes	75.00
42	"Wally" Moses	75.00
43	Albert "Bronk" Brancato	75.00
44	"Sam" Chapman	75.00
45	Elden Auker (Eldon)	75.00
46	"Sid" Hudson	75.00
47	"Buddy" Lewis	75.00
48	Cecil Travis	75.00
49	"Babe" Dahlgren	100.00
50	"Johnny" Cooney	100.00
51	"Dolph" Camilli	75.00
52	Kirby Higbe	100.00
53	Luke "Hot Potato" Hamlin	100.00
54	"Pee Wee" Reese	1000.00
55	"Whit" Wyatt	100.00
56	"Vandy" Vander Meer	100.00
57	"Moe" Arnovich	100.00
58	"Frank" Demaree	100.00
59	"Bill" Jurges	100.00
60	"Chuck" Klein	300.00
61	"Vince" DiMaggio	250.00
62	"Elbie" Fletcher	100.00
63	"Dom" DiMaggio	250.00
64	"Bobby" Doerr	275.00
65	"Tommy" Bridges	100.00
66	Harland Clift (Harland)	100.00
67	"Walt" Judnich	100.00
68	"Jack" Knott	100.00
69	George Case	100.00
70	"Bill" Dickey	850.00
71	"Joe" DiMaggio	3500.00
72	"Lefty" Gomez	1000.00

1954 Red Heart Dog Food

This set of 33 cards was issued in three color-coded series by the Red Heart Dog Food Co. Card fronts feature hand-colored photos on either a blue, green or red background. The 11 red-background cards are scarcer than the 11-card blue or green series. Backs of the 2-5/8" by 3-3/4" cards contain biographical and statistical information along with a Red Heart ad. Each 11-card series was available via a mail-in offer. As late as the early 1970s, the company was still sending cards to collectors who requested them.

ST. LOUIS CARDINALS

Mr. Mint Says - This has always been one of the really popular, more sought after regional issues because sets are simple to complete, they are colorful and attractive and almost every card is a star or minor star. They are also relatively inexpensive. The red background cards are much more difficult than the blues or greens, and the price of the commons reflects that.

These are often found in mint condition because they were sold as a set, and I think you see them in top grades more often than you do in off condition. I think that the companies that made these oddball, small sets often dumped them at the end of the promotion, and when I bought out Herb Ross he had a couple of thousand of these. I had 150 to 200 Mantles that still had the cutting marks on them, little pieces of paper on the outside edges.

I consistently get $600 or $700 for the Mantle at auction, and the Musial is the next toughest card in the set. It is actually harder to find than Mantle, but Mickey is more popular. The set also has a lot of players with regional interest, which helps the popularity.

		MT
Complete Set (33):		3000.
Common Player:		35.00
(1)	Richie Ashburn	75.00
(2)	Frankie Baumholtz	35.00
(3)	Gus Bell	35.00
(4)	Billy Cox	35.00
(5)	Alvin Dark	35.00
(6)	Carl Erskine	45.00
(7)	Ferris Fain	35.00
(8)	Dee Fondy	35.00
(9)	Nelson Fox	50.00
(10)	Jim Gilliam	40.00
(11)	Jim Hegan	35.00
(12)	George Kell	45.00
(13)	Ted Kluszewski	45.00
(14)	Ralph Kiner	60.00
(15)	Harvey Kuenn	35.00
(16)	Bob Lemon	60.00
(17)	Sherman Lollar	35.00
(18)	Mickey Mantle	600.00
(19)	Billy Martin	60.00
(20)	Gil McDougald	45.00
(21)	Roy McMillan	35.00
(22)	Minnie Minoso	35.00
(23)	Stan Musial	400.00
(24)	Billy Pierce	35.00
(25)	Al Rosen	45.00
(26)	Hank Sauer	35.00
(27)	Red Schoendienst	45.00
(28)	Enos Slaughter	45.00
(29)	Duke Snider	140.00
(30)	Warren Spahn	85.00
(31)	Sammy White	35.00
(32)	Eddie Yost	35.00
(33)	Gus Zernial	35.00

1933 Sport Kings

This 48-card set was issued by the Goudey Gum Company. Participants in 18 different sports are included in the set, which honors the top sports figures of the era. Three baseball players are pictured on the 2-3/8" x 2-7/8" cards. The card fronts are color portraits and include the player's name and silhouette representations of the respective sport. The card backs are numbered and list biographical information and a company ad.

Mr. Mint Says - This is one of the most popular collector sets ever. It's a small, challenging set with gorgeous color graphics. There are only 48 cards in the set, so it is not that difficult to complete, and there are only about 10 or 15 major stars. Mint copies of singles sell for many times in excess of listed prices.

It is very scarce in mint, and when they are you can throw the book away (unless it's a Krause publication, in which case we advise that you simply set it aside for the moment). The higher numbers are much more difficult than the lower numbers. In a hoard that I purchased, with perhaps 400 cards in varying grades, there were twice as many low numbers as highs. I've seen the Cobb sell for thousands at auctions, and the Ruth is also a neat looking card. The boxers and golfers in the set are also popular with collectors.

In another instance, I bought about a dozen unopened packs, opened them all and got a Rockne out of it. I put it in my auction complete with the stick of gum, which was the size of the back of the card and had left a small stain, and got $2,200.

Printing was excellent with this issue, but off centering can be a problem.

		MT
Complete Set (48):		23500.
Common Player (1-24):		50.00
Common Player (25-48):		100.00
1	Ty Cobb	2750.00
2	Babe Ruth	5500.00
3	Nat Holman (basketball)	250.00
4	Red Grange (football)	1000.00
5	Ed Wachter (basketball)	200.00
6	Jim Thorpe (football)	1400.00
7	Bobby Walthour, Sr. (bicycling)	50.00
8	Walter Hagen (golf)	200.00
9	Ed Blood (skiiing)	50.00
10	Anston Lekang (skiing)	50.00
11	Charles Jewtraw (ice skating)	50.00
12	Bobby McLean (ice skating)	50.00
13	Laverne Fator (jockey)	50.00
14	Jim Londos (wrestling)	50.00
15	Reggie McNamara (bicycling)	50.00
16	Bill Tilden (tennis)	200.00
17	Jack Dempsey (boxing)	500.00
18	Gene Tunney (boxing)	500.00
19	Eddie Shore (hockey)	250.00
20	Duke Kahanamoku (surfing/swimming)	200.00
21	Johnny Weissmuller (swimming/ "Tarzan")	350.00
22	Gene Sarazen (golf)	250.00
23	Vincent Richards (tennis)	100.00
24	Howie Morenz (hockey)	400.00
25	Ralph Snoddy (speedboating)	100.00
26	James Wedell (aviator)	100.00
27	Roscoe Turner (aviator)	100.00
28	James Doolittle (aviator)	250.00
29	Ace Bailey (hockey)	300.00
30	Irvin Johnson (hockey)	300.00
31	Bobby Walthour, Jr. (bicycling)	100.00
32	Joe Lopchick (basketball)	250.00
33	Eddie Burke (basketball)	100.00
34	Irving Jaffee (ice skating)	100.00
35	Knute Rockne (football)	1500.00
36	Willie Hoppe (billiards)	100.00
37	Helene Madison (swimming)	100.00
38	Bobby Jones (golf)	350.00
39	Jack Westrope (jockey)	100.00
40	Don George (wrestling)	100.00
41	Jim Browning (wrestling)	100.00
42	Carl Hubbell	850.00
43	Primo Carnera (boxing)	200.00
44	Max Baer (boxing)	200.00
45	Babe Didrickson (track)	1200.00
46	Ellsworth Vines (tennis)	100.00
47	J.H. Stevens (bobsled)	100.00
48	Leonard Seppala (dog sled)	250.00

1948 Sport Thrills

This is a set of black and white cards which depict memorable events in baseball history. The cards measure 2-1/2" by 3" and have a picture frame border and event title on the card fronts. The card backs describe the event in detail. Twenty cards were produced in this set by the Swell Gum Company of Philadelphia. Each card is numbered, and card numbers 9, 11, 16 and 20 are considered more difficult to obtain.

6	Home Run Wins Series (Bill Dickey)	25.00
7	Never Say Die Pitcher (Hal Schumacher)	20.00
8	Five Strikeouts! (Carl Hubbell)	25.00
9	Greatest Catch! (Al Gionfriddo)	50.00
10	No Hits! No Runs! (Johnny Vander Meer)	20.00
11	Bases Loaded! (Tony Lazzeri, Bob O'Farrell)	50.00
12	Most Dramatic Home Run (Lou Gehrig, Babe Ruth)	250.00
13	Winning Run	
	(Tommy Bridges, Mickey Cochrane, Goose Goslin)	20.00
14	Great Slugging (Lou Gehrig)	225.00
15	Four Men to Stop Him! (Jim Bagby, Al Smith)	20.00
16	Three Run Homer in Ninth!	
	(Joe DiMaggio, Joe Gordon, Ted Williams)	250.00
17	Football Block! (Whitey Kurowski, Johnny Lindell)	20.00
18	Home Run to Fame (Pee Wee Reese)	50.00
19	Strikout Record! (Bob Feller)	60.00
20	Rifle Arm! (Carl Furillo)	60.00

Mr. Mint Says - This is a set that not a lot of people are familiar with. It is a very challenging 20-card set, and relative to rarity should be worth a great deal more. The white border seems to degenerate quickly, and when they get really gray they don't sell that well. There are also centering problems. In my years in the business I have only owned two sets.

You can easily get $250 or $300 for the Gehrig and Ruth cards. The DiMaggio card is amazing; $150 for that card and I've only seen two or three of them.

		MT
Complete Set:		1400.
Common Player:		20.00
1	Greatest Single Inning (Mickey Cochrane, Jimmy Foxx, George Haas, Bing Miller, Al Simmons)	60.00
2	Amazing Record (Pete Reiser)	20.00
3	Dramatic Debut (Jackie Robinson)	125.00
4	Greatest Pitcher (Walter Johnson)	75.00
5	Three Strikes Not Out!	
	(Tommy Henrich, Mickey Owen)	20.00

1911 Turkey Red (T3)

Turkey Reds are the only cabinet cards the average collector can have a realistic chance to complete. Obtained by mailing in coupons found in Turkey Red, Fez and Old Mill brand cigarettes, the Turkey Reds measure 5-3/4" by 8", a size known to collectors as "cabinet cards." Turkey Reds feature full color lithograph fronts with wide gray frames. Backs carried either a numbered ordering list or an ad for Turkey Red cigarettes. The Turkey Red series consists of 25 boxers and 100 baseball players. Despite their cost, Turkey Reds remain very popular today as the most attractive of the cabinet sets.

Mr. Mint Says - Probably the most popular tobacco issue. The pictures are gorgeous, so realistic. There are not many people putting sets together these days, but when quality cards show up they are snapped up quickly. There is no availability.

		MT
Complete Set:		75000.
Common Player:		300.00

1	Mordecai Brown	1000.00
2	Bill Bergen	300.00
3	Tommy Leach	300.00
4	Roger Bresnahan	1200.00
5	Sam Crawford	1200.00
6	Hal Chase	400.00
7	Howie Camnitz	300.00
8	Fred Clarke	1000.00
9	Ty Cobb	11500.00
10	Art Devlin	300.00

11	Bill Dahlen	300.00
12	Wild Bill Donovan	300.00
13	Larry Doyle	300.00
14	Red Dooin	300.00
15	Kid Elberfeld	300.00
16	Johnny Evers	1200.00
17	Clark Griffith	1200.00
18	Hughie Jennings	1200.00
19	Addie Joss	1200.00
20	Tim Jordan	300.00
21	Red Kleinow	300.00
22	Harry Krause	300.00
23	Nap Lajoie	2800.00
24	Mike Mitchell	300.00
25	Matty McIntyre	300.00
26	John McGraw	1350.00
27	Christy Mathewson	3750.00
28a	Harry McIntyre (Brooklyn)	300.00
28b	Harry McIntyre (Brooklyn and Chicago)	350.00
29	Amby McConnell	300.00
30	George Mullin	300.00
31	Sherry Magee	300.00
32	Orval Overall	300.00
33	Jake Pfeister	300.00
34	Nap Rucker	300.00
35	Joe Tinker	1200.00
36	Tris Speaker	2800.00
37	Slim Sallee	300.00
38	Jake Stahl	300.00
39	Rube Waddell	1200.00
40a	Vic Willis (Pittsburgh)	300.00
40b	Vic Willis (Pittsburgh and St. Louis)	350.00
41	Hooks Wiltse	300.00
42	Cy Young	3500.00
43	Out At Third	200.00
44	Trying To Catch Him Napping	200.00
45	Jordan & Herzog At First	300.00
46	Safe At Third	200.00
47	Frank Chance At Bat	1000.00
48	Jack Murray At Bat	300.00
49	A Close Play At Second	300.00
50	Chief Myers At Bat	300.00
77	Red Ames	325.00
78	Home Run Baker	1200.00
79	George Bell	325.00
80	Chief Bender	1000.00
81	Bob Bescher	325.00
82	Kitty Bransfield	325.00
83	Al Bridwell	325.00
84	George Browne	325.00
85	Bill Burns	325.00
86	Bill Carrigan	325.00
87	Eddie Collins	1000.00
88	Harry Coveleski	325.00
89	Lou Criger	325.00
90a	Mickey Doolin (name incorrect)	375.00
90b	Mickey Doolan (name correct)	325.00
91	Tom Downey	325.00
92	Jimmy Dygert	325.00
93	Art Fromme	325.00
94	George Gibson	325.00
95	Peaches Graham	325.00
96	Bob Groom	325.00
97	Dick Hoblitzell	325.00
98	Solly Hofman	325.00
99	Walter Johnson	4000.00
100	Davy Jones	325.00
101	Wee Willie Keeler	450.00
102	Johnny Kling	325.00

103	Ed Konetchy	325.00
104	Ed Lennox	325.00
105	Hans Lobert	325.00
106	Harry Lord	325.00
107	Rube Manning	325.00
108	Fred Merkle	325.00
109	Pat Moran	325.00
110	George McBride	325.00
111	Harry Niles	325.00
112a	Dode Paskert (Cincinnati)	350.00
112b	Dode Paskert (Cincinnati and Philadelphia)	325.00
113	Bugs Raymond	325.00
114	Bob Rhoades (Rhoads)	350.00
115	Admiral Schlei	325.00
116	Boss Schmidt	325.00
117	Wildfire Schulte	325.00
118	Frank Smith	325.00
119	George Stone	325.00
120	Gabby Street	325.00
121	Billy Sullivan	325.00
122a	Fred Tenney (New York)	350.00
122b	Fred Tenney (New York and Boston)	325.00
123	Ira Thomas	325.00
124	Bobby Wallace	1000.00
125	Ed Walsh	1200.00
126	Owen Wilson	325.00

1900 T201

Mecca Double Folders

These cards found in packages of Mecca cigarettes feature one player when the card is open, and another when the card is folded; two players sharing the same pair of legs. Mecca Double Folders measure 2-1/4" by 4-11/16". The fronts are color lithographs with the player's name appearing in black script in the upper left. The backs are printed in red and contain an innovation in the form of player statistics. The 50-card set contains 100 different players including a number of Hall of Famers. The Mecca Double Folders, with two players (Topps "borrowed" the idea in 1955) and statistics, were one of the most innovative of the tobacco card era.

Mr. Mint Says - These are great old cards with super lithography. In addition, because of the small size of the set, they are very collectable. Like the T-202 set, I don't think that many people sit down and decide to piece together a T-201 set. I've had several that were near-mint, but they are not around that much.

They are neat, they depict two players, and though you often see them off-center to the left or right, overall they seem to have had better quality control than some Topps issues.

I don't think a top grade set can be sold for much more than $7,000 or $10,000.

		MT
Complete Set (50):		9000.
Common Player:		67.50
(1)	William Abstein, John Butler	67.50
(2)	Frank Baker, Edward Collins	360.00
(3)	Harry Baker, Thomas Downie (Downey)	67.50
(4)	James Barrett, Grant McGlynn	67.50
(5)	John Barry, John Lapp	67.50
(6)	Charles Bender, Reuben Oldring	225.00
(7)	William Bergen, Zack Wheat	225.00
(8)	Walter Blair, Roy Hartzell	67.50
(9)	Roger Bresnahan, Miller Huggins	450.00
(10)	Albert Bridwell, Christy Matthewson (Mathewson)	675.00
(11)	Mordecai Brown, Arthur Hofman	225.00
(12)	Robert Byrne, Fred Clarke	180.00
(13)	Frank Chance, John Evers	400.00
(14)	Harold Chase, Edward Sweeney	115.00
(15)	Edward Cicotte, John Thoney	90.00
(16)	Thomas Clarke, Harry Gaspar	67.50
(17)	Ty Cobb, Sam Crawford	1750.00
(18)	Leonard Cole, John Kling	67.50
(19)	John Coombs, Ira Thomas	67.50
(20)	Jake Daubert, Nap Rucker	90.00
(21)	Bill Donovan, Ralph Stroud, Bill Donovan	75.00
(22)	Charles Dooin, John Titus	67.50
(23)	Patsy Dougherty, Harry Lord	360.00
(24)	Jerry Downs, Fred Odwell	67.50
(25)	Larry Doyle, Chief Meyers	67.50
(26)	James Dygert, Cy Seymour	67.50
(27)	Norman Elberfeld, George McBride	67.50
(28)	Fred Falkenberg, Napoleon Lajoie	450.00
(29)	Edward Fitzpatrick, Ed Killian	67.50
(30)	Russell Ford, Otis Johnson	67.50
(31)	Edward Foster, Joseph Ward	67.50
(32)	Earl Gardner, Tris Speaker	135.00
(33)	George Gibson, Thomas Leach	67.50
(34)	George Graham, Al Mattern	67.50
(35)	Edward Grant, John McLean	67.50
(36)	Arnold Hauser, Ernest Lush	67.50
(37)	Charles Herzog, Roy Miller	67.50
(38)	Charles Hickman, Harry Hinchman	67.50
(39)	Hugh Jennings, Edgar Summers	225.00
(40)	Walter Johnson, Charles Street	675.00
(41)	Frank LaPorte, James Stephens	67.50
(42)	Joseph Lake, Robert Wallace	180.00
(43)	Albert Leifield, Mike Simon	67.50
(44)	John Lobert, Earl Moore	67.50
(45)	Arthur McCabe, Charles Starr	67.50
(46)	Lewis McCarty, Joseph McGinnity	180.00
(47)	Fred Merkle, George Wiltse	90.00
(48)	Grederick Payne, Edward Walsh	225.00
(49)	George Stovall, Torrence Turner	67.50
(50)	Williams, Orville Woodruff	67.50

1912 T202 Hassan

Triple Folders

Measuring 5-1/2" by 2-1/4", Hassan cigarette cards carried the concept of multiple-player cards even further than the innovative Mecca set of the previous year. Scored so that the two end cards - which are full-color and very close to exact duplicates of T205 "Gold Borders" - can fold over the black and white center panel, the Hassan Triple Folder appears like a booklet when closed. The two end cards are individual player cards, while the larger center panel contains an action scene. Usually the two player cards are not related to the action scene. The unique Hassan Triple Folders feature player biographies on the back of the two individual cards with a description of the action on the back of the center panel. Values depend on the player featured in the center panel, as well as the players featured on the end cards.

Mr. Mint Says - The relatively
large number of cards, the high individual price tags and the limited availability conspire to make piecing this set together a difficult task. The individual Hall of Famers are still in demand, but the Ty Cobb cards still sell the best. For all of these tobacco issues, I think there should be a bigger difference between the near-mint price and the price of an actual mint set.

Very salable, very pretty and one of the most popular tobacco sets ever made. When these cards are mint and the center panel not folded, they are just fabulous.

		MT
Complete Set (132):		78000.
Common Player:		200.00
(1a)	A Close Play At The Home Plate LaPorte	225.00
(1a)	A Close Play At The Home Plate Wallace	225.00
(1b)	A Close Play At The Home Plate Pelty	225.00
(1b)	A Close Play At The Home Plate Wallace	225.00
(2)	A Desperate Slide For Third (Ty Cobb, O'Leary)	3000.00
(3a)	A Great Batsman Barger	200.00
(3a)	A Great Batsman Bergen	200.00
(3b)	A Great Batsman Bergen	200.00
(3b)	A Great Batsman Rucker	200.00

(4)	Ambrose McConnell At Bat (Blair, Quinn)	200.00
(5)	A Wide Throw Saves Crawford (Mullin, Stanage)	200.00
(6)	Baker Gets His Man (Baker, Collins)	450.00
(7)	Birmingham Gets To Third (Johnson, Street)	675.00
(8)	Birmingham's Home Run (Birmingham, Turner)	725.00
(9)	Bush Just Misses Austin (Magee, Moran)	200.00
(10a)	Carrigan Blocks His Man Gaspar	200.00
(10a)	Carrigan Blocks His Man McLean	200.00
(10b)	Carrigan Blocks His Man Carrigan	200.00
(10b)	Carrigan Blocks His Man Wagner	200.00
(11)	Catching Him Napping (Bresnahan, Oakes)	350.00
(12)	Caught Asleep Off First (Bresnahan, Harmon)	350.00
(13a)	Chance Beats Out A Hit Chance	350.00
(13a)	Chance Beats Out A Hit Foxen	350.00
(13b)	Chance Beats Out A Hit Archer	200.00
(13b)	Chance Beats Out A Hit McIntyre	200.00
(13c)	Chance Beats Out A Hit Archer	200.00
(13c)	Chance Beats Out A Hit Overall	200.00
(13d)	Chance Beats Out A Hit Archer	200.00
(13d)	Chance Beats Out A Hit Rowan	200.00
(13e)	Chance Beats Out A Hit Chance	350.00
(13e)	Chance Beats Out A Hit Shean	350.00
(14a)	Chase Dives Into Third Chase	200.00
(14a)	Chase Dives Into Third Wolter	200.00
(14b)	Chase Dives Into Third Clarke	225.00
(14b)	Chase Dives Into Third Gibson	225.00
(14c)	Chase Dives Into Third Gibson	200.00
(14c)	Chase Dives Into Third Phillippe	200.00
(15a)	Chase Gets Ball Too Late Egan	200.00
(15a)	Chase Gets Ball Too Late Mitchell	200.00
(15b)	Chase Gets Ball Too Late Chase	200.00
(15b)	Chase Gets Ball Too Late Wolter	200.00
(16a)	Chase Guarding First Chase	200.00
(16a)	Chase Guarding First Wolter	200.00
(16b)	Chase Guarding First Clarke	225.00
(16b)	Chase Guarding First Gibson	225.00
(16c)	Chase Guarding First Gibson	200.00
(16c)	Chase Guarding First Leifield	200.00
(17)	Chase Ready For The Squeeze Play (Magee, Paskert)	200.00
(18)	Chase Safe At Third (Baker, Barry)	350.00
(19)	Chief Bender Waiting For A Good One (Bender, Thomas)	350.00
(20)	Clarke Hikes For Home (Bridwell, Kling)	200.00
(21)	Close At First (Ball, Stovall)	200.00
(22a)	Close At The Plate Payne	350.00
(22a)	Close At The Plate Walsh	350.00
(22b)	Close At The Plate Payne	200.00
(22b)	Close At The Plate White	200.00
(23)	Close At Third - (Speaker Speaker, Wood)	450.00
(24)	Close At Third - (Wagner Carrigan, Wagner)	200.00
(25a)	Collins Easily Safe Byrne	275.00
(25a)	Collins Easily Safe Clarke	275.00
(25b)	Collins Easily Safe Baker	450.00
(25b)	Collins Easily Safe Collins	450.00
(25c)	Collins Easily Safe Collins	350.00
(25c)	Collins Easily Safe Murphy	350.00
(26)	Crawford About To Smash One (Stanage, Summers)	200.00
(27)	Cree Rolls Home (Daubert, Hummel)	200.00
(28)	Davy Jones' Great Slide (Delahanty, Jones)	200.00
(29a)	Devlin Gets His Man Devlin (Giants)	1000.00
(29a)	Devlin Gets His Man Mathewson	1000.00
(29b)	Devlin Gets His Man Devlin (Rustlers)	575.00
(29b)	Devlin Gets His Man Mathewson	575.00
(29c)	Devlin Gets His Man Fletcher	575.00
(29c)	Devlin Gets His Man Mathewson	575.00
(29d)	Devlin Gets His Man Mathewson	575.00
(29d)	Devlin Gets His Man Meyers	575.00

(30a) Donlin Out At First Camnitz	200.00
(30a) Donlin Out At First Gibson	200.00
(30b) Donlin Out At First Doyle	200.00
(30b) Donlin Out At First Merlke	200.00
(30c) Donlin Out At First Leach	200.00
(30c) Donlin Out At First Wilson	200.00
(30d) Donlin Out At First Dooin	200.00
(30d) Donlin Out At First Magee	200.00
(30e) Donlin Out At First Gibson	200.00
(30e) Donlin Out At First Phillippe	200.00
(31a) Dooin Gets His Man Dooin	200.00
(31a) Dooin Gets His Man Doolan	200.00
(31b) Dooin Gets His Man Dooin	200.00
(31b) Dooin Gets His Man Lobert	200.00
(31c) Dooin Gets His Man Dooin	200.00
(31c) Dooin Gets His Man Titus	200.00
(32) Easy For Larry Doyle, Merlke)	200.00
(33) Elberfeld Beats The Throw (Elberfeld, Milan)	200.00
(34) Elberfeld Gets His Man (Elberfeld, Milan)	200.00
(35) Engle In A Close Play (Engle, Speaker)	400.00
(36a) Evers Makes A Safe Slide Archer	350.00
(36a) Evers Makes A Safe Slide Evers	350.00
(36b) Evers Makes A Safe Slide Chance	450.00
(36b) Evers Makes A Safe Slide Evers	450.00
(36c) Evers Makes A Safe Slide Archer	200.00
(36c) Evers Makes A Safe Slide Overall	200.00
(36d) Evers Makes A Safe Slide Archer	200.00
(36d) Evers Makes A Safe Slide Reulbach	200.00
(36e) Evers Makes A Safe Slide Chance	500.00
(36e) Evers Makes A Safe Slide Tinker	500.00
(37) Fast Work At Third (Cobb, O'Leary)	3000.00
(38a) Ford Putting Over A Spitter Ford	200.00
(38a) Ford Putting Over A Spitter Vaughn	200.00
(38b) Ford Putting Over A Spitter Sweeney	200.00
(38b) Ford Putting Over A SpitterFord	200.00
(39) Good Play At Third (Cobb, Moriarity)	2225.00
(40) Grant Gets His Man (Grant, Hoblitzell)	200.00
(41a) Hal Chase Too Late McConnell	200.00
(41a) Hal Chase Too Late McIntyre	200.00
(41b) Hal Chase Too Late McLean	200.00
(41b) Hal Chase Too Late Suggs	200.00
(42) Harry Lord At Third (Lennox, Tinker)	200.00
(43) Hartzell Covering Third (Dahlen, Scanlan)	200.00
(44) Hartsel Strikes Out (Gray, Groom)	200.00
(45) Held At Third (Lord, Tannehill)	200.00
(46) Jake Stahl Guarding First (Cicotte, Stahl)	200.00
(47) Jim Delahanty At Bat (Delahanty, Jones)	200.00
(48a) Just Before The Battle Ames	200.00
(48a) Just Before The Battle Meyers	200.00
(48b) Just Before The Battle Bresnahan	450.00
(48b) Just Before The Battle McGraw	450.00
(48c) Just Before The Battle Crandall	200.00
(48c) Just Before The Battle Meyers	200.00
(48d) Just Before The Battle Becker	200.00
(48d) Just Before The Battle Devore	200.00
(48e) Just Before The Battle Fletcher	575.00
(48e) Just Before The Battle Mathewson	575.00
(48f) Just Before The Battle Marquard	350.00
(48f) Just Before The Battle Meyers	350.00
(48g) Just Before The Battle Jennings	500.00
(48g) Just Before The Battle McGraw	500.00
(48h) Just Before The Battle Mathewson	575.00
(48h) Just Before The Battle Meyers	575.00
(48i) Just Before The Battle Murray	200.00
(48i) Just Before The Battle Snodgrass	200.00
(48j) Just Before The Battle Meyers	200.00
(48j) Just Before The Battle Wiltse	200.00
(49) Knight Catches A Runner (Johnson, Knight)	675.00
(50a) Lobert Almost Caught Bridwell	200.00
(50a) Lobert Almost Caught Kling	200.00
(50b) Lobert Almost Caught Kling	500.00
(50b) Lobert Almost Caught Young	500.00
(50c) Lobert Almost Caught Kling	200.00
(50c) Lobert Almost Caught Mattern	200.00
(50d) Lobert Almost Caught Kling	200.00
(50d) Lobert Almost Caught Steinfeldt	200.00
(51) Lobert Gets Tenney (Dooin, Lobert)	200.00
(52) Lord Catches His Man (Lord, Tannehil)	200.00
(53) McConnell Caught (Needham, Richie)	200.00
(54) McIntyre At Bat (McConnell, McIntyre)	200.00
(55) Moriarty Spiked (Stanage, Willett)	200.00
(56) Nearly Caught (Bates, Bescher)	200.00
(57) Oldring Almost Home (Lord, Oldring)	200.00
(58) Schaefer On First (McBride, Milan)	200.00
(59) Schaefer Steals Second (Clark Griffith, McBride)	350.00
(60) Scoring From Second (Lord, Oldring)	200.00
(61a) Scrambling Back To First Barger	200.00
(61a) Scrambling Back To First Bergen	200.00
(61b) Scrambling Back To First Chase	200.00
(61b) Scrambling Back To First Wolter	200.00
(62) Speaker Almost Caught (Clarke, Miller)	275.00
(63) Speaker Rounding Third (Speaker, Wood)	450.00
(64) Speaker Scores (Engle, Speaker)	450.00
(65) Stahl Safe (Austin, Stovall)	200.00
(66) Stone About To Swing (Schulte, Sheckard)	200.00
(67a) Sullivan Puts Up A High One Evans	350.00
(67a) Sullivan Puts Up A High One Huggins	350.00
(67b) Sullivan Puts Up A High One Gray	200.00
(67b) Sullivan Puts Up A High One Groom	200.00
(68a) Sweeney Gets Stahl Ford	200.00
(68a) Sweeney Gets Stahl Vaughn	200.00
(68b) Sweeney Gets Stahl Ford	200.00
(68b) Sweeney Gets Stahl Sweeney	200.00
(69) Tenney Lands Safely (Latham, Raymond)	200.00
(70a) The Athletic Infield Baker	350.00
(70a) The Athletic Infield Barry	350.00
(70b) The Athletic Infield Brown	350.00
(70b) The Athletic Infield Graham	350.00
(70c) The Athletic Infield Hauser	200.00
(70c) The Athletic Infield Konetchy	200.00
(70d) The Athletic Infield Krause	200.00
(70d) The Athletic Infield Thomas	200.00
(71) The Pinch Hitter (Egan, Hoblitzell)	200.00
(72) The Scissors Slide (Birmingham, Turner)	200.00
(73a) Tom Jones At Bat Fromme	200.00
(73a) Tom Jones At Bat McLean	200.00
(73b) Tom Jones At Bat Gaspar	200.00
(73b) Tom Jones At Bat McLean	200.00
(74a) Too Late For Devlin Ames	200.00
(74a) Too Late For Devlin Meyers	200.00
(74b) Too Late For Devlin Crandall	200.00
(74b) Too Late For Devlin Meyers	200.00
(74c) Too Late For Devlin Devlin (Giants)	750.00
(74c) Too Late For Devlin Mathewson	750.00
(74d) Too Late For Devlin Devlin (Rustlers)	575.00
(74d) Too Late For Devlin Mathewson	575.00
(74e) Too Late For Devlin Marquard	350.00
(74e) Too Late For Devlin Meyers	350.00
(74f) Too Late For Devlin Meyers	200.00
(74f) Too Late For Devlin Wiltse	200.00
(75a) Ty Cobb Steals Third Cobb	3500.00
(75a) Ty Cobb Steals Third Jennings	3500.00
(75b) Ty Cobb Steals Third Cobb	3000.00
(75b) Ty Cobb Steals Third Moriarty	3000.00
(75c) Ty Cobb Steals Third Austin	1075.00
(75c) Ty Cobb Steals Third Stovall	1075.00
(76) Wheat Strikes Out (Dahlen, Wheat)	400.00

1911 T205 Gold Border

Taking their hobby nickname from their border color, these cards were issued in a number of different cigarette brands. The cards measure 1-1/2" by 2-5/8". American League cards feature a color lithograph of the player inside a stylized baseball diamond. National League cards have head and shoulders portraits and a plain background, plus the first ever use of a facsimile autograph in a major card set. The 12 minor league players in the set feature three-quarter length portraits or action pictures in an elaborate frame of columns and other devices. Card backs of the major leaguers carry the player's full name (a first) and statistics. Card backs of the minor leaguers lack the statistics. The complete set price does not include the scarcer variations.

Mr. Mint Says - These are the most beautiful tobacco cards, along with the T-3s. I've never seen a set in my life that could be considered mint, and relative to rarity, a mint one could be worth whatever price you can name. True mint Hall of Famers, especially Cobb, would easily command in excess of book. If I could find a full gold Cobb, a mint

one, I would be a buyer at $7,500 and then try to get a little more for it.

Collectors have to be careful with these cards to watch out for the handiwork of those with gold-tipped pens, just as you might be cautious about any colored border.

You must also be careful about trimming. In that Baltimore find, there were almost 800 cards, and they were all the same size, which was over the size listed in the books. And the Southern find was the same way. If I get handed a T-205 or T-206 that is shorter than what is listed in the book, I don't buy it.

		MT
Complete Set:		80000.
Common Player:		90.00
(1)	Edward J. Abbaticchio	90.00
(2)	Doc Adkins	300.00
(3)	Leon K. Ames	90.00
(4)	Jas. P. Archer	90.00
(5)	Jimmy Austin	90.00
(6)	Bill Bailey	90.00
(7)	Home Run Baker	450.00
(8)	Neal Ball	90.00
(9)	E.B. Barger (full "B" on cap)	90.00
(10)	E.B. Barger (partial "B" on cap)	450.00
(11)	Jack Barry	90.00
(12)	Emil Batch	300.00
(13)	John W. Bates	90.00
(14)	Fred Beck	90.00
(15)	B. Becker	90.00
(16)	George G. Bell	90.00
(17)	Chas. Bender	600.00
(18)	William Bergen	90.00
(19)	Bob Bescher	90.00
(20)	Joe Birmingham	90.00
(21)	Lena Blackburne	90.00
(22)	William E. Bransfield	90.00
(23)	Roger P. Bresnahan (mouth closed)	600.00
(24)	Roger P. Bresnahan (mouth open)	575.00
(25)	A.H. Bridwell	90.00
(26)	Mordecai Brown	600.00
(27)	Robert Byrne	90.00
(28)	Hick Cady	300.00
(29)	H. Camnitz	90.00
(30)	Bill Carrigan	90.00
(31)	Frank J. Chance	600.00
(32a)	Hal Chase (both ears show, gold diamond frame extends below shoulders)	150.00
(32b)	Hal Chase (both ears show, gold diamond frame ends at shoulders)	150.00
(33)	Hal Chase (only left ear shows)	475.00
(34)	Ed Cicotte	125.00
(35)	Fred C. Clarke	275.00
(36)	Ty Cobb	7500.00
(37)	Eddie Collins (mouth closed)	600.00
(38)	Eddie Collins (mouth open)	575.00
(39)	Jimmy Collins	600.00
(40)	Frank J. Corridon	90.00
(41a)	Otis Crandall ("t" not crossed in name)	90.00
(41b)	Otis Crandall ("t" crossed in name)	90.00
(42)	Lou Criger	90.00
(43)	W.F. Dahlen	250.00

(44)	Jake Daubert	95.00
(45)	Jim Delahanty	90.00
(46)	Arthur Devlin	90.00
(47)	Josh Devore	90.00
(48)	W.R. Dickson	90.00
(49)	Jiggs Donohue (Donahue)	450.00
(50)	Chas. S. Dooin	90.00
(51)	Michael J. Doolan	90.00
(52a)	Patsy Dougherty (red sock for team emblem)	90.00
(52b)	Patsy Dougherty (white sock for team emblem)	275.00
(53)	Thomas Downey	90.00
(54)	Larry Doyle	90.00
(55)	Hugh Duffy	600.00
(56)	Jack Dunn	325.00
(57)	Jimmy Dygert	90.00
(58)	R. Egan	90.00
(59)	Kid Elberfeld	90.00
(60)	Clyde Engle	90.00
(61)	Louis Evans	90.00
(62)	John J. Evers	450.00
(63)	Robert Ewing	90.00
(64)	G.C. Ferguson	90.00
(65)	Ray Fisher	350.00
(66)	Arthur Fletcher	90.00
(67)	John A. Flynn	90.00
(68)	Russ Ford (black cap)	90.00
(69)	Russ Ford (white cap)	325.00
(70)	Wm. A. Foxen	90.00
(71)	Jimmy Frick	300.00
(72)	Arthur Fromme	90.00
(73)	Earl Gardner	90.00
(74)	H.L. Gaspar	90.00
(75)	George Gibson	90.00
(76)	Wilbur Goode	90.00
(77)	George F. Graham (Rustlers)	90.00
(78)	George F. Graham (Cubs)	450.00
(79)	Edward L. Grant	325.00
(80a)	Dolly Gray (no stats on back)	90.00
(80b)	Dolly Gray (stats on back)	200.00
(81)	Clark Griffith	450.00
(82)	Bob Groom	90.00
(83)	Charlie Hanford	300.00
(84)	Bob Harmon (both ears show)	90.00
(85)	Bob Harmon (only left ear shows)	450.00
(86)	Topsy Hartsel	90.00
(87)	Arnold J. Hauser	90.00
(88)	Charlie Hemphill	90.00
(89)	C.L. Herzog	90.00
(90a)	R. Hoblitzell (no stats on back)	600.00
(90b)	R. Hoblitzell ("Cin." after 2nd 1908 in stats)	225.00
(90c)	R. Hoblitzel (name incorrect, no "Cin." after 1908 in stats)	90.00
(90d)	R. Hoblitzell (name correct, no "Cin." after 1908 in stats)	225.00
(91)	Danny Hoffman	90.00
(92)	Miller J. Huggins	325.00
(93)	John E. Hummel	90.00
(94)	Fred Jacklitsch	90.00
(95)	Hughie Jennings	600.00
(96)	Walter Johnson	1875.00
(97)	D. Jones	90.00
(98)	Tom Jones	90.00
(99)	Addie Joss	600.00
(100)	Ed Karger	300.00
(101)	Ed Killian	90.00
(102)	Red Kleinow	300.00
(103)	John G. Kling	90.00
(104)	Jack Knight	90.00
(105)	Ed Konetchy	90.00
(106)	Harry Krause	90.00
(107)	Floyd M. Kroh	90.00
(108)	Frank LaPorte	90.00
(109)	Frank Lang (Lange)	90.00
(110a)	A. Latham (A. Latham on back)	90.00
(110b)	A. Latham (W.A. Latham on back)	90.00
(111)	Thomas W. Leach	90.00
(112)	Watty Lee	300.00
(113)	Sam Leever	90.00
(114a)	A. Leifield (initial "A." on front)	90.00
(114b)	A.P. Leifield (initials "A.P." on front)	90.00
(115)	Edgar Lennox	90.00
(116)	Paddy Livingston	90.00
(117)	John B. Lobert	90.00
(118)	Bris Lord (Athletics)	90.00
(119)	Harry Lord (White Sox)	90.00
(120)	Jno. C. Lush	90.00
(121)	Nick Maddox	90.00
(122)	Sherwood R. Magee	90.00
(123)	R.W. Marquard	400.00
(124)	C. Mathewson	1200.00
(125)	A.A. Mattern	90.00
(126)	Sport McAllister	300.00
(127)	George McBride	90.00
(128)	Amby McConnell	90.00
(129)	P.M. McElveen	90.00
(130)	J.J. McGraw	600.00
(131)	Harry McIntyre (Cubs)	90.00
(132)	Matty McIntyre (White Sox)	90.00
(133)	M.A. McLean (initials actually J.B.)	90.00
(134)	Fred Merkle	95.00
(135)	George Merritt	300.00
(136)	J.T. Meyers	90.00
(137)	Clyde Milan	90.00
(138)	J.D. Miller	90.00
(139)	M.F. Mitchell	90.00
(140a)	P.J. Moran (stray line of type below stats)	90.00
(140b)	P.J. Moran (no stray line)	90.00
(141)	George Moriarty	90.00
(142)	George Mullin	90.00
(143)	Danny Murphy	90.00
(144)	Jack Murray	90.00
(145)	John Nee	300.00
(146)	Thomas J. Needham	90.00
(147)	Rebel Oakes	90.00
(148)	Rube Oldring	90.00
(149)	Charley O'Leary	90.00
(150)	Fred Olmstead	90.00
(151)	Orval Overall	90.00
(152)	Freddy Parent	90.00
(153)	George Paskert	90.00
(154)	Billy Payne	90.00
(155)	Barney Pelty	90.00
(156)	John Pfeister	90.00
(157)	Jimmy Phelan	300.00
(158)	E.J. Phelps	90.00
(159)	C. Phillippe	90.00
(160)	Jack Quinn	90.00
(161)	A.L. Raymond	400.00
(162)	E.M. Reulbach	90.00
(163)	Lewis Richie	90.00
(164)	John A. Rowan	300.00
(165)	George N. Rucker	90.00
(166)	W.D. Scanlan	300.00
(167)	Germany Schaefer	90.00
(168)	George Schlei	90.00
(169)	Boss Schmidt	90.00
(170)	F.M. Schulte	90.00
(171)	Jim Scott	90.00
(172)	B.H. Sharpe	90.00
(173)	David Shean (Rustlers)	90.00
(174)	David Shean (Cubs)	450.00
(175)	Jas. T. Sheckard	90.00
(176)	Hack Simmons	90.00
(177)	Tony Smith	90.00
(178)	Fred C. Snodgrass	90.00
(179)	Tris Speaker	550.00
(180)	Jake Stahl	90.00

(181) Oscar Stanage 90.00
(182) Harry Steinfeldt 95.00
(183) George Stone 90.00
(184) George Stovall 90.00
(185) Gabby Street 90.00
(186) George F. Suggs 450.00
(187) Ed Summers 90.00
(188) Jeff Sweeney 300.00
(189) Lee Tannehill 90.00
(190) Ira Thomas 90.00
(191) Joe Tinker 650.00
(192) John Titus 90.00
(193) Terry Turner 450.00
(194) James Vaughn 90.00
(195) Heinie Wagner 300.00
(196) Bobby Wallace (with cap) 300.00
(197a) Bobby Wallace (no cap, one line of 1910 stats) 600.00
(197b) Bobby Wallace (no cap, two lines of 1910 stats) 450.00
(198) Ed Walsh 475.00
(199) Z.D. Wheat 450.00
(200) Doc White (White Sox) 90.00
(201) Kirb. White (Pirates) 300.00
(202) Irvin K. Wilhelm 450.00
(203) Ed Willett 90.00
(204) J. Owen Wilson 90.00
(205) George R. Wiltse (both ears show) 90.00
(206) George R. Wiltse (only right ear shows) 450.00
(207) Harry Wolter 90.00
(208) Cy Young 1200.00

1909 - 11 T206

White Border

The nearly 525 cards which make up the T206 set are the most popular of the early tobacco card issues. Players are depicted in a color lithograph against a variety of colorful backgrounds, surrounded by a white border. The player names on the 1-1/2" by 2-5/8" cards appear at the bottom with the city and league, when a city had more than one team. Backs contain an ad for one of 16 brands of cigarettes. There are 389 major leaguer cards and 134 minor leaguer cards in the set, but with front/back varieties the number of potentially different cards runs into the thousands. The set features many expensive cards including a number of pose and/or team variations, along with the very scarce Eddie Plank card and the "King of Baseball Cards," the T206 Honus Wagner, the most avidly sought of all baseball cards. The complete set price does not include the Ty Cobb card with Ty Cobb brand back, Doyle (N.Y. Nat'l.), Magie, Plank and Wagner cards.

MAGIE, PHILA. NAT'L

Mr. Mint Says - The king and the most famous of tobacco sets because of the Wagner card. I like to refer to it as the Sistine Chapel, or Mona Lisa, of baseball cards. When collectors gaze at the hobby's rarest card, a smile comes to their face. A monumental task to complete because of its size, but I believe there would be a couple of guys in line at $100,000 for really good one.

In addition to the Wagner rarity, there are several other cards in the set that elude even the most advanced collector's holdings. A real sharp Magee error would easily bring $30,000, maybe more, and a great Plank would fetch maybe $35,000. Other real toughies in the set include Demmitt, Doyle and O'Hara. There are buyers of the Wagner, Magee and Plank at high levels, but I don't think that there are still buyers of the Cobb at high levels anymore.

In the Baltimore find, I had nearly 800 near-mint to mint or better T-206s, and there was also the famous Southern find.

		MT
Complete Set:		
Common Player:		75.00
Common Minor Leaguer:		80.00
Common Southern Leaguer:		175.00
(1)	Ed Abbaticchio (blue sleeves)	115.00
(2)	Ed Abbaticchio (brown sleeves)	75.00
(3)	Fred Abbott	80.00
(4)	Bill Abstein	75.00
(5)	Doc Adkins	80.00
(6)	Whitey Alperman	95.00
(7)	Red Ames (hands at chest)	95.00
(8)	Red Ames (hands above head)	95.00
(9)	Red Ames (portrait)	75.00
(10)	John Anderson	80.00
(11)	Frank Arellanes	75.00
(12)	Herman Armbruster	80.00
(13)	Harry Arndt	80.00
(14)	Jake Atz	75.00
(15)	Home Run Baker	500.00
(16)	Neal Ball (New York)	95.00
(17)	Neal Ball (Cleveland)	75.00
(18)	Jap Barbeau	95.00
(19)	Cy Barger	80.00
(20)	Jack Barry (Philadelphia)	75.00
(21)	Shad Barry (Milwaukee)	80.00
(22)	Jack Bastian	175.00
(23)	Emil Batch	80.00
(24)	Johnny Bates	95.00
(25)	Harry Bay	225.00
(26)	Ginger Beaumont	95.00
(27)	Fred Beck	75.00
(28)	Beals Becker	75.00
(29)	Jake Beckley	250.00
(30)	George Bell (hands above head)	95.00
(31)	George Bell (pitching follow thru)	75.00
(32)	Chief Bender (pitching, no trees in background)	300.00
(33)	Chief Bender (pitching, trees in background)	300.00
(34)	Chief Bender (portrait)	375.00
(35)	Bill Bergen (batting)	95.00
(36)	Bill Bergen (catching)	80.00
(37)	Heinie Berger	75.00
(38)	Bill Bernhard	175.00
(39)	Bob Bescher (hands in air)	75.00
(40)	Bob Bescher (portrait)	75.00
(41)	Joe Birmingham	100.00
(42)	Lena Blackburne	80.00
(43)	Jack Bliss	75.00
(44)	Frank Bowerman	95.00

(45)	Bill Bradley (portrait)	95.00
(46)	Bill Bradley (with bat)	75.00
(47)	Dave Brain	80.00
(48)	Kitty Bransfield	95.00
(49)	Roy Brashear	80.00
(50)	Ted Breitenstein	175.00
(51)	Roger Bresnahan (portrait)	400.00
(52)	Roger Bresnahan (with bat)	300.00
(53)	Al Bridwell (portrait, no cap)	75.00
(54)	Al Bridwell (portrait, with cap)	95.00
(55a)	George Brown (Browne) (Chicago)	95.00
(55b)	George Brown (Browne) (Washington)	750.00
(56)	Mordecai Brown (Chicago on shirt)	300.00
(57)	Mordecai Brown (Cubs on shirt)	400.00
(58)	Mordecai Brown (portrait)	350.00
(59)	Al Burch (batting)	200.00
(60)	Al Burch (fielding)	75.00
(61)	Fred Burchell	80.00
(62)	Jimmy Burke	80.00
(63)	Bill Burns	75.00
(64)	Donie Bush	75.00
(65)	John Butler	80.00
(66)	Bobby Byrne	75.00
(67)	Howie Camnitz (arm at side)	75.00
(68)	Howie Camnitz (arms folded)	95.00
(69)	Howie Camnitz (hands above head)	75.00
(70)	Billy Campbell	75.00
(71)	Scoops Carey	130.00
(72)	Charley Carr	80.00
(73)	Bill Carrigan	75.00
(74)	Doc Casey	80.00
(75)	Peter Cassidy	80.00
(76)	Frank Chance (batting)	300.00
(77)	Frank Chance (portrait, red background)	400.00
(78)	Frank Chance (portrait, yellow background)	350.00
(79)	Bill Chappelle	80.00
(80)	Chappie Charles	75.00
(81)	Hal Chase (holding trophy)	200.00
(82)	Hal Chase (portrait, blue background)	190.00
(83)	Hal Chase (portrait, pink background)	275.00
(84)	Hal Chase (throwing, dark cap)	175.00
(85)	Hal Chase (throwing, white cap)	400.00
(86)	Jack Chesbro	450.00
(87)	Ed Cicotte	150.00
(88)	Bill Clancy (Clancey)	80.00
(89)	Josh Clark (Clarke) (Columbus)	80.00
(90)	Fred Clarke (Pittsburgh, holding bat)	300.00
(91)	Fred Clarke (Pittsburgh, portrait)	350.00
(92)	Nig Clarke (Cleveland)	95.00
(93)	Bill Clymer	80.00
(94)	Ty Cobb (portrait, green background)	3000.00
(95a)	Ty Cobb (portrait, red background)	2500.00
(95b)	Ty Cobb (portrait, red background, Ty Cobb brand back)	2500.00
(96)	Ty Cobb (bat off shoulder)	2500.00
(97)	Ty Cobb (bat on shoulder)	2500.00
(98)	Cad Coles	175.00
(99)	Eddie Collins (Philadelphia)	375.00
(100)	Jimmy Collins (Minneapolis)	275.00
(101)	Bunk Congalton	80.00
(102)	Wid Conroy (fielding)	95.00
(103)	Wid Conroy (with bat)	75.00
(104)	Harry Covaleski (Coveleski)	90.00
(105)	Doc Crandall (portrait, no cap)	90.00
(106)	Doc Crandall (portrait, with cap)	75.00
(107)	Bill Cranston	190.00
(108)	Gavvy Cravath	125.00
(109)	Sam Crawford (throwing)	375.00
(110)	Sam Crawford (with bat)	350.00
(111)	Birdie Cree	75.00
(112)	Lou Criger	95.00
(113)	Dode Criss	95.00
(114)	Monte Cross	80.00
(115a)	Bill Dahlen (Boston)	100.00
(115b)	Bill Dahlen (Brooklyn)	425.00
(116)	Paul Davidson	80.00

(117)	George Davis (Chicago)	95.00
(118)	Harry Davis (Philadelphia, Davis on front)	75.00
(119)	Harry Davis (Philadelphia, H. Davis on front)	95.00
(120)	Frank Delehanty (Delahanty) (Louisville)	80.00
(121)	Jim Delehanty (Delahanty) (Washington)	95.00
(122a)	Ray Demmitt (New York)	75.00
(122b)	Ray Demmitt (St. Louis)	7500.00
(123)	Rube Dessau	80.00
(124)	Art Devlin	95.00
(125)	Josh Devore	75.00
(126)	Bill Dineen (Dinneen)	75.00
(127)	Mike Donlin (fielding)	250.00
(128)	Mike Donlin (seated)	95.00
(129)	Mike Donlin (with bat)	75.00
(130)	Jiggs Donohue (Donahue)	95.00
(131)	Wild Bill Donovan (portrait)	95.00
(132)	Wild Bill Donovan (throwing)	75.00
(133)	Red Dooin	95.00
(134)	Mickey Doolan (batting)	75.00
(135)	Mickey Doolan (fielding)	75.00
(136)	Mickey Doolin (Doolan)	95.00
(137)	Gus Dorner	80.00
(138)	Patsy Dougherty (arm in air)	75.00
(139)	Patsy Dougherty (portrait)	95.00
(140)	Tom Downey (batting)	75.00
(141)	Tom Downey (fielding)	75.00
(142)	Jerry Downs	80.00
(143a)	Joe Doyle (N.Y. Natl., hands above head)	30000.00
(143b)	Joe Doyle (N.Y., hands above head)	75.00
(144)	Larry Doyle (N.Y. Nat'l., portrait)	95.00
(145)	Larry Doyle (N.Y. Nat'l., throwing)	125.00
(146)	Larry Doyle (N.Y. Nat'l., with bat)	95.00
(147)	Jean Dubuc	75.00
(148)	Hugh Duffy	300.00
(149)	Jack Dunn (Baltimore)	80.00
(150)	Joe Dunn (Brooklyn)	75.00
(151)	Bull Durham	100.00
(152)	Jimmy Dygert	75.00
(153)	Ted Easterly	75.00
(154)	Dick Egan	75.00
(155a)	Kid Elberfeld (New York)	95.00
(155b)	Kid Elberfeld (Washington, portrait)	1875.00
(156)	Kid Elberfeld (Washington, fielding)	75.00
(157)	Roy Ellam	175.00
(158)	Clyde Engle	75.00
(159)	Steve Evans	75.00
(160)	Johnny Evers (portrait)	475.00
(161)	Johnny Evers (with bat, Chicago on shirt)	300.00
(162)	Johnny Evers (with bat, Cubs on shirt)	375.00
(163)	Bob Ewing	95.00
(164)	Cecil Ferguson	75.00
(165)	Hobe Ferris	95.00
(166)	Lou Fiene (portrait)	75.00
(167)	Lou Fiene (throwing)	75.00
(168)	Steamer Flanagan	80.00
(169)	Art Fletcher	75.00
(170)	Elmer Flick	325.00
(171)	Russ Ford	75.00
(172)	Ed Foster	175.00
(173)	Jerry Freeman	80.00
(174)	John Frill	75.00
(175)	Charlie Fritz	175.00
(176)	Art Fromme	75.00
(177)	Chick Gandil	95.00
(178)	Bob Ganley	95.00
(179)	John Ganzel	80.00
(180)	Harry Gasper	75.00
(181)	Rube Geyer	75.00
(182)	George Gibson	95.00
(183)	Billy Gilbert	95.00
(184)	Wilbur Goode (Good)	95.00
(185)	Bill Graham (St. Louis)	75.00
(186)	Peaches Graham (Boston)	75.00
(187)	Dolly Gray	75.00
(188)	Ed Greminger	175.00

(189)	Clark Griffith (batting)	325.00	(263)	Nap Lajoie (throwing)	525.00
(190)	Clark Griffith (portrait)	350.00	(264)	Nap Lajoie (with bat)	525.00
(191)	Moose Grimshaw	80.00	(265)	Joe Lake (New York)	95.00
(192)	Bob Groom	75.00	(266)	Joe Lake (St. Louis, ball in hand)	75.00
(193)	Tom Guiheen	200.00	(267)	Joe Lake (St. Louis, no ball in hand)	75.00
(194)	Ed Hahn	95.00	(268)	Frank LaPorte	75.00
(195)	Bob Hall	80.00	(269)	Arlie Latham	75.00
(196)	Bill Hallman	80.00	(270)	Bill Lattimore	80.00
(197)	Jack Hannifan (Hannifin)	80.00	(271)	Jimmy Lavender	80.00
(198)	Bill Hart (Little Rock)	225.00	(272)	Tommy Leach (bending over)	75.00
(199)	Jimmy Hart (Montgomery)	190.00	(273)	Tommy Leach (portrait)	95.00
(200)	Topsy Hartsel	75.00	(274)	Lefty Leifield (batting)	75.00
(201)	Jack Hayden	80.00	(275)	Lefty Leifield (pitching)	95.00
(202)	J. Ross Helm	175.00	(276)	Ed Lennox	75.00
(203)	Charlie Hemphill	95.00	(277)	Harry Lentz (Sentz)	175.00
(204)	Buck Herzog (Boston)	75.00	(278)	Glenn Liebhardt	95.00
(205)	Buck Herzog (New York)	95.00	(279)	Vive Lindaman	95.00
(206)	Gordon Hickman	175.00	(280)	Perry Lipe	175.00
(207)	Bill Hinchman (Cleveland)	95.00	(281)	Paddy Livingstone (Livingston)	75.00
(208)	Harry Hinchman (Toledo)	80.00	(282)	Hans Lobert	95.00
(209)	Dick Hoblitzell	75.00	(283)	Harry Lord	75.00
(210)	Danny Hoffman (St. Louis)	75.00	(284)	Harry Lumley	95.00
(211)	Izzy Hoffman (Providence)	80.00	(285a)	Carl Lundgren (Chicago)	550.00
(212)	Solly Hofman	75.00	(285b)	Carl Lundgren (Kansas City)	80.00
(213)	Bock Hooker	175.00	(286)	Nick Maddox	75.00
(214)	Del Howard (Chicago)	75.00	(287a)	Sherry Magie (Magee)	30000.00
(215)	Ernie Howard (Savannah)	175.00	(287b)	Sherry Magee (portrait)	125.00
(216)	Harry Howell (hand at waist)	75.00	(288)	Sherry Magee (with bat)	95.00
(217)	Harry Howell (portrait)	75.00	(289)	Bill Malarkey	80.00
(218)	Miller Huggins (hands at mouth)	300.00	(290)	Billy Maloney	80.00
(219)	Miller Huggins (portrait)	325.00	(291)	George Manion	175.00
(220)	Rudy Hulswitt	75.00	(292)	Rube Manning (batting)	95.00
(221)	John Hummel	75.00	(293)	Rube Manning (pitching)	75.00
(222)	George Hunter	75.00	(294)	Rube Marquard (hands at thighs)	375.00
(223)	Frank Isbell	100.00	(295)	Rube Marquard (pitching follow thru)	350.00
(224)	Fred Jacklitsch	100.00	(296)	Rube Marquard (portrait)	360.00
(225)	Jimmy Jackson	80.00	(297)	Doc Marshall	75.00
(226)	Hughie Jennings (one hand showing)	300.00	(298)	Christy Mathewson (dark cap)	600.00
(227)	Hughie Jennings (both hands showing)	300.00	(299)	Christy Mathewson (portrait)	1000.00
(228)	Hughie Jennings (portrait)	325.00	(300)	Christy Mathewson (white cap)	900.00
(229)	Walter Johnson (hands at chest)	950.00	(301)	Al Mattern	75.00
(230)	Walter Johnson (portrait)	1000.00	(302)	John McAleese	75.00
(231)	Fielder Jones (Chicago, hands at hips)	95.00	(303)	George McBride	75.00
(232)	Fielder Jones (Chicago, portrait)	95.00	(304)	Pat McCauley	175.00
(233)	Davy Jones (Detroit)	75.00	(305)	Moose McCormick	75.00
(234)	Tom Jones (St. Louis)	95.00	(306)	Pryor McElveen	75.00
(235)	Dutch Jordan (Atlanta)	175.00	(307)	Dan McGann	80.00
(236)	Tim Jordan (Brooklyn, batting)	75.00	(308)	Jim McGinley	80.00
(237)	Tim Jordan (Brooklyn, portrait)	95.00	(309)	Iron Man McGinnity	250.00
(238)	Addie Joss (hands at chest)	350.00	(310)	Stoney McGlynn	80.00
(239)	Addie Joss (portrait)	425.00	(311)	John McGraw (finger in air)	360.00
(240)	Ed Karger	95.00	(312)	John McGraw (glove at hip)	360.00
(241)	Willie Keeler (portrait)	550.00	(313)	John McGraw (portrait, no cap)	450.00
(242)	Willie Keeler (with bat)	525.00	(314)	John McGraw (portrait, with cap)	300.00
(243)	Joe Kelley	225.00	(315)	Harry McIntyre (Brooklyn)	95.00
(244)	J.F. Kiernan	175.00	(316)	Harry McIntyre (Brooklyn & Chicago)	75.00
(245)	Ed Killian (hands at chest)	75.00	(317)	Matty McIntyre (Detroit)	75.00
(246)	Ed Killian (portrait)	95.00	(318)	Larry McLean	75.00
(247)	Frank King	175.00	(319)	George McQuillan (ball in hand)	95.00
(248)	Rube Kisinger (Kissinger)	80.00	(320)	George McQuillan (with bat)	75.00
(249a)	Red Kleinow (Boston)	1500.00	(321)	Fred Merkle (portrait)	125.00
(249b)	Red Kleinow (New York, catching)	75.00	(322)	Fred Merkle (throwing)	95.00
(250)	Red Kleinow (New York, with bat)	95.00	(323)	George Merritt	80.00
(251)	Johnny Kling	95.00	(324)	Chief Meyers	75.00
(252)	Otto Knabe	75.00	(325)	Clyde Milan	75.00
(253)	Jack Knight (portrait)	75.00	(326)	Dots Miller (Pittsburgh)	75.00
(254)	Jack Knight (with bat)	75.00	(327)	Molly Miller (Dallas)	175.00
(255)	Ed Konetchy (glove above head)	95.00	(328)	Bill Milligan	80.00
(256)	Ed Konetchy (glove near ground)	75.00	(329)	Fred Mitchell (Toronto)	80.00
(257)	Harry Krause (pitching)	75.00	(330)	Mike Mitchell (Cincinnati)	75.00
(258)	Harry Krause (portrait)	75.00	(331)	Dan Moeller	80.00
(259)	Rube Kroh	75.00	(332)	Carlton Molesworth	175.00
(260)	Otto Kruger (Krueger)	80.00	(333)	Herbie Moran (Providence)	80.00
(261)	James Lafitte	175.00	(334)	Pat Moran (Chicago)	75.00
(262)	Nap Lajoie (portrait)	950.00	(335)	George Moriarty	75.00

(336)	Mike Mowrey	75.00
(337)	Dom Mullaney	175.00
(338)	George Mullen (Mullin)	75.00
(339)	George Mullin (throwing)	95.00
(340)	George Mullin (with bat)	75.00
(341)	Danny Murphy (batting)	75.00
(342)	Danny Murphy (throwing)	95.00
(343)	Red Murray (batting)	75.00
(344)	Red Murray (portrait)	75.00
(345)	Chief Myers (Meyers) (batting)	75.00
(346)	Chief Myers (Meyers) (fielding)	75.00
(347)	Billy Nattress	80.00
(348)	Tom Needham	75.00
(349)	Simon Nicholls (hands on knees)	95.00
(350)	Simon Nichols (Nicholls) (batting)	75.00
(351)	Harry Niles	95.00
(352)	Rebel Oakes	75.00
(353)	Frank Oberlin	80.00
(354)	Peter O'Brien	80.00
(355a)	Bill O'Hara (New York)	75.00
(355b)	Bill O'Hara (St. Louis)	7500.00
(356)	Rube Oldring (batting)	75.00
(357)	Rube Oldring (fielding)	95.00
(358)	Charley O'Leary (hands on knees)	75.00
(359)	Charley O'Leary (portrait)	95.00
(360)	William J. O'Neil	80.00
(361)	Al Orth	175.00
(362)	William Otey	175.00
(363)	Orval Overall (hand face level)	75.00
(364)	Orval Overall (hands waist level)	75.00
(365)	Orval Overall (portrait)	95.00
(366)	Frank Owen	95.00
(367)	George Paige	175.00
(368)	Fred Parent	95.00
(369)	Dode Paskert	75.00
(370)	Jim Pastorius	95.00
(371)	Harry Pattee	400.00
(372)	Billy Payne	75.00
(373)	Barney Pelty (horizontal photo)	250.00
(374)	Barney Pelty (vertical photo)	75.00
(375)	Hub Perdue	175.00
(376)	George Perring	75.00
(377)	Arch Persons	175.00
(378)	Francis (Big Jeff) Pfeffer	75.00
(379)	Jake Pfeister (Pfiester) (seated)	75.00
(380)	Jake Pfeister (Pfiester) (throwing)	75.00
(381)	Jimmy Phelan	80.00
(382)	Eddie Phelps	75.00
(383)	Deacon Phillippe	75.00
(384)	Ollie Pickering	80.00
(385)	Eddie Plank	35000.00
(386)	Phil Poland	80.00
(387)	Jack Powell	95.00
(388)	Mike Powers	260.00
(389)	Billy Purtell	75.00
(390)	Ambrose Puttman (Puttmann)	80.00
(391)	Lee Quillen (Quillin)	80.00
(392)	Jack Quinn	75.00
(393)	Newt Randall	80.00
(394)	Bugs Raymond	75.00
(395)	Ed Reagan	175.00
(396)	Ed Reulbach (glove showing)	200.00
(397)	Ed Reulbach (no glove showing)	75.00
(398)	Dutch Revelle	175.00
(399)	Bob Rhoades (Rhoads) (hands at chest)	75.00
(400)	Bob Rhoades (Rhoads) (right arm extended)	75.00
(401)	Charlie Rhodes	75.00
(402)	Claude Ritchey	95.00
(403)	Lou Ritter	80.00
(404)	Ike Rockenfeld	175.00
(405)	Claude Rossman	75.00
(406)	Nap Rucker (portrait)	95.00
(407)	Nap Rucker (throwing)	75.00
(408)	Dick Rudolph	80.00
(409)	Ray Ryan	175.00

(410)	Germany Schaefer (Detroit)	95.00
(411)	Germany Schaefer (Washington)	75.00
(412)	George Schirm	80.00
(413)	Larry Schlafly	80.00
(414)	Admiral Schlei (batting)	75.00
(415)	Admiral Schlei (catching)	95.00
(416)	Admiral Schlei (portrait)	75.00
(417)	Boss Schmidt (portrait)	75.00
(418)	Boss Schmidt (throwing)	95.00
(419)	Ossee Schreck (Schreckengost)	80.00
(420)	Wildfire Schulte (front view)	95.00
(421)	Wildfire Schulte (back view)	75.00
(422)	Jim Scott	75.00
(423)	Charles Seitz	175.00
(424)	Cy Seymour (batting)	95.00
(425)	Cy Seymour (portrait)	75.00
(426)	Cy Seymour (throwing)	75.00
(427)	Spike Shannon	80.00
(428)	Bud Sharpe	80.00
(429)	Shag Shaughnessy	175.00
(430)	Al Shaw (St. Louis)	95.00
(431)	Hunky Shaw (Providence)	80.00
(432)	Jimmy Sheckard (glove showing)	75.00
(433)	Jimmy Sheckard (no glove showing)	95.00
(434)	Bill Shipke	95.00
(435)	Jimmy Slagle	80.00
(436)	Carlos Smith (Shreveport)	175.00
(437)	Frank Smith (Chicago, F. Smith on front)	185.00
(438a)	Frank Smith (Chicago, white cap)	75.00
(438b)	Frank Smith (Chicago & Boston)	950.00
(439)	"Happy" Smith (Brooklyn)	75.00
(440)	Heinie Smith (Buffalo)	80.00
(441)	Sid Smith (Atlanta)	175.00
(442)	Fred Snodgrass (batting)	95.00
(443)	Fred Snodgrass (catching)	95.00
(444)	Bob Spade	75.00
(445)	Tris Speaker	950.00
(446)	Tubby Spencer	95.00
(447)	Jake Stahl (glove shows)	75.00
(448)	Jake Stahl (no glove shows)	95.00
(449)	Oscar Stanage	75.00
(450)	Dolly Stark	175.00
(451)	Charlie Starr	75.00
(452)	Harry Steinfeldt (portrait)	125.00
(453)	Harry Steinfeldt (with bat)	95.00
(454)	Jim Stephens	75.00
(455)	George Stone	95.00
(456)	George Stovall (batting)	75.00
(457)	George Stovall (portrait)	95.00
(458)	Sam Strang	80.00
(459)	Gabby Street (catching)	75.00
(460)	Gabby Street (portrait)	75.00
(461)	Billy Sullivan	95.00
(462)	Ed Summers	75.00
(463)	Bill Sweeney (Boston)	75.00
(464)	Jeff Sweeney (New York)	75.00
(465)	Jesse Tannehill (Washington)	75.00
(466)	Lee Tannehill (Chicago, L. Tannehill on front)	95.00
(467)	Lee Tannehill (Chicago, Tannehill on front)	75.00
(468)	Dummy Taylor	80.00
(469)	Fred Tenney	95.00
(470)	Tony Thebo	175.00
(471)	Jake Thielman	80.00
(472)	Ira Thomas	75.00
(473)	Woodie Thornton	175.00
(474)	Joe Tinker (bat off shoulder)	350.00
(475)	Joe Tinker (bat on shoulder)	350.00
(476)	Joe Tinker (hands on knees)	375.00
(477)	Joe Tinker (portrait)	400.00
(478)	John Titus	75.00
(479)	Terry Turner	95.00
(480)	Bob Unglaub	75.00
(481)	Juan Violat (Viola)	175.00
(482)	Rube Waddell (portrait)	375.00
(483)	Rube Waddell (throwing)	375.00

(484) Heinie Wagner (bat on left shoulder)	95.00
(485) Heinie Wagner (bat on right shoulder)	75.00
(486) Honus Wagner	
(487) Bobby Wallace	300.00
(488) Ed Walsh	400.00
(489) Jack Warhop	75.00
(490) Jake Weimer	95.00
(491) James Westlake	175.00
(492) Zack Wheat	400.00
(493) Doc White (Chicago, pitching)	75.00
(494) Doc White (Chicago, portrait)	95.00
(495) Foley White (Houston)	175.00
(496) Jack White (Buffalo)	80.00
(497) Kaiser Wilhelm (hands at chest)	95.00
(498) Kaiser Wilhelm (with bat)	750.00
(499) Ed Willett	750.00
(500) Ed Willetts (Willett)	750.00
(501) Jimmy Williams	95.00
(502) Vic Willis (Pittsburgh)	75.00
(503) Vic Willis (St. Louis, throwing)	75.00
(504) Vic Willis (St. Louis, with bat)	75.00
(505) Owen Wilson	75.00
(506) Hooks Wiltse (pitching)	80.00
(507) Hooks Wiltse (portrait, no cap)	95.00
(508) Hooks Wiltse (portrait, with cap)	75.00
(509) Lucky Wright	80.00
(510) Cy Young (Cleveland, glove shows)	550.00
(511) Cy Young (Cleveland, bare hand shows)	550.00
(512) Cy Young (Cleveland, portrait)	1100.00
(513) Irv Young (Minneapolis)	80.00
(514) Heinie Zimmerman	75.00

PLANK, PHILA. AMER.

1933 Tattoo Orbit

Found in 1¢ packages of Tattoo gum, these 2" by 2-1/4" cards were produced by the Orbit Gum Company of Chicago, Illinois. The fronts feature a photograph which is tinted to give skin some color. Stylized baseball park backgrounds are separated from the photograph by a black line. The rest of the background is printed in vivid red, yellow and green. Card backs have the player's name, team, position, birth date, height and weight. The 60-card set is not common, but their interesting format does not seem to have struck a responsive chord in today's collectors. Cards of Bump Hadley and George Blaeholder are the most elusive, followed by those of Ivy Andrews and Rogers Hornsby.

ROGERS HORNSBY

Mr. Mint Says - It's printed on a very thin card stock with that light yellow background, which doesn't hold up very well. Very hard to find in true mint condition because of the lily white borders, and really is a tough set to find in any condition, much less in mint. A lot of advanced collectors that I know have been looking for these cards for years.

		MT
Complete Set (60):		5200.
Common Player:		50.00

(1)	Dale Alexander	150.00
(2)	Ivy Paul Andrews	350.00
(3)	Earl Averill	125.00
(4)	Richard Bartell	50.00
(5)	Walter Berger	50.00
(6)	George F. Blaeholder	175.00
(7)	Irving J. Burns	50.00
(8)	Guy T. Bush	50.00
(9)	Bruce D. Campbell	50.00
(10)	William Cissell	50.00
(11)	Lefty Clark	50.00
(12)	Mickey Cochrane	100.00
(13)	Phil Collins	50.00
(14)	Hazen Kiki Cuyler	100.00
(15)	Dizzy Dean	250.00
(16)	Jimmy Dykes	50.00
(17)	George L. Earnshaw	50.00
(18)	Woody English	50.00
(19)	Lewis A. Fonseca	50.00
(20)	Jimmy Foxx	250.00
(21)	Burleigh A. Grimes	85.00
(22)	Charles John Grimm	50.00
(23)	Robert M. Grove	100.00
(24)	Frank Grube	50.00
(25)	George W. Haas	50.00
(26)	Irving D. Hadley	175.00
(27)	Chick Hafey	85.00
(28)	Jesse Joseph Haines	85.00
(29)	William Hallahan	50.00
(30)	Melvin Harder	50.00
(31)	Gabby Hartnett	100.00
(32)	Babe Herman	50.00
(33)	William Herman	85.00
(34)	Rogers Hornsby	300.00
(35)	Roy C. Johnson	50.00
(36)	J. Smead Jolley	50.00
(37)	William Jurges	50.00
(38)	William Kamm	50.00
(39)	Mark A. Koenig	50.00
(40)	James J. Levey	50.00
(41)	Ernie Lombardi	85.00
(42)	Red Lucas	50.00
(43)	Ted Lyons	85.00
(44)	Connie Mack	175.00
(45)	Pat Malone	50.00
(46)	Pepper Martin	50.00
(47)	Marty McManus	50.00
(48)	Frank J. O'Doul	50.00
(49)	Richard Porter	50.00
(50)	Carl N. Reynolds	50.00
(51)	Charles Henry Root	50.00
(52)	Robert Seeds	50.00
(53)	Al H. Simmons	90.00
(54)	Jackson Riggs Stepheson	50.00
(55)	Bud Tinning	50.00
(56)	Joe Vosmik	50.00
(57)	Rube Walberg	50.00
(58)	Paul Waner	90.00
(59)	Lonnie Warneke	50.00
(60)	Arthur C. Whitney	50.00

1951 Topps

Connie Mack's All-Stars

A set of die-cut, 2-1/16" by 5-1/4" cards, all eleven players are Hall of Famers. The cards feature a black and white photograph of the player printed on a red background with a red, white, blue, yellow and black plaque underneath. Like the "Current All-Stars," with which they were issued, the background could be removed making it possible for the card to stand up. This practice, however, resulted in the card's mutilation and lowers its condition in the eyes of today's collectors. Connie Mack All-Stars are scarce today and, despite being relatively expensive, retain a certain popularity as one of Topps first issues.

Mr. Mint Says - From the collections that I buy, most do not have this set included. Perhaps one of 30 major collections will have it. It is a scarce, regional test issue distributed on the East Coast.

It is tough to get mint without the paper wrinkles, and most the time the wrinkles are on the top of the card and the side where the player's body comes closest to the card background. A lot of oldtime collectors taped the back so that they wouldn't come apart because of the die cut.

The Ruth and Gehrig cards sell well when they are defect-free and in mint condition, and I have sold many sets in the $7,000 to $10,000 range.

Though I have never had a major purchase, I've seen and owned unopened packs with the 1951 Team Cards.

		MT
Complete Set (11):		10750.
Common Player:		450.00
(1)	Grover Cleveland Alexander	650.00
(2)	Mickey Cochrane	500.00
(3)	Eddie Collins	450.00
(4)	Jimmy Collins	450.00
(5)	Lou Gehrig	2500.00
(6)	Walter Johnson	900.00
(7)	Connie Mack	500.00
(8)	Christy Mathewson	900.00
(9)	Babe Ruth	2750.00
(10)	Tris Speaker	650.00
(11)	Honus Wagner	600.00

1951 Topps Current All-Stars

A set of die-cut, 2-1/16" by 5-1/4" cards, all Connie Mack All-Stars of the same year. The 2-1/16" by 5-1/4" cards have a black and white photograph on a red die cut background. Most of the background could be folded over or removed so that the card would stand up. A plaque at the base carries brief biographical information. The set was to contain 11 cards, but only eight were actually issued in gum packs. Those of Jim Konstanty, Robin Roberts and Eddie Stanky were not released and are very rare. A big problem with the set is that if the card was used as it was intended it was folded and, thus, damaged from a collector's viewpoint. That makes top quality examples of any players difficult to find and quite expensive.

Mr. Mint Says - These are much harder to find than the Connie Mack All-Stars and the Team Cards. It is a much more attractive set to collect because of the scarcity and the modern players, but it is mostly unaffordable to normal collectors.

I have had the Konstanty, Roberts and Stanky cards on two occasions, both around ex-mt, which I sold for $30,000, and another set in poor condition for half that much. I don't know if there are any mint examples of these three cards in existence.

		MT
Complete Set (11):		45000.
Common Player:		500.00
(1)	Yogi Berra	2000.00
(2)	Larry Doby	750.00
(3)	Walt Dropo	750.00
(4)	"Hoot" Evers	500.00
(5)	George Kell	1100.00
(6)	Ralph Kiner	1100.00
(7)	Jim Konstanty	12500.00
(8)	Bob Lemon	1100.00
(9)	Phil Rizzuto	1500.00
(10)	Robin Roberts	12500.00
(11)	Ed Stanky	12500.00

1951 Topps Teams

An innovative issue for 1951, the Topps team cards were a nine-card set, 5-1/4" by 2-1/16", which carried a black and white picture of a major league team surrounded by a yellow border on the front. The back identifies team members with red printing on white cardboard. There are two versions of each card, with and without the date "1950" in the banner that carries the team name. Undated versions are valued slightly higher than the cards with dates. Strangely only nine teams were issued. Scarcity varies, with the Cardinals and Red Sox being the most difficult to obtain. The complete set price does not include the scarcer variations.

creased because of the size and because they are so long and narrow. The color contrast is terrible and the photos often are blurry.

Still, it's a tough set. I've never purchased a complete set of undated and dated, and have only seen a couple unopened.

There is considerable regional interest in the more popular teams like the Dodgers, Red Sox and Giants, and there was no Yankee card in the set.

Mr. Mint Says - There are 18 cards in the set, with dated and undated versions. The dated cards are much easier to find than the undated. The cards were issued one to a pack with the Connie Mack Current All-Stars. Most of the time the cards are found

		MT
Complete Set (Dated):		2900
Common Card:		225.00
(1a)	Boston Red Sox (1950)	350.00
(1b)	Boston Red Sox (undated)	450.00
(2a)	Brooklyn Dodgers (1950)	450.00
(2b)	Brooklyn Dodgers (undated)	475.00
(3a)	Chicago White Sox (1950)	225.00
(3b)	Chicago White Sox (undated)	300.00
(4a)	Cincinnati Reds (1950)	225.00
(4b)	Cincinnati Reds (undated)	300.00
(5a)	New York Giants (1950)	350.00
(5b)	New York Giants (undated)	450.00
(6a)	Philadelphia Athletics (1950)	225.00
(6b)	Philadelphia Athletics (undated)	300.00
(7a)	Philadelphia Phillies (1950)	225.00
(7b)	Philadelphia Phillies (undated)	300.00
(8a)	St. Louis Cardinals (1950)	225.00
(8b)	St. Louis Cardinals (undated)	300.00
(9a)	Washington Senators (1950)	225.00
(9b)	Washington Senators (undated)	300.00

1951 Topps Red Backs

Like the Blue Backs, the Topps Red Backs which were sold at the same time, came two to a package for 1¢. Their black and white photographs appear on a red, white, blue and yellow background. The back printing is red on white. Their 2" by 2-5/8" size is the same as Blue Backs. Also identical is the set size (52 cards) and the game situations to be found on the fronts of the cards, for use in playing a card game of baseball. Red Backs are more common than the Blue Backs by virtue of a recent discovery of a large hoard of unopened boxes.

Mr. Mint Says - Most of the time when you run across these they are in great shape. The Blue Backs sell for more because they are scarcer, but the Red Backs are more popular because they have great players and stars.

The #1 Berra card is real tough, as are a couple of the variations. Paper wrinkles can be a real problem with this issue, especially with the red on the back. There was a major find (not by me) several years ago involving hundreds of boxes. After that find, Red Back sets were selling for a couple of hundred dollars, but the price has escalated a bit in recent years.

		MT
Complete Set (52):		850.00
Common Player:		12.00
1	Yogi Berra	125.00
2	Sid Gordon	12.00
3	Ferris Fain	12.00
4	Vern Stephens	12.00
5	Phil Rizzuto	50.00
6	Allie Reynolds	20.00
7	Howie Pollet	12.00
8	Early Wynn	30.00
9	Roy Sievers	12.00
10	Mel Parnell	12.00
11	Gene Hermanski	12.00
12	Jim Hegan	12.00
13	Dale Mitchell	12.00
14	Wayne Terwilliger	12.00
15	Ralph Kiner	30.00
16	Preacher Roe	14.00
17	Gus Bell	12.00
18	Gerry Coleman	12.00
19	Dick Kokos	12.00
20	Dom DiMaggio	12.00
21	Larry Jansen	12.00
22	Bob Feller	30.00
23	Ray Boone	12.00
24	Hank Bauer	12.00
25	Cliff Chambers	12.00
26	Luke Easter	12.00
27	Wally Westlake	12.00
28	Elmer Valo	12.00
29	Bob Kennedy	12.00
30	Warren Spahn	35.00
31	Gil Hodges	30.00
32	Henry Thompson	12.00
33	William Werle	12.00
34	Grady Hatton	12.00
35	Al Rosen	12.00
36a	Gus Zernial (Chicago in bio)	35.00
36b	Gus Zernial (Philadelphia in bio)	12.00
37	Wes Westrum	12.00
38	Duke Snider	40.00
39	Ted Kluszewski	14.00
40	Mike Garcia	12.00
41	Whitey Lockman	12.00
42	Ray Scarborough	12.00
43	Maurice McDermott	12.00
44	Sid Hudson	12.00
45	Andy Seminick	12.00
46	Billy Goodman	12.00
47	Tommy Glaviano	12.00
48	Eddie Stanky	12.00
49	Al Zarilla	12.00
50	Monte Irvin	30.00
51	Eddie Robinson	12.00
52a	Tommy Holmes (Boston in bio)	30.00

1951 Topps Blue Backs

Sold two cards in a package with a piece of candy for 1¢, the Topps Blue Backs are considerably scarcer than their Red Back counterparts. The 2" by 2-5/8" cards carry a black and white player photograph on a red, white, yellow and green background along with the player's name and other information including their 1950 record on the front. The back is printed in blue on a white background. The 52-card set has varied baseball situations on them, making the playing of a rather elementary game of baseball possible. Although scarce, Blue Backs were printed on thick cardboard and have survived quite well over the years. There are, however, few stars (Johnny Mize and Enos Slaughter are two) in the set. Despite being a Topps product, Blue Backs do not currently enjoy great popularity.

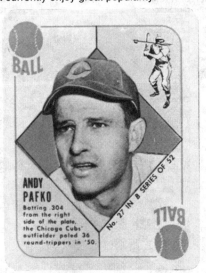

Mr. Mint Says - I think these are three to four times as scarce as the Red Backs. They also came in some instances in pairs, joined at the top the card.

Though there is not much call for it, I always need the #1 Eddie Yost card because most of those that I have seen had rubber band marks. In this series you also have

Schoendienst, Doerr, Mize, Slaughter and Ashburn, much rarer than the Red Backs, but they don't sell as well.

		MT
Complete Set (52):		2200.
Common Player:		50.00
1	Eddie Yost	100.00
2	Henry Majeski	50.00
3	Richie Ashburn	75.00
4	Del Ennis	50.00
5	Johnny Pesky	50.00
6	Red Schoendienst	75.00
7	Gerry Staley	75.00
8	Dick Sisler	75.00
9	Johnny Sain	75.00
10	Joe Page	50.00
11	Johnny Groth	50.00
12	Sam Jethroe	50.00
13	Mickey Vernon	50.00
14	Red Munger	50.00
15	Eddie Joost	50.00
16	Murry Dickson	50.00
17	Roy Smalley	50.00
18	Ned Garver	50.00
19	Phil Masi	50.00
20	Ralph Branca	50.00
21	Billy Johnson	50.00
22	Bob Kuzava	50.00
23	Dizzy Trout	50.00
24	Sherman Lollar	50.00
25	Sam Mele	50.00
26	Chico Carrasquel	50.00
27	Andy Pafko	50.00
28	Harry (The Cat) Brecheen	50.00
29	Granny Hamner	50.00
30	Enos Slaughter	70.00
31	Lou Brissie	50.00
32	Bob Elliott	50.00
33	Don Lenhardt	50.00
34	Earl Torgeson	50.00
35	Tommy Byrne	50.00
36	Cliff Fannin	50.00
37	Bobby Doerr	70.00
38	Irv Noren	50.00
39	Ed Lopat	50.00
40	Vic Wertz	50.00
41	Johnny Schmitz	50.00
42	Bruce Edwards	50.00
43	Willie Jones	50.00
44	Johnny Wyrostek	50.00
45	Bill Pierce	50.00
46	Gerry Priddy	50.00
47	Herman Wehmeier	50.00
48	Billy Cox	50.00
49	Hank Sauer	50.00
50	Johnny Mize	70.00
51	Eddie Waitkus	50.00
52	Sam Chapman	50.00

1952 Topps

At 407 cards, the 1952 Topps set was the largest set of its day, both in number of cards and physical dimensions of the cards. Cards are 2-5/8" by 3-3/4" with a hand-colored black and white photo on front. Major baseball card innovations presented in the set include the first-ever use of color team logos as part of the design, and the inclusion of stats for the previous season and overall career on the backs. A major variety in the set is that first 80 cards can be found with backs printed entirely in black or black and red. Backs entirely in black command a $10-15 premium. Card numbers 311-407 were printed in limited supplies and are extremely rare.

Mr. Mint Says - This is the set that put "Mr. Mint" on the map. Shiny, new Topps baseball cards; the first coated set. They are scarce, expensive but still available, and the hard cardboard held up pretty well.

I am amazed at how tough the high numbers are. My famous find of 1952 Topps cards provided a lot of insight about collation within the set. When you have 5,500 cards that gives you a pretty good indication about splits and distribution patterns. I found it interesting that in the find there were 35 of every mid-number except 271-280 and 301-310, and 17 or 18 of each of those. That seems like solid evidence that the others were doubled printed.

In the high numbers, there were 17 to 18 of every single card except for the three famous cards thought (correctly) to have been double printed; Mantle, Robinson and Thomson. In most collections that I buy, only two out of 10 will have the high numbers series. Most of the time it's 1-310.

In my Seattle find of unopened 1952 Topps we had low numbers, so finding 151-250 in mint condition is pretty difficult. From the packs that I opened in that find, all the Pafko and Loes cards had little pulls in the corner (probably from the gripper on the press).

The cards from my finds are quite distinctive and I still see ads from other dealers mentioning particular cards.

As a final note to collectors, I would suggest that the 1952 Topps set is expensive enough without fiddling with a black back or red back run.

		MT
Complete Set (407):		87000.
Common Player (1-80):		75.00
Common Player (81-250):		35.00
Common Player (251-310):		75.00
Common Player (311-407):		300.00
1	Andy Pafko	5000.00
2	*Pete Runnels*	200.00
3	Hank Thompson	75.00
4	Don Lenhardt	75.00
5	Larry Jansen	75.00
6	Grady Hatton	75.00
7	Wayne Terwilliger	75.00
8	Fred Marsh	75.00
9	Bobby Hogue	75.00
10	Al Rosen	75.00
11	Phil Rizzuto	300.00
12	Monty Basgall	75.00
13	Johnny Wyrostek	75.00
14	Bob Elliott	75.00
15	Johnny Pesky	75.00
16	Gene Hermanski	75.00
17	Jim Hegan	75.00
18	Merrill Combs	75.00
19	Johnny Bucha	75.00
20	*Billy Loes*	400.00
21	Ferris Fain	75.00
22	Dom DiMaggio	150.00
23	Billy Goodman	75.00
24	Luke Easter	75.00
25	Johnny Groth	75.00
26	Monte Irvin	150.00
27	Sam Jethroe	75.00
28	Jerry Priddy	75.00
29	Ted Kluszewski	150.00
30	Mel Parnell	75.00
31	Gus Zernial	75.00
32	Eddie Robinson	75.00
33	Warren Spahn	350.00
34	Elmer Valo	75.00

35	Hank Sauer	75.00	106	Mickey Vernon	35.00
36	Gil Hodges	350.00	107	Connie Ryan	35.00
37	Duke Snider	450.00	108	Jim Konstanty	35.00
38	Wally Westlake	75.00	109	Ted Wilks	35.00
39	"Dizzy" Trout	75.00	110	Dutch Leonard	35.00
40	Irv Noren	75.00	111	Harry Lowrey	35.00
41	Bob Wellman	75.00	112	Henry Majeski	35.00
42	Lou Kretlow	75.00	113	Dick Sisler	35.00
43	Ray Scarborough	75.00	114	Willard Ramsdell	35.00
44	Con Dempsey	75.00	115	George Munger	35.00
45	Eddie Joost	75.00	116	Carl Scheib	35.00
46	Gordon Goldsberry	75.00	117	Sherman Lollar	35.00
47	Willie Jones	75.00	118	Ken Raffensberger	35.00
48a	Joe Page (Johnny Sain back)	550.00	119	Maurice McDermott	35.00
48b	Joe Page (Joe Page back)	125.00	120	Bob Chakales	35.00
49a	Johnny Sain (Joe Page back)	550.00	121	Gus Niarhos	35.00
49b	Johnny Sain (Johnny Sain back)	125.00	122	Jack Jensen	85.00
50	Marv Rickert	75.00	123	Eddie Yost	35.00
51	Jim Russell	75.00	124	Monte Kennedy	35.00
52	Don Mueller	75.00	125	Bill Rigney	35.00
53	Chris Van Cuyk	75.00	126	Fred Hutchinson	35.00
54	Leo Kiely	75.00	127	Paul Minner	35.00
55	Ray Boone	75.00	128	Don Bollweg	35.00
56	Tommy Glaviano	75.00	129	Johnny Mize	100.00
57	Ed Lopat	100.00	130	Sheldon Jones	35.00
58	Bob Mahoney	75.00	131	Morrie Martin	35.00
59	Robin Roberts	200.00	132	Clyde Kluttz	35.00
60	Sid Hudson	75.00	133	Al Widmar	35.00
61	"Tookie" Gilbert	75.00	134	Joe Tipton	35.00
62	Chuck Stobbs	75.00	135	Dixie Howell	35.00
63	Howie Pollet	75.00	136	Johnny Schmitz	35.00
64	Roy Sievers	75.00	137	*Roy McMillan*	35.00
65	Enos Slaughter	150.00	138	Bill MacDonald	35.00
66	Preacher Roe	135.00	139	Ken Wood	35.00
67	Allie Reynolds	135.00	140	John Antonelli	35.00
68	Cliff Chambers	75.00	141	Clint Hartung	35.00
69	Virgil Stallcup	75.00	142	Harry Perkowski	35.00
70	Al Zarilla	75.00	143	Les Moss	35.00
71	Tom Upton	75.00	144	Ed Blake	35.00
72	Karl Olson	75.00	145	Joe Haynes	35.00
73	William Werle	75.00	146	Frank House	35.00
74	Andy Hansen	75.00	147	Bob Young	35.00
75	Wes Westrum	75.00	148	Johnny Klippstein	35.00
76	Eddie Stanky	75.00	149	Dick Kryhoski	35.00
77	Bob Kennedy	75.00	150	Ted Beard	35.00
78	Ellis Kinder	75.00	151	Wally Post	35.00
79	Gerald Staley	75.00	152	Al Evans	35.00
80	Herman Wehmeier	75.00	153	Bob Rush	35.00
81	Vernon Law	35.00	154	Joe Muir	35.00
82	Duane Pillette	35.00	155	Frank Overmire	35.00
83	Billy Johnson	35.00	156	Frank Hiller	35.00
84	Vern Stephens	35.00	157	Bob Usher	35.00
85	Bob Kuzava	35.00	158	Eddie Waitkus	35.00
86	Ted Gray	35.00	159	Saul Rogovin	35.00
87	Dale Coogan	35.00	160	Owen Friend	35.00
88	Bob Feller	300.00	161	Bud Byerly	35.00
89	Johnny Lipon	35.00	162	Del Crandall	35.00
90	Mickey Grasso	35.00	163	Stan Rojek	35.00
91	Red Schoendienst	100.00	164	Walt Dubiel	35.00
92	Dale Mitchell	35.00	165	Eddie Kazak	35.00
93	Al Sima	35.00	166	Paul LaPalme	35.00
94	Sam Mele	35.00	167	Bill Howerton	35.00
95	Ken Holcombe	35.00	168	*Charlie Silvera*	35.00
96	Willard Marshall	35.00	169	Howie Judson	35.00
97	Earl Torgeson	35.00	170	Gus Bell	35.00
98	Bill Pierce	35.00	171	Ed Erautt	35.00
99	Gene Woodling	60.00	172	Eddie Miksis	35.00
100	Del Rice	35.00	173	Roy Smalley	35.00
101	Max Lanier	35.00	174	Clarence Marshall	35.00
102	Bill Kennedy	35.00	175	*Billy Martin*	500.00
103	Cliff Mapes	35.00	176	Hank Edwards	35.00
104	Don Kolloway	35.00	177	Bill Wight	35.00
105	John Pramesa	35.00	178	Cass Michaels	35.00

179	Frank Smith	35.00
180	*Charley Maxwell*	35.00
181	Bob Swift	35.00
182	Billy Hitchcock	35.00
183	Erv Dusak	35.00
184	Bob Ramazzotti	35.00
185	Bill Nicholson	35.00
186	Walt Masterson	35.00
187	Bob Miller	35.00
188	Clarence Podbielan	35.00
189	Pete Reiser	35.00
190	Don Johnson	35.00
191	Yogi Berra	750.00
192	Myron Ginsberg	35.00
193	Harry Simpson	35.00
194	Joe Hatten	35.00
195	*Minnie Minoso*	200.00
196	Solly Hemus	35.00
197	George Strickland	35.00
198	Phil Haugstad	35.00
199	George Zuverink	35.00
200	Ralph Houk	75.00
201	Alex Kellner	35.00
202	Joe Collins	35.00
203	Curt Simmons	35.00
204	Ron Northey	35.00
205	Clyde King	35.00
206	Joe Ostrowski	35.00
207	Mickey Harris	35.00
208	Marlin Stuart	35.00
209	Howie Fox	35.00
210	Dick Fowler	35.00
211	Ray Coleman	35.00
212	Ned Garver	35.00
213	Nippy Jones	35.00
214	Johnny Hopp	35.00
215	Hank Bauer	75.00
216	Richie Ashburn	150.00
217	George Stirnweiss	35.00
218	Clyde McCullough	35.00
219	Bobby Shantz	35.00
220	Joe Presko	35.00
221	Granny Hamner	35.00
222	"Hoot" Evers	35.00
223	Del Ennis	35.00
224	Bruce Edwards	35.00
225	Frank Baumholtz	35.00
226	Dave Philley	35.00
227	Joe Garagiola	125.00
228	Al Brazle	35.00
229	Gene Bearden	35.00
230	Matt Batts	35.00
231	Sam Zoldak	35.00
232	Billy Cox	50.00
233	*Bob Friend*	35.00
234	Steve Souchock	35.00
235	Walt Dropo	35.00
236	Ed Fitz Gerald	35.00
237	Jerry Coleman	45.00
238	Art Houtteman	35.00
239	*Rocky Bridges*	35.00
240	Jack Phillips	35.00
241	Tommy Byrne	35.00
242	Tom Poholsky	35.00
243	Larry Doby	60.00
244	Vic Wertz	35.00
245	Sherry Robertson	35.00
246	George Kell	100.00
247	Randy Gumpert	35.00
248	Frank Shea	35.00
249	Bobby Adams	35.00
250	Carl Erskine	85.00
251	Chico Carrasquel	75.00
252	Vern Bickford	75.00
253	Johnny Berardino	75.00
254	Joe Dobson	75.00
255	Clyde Vollmer	75.00
256	Pete Suder	75.00
257	Bobby Avila	75.00
258	Steve Gromek	75.00
259	Bob Addis	75.00
260	Pete Castiglione	75.00
261	Willie Mays	3500.00
262	Virgil Trucks	75.00
263	Harry Brecheen	75.00
264	Roy Hartsfield	75.00
265	Chuck Diering	75.00
266	Murry Dickson	75.00
267	Sid Gordon	75.00
268	Bob Lemon	200.00
269	Willard Nixon	75.00
270	Lou Brissie	75.00
271	Jim Delsing	100.00
272	Mike Garcia	100.00
273	Erv Palica	100.00
274	Ralph Branca	125.00
275	Pat Mullin	100.00
276	Jim Wilson	100.00
277	Early Wynn	300.00
278	Al Clark	100.00
279	Ed Stewart	100.00
280	Cloyd Boyer	100.00
281	Tommy Brown	75.00
282	Birdie Tebbetts	75.00
283	Phil Masi	75.00
284	Hank Arft	75.00
285	Cliff Fannin	75.00
286	Joe DeMaestri	75.00
287	Steve Bilko	75.00
288	Chet Nichols	75.00
289	Tommy Holmes	75.00
290	Joe Astroth	75.00
291	Gil Coan	75.00
292	Floyd Baker	75.00
293	Sibby Sisti	75.00
294	Walker Cooper	75.00
295	Phil Cavarretta	75.00
296	Red Rolfe	75.00
297	Andy Seminick	75.00
298	Bob Ross	75.00
299	Ray Murray	75.00
300	Barney McCosky	75.00
301	Bob Porterfield	100.00
302	Max Surkont	100.00
303	Harry Dorish	100.00
304	Sam Dente	100.00
305	Paul Richards	100.00
306	Lou Sleator	100.00
307	Frank Campos	100.00
308	Luis Aloma	100.00
309	Jim Busby	100.00
310	George Metkovich	100.00
311	Mickey Mantle	25000.00
312	Jackie Robinson	2500.00
313	Bobby Thomson	300.00
314	Roy Campanella	3000.00
315	Leo Durocher	750.00
316	Davey Williams	300.00
317	Connie Marrero	300.00
318	Hal Gregg	300.00
319	Al Walker	300.00
320	John Rutherford	300.00
321	*Joe Black*	450.00
322	Randy Jackson	300.00
323	Bubba Church	300.00
324	Warren Hacker	300.00

325	Bill Serena	300.00		383	Del Wilber	300.00
326	George Shuba	300.00		384	Frank Crosetti	500.00
327	Archie Wilson	300.00		385	Herman Franks	300.00
328	Bob Borkowski	300.00		386	Eddie Yuhas	300.00
329	Ike Delock	300.00		387	Billy Meyer	300.00
330	Turk Lown	300.00		388	Bob Chipman	300.00
331	Tom Morgan	300.00		389	Ben Wade	300.00
332	Tony Bartirome	300.00		390	Rocky Nelson	300.00
333	Pee Wee Reese	2500.00		391	Ben Chapman (photo actually Sam Chapman)	300.00
334	Wilmer Mizell	300.00		392	*Hoyt Wilhelm*	1250.00
335	Ted Lepcio	300.00		393	Ebba St. Claire	300.00
336	Dave Koslo	300.00		394	Billy Herman	350.00
337	Jim Hearn	300.00		395	Jake Pitler	300.00
338	Sal Yvars	300.00		396	*Dick Williams*	350.00
339	Russ Meyer	300.00		397	Forrest Main	300.00
340	Bob Hooper	300.00		398	Hal Rice	300.00
341	Hal Jeffcoat	300.00		399	Jim Fridley	300.00
342	*Clem Labine*	350.00		400	Bill Dickey	1000.00
343	Dick Gernert	300.00		401	Bob Schultz	300.00
344	Ewell Blackwell	300.00		402	Earl Harrist	300.00
345	Sam White	300.00		403	Bill Miller	300.00
346	George Spencer	300.00		404	Dick Brodowski	300.00
347	Joe Adcock	350.00		405	Eddie Pellagrini	300.00
348	Bob Kelly	300.00		406	*Joe Nuxhall*	300.00
349	Bob Cain	300.00		407	*Eddie Mathews*	5000.00
350	Cal Abrams	300.00				
351	Al Dark	350.00				
352	Karl Drews	300.00				
353	Bob Del Greco	300.00				
354	Fred Hatfield	300.00				
355	Bobby Morgan	300.00				
356	Toby Atwell	300.00				
357	Smoky Burgess	300.00				
358	John Kucab	300.00				
359	Dee Fondy	300.00				
360	George Crowe	300.00				
361	Bill Posedel	300.00				
362	Ken Heintzelman	300.00				
363	Dick Rozek	300.00				
364	Clyde Sukeforth	300.00				
365	Cookie Lavagetto	300.00				
366	Dave Madison	300.00				
367	Bob Thorpe	300.00				
368	Ed Wright	300.00				
369	*Dick Groat*	750.00				
370	Billy Hoeft	300.00				
371	Bob Hofman	300.00				
372	*Gil McDougald*	500.00				
373	Jim Turner	300.00				
374	Al Benton	300.00				
375	Jack Merson	300.00				
376	Faye Throneberry	300.00				
377	Chuck Dressen	300.00				
378	Les Fusselman	300.00				
379	Joe Rossi	300.00				
380	Clem Koshorek	300.00				
381	Milton Stock	300.00				
382	Sam Jones	300.00				

1953 Topps

The 1953 Topps set reflects the company's continuing legal battles with Bowman. The set, originally intended to consist of 280 cards, is lacking six numbers (#'s 253, 261, 267, 268, 271 and 275) which probably represent players whose contracts were lost to the competition. The 2-5/8" by 3-3/4" cards feature painted player pictures. A color team logo appears at a bottom panel (red for American League and black for National.) Card backs contain the first baseball trivia questions along with brief statistics and player biographies. In the red panel at the top which lists the player's personal data, cards from the 2nd Series (#'s 86-165 plus 10, 44, 61, 72 and 81) can be found with that data printed in either black or white, black being the scarcer variety. Cards 221-280 are the scarce high numbers, with even scarcer short-printed cards interspersed in the series.

Mr. Mint Says - This is my favorite set. The set is probably tougher to find in mint condition than the 1952 set because of the black and red panels, and I even think the 1953 Mantle is harder to find in top condition than its more famous predecessor.

There were many miscuts, and you often find the rough cut, which I think makes the card look authentic and uncirculated. I also think that collectors are catching on to that notion and not objecting to rough cuts as much as they might have in the past.

The high numbers (221-280) are very hard to find, and the short prints within that series are even tougher. The #1 card of Jackie Robinson is difficult in mint, and the last card, Milt Bolling, is even harder because it's in the high series.

The Mays and Mantle cards are obviously the keys, and all of the Hall of Fame cards are popular. There is also a three card advertising panel, with a commercial message on the back, that shows up from time to time.

Collectors must also be wary, since this is an easy set to fall victim to tinkering with a magic marker to cover nicks and dings in the red and black panels at the bottom of the card. Don't rely solely on the front of the card; look at the edge itself. It should be cardboard color, and indications of red or black can suggest that the card may have been tampered with.

		MT
Complete Set (274):		22000.
Common Player (1-165):		35.00
Common Player (166-220):		25.00
Common Player (221-280):		55.00
Short-print Player (221-280):		125.00
1	Jackie Robinson	750.00
2	Luke Easter	25.00
3	George Crowe	35.00
4	Ben Wade	35.00
5	Joe Dobson	35.00
6	Sam Jones	35.00
7	Bob Borkowski	25.00
8	Clem Koshorek	25.00
9	Joe Collins	50.00
10	Smoky Burgess	75.00
11	Sal Yvars	35.00
12	Howie Judson	25.00
13	Connie Marrero	25.00
14	Clem Labine	35.00
15	Bobo Newsom	25.00
16	Harry Lowrey	25.00
17	Billy Hitchcock	35.00
18	Ted Lepcio	25.00
19	Mel Parnell	25.00
20	Hank Thompson	35.00
21	Billy Johnson	35.00
22	Howie Fox	35.00
23	Toby Atwell	25.00
24	Ferris Fain	35.00
25	Ray Boone	35.00
26	Dale Mitchell	25.00
27	Roy Campanella	300.00
28	Eddie Pellagrini	35.00

Jackie ROBINSON
second base BROOKLYN DODGERS

No.	Player	Price	No.	Player	Price
29	Hal Jeffcoat	35.00	102	Connie Ryan	25.00
30	Willard Nixon	35.00	103	Joe Astroth	25.00
31	Ewell Blackwell	60.00	104	Yogi Berra	350.00
32	Clyde Vollmer	35.00	105	Joe Nuxhall	25.00
33	Bob Kennedy	25.00	106	Johnny Antonelli	25.00
34	George Shuba	35.00	107	Danny O'Connell	25.00
35	Irv Noren	35.00	108	Bob Porterfield	25.00
36	Johnny Groth	25.00	109	Alvin Dark	30.00
37	Eddie Mathews	150.00	110	Herman Wehmeier	25.00
38	Jim Hearn	25.00	111	Hank Sauer	25.00
39	Eddie Miksis	35.00	112	Ned Garver	25.00
40	John Lipon	35.00	113	Jerry Priddy	35.00
41	Enos Slaughter	100.00	114	Phil Rizzuto	200.00
42	Gus Zernial	25.00	115	George Spencer	35.00
43	Gil McDougald	75.00	116	Frank Smith	25.00
44	Ellis Kinder	50.00	117	Sid Gordon	25.00
45	Grady Hatton	25.00	118	Gus Bell	25.00
46	Johnny Klippstein	25.00	119	Johnny Sain	50.00
47	Bubba Church	25.00	120	Davey Williams	35.00
48	Bob Del Greco	25.00	121	Walt Dropo	35.00
49	Faye Throneberry	25.00	122	Elmer Valo	35.00
50	Chuck Dressen	40.00	123	Tommy Byrne	25.00
51	Frank Campos	25.00	124	Sibby Sisti	25.00
52	Ted Gray	25.00	125	Dick Williams	25.00
53	Sherman Lollar	25.00	126	Bill Connelly	25.00
54	Bob Feller	150.00	127	Clint Courtney	25.00
55	Maurice McDermott	25.00	128	Wilmer Mizell	25.00
56	Gerald Staley	25.00	129	Keith Thomas	35.00
57	Carl Scheib	35.00	130	Turk Lown	25.00
58	George Metkovich	35.00	131	Harry Byrd	25.00
59	Karl Drews	25.00	132	Tom Morgan	50.00
60	Cloyd Boyer	25.00	133	Gil Coan	25.00
61	Early Wynn	150.00	134	Rube Walker	25.00
62	Monte Irvin	100.00	135	Al Rosen	45.00
63	Gus Niarhos	25.00	136	Ken Heintzelman	25.00
64	Dave Philley	35.00	137	John Rutherford	25.00
65	Earl Harrist	35.00	138	George Kell	100.00
66	Minnie Minoso	75.00	139	Sammy White	35.00
67	Roy Sievers	25.00	140	Tommy Glaviano	35.00
68	Del Rice	35.00	141	Allie Reynolds	50.00
69	Dick Brodowski	35.00	142	Vic Wertz	35.00
70	Ed Yuhas	35.00	143	Billy Pierce	40.00
71	Tony Bartirome	35.00	144	Bob Schultz	25.00
72	Fred Hutchinson	35.00	145	Harry Dorish	25.00
73	Eddie Robinson	35.00	146	Granny Hamner	35.00
74	Joe Rossi	35.00	147	Warren Spahn	200.00
75	Mike Garcia	35.00	148	Mickey Grasso	35.00
76	Pee Wee Reese	250.00	149	Dom DiMaggio	50.00
77	Johnny Mize	100.00	150	Harry Simpson	25.00
78	Red Schoendienst	90.00	151	Hoyt Wilhelm	100.00
79	Johnny Wyrostek	35.00	152	Bob Adams	25.00
80	Jim Hegan	35.00	153	Andy Seminick	25.00
81	Joe Black	100.00	154	Dick Groat	40.00
82	Mickey Mantle	5000.00	155	Dutch Leonard	35.00
83	Howie Pollet	35.00	156	Jim Rivera	25.00
84	Bob Hooper	25.00	157	Bob Addis	25.00
85	Bobby Morgan	25.00	158	*Johnny Logan*	25.00
86	Billy Martin	200.00	159	Wayne Terwilliger	25.00
87	Ed Lopat	50.00	160	Bob Young	35.00
88	Willie Jones	25.00	161	Vern Bickford	25.00
89	Chuck Stobbs	25.00	162	Ted Kluszewski	75.00
90	Hank Edwards	25.00	163	Fred Hatfield	25.00
91	Ebba St. Claire	25.00	164	Frank Shea	25.00
92	Paul Minner	25.00	165	Billy Hoeft	35.00
93	Hal Rice	25.00	166	Bill Hunter	25.00
94	William Kennedy	25.00	167	Art Schult	25.00
95	Willard Marshall	25.00	168	Willard Schmidt	25.00
96	Virgil Trucks	35.00	169	Dizzy Trout	25.00
97	Don Kolloway	25.00	170	Bill Werle	25.00
98	Cal Abrams	25.00	171	Bill Glynn	25.00
99	Dave Madison	35.00	172	Rip Repulski	25.00
100	Bill Miller	35.00	173	Preston Ward	25.00
101	Ted Wilks	35.00	174	Billy Loes	25.00

#	Player	Price		#	Player	Price
175	Ron Kline	25.00		228	Hal Newhouser	200.00
176	*Don Hoak*	30.00		229	Rocky Krsnich	125.00
177	Jim Dyck	25.00		230	Johnny Lindell	75.00
178	Jim Waugh	25.00		231	Solly Hemus	75.00
179	Gene Hermanski	25.00		232	Dick Kokos	125.00
180	Virgil Stallcup	25.00		233	Al Aber	125.00
181	Al Zarilla	25.00		234	Ray Murray	75.00
182	Bob Hofman	25.00		235	John Hetki	75.00
183	*Stu Miller*	25.00		236	Harry Perkowski	75.00
184	*Hal Brown*	25.00		237	Clarence Podbielan	75.00
185	*Jim Pendleton*	25.00		238	Cal Hogue	75.00
186	Charlie Bishop	25.00		239	Jim Delsing	125.00
187	Jim Fridley	25.00		240	Freddie Marsh	75.00
188	*Andy Carey*	30.00		241	Al Sima	75.00
189	Ray Jablonski	25.00		242	*Charlie Silvera*	125.00
190	Dixie Walker	25.00		243	Carlos Bernier	75.00
191	Ralph Kiner	125.00		244	Willie Mays	3750.00
192	Wally Westlake	25.00		245	Bill Norman	125.00
193	Mike Clark	25.00		246	*Roy Face*	125.00
194	Eddie Kazak	25.00		247	Mike Sandlock	75.00
195	Ed McGhee	25.00		248	Gene Stephens	75.00
196	Bob Keegan	25.00		249	Ed O'Brien	125.00
197	Del Crandall	25.00		250	Bob Wilson	125.00
198	Forrest Main	25.00		251	Sid Hudson	125.00
199	Marion Fricano	25.00		252	Henry Foiles	125.00
200	Gordon Goldsberry	25.00		253	Not Issued	
201	Paul LaPalme	25.00		254	Preacher Roe	125.00
202	Carl Sawatski	25.00		255	Dixie Howell	125.00
203	Cliff Fannin	25.00		256	Les Peden	125.00
204	Dick Bokelmann	25.00		257	Bob Boyd	125.00
205	Vern Benson	25.00		258	*Jim Gilliam*	375.00
206	*Ed Bailey*	25.00		259	Roy McMillan	75.00
207	Whitey Ford	200.00		260	Sam Calderone	125.00
208	Jim Wilson	25.00		261	Not Issued	
209	Jim Greengrass	25.00		262	Bob Oldis	125.00
210	*Bob Cerv*	30.00		263	*Johnny Podres*	300.00
211	J.W. Porter	25.00		264	Gene Woodling	100.00
212	Jack Dittmer	25.00		265	Jackie Jensen	175.00
213	Ray Scarborough	25.00		266	Bob Cain	125.00
214	*Bill Bruton*	25.00		267	Not Issued	
215	*Gene Conley*	25.00		268	Not Issued	
216	Jim Hughes	25.00		269	Duane Pillette	125.00
217	Murray Wall	25.00		270	Vern Stephens	125.00
218	Les Fusselman			271	Not Issued	
219	Pete Runnels (picture actually Don Johnson)	25.00		272	Bill Antonello	125.00
220	Satchel Paige	600.00		273	*Harvey Haddix*	175.00
221	Bob Milliken	125.00		274	John Riddle	125.00
222	Vic Janowicz	75.00		275	Not Issued	
223	John O'Brien	75.00		276	Ken Raffensberger	125.00
224	Lou Sleater	75.00		277	Don Lund	125.00
225	Bobby Shantz	150.00		278	Willie Miranda	125.00
226	Ed Erautt	125.00		279	Joe Coleman	75.00
227	Morris Martin	75.00		280	Milt Bolling	500.00

1954 Topps

The first issue to use two player pictures on the front, the 1954 Topps set is very popular today. Solid color backgrounds frame both color head-and-shoulders and black and white action pictures of the player. The player's name, position, team and team logo appear at the top. Backs include an "Inside Baseball" cartoon regarding the player as well as statistics and biography. The 250-card, 2-5/8" by 3-3/4", set includes manager and coaches cards, and the first use by Topps of two players together on a card; the players were, appropriately, the O'Brien twins.

Mr. Mint Says - To me, these are the neatest cards ever made with the large picture and the smaller action photo.

The cards also have the rousgh cut along the vertical edges, and centering is basically pretty good. The set is extremely popular and sells well.

Cards 51-75 are brutal; collections that I buy invariably are called near sets, with those numbers missing, suggesting that all the cards around them were double printed. Most of the cards within that short stretch are commons.

The three rookie cards are the keys, plus the two Williams cards, Mays, Robinson and Berra. The Williams cards, the first and last in the set, are really tough to find in mint condition.

		MT
Complete Set (250):		12000.
Common Player (1-50):		15.00
Common Player (51-75):		35.00
Common Player (76-250):		15.00

1	Ted Williams	1000.00
2	Gus Zernial	15.00
3	Monte Irvin	35.00
4	Hank Sauer	15.00
5	Ed Lopat	20.00
6	Pete Runnels	15.00
7	Ted Kluszewski	30.00
8	Bobby Young	15.00
9	Harvey Haddix	15.00
10	Jackie Robinson	325.00
11	Paul Smith	15.00
12	Del Crandall	15.00
13	Billy Martin	75.00
14	Preacher Roe	30.00
15	Al Rosen	18.00
16	Vic Janowicz	18.00
17	Phil Rizzuto	100.00
18	Walt Dropo	15.00
19	Johnny Lipon	15.00
20	Warren Spahn	150.00
21	Bobby Shantz	18.00
22	Jim Greengrass	15.00
23	Luke Easter	15.00
24	Granny Hamner	15.00
25	*Harvey Kuenn*	35.00
26	Ray Jablonski	15.00
27	Ferris Fain	15.00
28	Paul Minner	15.00
29	Jim Hegan	15.00
30	Eddie Mathews	85.00
31	Johnny Klippstein	15.00
32	Duke Snider	175.00
33	Johnny Schmitz	15.00
34	Jim Rivera	15.00
35	Junior Gilliam	25.00
36	Hoyt Wilhelm	45.00
37	Whitey Ford	120.00
38	Eddie Stanky	15.00
39	Sherm Lollar	15.00
40	Mel Parnell	15.00
41	Willie Jones	15.00
42	Don Mueller	15.00
43	Dick Groat	15.00
44	Ned Garver	15.00
45	Richie Ashburn	65.00
46	Ken Raffensberger	15.00
47	Ellis Kinder	15.00
48	Billy Hunter	15.00
49	Ray Murray	15.00
50	Yogi Berra	300.00
51	Johnny Lindell	35.00
52	Vic Power	35.00
53	Jack Dittmer	35.00
54	Vern Stephens	35.00
55	Phil Cavarretta	35.00
56	Willie Miranda	35.00

#	Player	Price		#	Player	Price
57	Luis Aloma	35.00		130	Hank Bauer	50.00
58	Bob Wilson	35.00		131	Reno Bertoia	15.00
59	Gene Conley	35.00		132	*Tom Lasorda*	175.00
60	Frank Baumholtz	35.00		133	Del Baker	15.00
61	Bob Cain	35.00		134	Cal Hogue	15.00
62	Eddie Robinson	35.00		135	Joe Presko	15.00
63	Johnny Pesky	35.00		136	Connie Ryan	15.00
64	Hank Thompson	35.00		137	*Wally Moon*	15.00
65	Bob Swift	35.00		138	Bob Borkowski	15.00
66	Ted Lepcio	35.00		139	Ed & Johnny O'Brien	65.00
67	Jim Willis	35.00		140	Tom Wright	15.00
68	Sam Calderone	35.00		141	*Joe Jay*	15.00
69	Bud Podbielan	35.00		142	Tom Poholsky	15.00
70	Larry Doby	100.00		143	Rollie Hemsley	15.00
71	Frank Smith	35.00		144	Bill Werle	15.00
72	Preston Ward	35.00		145	Elmer Valo	15.00
73	Wayne Terwilliger	35.00		146	Don Johnson	15.00
74	Bill Taylor	35.00		147	John Riddle	15.00
75	Fred Haney	35.00		148	Bob Trice	15.00
76	Bob Scheffing	15.00		149	Jim Robertson	15.00
77	Ray Boone	15.00		150	Dick Kryhoski	15.00
78	Ted Kazanski	15.00		151	Alex Grammas	15.00
79	Andy Pafko	15.00		152	Mike Blyzka	15.00
80	Jackie Jensen	15.00		153	Rube Walker	15.00
81	Dave Hoskins	15.00		154	Mike Fornieles	15.00
82	Milt Bolling	15.00		155	Bob Kennedy	15.00
83	Joe Collins	15.00		156	Joe Coleman	15.00
84	Dick Cole	15.00		157	Don Lenhardt	15.00
85	*Bob Turley*	15.00		158	Peanuts Lowrey	15.00
86	Billy Herman	30.00		159	Dave Philley	15.00
87	Roy Face	15.00		160	Red Kress	15.00
88	Matt Batts	15.00		161	John Hetki	15.00
89	Howie Pollet	15.00		162	Herman Wehmeier	15.00
90	Willie Mays	700.00		163	Frank House	15.00
91	Bob Oldis	15.00		164	Stu Miller	15.00
92	Wally Westlake	15.00		165	Jim Pendleton	15.00
93	Sid Hudson	15.00		166	Johnny Podres	25.00
94	*Ernie Banks*	1000.00		167	Don Lund	15.00
95	Hal Rice	15.00		168	Morrie Martin	15.00
96	Charlie Silvera	15.00		169	Jim Hughes	15.00
97	Jerry Lane	15.00		170	*Dusty Rhodes*	15.00
98	Joe Black	15.00		171	Leo Kiely	15.00
99	Bob Hofman	15.00		172	Hal Brown	15.00
100	Bob Keegan	15.00		173	Jack Harshman	15.00
101	Gene Woodling	15.00		174	Tom Qualters	15.00
102	Gil Hodges	125.00		175	Frank Leja	15.00
103	*Jim Lemon*	15.00		176	Bob Keely	15.00
104	Mike Sandlock	15.00		177	Bob Milliken	15.00
105	Andy Carey	15.00		178	Bill Gylnn (Glynn)	15.00
106	Dick Kokos	15.00		179	Gair Allie	15.00
107	Duane Pillette	15.00		180	Wes Westrum	15.00
108	Thornton Kipper	15.00		181	Mel Roach	15.00
109	Bill Bruton	15.00		182	Chuck Harmon	15.00
110	Harry Dorish	15.00		183	Earle Combs	30.00
111	Jim Delsing	15.00		184	Ed Bailey	15.00
112	Bill Renna	15.00		185	Chuck Stobbs	15.00
113	Bob Boyd	15.00		186	Karl Olson	15.00
114	Dean Stone	15.00		187	Heinie Manush	30.00
115	"Rip" Repulski	15.00		188	Dave Jolly	15.00
116	Steve Bilko	15.00		189	Bob Ross	15.00
117	Solly Hemus	15.00		190	Ray Herbert	15.00
118	Carl Scheib	15.00		191	*Dick Schofield*	15.00
119	Johnny Antonelli	15.00		192	Cot Deal	15.00
120	Roy McMillan	15.00		193	Johnny Hopp	15.00
121	Clem Labine	15.00		194	Bill Sarni	15.00
122	Johnny Logan	15.00		195	Bill Consolo	15.00
123	Bobby Adams	15.00		196	Stan Jok	15.00
124	Marion Fricano	15.00		197	Schoolboy Rowe	15.00
125	Harry Perkowski	15.00		198	Carl Sawatski	15.00
126	Ben Wade	15.00		199	Rocky Nelson	15.00
127	Steve O'Neill	15.00		200	Larry Jansen	15.00
128	*Hank Aaron*	2500.00		201	*Al Kaline*	900.00
129	Forrest Jacobs	15.00		202	*Bob Purkey*	15.00

203	Harry Brecheen	15.00
204	Angel Scull	15.00
205	Johnny Sain	25.00
206	Ray Crone	15.00
207	Tom Oliver	15.00
208	Grady Hatton	15.00
209	Charlie Thompson	15.00
210	*Bob Buhl*	15.00
211	Don Hoak	15.00
212	Mickey Micelotta	15.00
213	John Fitzpatrick	15.00
214	Arnold Portocarrero	15.00
215	Ed McGhee	15.00
216	Al Sima	15.00
217	Paul Schreiber	15.00
218	Fred Marsh	15.00
219	Charlie Kress	15.00
220	Ruben Gomez	15.00
221	Dick Brodowski	15.00
222	Bill Wilson	15.00
223	Joe Haynes	15.00
224	Dick Weik	15.00
225	Don Liddle	15.00
226	Jehosie Heard	15.00
227	Buster Mills	15.00
228	Gene Hermanski	15.00
229	Bob Talbot	15.00
230	Bob Kuzava	15.00
231	Roy Smalley	15.00
232	Lou Limmer	15.00
233	Augie Galan	15.00
234	*Jerry Lynch*	15.00
235	Vern Law	15.00
236	Paul Penson	15.00
237	Mike Ryba	15.00
238	Al Aber	15.00
239	*Bill Skowron*	100.00
240	Sam Mele	15.00
241	Bob Miller	15.00
242	Curt Roberts	15.00
243	Ray Blades	15.00
244	Leroy Wheat	15.00
245	Roy Sievers	15.00
246	Howie Fox	15.00
247	Eddie Mayo	15.00
248	*Al Smith*	15.00
249	Wilmer Mizell	15.00
250	Ted Williams	900.00

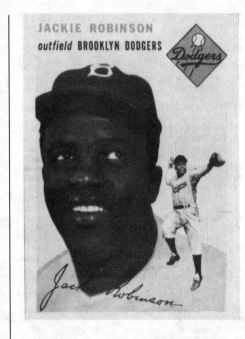

1955 Topps

The 1955 Topps set is numerically the smallest of the regular issue Topps sets. The 3-3/4" by 2-5/8" cards mark the first time that Topps used a horizontal format. While that format was new, the design was not; they are very similar to the 1954 cards to the point many pictures appeared in both years. Although it was slated for a 210-card set, the 1955 Topps set turned out to be only 206 cards with numbers 175, 186, 203 and 209 never being released. The scarce high numbers in this set begin with #161.

"SANDY" KOUFAX   pitcher BROOKLYN DODGERS

Mr. Mint Says - This is a difficult, undervalued issue, and the first year Topps tried a horizontal set. It is also a year where the card backs can turn color, and it is seldom that you see a nice, white back. The set also had much better gloss than in 1954, and true mint condition cards can be absolutely breathtaking.

Cards 151-160 are difficult, and 161-210 even worse, not only because of off-centering. With Duke Snider, a variety of factors, like being a Brooklyn Dodger, a high number card in that most famous Brooklyn year, and the last card in the set, conspire to make it a pricey item. The Aaron, Banks and Kaline second-year cards are also very popular, as are Jackie Robinson and Mays.

		MT
Complete Set (206):		12250.
Common Player (1-150):		15.00
Common Player (151-160):		30.00
Common Player (161-210):		40.00
1	Dusty Rhodes	75.00
2	Ted Williams	500.00
3	Art Fowler	15.00
4	Al Kaline	250.00
5	Jim Gilliam	25.00
6	Stan Hack	15.00
7	Jim Hegan	15.00
8	Hal Smith	15.00
9	Bob Miller	15.00
10	Bob Keegan	15.00
11	15. (Ferris Fain)	
12	"Jake" Thies	15.00
13	Fred Marsh	15.00
14	Jim Finigan	15.00
15	Jim Pendleton	15.00
16	Roy Sievers	15.00
17	Bobby Hofman	15.00
18	Russ Kemmerer	15.00
19	Billy Herman	17.00
20	Andy Carey	15.00
21	Alex Grammas	15.00
22	Bill Skowron	30.00
23	Jack Parks	15.00
24	Hal Newhouser	30.00
25	Johnny Podres	30.00
26	Dick Groat	25.00
27	Billy Gardner	15.00
28	Ernie Banks	300.00
29	Herman Wehmeier	15.00
30	Vic Power	15.00
31	Warren Spahn	110.00
32	Ed McGhee	15.00
33	Tom Qualters	15.00
34	Wayne Terwilliger	15.00
35	Dave Jolly	15.00
36	Leo Kiely	15.00
37	*Joe Cunningham*	15.00
38	Bob Turley	20.00
39	Bill Glynn	15.00
40	Don Hoak	15.00
41	Chuck Stobbs	15.00
42	Windy McCall	15.00
43	Harvey Haddix	15.00
44	Corky Valentine	15.00
45	Hank Sauer	15.00
46	Ted Kazanski	15.00
47	Hank Aaron	500.00
48	Bob Kennedy	15.00
49	J.W. Porter	15.00
50	Jackie Robinson	275.00
51	Jim Hughes	15.00
52	Bill Tremel	15.00
53	Bill Taylor	15.00
54	Lou Limmer	15.00
55	"Rip" Repulski	15.00
56	Ray Jablonski	15.00
57	*Billy O'Dell*	15.00
58	Jim Rivera	15.00
59	Gair Allie	15.00
60	Dean Stone	15.00
61	"Spook" Jacobs	15.00
62	Thornton Kipper	15.00
63	Joe Collins	15.00
64	*Gus Triandos*	15.00
65	Ray Boone	15.00
66	Ron Jackson	15.00
67	Wally Moon	15.00
68	Jim Davis	15.00
69	Ed Bailey	15.00
70	Al Rosen	20.00
71	Ruben Gomez	15.00
72	Karl Olson	15.00
73	Jack Shepard	15.00
74	Bob Borkowski	15.00
75	*Sandy Amoros*	30.00
76	Howie Pollet	15.00
77	Arnold Portocarrero	15.00
78	Gordon Jones	15.00
79	Danny Schell	15.00

80	Bob Grim	15.00
81	Gene Conley	15.00
82	Chuck Harmon	15.00
83	Tom Brewer	15.00
84	*Camilo Pascual*	15.00
85	*Don Mossi*	15.00
86	Bill Wilson	15.00
87	Frank House	15.00
88	*Bob Skinner*	15.00
89	*Joe Frazier*	15.00
90	*Karl Spooner*	15.00
91	Milt Bolling	15.00
92	*Don Zimmer*	35.00
93	Steve Bilko	15.00
94	Reno Bertoia	15.00
95	Preston Ward	15.00
96	Charlie Bishop	15.00
97	Carlos Paula	15.00
98	Johnny Riddle	15.00
99	Frank Leja	15.00
100	Monte Irvin	45.00
101	Johnny Gray	15.00
102	Wally Westlake	15.00
103	Charlie White	15.00
104	Jack Harshman	15.00
105	Chuck Diering	15.00
106	*Frank Sullivan*	15.00
107	Curt Roberts	15.00
108	Rube Walker	15.00
109	Ed Lopat	20.00
110	Gus Zernial	15.00
111	Bob Milliken	15.00
112	Nelson King	15.00
113	Harry Brecheen	15.00
114	Lou Ortiz	15.00
115	Ellis Kinder	15.00
116	Tom Hurd	15.00
117	Mel Roach	15.00
118	Bob Purkey	15.00
119	Bob Lennon	15.00
120	Ted Kluszewski	35.00
121	Bill Renna	15.00
122	Carl Sawatski	15.00
123	*Sandy Koufax*	1500.00
124	*Harmon Killebrew*	475.00
125	*Ken Boyer*	100.00
126	*Dick Hall*	15.00
127	*Dale Long*	15.00
128	Ted Lepcio	15.00
129	Elvin Tappe	15.00
130	Mayo Smith	15.00
131	Grady Hatton	15.00
132	Bob Trice	15.00
133	Dave Hoskins	15.00
134	Joe Jay	15.00
135	Johnny O'Brien	15.00
136	"Bunky" Stewart	15.00
137	Harry Elliott	15.00
138	Ray Herbert	15.00
139	Steve Kraly	15.00
140	Mel Parnell	15.00
141	Tom Wright	15.00
142	Jerry Lynch	15.00
143	Dick Schofield	15.00
144	Joe Amalfitano	15.00
145	Elmer Valo	15.00
146	*Dick Donovan*	15.00
147	Laurin Pepper	15.00
148	Hal Brown	15.00
149	Ray Crone	15.00
150	Mike Higgins	15.00
151	Red Kress	15.00
152	*Harry Agganis*	100.00

153	Bud Podbielan	25.00
154	Willie Miranda	25.00
155	Eddie Mathews	125.00
156	Joe Black	35.00
157	Bob Miller	25.00
158	Tom Carroll	25.00
159	Johnny Schmitz	25.00
160	Ray Narleski	25.00
161	*Chuck Tanner*	25.00
162	Joe Coleman	25.00
163	Faye Throneberry	25.00
164	*Roberto Clemente*	2500.00
165	Don Johnson	25.00
166	Hank Bauer	50.00
167	Tom Casagrande	40.00
168	Duane Pillette	40.00
169	Bob Oldis	40.00
170	Jim Pearce	40.00
171	Dick Brodowski	40.00
172	Frank Baumholtz	40.00
173	Bob Kline	40.00
174	Rudy Minarcin	40.00
175	Not Issued	
176	Norm Zauchin	40.00
177	Jim Robertson	40.00
178	Bobby Adams	40.00
179	Jim Bolger	40.00
180	Clem Labine	50.00
181	Roy McMillan	40.00
182	Humberto Robinson	40.00
183	Tony Jacobs	40.00
184	Harry Perkowski	40.00
185	Don Ferrarese	40.00
186	Not Issued	
187	Gil Hodges	200.00
188	Charlie Silvera	40.00
189	Phil Rizzuto	200.00
190	Gene Woodling	40.00
191	Ed Stanky	40.00
192	Jim Delsing	40.00
193	Johnny Sain	50.00
194	Willie Mays	750.00
195	Ed Roebuck	40.00
196	Gale Wade	40.00
197	Al Smith	40.00
198	Yogi Berra	300.00
199	Bert Hamric	40.00
200	Jack Jensen	50.00
201	Sherm Lollar	40.00
202	Jim Owens	40.00
203	Not Issued	
204	Frank Smith	40.00
205	Gene Freese	40.00
206	Pete Daley	40.00
207	Bill Consolo	40.00
208	Ray Moore	40.00
209	Not Issued	
210	Duke Snider	750.00

HANK AARON   outfield MILWAUKEE BRAVES

1955 Topps Doubleheaders

This set is a throwback to the 1911 T201 Mecca Double Folders. The cards were perforated allowing them to be folded. Open, there is a color painting of a player set against a ballpark background. When folded, a different stadium and player appears, although both share the same lower legs and feet. Back gives abbreviated career histories. Placed side by side in reverse numerical order, the backgrounds form a continuous stadium scene. When open, the cards measure 2-1/16" by 4-7/8." The 66 cards in the set mean 132 total players, all of whom also appeared in the lower number regular 1955 Topps

Mr. Mint Says - These are popular and they still sell pretty well when they turn up. There are not that many stars in the set, but the Hall of Famers that there are, like Robinson, Banks, Kaline, Williams, Aaron and Spahn, draw a lot of interest.

I've had packs from time to time. The cards come folded, or some that I've seen were unperforated in the middle.

		MT
Complete Set (66):		5150.
Common Player:		40.00

1	Al Rosen	
2	Chuck Diering	40.00
3	Monte Irvin	
4	Russ Kemmerer	40.00
5	Ted Kazanski	
6	Gordon Jones	40.00
7	Bill Taylor	
8	Billy O'Dell	40.00
9	J.W. Porter	
10	Thornton Kipper	40.00
11	Curt Roberts	
12	Arnie Portocarrero	40.00
13	Wally Westlake	
14	Frank House	40.00
15	"Rube" Walker	
16	Lou Limmer	40.00
17	Dean Stone	
18	Charlie White	40.00
19	Karl Spooner	
20	Jim Hughes	40.00
21	Bill Skowron	
22	Frank Sullivan	40.00
23	Jack Shepard	
24	Stan Hack	40.00
25	Jackie Robinson	
26	Don Hoak	400.00
27	"Dusty" Rhodes	
28	Jim Davis	40.00
29	Vic Power	
30	Ed Bailey	40.00
31	Howie Pollet	
32	Ernie Banks	250.00
33	Jim Pendleton	
34	Gene Conley	40.00
35	Karl Olson	
36	Andy Carey	40.00
37	Wally Moon	
38	Joe Cunningham	40.00
39	Fred Marsh	
40	"Jake" Thies	40.00
41	Ed Lopat	
42	Harvey Haddix	40.00
43	Leo Kiely	
44	Chuck Stobbs	40.00
45	Al Kaline	
46	"Corky" Valentine	425.00
47	"Spook" Jacobs	
48	Johnny Gray	40.00
49	Ron Jackson	
50	Jim Finigan	40.00
51	Ray Jablonski	
52	Bob Keegan	40.00
53	Billy Herman	
54	Sandy Amoros	40.00
55	Chuck Harmon	
56	Bob Skinner	40.00
57	Dick Hall	
58	Bob Grim	40.00
59	Billy Glynn	
60	Bob Miller	40.00
61	Billy Gardner	
62	John Hetki	40.00
63	Bob Borkowski	
64	Bob Turley	40.00
65	Joe Collins	
66	Jack Harshman	40.00
67	Jim Hegan	
68	Jack Parks	40.00
69	Ted Williams	
70	Hal Smith	425.00
71	Gair Allie	
72	Grady Hatton	40.00
73	Jerry Lynch	
74	Harry Brecheen	40.00
75	Tom Wright	
76	"Bunky" Stewart	40.00
77	Dave Hoskins	
78	Ed McGhee	40.00

79	Roy Sievers	
80	Art Fowler	40.00
81	Danny Schell	
82	Gus Triandos	40.00
83	Joe Frazier	
84	Don Mossi	40.00
85	Elmer Valo	
86	Hal Brown	40.00
87	Bob Kennedy	
88	"Windy" McCall	40.00
89	Ruben Gomez	
90	Jim Rivera	40.00
91	Lou Ortiz	
92	Milt Bolling	40.00
93	Carl Sawatski	
94	Elvin Tappe	40.00
95	Dave Jolly	
96	Bobby Hofman	40.00
97	Preston Ward	
98	Don Zimmer	40.00
99	Bill Renna	
100	Dick Groat	40.00
101	Bill Wilson	
102	Bill Tremel	40.00
103	Hank Sauer	
104	Camilo Pascual	40.00
105	Hank Aaron	
106	Ray Herbert	600.00
107	Alex Grammas	
108	Tom Qualters	40.00
109	Hal Newhouser	
110	Charlie Bishop	40.00
111	Harmon Killebrew	
112	John Podres	350.00
113	Ray Boone	
114	Bob Purkey	40.00
115	Dale Long	
116	Ferris Fain	40.00
117	Steve Bilko	
118	Bob Milliken	40.00
119	Mel Parnell	
120	Tom Hurd	40.00
121	Ted Kluszewski	
122	Jim Owens	40.00
123	Gus Zernial	
124	Bob Trice	40.00
125	"Rip" Repulski	
126	Ted Lepcio	40.00
127	Warren Spahn	
128	Tom Brewer	300.00
129	Jim Gilliam	
130	Ellis Kinder	40.00
131	Herm Wehmeier	
132	Wayne Terwilliger	40.00

1956 Topps

This 340-card set is quite similar in design to the 1955 Topps set, again using both a portrait and an "action" picture. Some portraits are the same as those used in 1955 (and even 1954). Innovations found in the 1956 Topps set of 2-5/8" by 3-3/4" cards include team cards introduced as part of a regular set. Additionally, there are two unnumbered checklist cards (the complete set price quoted below does not include the checklist cards). Finally, there are cards of the two league presidents, William Harridge and Warren Giles. On the backs, a three-panel cartoon depicts big moments from the player's career while biographical information appears above the cartoon and the statistics below. Card backs for numbers 1-180 can be found with either white or grey cardboard. Some dealers charge a premium for grey backs (#'s 1-100) and white backs (#'s 101-180).

outfield BOSTON RED SOX

Mr. Mint Says - If these cards had gloss it would be the best set on earth. I like the texture, the grass, the double photos and the horizontal format. The 1954 and 1956 cards are often found with the rough cut, and when they are they look very nice. The card stock seems a little softer than 1955. A very popular set, and the the last one in the oversized format. But no gloss.

I have never had a major purchase or find, that there seem to be more 1956s available than 1952-55. If I see a group of gray and white backs in the same collection, the gray often appear to be in better shape. I don't know why that is.

The white backs 101-180 are tough to find, and 1-100 gray backs and white backs are priced the same. I once purchased 1,100 1956 checklists, and I am convinced that the 1957 checklists are much harder to find. Checklists from 1956 are hardly easy, but they are not as difficult as people make them out to be.

Dated team cards are very much in demand and scarce, but I don't put too much stock in the center, and left team card variations. Few collectors seem to care about that. I don't find any difference between the 1/3 and 2/4 checklists and have priced them accordingly.

There are a few print lines here and there, but centering is not usually a problem. There is a printing dot that shows up on the 1956 Mantle, one of the great cards of all time and obviously the key to the set. All of the Hall of Famers are popular, and for the first time since Topps and Bowman began their wrangle over exclusive contracts, they are all present and accounted for in the 1956 set. The set also has the most popular team cards (and the first) from the 1950s, plus a host of high-demand Brooklyn Dodger and Yankee cards. The 1956 Don Larsen card is also sneaky, because of the perfect game.

		MT
Complete Set (340):		10000.
Common Player (1-100):		10.00
Common Player (101-180):		12.00
Common Player (181-260):		18.00
Common Player (261-340):		12.00

1	William Harridge	200.00
2	Warren Giles	40.00
3	Elmer Valo	10.00
4	Carlos Paula	10.00
5	Ted Williams	425.00
6	Ray Boone	10.00
7	Ron Negray	10.00
8	Walter Alston	50.00
9	Ruben Gomez	10.00
10	Warren Spahn	100.00
11a	Cubs Team (with date)	85.00
11b	Cubs Team (no date, name centered)	35.00
11c	Cubs Team (no date, name at left)	35.00
12	Andy Carey	10.00
13	Roy Face	10.00
14	Ken Boyer	20.00
15	Ernie Banks	100.00
16	*Hector Lopez*	10.00
17	Gene Conley	10.00
18	Dick Donovan	10.00
19	Chuck Diering	10.00
20	Al Kaline	125.00
21	Joe Collins	10.00
22	Jim Finigan	10.00
23	Freddie Marsh	10.00
24	Dick Groat	10.00
25	Ted Kluszewski	35.00
26	Grady Hatton	10.00
27	Nelson Burbrink	10.00
28	Bobby Hofman	10.00
29	Jack Harshman	10.00
30	Jackie Robinson	200.00
31	Hank Aaron	250.00
32	Frank House	10.00
33	Roberto Clemente	500.00

34	Tom Brewer	10.00
35	Al Rosen	14.00
36	Rudy Minarcin	10.00
37	Alex Grammas	10.00
38	Bob Kennedy	10.00
39	Don Mossi	10.00
40	Bob Turley	10.00
41	Hank Sauer	10.00
42	Sandy Amoros	10.00
43	Ray Moore	10.00
44	"Windy" McCall	10.00
45	Gus Zernial	10.00
46	Gene Freese	10.00
47	Art Fowler	10.00
48	Jim Hegan	10.00
49	*Pedro Ramos*	10.00
50	"Dusty" Rhodes	10.00
51	Ernie Oravetz	10.00
52	Bob Grim	10.00
53	Arnold Portocarrero	10.00
54	Bob Keegan	10.00
55	Wally Moon	10.00
56	Dale Long	10.00
57	"Duke" Maas	10.00
58	Ed Roebuck	10.00
59	Jose Santiago	10.00
60	Mayo Smith	10.00
61	Bill Skowron	25.00
62	Hal Smith	10.00
63	*Roger Craig*	35.00
64	Luis Arroyo	10.00
65	Johnny O'Brien	10.00
66	Bob Speake	10.00
67	Vic Power	10.00
68	Chuck Stobbs	10.00
69	Chuck Tanner	10.00
70	Jim Rivera	10.00
71	Frank Sullivan	10.00
72a	Phillies Team (with date)	85.00
72b	Phillies Team (no date, name centered)	30.00
72c	Philadelphia Phillies (no date, name at left)	30.00
73	Wayne Terwilliger	10.00
74	Jim King	10.00
75	Roy Sievers	10.00
76	Ray Crone	10.00
77	Harvey Haddix	10.00
78	Herman Wehmeier	10.00
79	Sandy Koufax	450.00
80	Gus Triandos	10.00
81	Wally Westlake	10.00
82	Bill Renna	10.00
83	Karl Spooner	10.00
84	Babe Birrer	10.00
85a	Indians Team (with date)	85.00
85b	Indians Team (no date, name centered)	30.00
85c	Indians Team (no date, name at left)	30.00
86	Ray Jablonski	10.00
87	Dean Stone	10.00
88	Johnny Kucks	10.00
89	Norm Zauchin	10.00
90a	Redlegs Team (with date)	85.00
90b	Redlegs Team (no date, name centered)	30.00
90c	Redlegs Team (no date, name at left)	30.00
91	Gail Harris	10.00
92	"Red" Wilson	10.00
93	George Susce, Jr.	10.00
94	Ronnie Kline	10.00
95a	Braves Team (with date)	85.00
95b	Braves Team (no date, name centered)	30.00
95c	Braves Team (no date, name at left)	30.00
96	Bill Tremel	10.00
97	Jerry Lynch	10.00
98	Camilo Pascual	10.00

99	Don Zimmer	20.00
100a	Orioles Team (with date)	85.00
100b	Orioles Team (no date, name centered)	35.00
100c	Orioles Team (no date, name at left)	35.00
101	Roy Campanella	175.00
102	Jim Davis	12.00
103	Willie Miranda	12.00
104	Bob Lennon	12.00
105	Al Smith	12.00
106	Joe Astroth	12.00
107	Eddie Mathews	75.00
108	Laurin Pepper	12.00
109	Enos Slaughter	40.00
110	Yogi Berra	175.00
111	Red Sox Team	35.00
112	Dee Fondy	12.00
113	Phil Rizzuto	100.00
114	Jim Owens	12.00
115	Jackie Jensen	20.00
116	Eddie O'Brien	12.00
117	Virgil Trucks	12.00
118	Nellie Fox	50.00
119	*Larry Jackson*	12.00
120	Richie Ashburn	45.00
121	Pirates Team	45.00
122	Willard Nixon	12.00
123	Roy McMillan	12.00
124	Don Kaiser	12.00
125	Minnie Minoso	25.00
126	Jim Brady	12.00
127	Willie Jones	12.00
128	Eddie Yost	12.00
129	Jake Martin	12.00
130	Willie Mays	450.00
131	Bob Roselli	12.00
132	Bobby Avila	12.00
133	Ray Narleski	12.00
134	Cardinals Team	35.00
135	Mickey Mantle	1500.00
136	Johnny Logan	12.00
137	Al Silvera	12.00
138	Johnny Antonelli	12.00
139	Tommy Carroll	12.00
140	*Herb Score*	40.00
141	Joe Frazier	12.00
142	Gene Baker	12.00
143	Jim Piersall	12.00
144	Leroy Powell	12.00
145	Gil Hodges	75.00
146	Nationals Team	35.00
147	Earl Torgeson	12.00
148	Alvin Dark	12.00
149	Dixie Howell	12.00
150	Duke Snider	150.00
151	Spook Jacobs	12.00
152	Billy Hoeft	12.00
153	Frank J. Thomas	12.00
154	Dave Pope	12.00
155	Harvey Kuenn	12.00
156	Wes Westrum	12.00
157	Dick Brodowski	12.00
158	Wally Post	12.00
159	Clint Courtney	12.00
160	Billy Pierce	12.00
161	Joe DeMaestri	12.00
162	Gus Bell	12.00
163	Gene Woodling	12.00
164	Harmon Killebrew	175.00
165	Red Schoendienst	35.00
166	Dodgers Team	225.00
167	Harry Dorish	12.00
168	Sammy White	12.00
169	Bob Nelson	12.00

No.	Player	Price	No.	Player	Price
170	Bill Virdon	20.00	243	Sherm Lollar	18.00
171	Jim Wilson	12.00	244	Bob Buhl	18.00
172	*Frank Torre*	12.00	245	Billy Goodman	18.00
173	Johnny Podres	20.00	246	Tom Gorman	18.00
174	Glen Gorbous	12.00	247	Bill Sarni	18.00
175	Del Crandall	12.00	248	Bob Porterfield	18.00
176	Alex Kellner	12.00	249	Johnny Klippstein	18.00
177	Hank Bauer	20.00	250	Larry Doby	30.00
178	Joe Black	12.00	251	Yankees Team	250.00
179	Harry Chiti	12.00	252	Vernon Law	18.00
180	Robin Roberts	50.00	253	Irv Noren	18.00
181	Billy Martin	100.00	254	George Crowe	18.00
182	Paul Minner	18.00	255	Bob Lemon	40.00
183	Stan Lopata	18.00	256	Tom Hurd	18.00
184	Don Bessent	18.00	257	Bobby Thomson	25.00
185	Bill Bruton	18.00	258	Art Ditmar	18.00
186	Ron Jackson	18.00	259	Sam Jones	18.00
187	Early Wynn	50.00	260	Pee Wee Reese	175.00
188	White Sox Team	50.00	261	Bobby Shantz	12.00
189	Ned Garver	18.00	262	Howie Pollet	12.00
190	Carl Furillo	40.00	263	Bob Miller	12.00
191	Frank Lary	18.00	264	Ray Monzant	12.00
192	Smoky Burgess	18.00	265	Sandy Consuegra	12.00
193	Wilmer Mizell	18.00	266	Don Ferrarese	12.00
194	Monte Irvin	40.00	267	Bob Nieman	12.00
195	George Kell	40.00	268	Dale Mitchell	12.00
196	Tom Poholsky	18.00	269	Jack Meyer	12.00
197	Granny Hamner	18.00	270	Billy Loes	12.00
198	Ed Fitzgerald (Fitz Gerald)	18.00	271	Foster Castleman	12.00
199	Hank Thompson	18.00	272	Danny O'Connell	12.00
200	Bob Feller	165.00	273	Walker Cooper	12.00
201	Rip Repulski	18.00	274	Frank Baumholtz	12.00
202	Jim Hearn	18.00	275	Jim Greengrass	12.00
203	Bill Tuttle	18.00	276	George Zuverink	12.00
204	Art Swanson	18.00	277	Daryl Spencer	12.00
205	"Whitey" Lockman	18.00	278	Chet Nichols	12.00
206	Erv Palica	18.00	279	Johnny Groth	12.00
207	Jim Small	18.00	280	Jim Gilliam	30.00
208	Elston Howard	50.00	281	Art Houtteman	12.00
209	Max Surkont	18.00	282	Warren Hacker	12.00
210	Mike Garcia	18.00	283	Hal Smith	12.00
211	Murry Dickson	18.00	284	Ike Delock	12.00
212	Johnny Temple	18.00	285	Eddie Miksis	12.00
213	Tigers Team	75.00	286	Bill Wight	12.00
214	Bob Rush	18.00	287	Bobby Adams	12.00
215	Tommy Byrne	18.00	288	Bob Cerv	50.00
216	Jerry Schoonmaker	18.00	289	Hal Jeffcoat	12.00
217	Billy Klaus	18.00	290	Curt Simmons	12.00
218	Joe Nuxall (Nuxhall)	18.00	291	Frank Kellert	12.00
219	Lew Burdette	18.00	292	*Luis Aparicio*	175.00
220	Del Ennis	18.00	293	Stu Miller	12.00
221	Bob Friend	18.00	294	Ernie Johnson	12.00
222	Dave Philley	18.00	295	Clem Labine	12.00
223	Randy Jackson	18.00	296	Andy Seminick	12.00
224	Bud Podbielan	18.00	297	Bob Skinner	12.00
225	Gil McDougald	18.00	298	Johnny Schmitz	12.00
226	Giants Team	100.00	299	Charley Neal	40.00
227	Russ Meyer	18.00	300	Vic Wertz	12.00
228	Mickey Vernon	18.00	301	Marv Grissom	12.00
229	Harry Brecheen	18.00	302	Eddie Robinson	12.00
230	Chico Carrasquel	18.00	303	Jim Dyck	12.00
231	Bob Hale	18.00	304	Frank Malzone	12.00
232	Toby Atwell	18.00	305	Brooks Lawrence	12.00
233	Carl Erskine	35.00	306	Curt Roberts	12.00
234	Pete Runnels	18.00	307	Hoyt Wilhelm	45.00
235	Don Newcombe	50.00	308	Chuck Harmon	12.00
236	Athletics Team	40.00	309	*Don Blasingame*	12.00
237	Jose Valdivielso	18.00	310	Steve Gromek	12.00
238	Walt Dropo	18.00	311	Hal Naragon	12.00
239	Harry Simpson	18.00	312	Andy Pafko	12.00
240	Whitey Ford	200.00	313	Gene Stephens	12.00
241	Don Mueller	18.00	314	Hobie Landrith	12.00
242	Hershell Freeman	18.00	315	Milt Bolling	12.00

316	Jerry Coleman	12.00
317	Al Aber	12.00
318	Fred Hatfield	12.00
319	Jack Crimian	12.00
320	Joe Adcock	12.00
321	Jim Konstanty	12.00
322	Karl Olson	12.00
323	Willard Schmidt	12.00
324	"Rocky" Bridges	12.00
325	Don Liddle	12.00
326	Connie Johnson	12.00
327	Bob Wiesler	12.00
328	Preston Ward	12.00
329	Lou Berberet	12.00
330	Jim Busby	12.00
331	Dick Hall	12.00
332	Don Larsen	75.00
333	Rube Walker	12.00
334	Bob Miller	12.00
335	Don Hoak	12.00
336	Ellis Kinder	12.00
337	Bobby Morgan	12.00
338	Jim Delsing	12.00
339	Rance Pless	12.00
340	Mickey McDermott	50.00
----	Checklist 1/3	350.00
----	Checklist 2/4	350.00

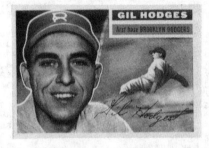

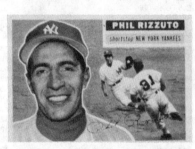

1957 Topps

For 1957, Topps reduced the size of its cards to the now-standard 2-1/2" by 3-1/2." Set size was increased to 407 cards. Another change came in the form of the use of real color photographs as opposed to the hand-colored black and whites of previous years. For the first time since 1954, there were also cards with more than one player. The two, "Dodger Sluggers" and "Yankees' Power Hitters" began a trend toward the increased use of multiple-player cards. Another first-time innovation, found on the backs, is complete player statistics. The scarce cards in the set are not the highest numbers, but rather numbers 265-352. Four unnumbered checklist cards were issued along with the set. They are quite expensive and are not included in the complete set prices quoted below.

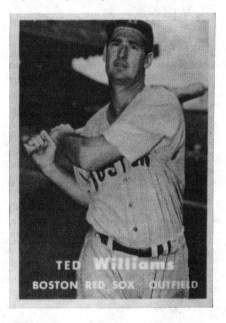

Mr. Mint Says - This was the first set of the modern era, now in the standard size of 2-1/2" x 3-1/2". One of the most popular, if not the most popular, of the modern sets.

The mid-numbers, 265-352, are genuinely difficult to find and priced accordingly, and the 3/4 and 4/5 checklists are super tough. I've probably only had one 4/5 checklist in my life that I would consider mint.

The Mantle is a super popular card, but frequently found off-center to the right. The #1 Williams card is always tricky in top condition. All of the Hall of Famers are highly sought, as are the Dodgers Sluggers and Power Hitters combination cards.

		MT
Complete Set (407):		9750.
Common Player (1-176):		7.00
Common Player (177-264):		5.00
Common Player (265-352):		20.00
Common Player (353-407):		7.00

1	Ted Williams	700.00
2	Yogi Berra	20.00
3	Dale Long	7.00
4	Johnny Logan	7.00
5	Sal Maglie	7.00
6	Hector Lopez	7.00
7	Luis Aparicio	50.00
8	Don Mossi	7.00
9	Johnny Temple	7.00
10	Willie Mays	275.00
11	George Zuverink	7.00
12	Dick Groat	8.00
13	Wally Burnette	7.00
14	Bob Nieman	7.00
15	Robin Roberts	40.00
16	Walt Moryn	7.00
17	Billy Gardner	7.00
18	*Don Drysdale*	300.00
19	Bob Wilson	7.00
20	Hank Aaron (negative reversed)	300.00
21	Frank Sullivan	7.00
22	Jerry Snyder (photo actually Ed Fitz Gerald)	7.00
23	Sherm Lollar	7.00
24	*Bill Mazeroski*	85.00
25	Whitey Ford	75.00
26	Bob Boyd	7.00
27	Ted Kazanski	7.00
28	Gene Conley	7.00
29	*Whitey Herzog*	30.00
30	Pee Wee Reese	100.00
31	Ron Northey	7.00
32	Hersh Freeman	7.00
33	Jim Small	7.00
34	Tom Sturdivant	8.00
35	*Frank Robinson*	350.00
36	Bob Grim	8.00
37	Frank Torre	7.00
38	Nellie Fox	35.00
39	Al Worthington	7.00
40	Early Wynn	25.00
41	Hal Smith	7.00
42	Dee Fondy	7.00
43	Connie Johnson	7.00
44	Joe DeMaestri	7.00
45	Carl Furillo	20.00
46	Bob Miller	7.00
47	Don Blasingame	7.00
48	Bill Bruton	7.00
49	Daryl Spencer	7.00
50	Herb Score	7.00
51	Clint Courtney	7.00
52	Lee Walls	7.00
53	Clem Labine	7.00
54	Elmer Valo	7.00

No.	Player	Price	No.	Player	Price
55	Ernie Banks	150.00	131	Milt Bolling	7.00
56	Dave Sisler	7.00	132	Art Ditmar	8.00
57	Jim Lemon	7.00	133	Del Crandall	8.00
58	Ruben Gomez	7.00	134	Don Kaiser	7.00
59	Dick Williams	8.00	135	Bill Skowron	20.00
60	Billy Hoeft	7.00	136	Jim Hegan	7.00
61	Dusty Rhodes	7.00	137	Bob Rush	7.00
62	Billy Martin	60.00	138	Minnie Minoso	15.00
63	Ike Delock	7.00	139	Lou Kretlow	7.00
64	Pete Runnels	7.00	140	Frank J. Thomas	7.00
65	Wally Moon	7.00	141	Al Aber	7.00
66	Brooks Lawrence	7.00	142	Charley Thompson	7.00
67	Chico Carrasquel	7.00	143	Andy Pafko	7.00
68	Ray Crone	7.00	144	Ray Narleski	7.00
69	Roy McMillan	7.00	145	Al Smith	7.00
70	Richie Ashburn	40.00	146	Don Ferrarese	7.00
71	Murry Dickson	7.00	147	Al Walker	8.00
72	Bill Tuttle	7.00	148	Don Mueller	7.00
73	George Crowe	7.00	149	Bob Kennedy	7.00
74	Vito Valentinetti	7.00	150	Bob Friend	7.00
75	Jim Piersall	8.00	151	Willie Miranda	7.00
76	Roberto Clemente	300.00	152	Jack Harshman	7.00
77	Paul Foytack	7.00	153	Karl Olson	7.00
78	Vic Wertz	7.00	154	Red Schoendienst	25.00
79	*Lindy McDaniel*	8.00	155	Jim Brosnan	7.00
80	Gil Hodges	75.00	156	Gus Triandos	7.00
81	Herm Wehmeier	7.00	157	Wally Post	7.00
82	Elston Howard	25.00	158	Curt Simmons	7.00
83	Lou Skizas	7.00	159	Solly Drake	7.00
84	Moe Drabowsky	7.00	160	Billy Pierce	8.00
85	Larry Doby	10.00	161	Pirates Team	12.50
86	Bill Sarni	7.00	162	Jack Meyer	7.00
87	Tom Gorman	7.00	163	Sammy White	7.00
88	Harvey Kuenn	8.00	164	Tommy Carroll	8.00
89	Roy Sievers	7.00	165	Ted Kluszewski	60.00
90	Warren Spahn	75.00	166	Roy Face	7.00
91	Mack Burk	7.00	167	Vic Power	7.00
92	Mickey Vernon	7.00	168	Frank Lary	7.00
93	Hal Jeffcoat	7.00	169	Herb Plews	7.00
94	Bobby Del Greco	7.00	170	Duke Snider	150.00
95	Mickey Mantle	1750.00	171	Red Sox Team	12.00
96	*Hank Aguirre*	7.00	172	Gene Woodling	7.00
97	Yankees Team	75.00	173	Roger Craig	12.50
98	Al Dark	8.00	174	Willie Jones	7.00
99	Bob Keegan	7.00	175	Don Larsen	20.00
100	League Presidents (Warren Giles, William Harridge)	9.00	176	Gene Baker	7.00
101	Chuck Stobbs	7.00	177	Eddie Yost	5.00
102	Ray Boone	7.00	178	Don Bessent	8.00
103	Joe Nuxhall	9.00	179	Ernie Oravetz	5.00
104	Hank Foiles	7.00	180	Gus Bell	5.00
105	Johnny Antonelli	7.00	181	Dick Donovan	5.00
106	Ray Moore	7.00	182	Hobie Landrith	5.00
107	Jim Rivera	7.00	183	Cubs Team	15.00
108	Tommy Byrne	8.00	184	*Tito Francona*	5.00
109	Hank Thompson	7.00	185	Johnny Kucks	8.00
110	Bill Virdon	8.00	186	Jim King	5.00
111	Hal Smith	7.00	187	Virgil Trucks	5.00
112	Tom Brewer	7.00	188	Felix Mantilla	5.00
113	Wilmer Mizell	7.00	189	Willard Nixon	5.00
114	Braves Team	20.00	190	Randy Jackson	8.00
115	Jim Gilliam	15.00	191	Joe Margoneri	5.00
116	Mike Fornieles	7.00	192	Jerry Coleman	9.00
117	Joe Adcock	7.00	193	Del Rice	5.00
118	Bob Porterfield	7.00	194	Hal Brown	5.00
119	Stan Lopata	7.00	195	Bobby Avila	5.00
120	Bob Lemon	25.00	196	Larry Jackson	5.00
121	*Cletis Boyer*	25.00	197	Hank Sauer	5.00
122	Ken Boyer	15.00	198	Tigers Team	15.00
123	Steve Ridzik	7.00	199	Vernon Law	5.00
124	Dave Philley	7.00	200	Gil McDougald	20.00
125	Al Kaline	100.00	201	Sandy Amoros	9.00
126	Bob Wiesler	7.00	202	Dick Gernert	5.00
127	Bob Buhl	7.00	203	Hoyt Wilhelm	25.00
128	Ed Bailey	7.00	204	Athletics Team	15.00
129	Saul Rogovin	7.00	205	Charley Maxwell	5.00
130	Don Newcombe	20.00	206	Willard Schmidt	5.00

207	Billy Hunter	5.00
208	Lew Burdette	5.00
209	Bob Skinner	5.00
210	Roy Campanella	150.00
211	Camilo Pascual	5.00
212	*Rocky Colavito*	175.00
213	Les Moss	5.00
214	Phillies Team	12.00
215	Enos Slaughter	25.00
216	Marv Grissom	5.00
217	Gene Stephens	5.00
218	Ray Jablonski	5.00
219	Tom Acker	5.00
220	Jackie Jensen	10.00
221	Dixie Howell	5.00
222	Alex Grammas	5.00
223	Frank House	5.00
224	Marv Blaylock	5.00
225	Harry Simpson	5.00
226	Preston Ward	5.00
227	Jerry Staley	5.00
228	Smoky Burgess	5.00
229	George Susce	5.00
230	George Kell	20.00
231	Solly Hemus	5.00
232	Whitey Lockman	5.00
233	Art Fowler	5.00
234	Dick Cole	5.00
235	Tom Poholsky	5.00
236	Joe Ginsberg	5.00
237	Foster Castleman	5.00
238	Eddie Robinson	5.00
239	Tom Morgan	5.00
240	Hank Bauer	15.00
241	Joe Lonnett	5.00
242	Charley Neal	8.00
243	Cardinals Team	15.00
244	Billy Loes	5.00
245	Rip Repulski	5.00
246	Jose Valdivielso	5.00
247	Turk Lown	5.00
248	Jim Finigan	5.00
249	Dave Pope	5.00
250	Eddie Mathews	50.00
251	Orioles Team	15.00
252	Carl Erskine	15.00
253	Gus Zernial	5.00
254	Ron Negray	5.00
255	Charlie Silvera	5.00
256	Ronnie Kline	5.00
257	Walt Dropo	5.00
258	Steve Gromek	5.00
259	Eddie O'Brien	5.00
260	Del Ennis	5.00
261	Bob Chakales	5.00
262	Bobby Thomson	10.00
263	George Strickland	5.00
264	Bob Turley	8.00
265	Harvey Haddix	20.00
266	Ken Kuhn	20.00
267	Danny Kravitz	20.00
268	Jackie Collum	20.00
269	Bob Cerv	20.00
270	Senators Team	75.00
271	Danny O'Connell	20.00
272	Bobby Shantz	30.00
273	Jim Davis	20.00
274	Don Hoak	20.00
275	Indians Team	75.00
276	Jim Pyburn	20.00
277	Johnny Podres	75.00
278	Fred Hatfield	20.00
279	Bob Thurman	20.00
280	Alex Kellner	20.00
281	Gail Harris	20.00
282	Jack Dittmer	20.00

283	*Wes Covington*	20.00
284	Don Zimmer	20.00
285	Ned Garver	20.00
286	*Bobby Richardson*	150.00
287	Sam Jones	20.00
288	Ted Lepcio	20.00
289	Jim Bolger	20.00
290	Andy Carey	20.00
291	Windy McCall	20.00
292	Billy Klaus	20.00
293	Ted Abernathy	20.00
294	Rocky Bridges	20.00
295	Joe Collins	20.00
296	Johnny Klippstein	20.00
297	Jack Crimian	20.00
298	Irv Noren	20.00
299	Chuck Harmon	20.00
300	Mike Garcia	20.00
301	Sam Esposito	20.00
302	Sandy Koufax	400.00
303	Billy Goodman	20.00
304	Joe Cunningham	20.00
305	Chico Fernandez	20.00
306	Darrell Johnson	20.00
307	Jack Phillips	20.00
308	Dick Hall	20.00
309	Jim Busby	20.00
310	Max Surkont	20.00
311	Al Pilarcik	20.00
312	*Tony Kubek*	150.00
313	Mel Parnell	20.00
314	Ed Bouchee	20.00
315	Lou Berberet	20.00
316	Billy O'Dell	20.00
317	Giants Team	75.00
318	Mickey McDermott	20.00
319	Gino Cimoli	20.00
320	Neil Chrisley	20.00
321	Red Murff	20.00
322	Redlegs Team	75.00
323	Wes Westrum	20.00
324	Dodgers Team	150.00
325	Frank Bolling	20.00
326	Pedro Ramos	20.00
327	Jim Pendleton	20.00
328	*Brooks Robinson*	450.00
329	White Sox Team	75.00
330	Jim Wilson	20.00
331	Ray Katt	20.00
332	Bob Bowman	20.00
333	Ernie Johnson	20.00
334	Jerry Schoonmaker	20.00
335	Granny Hamner	20.00
336	*Haywood Sullivan*	20.00
337	Rene Valdes	20.00
338	*Jim Bunning*	200.00
339	Bob Speake	20.00
340	Bill Wight	20.00
341	Don Gross	20.00
342	Gene Mauch	20.00
343	Taylor Phillips	20.00
344	Paul LaPalme	20.00
345	Paul Smith	20.00
346	Dick Littlefield	20.00
347	Hal Naragon	20.00
348	Jim Hearn	20.00
349	Nelson King	20.00
350	Eddie Miksis	20.00
351	Dave Hillman	20.00
352	Ellis Kinder	20.00
353	Cal Neeman	7.00
354	Rip Coleman	7.00
355	Frank Malzone	7.00
356	Faye Throneberry	7.00
357	Earl Torgeson	7.00
358	Jerry Lynch	7.00

359	Tom Cheney	7.00
360	Johnny Groth	7.00
361	Curt Barclay	7.00
362	Roman Mejias	7.00
363	Eddie Kasko	7.00
364	Cal McLish	7.00
365	Ossie Virgil	7.00
366	Ken Lehman	8.00
367	Ed Fitz Gerald	7.00
368	Bob Purkey	7.00
369	Milt Graff	7.00
370	Warren Hacker	7.00
371	Bob Lennon	7.00
372	Norm Zauchin	7.00
373	Pete Whisenant	7.00
374	Don Cardwell	7.00
375	*Jim Landis*	7.00
376	Don Elston	8.00
377	Andre Rodgers	7.00
378	Elmer Singleton	7.00
379	Don Lee	7.00
380	Walker Cooper	7.00
381	Dean Stone	7.00
382	Jim Brideweser	7.00
383	*Juan Pizarro*	7.00
384	Bobby Gene Smith	7.00
385	Art Houtteman	7.00
386	Lyle Luttrell	7.00
387	*Jack Sanford*	7.00
388	Pete Daley	7.00
389	Dave Jolly	7.00
390	Reno Bertoia	7.00
391	*Ralph Terry*	10.00
392	Chuck Tanner	7.00
393	Raul Sanchez	7.00
394	Luis Arroyo	7.00
395	Bubba Phillips	7.00
396	Casey Wise	7.00
397	Roy Smalley	7.00
398	Al Cicotte	7.00
399	Billy Consolo	7.00
400	Roy Campanella, Carl Furillo, Gil Hodges, DukeSnider	300.00
401	*Earl Battey*	8.00
402	Jim Pisoni	7.00
403	Dick Hyde	7.00
404	Harry Anderson	7.00
405	Duke Maas	7.00
406	Bob Hale	7.00
407	Yankees' Power Hitters (Mickey Mantle, Yogi Berra)	500.00
----	Checklist Series 1-2 (Big Blony ad on back)	250.00
----	Checklist Series 1-2 (Bazooka ad on back)	250.00
----	Checklist Series 2-3 (Big Blony ad on back)	350.00
----	Checklist Series 2-3 (Bazooka ad on back)	350.00
----	Checklist Series 3-4 (Big Blony ad on back)	650.00
----	Checklist Series 3-4 (Bazooka ad on back)	650.00
----	Checklist Series 4-5 (Big Blony ad on back)	1000.00
----	Checklist Series 4-5 (Bazooka ad on back)	1000.00
----	Contest May 4	50.00
----	Contest May 25	50.00
----	Contest June 22	50.00
----	Contest July 19	50.00
----	Lucky Penny Insert Card	15.00

1958 Topps

Topps continued to expand its set size in 1958 with the release of a 494-card set. One card (#145) was not issued after Ed Bouchee was suspended from baseball. Cards retained the 2-1/2" by 3-1/2" size. There are a number of variations, including yellow or white lettering on 33 cards between numbers 2-108 (higher priced yellow letter variations checklisted below are not included in the complete set prices). The number of multiple-player cards was increased. A major innovation is the addition of 20 "All-Star" cards. For the first time, checklists were incorporated into the numbered series, as the backs of team cards.

Mr. Mint Says - Here is one of the toughest sets in the late 50s and early 60s to complete in mint condition. It is probably harder than most other sets in the 50s except for 1952 and 1953. Perhaps it was the quality of the card stock, but it seems soft and did not hold up well. Cards #1-110 are virtually impossible in mint grades.

The yellow letter variation in 1958 Topps is probably the most actively collected variation in the 1950s. At one time, after a major purchase, I had literally hundreds of each of these, but the hobby consumed them quickly. The Harrell, Hardy, Ward and Geiger cards are overrated; there were several hundred of each in the Ross Collection, the same collection that yielded the yellow letter variations.

I have never seen an unopened box of 1958s, and they are much tougher than 59-61 in that regard. Finding a matched set in any kind of quantity is virtually impossible, but after 1958 Topps started coming out with presentation sets, many of which have survived in pristine condition. I also think that Topps production was cranked up following the 1958 set.

		MT
Complete Set (494):		7500.
Common Player (1-110):		10.00
Common Player (111-198):		6.50
Common Player (199-352):		5.50
Common Player (353-474):		4.00
Common Player (475-495):		5.50

1	Ted Williams	300.00
2a	Bob Lemon (yellow team letters)	75.00
2b	Bob Lemon (white team letters)	20.00
3	Alex Kellner	10.00
4	Hank Foiles	10.00
5	Willie Mays	300.00
6	George Zuverink	10.00
7	Dale Long	10.00
8a	Eddie Kasko (yellow name)	50.00
8b	Eddie Kasko (white name)	10.00
9	Hank Bauer	15.00
10	Lou Burdette	10.00
11a	Jim Rivera (yellow team letters)	50.00
11b	Jim Rivera (white team letters)	10.00
12	George Crowe	10.00
13a	Billy Hoeft (yellow name)	50.00
13b	Billy Hoeft (white name, orange triangle by foot)	10.00
13c	Billy Hoeft (white name, red triangle by foot)	10.00
14	Rip Repulski	10.00
15	Jim Lemon	10.00
16	Charley Neal	10.00
17	Felix Mantilla	10.00
18	Frank Sullivan	10.00
19	Giants Team/Checklist 1-88	30.00
20a	Gil McDougald (yellow name)	50.00
20b	Gil McDougald (white name)	10.00
21	Curt Barclay	10.00
22	Hal Naragon	10.00
23a	Bill Tuttle (yellow name)	50.00
23b	Bill Tuttle (white name)	10.00
24a	Hobie Landrith (yellow name)	50.00
24b	Hobie Landrith (white name)	10.00
25	Don Drysdale	100.00
26	Ron Jackson	10.00
27	Bud Freeman	10.00
28	Jim Busby	10.00
29	Ted Lepcio	10.00
30a	Hank Aaron (yellow name)	500.00
30b	Hank Aaron (white name)	300.00
31	Tex Clevenger	10.00
32a	J.W. Porter (yellow name)	50.00
32b	J.W. Porter (white name)	10.00
33a	Cal Neeman (yellow team letters)	50.00
33b	Cal Neeman (white team letters)	10.00
34	Bob Thurman	10.00
35a	Don Mossi (yellow team letters)	50.00
35b	Don Mossi (white team letters)	10.00
36	Ted Kazanski	10.00
37	*Mike McCormick (photo actually Ray Monzant)*	10.00

38	Dick Gernert	10.00		95	Frank Bolling	10.00
39	Bob Martyn	10.00		96	Joe Durham	10.00
40	George Kell	25.00		97a	Larry Jackson (yellow name)	50.00
41	Dave Hillman	10.00		97b	Larry Jackson (white name)	10.00
42	*John Roseboro*	10.00		98a	Billy Hunter (yellow name)	50.00
43	Sal Maglie	10.00		98b	Billy Hunter (white name)	10.00
44	Senators Team/Checklist 1-88	20.00		99	Bobby Adams	10.00
45	Dick Groat	10.00		100a	Early Wynn (yellow team letters)	100.00
46a	Lou Sleater (yellow name)	50.00		100b	Early Wynn (white team letters)	25.00
46b	Lou Sleater (white name)	10.00		101a	Bobby Richardson (yellow name)	100.00
47	*Roger Maris*	100.00		101b	Bobby Richardson (white name)	300.00
48	Chuck Harmon	10.00		102	George Strickland	10.00
49	Smoky Burgess	10.00		103	Jerry Lynch	10.00
50a	Billy Pierce (yellow team letters)	50.00		104	Jim Pendleton	10.00
50b	Billy Pierce (white team letters)	10.00		105	Billy Gardner	10.00
51	Del Rice	10.00		106	Dick Schofield	10.00
52a	Roberto Clemente (yellow team letters)	750.00		107	Ossie Virgil	10.00
52b	Roberto Clemente (white team letters)	350.00		108a	Jim Landis (yellow team letters)	10.00
53a	Morrie Martin (yellow name)	50.00		108b	Jim Landis (white team letters)	10.00
53b	Morrie Martin (white name)	10.00		109	Herb Plews	10.00
54	*Norm Siebern*	10.00		110	Johnny Logan	10.00
55	Chico Carrasquel	10.00		111	Stu Miller	6.50
56	Bill Fischer	10.00		112	Gus Zernial	6.50
57a	Tim Thompson (yellow name)	50.00		113	Jerry Walker	6.50
57b	Tim Thompson (white name)	10.00		114	Irv Noren	6.50
58a	Art Schult (yellow team letters)	50.00		115	Jim Bunning	25.00
58b	Art Schult (white team letters)	10.00		116	Dave Philley	6.50
59	Dave Sisler	10.00		117	Frank Torre	6.50
60a	Del Ennis (yellow name)	50.00		118	Harvey Haddix	6.50
60b	Del Ennis (white name)	10.00		119	Harry Chiti	6.50
61a	Darrell Johnson (yellow name)	50.00		120	Johnny Podres	7.50
61b	Darrell Johnson (white name)	10.00		121	Eddie Miksis	6.50
62	Joe DeMaestri	10.00		122	Walt Moryn	6.50
63	Joe Nuxhall	10.00		123	Dick Tomanek	6.50
64	Joe Lonnett	10.00		124	Bobby Usher	6.50
65a	Von McDaniel (yellow name)	50.00		125	Al Dark	6.50
65b	Von McDaniel (white name)	10.00		126	Stan Palys	6.50
66	Lee Walls	10.00		127	Tom Sturdivant	7.50
67	Joe Ginsberg	10.00		128	*Willie Kirkland*	6.50
68	Daryl Spencer	10.00		129	Jim Derrington	6.50
69	Wally Burnette	10.00		130	Jackie Jensen	7.50
70a	Al Kaline (yellow name)	300.00		131	Bob Henrich	6.50
70b	Al Kaline (white name)	100.00		132	Vernon Law	6.50
71	Dodgers Team	50.00		133	Russ Nixon	6.50
72	Bud Byerly	10.00		134	Phillies Team/Checklist 89-176	12.00
73	Pete Daley	10.00		135	Mike Drabowsky	6.50
74	Roy Face	10.00		136	Jim Finingan	6.50
75	Gus Bell	10.00		137	Russ Kemmerer	6.50
76a	Dick Farrell (yellow team letters)	50.00		138	Earl Torgeson	6.50
76b	Dick Farrell (white team letters)	10.00		139	George Brunet	6.50
77a	Don Zimmer (yellow team letters)	50.00		140	Wes Covington	6.50
77b	Don Zimmer (white team letters)	10.00		141	Ken Lehman	6.50
78a	Ernie Johnson (yellow name)	50.00		142	Enos Slaughter	25.00
78b	Ernie Johnson (white name)	10.00		143	Billy Muffett	6.50
79a	Dick Williams (yellow team letters)	50.00		144	Bobby Morgan	6.50
79b	Dick Williams (white team letters)	10.00		145	Not Issued	
80	Dick Drott	10.00		146	Dick Gray	6.50
81a	*Steve Boros* (yellow team letters)	50.00		147	*Don McMahon*	6.50
81b	*Steve Boros* (white team letters)	10.00		148	Billy Consolo	6.50
82	Ronnie Kline	10.00		149	Tom Acker	6.50
83	*Bob Hazle*	10.00		150	Mickey Mantle	1000.00
84	Billy O'Dell	10.00		151	Buddy Pritchard	6.50
85a	Luis Aparicio (yellow team letters)	100.00		152	Johnny Antonelli	6.50
85b	Luis Aparicio (white team letters)	40.00		153	Les Moss	6.50
86	Valmy Thomas	10.00		154	Harry Byrd	6.50
87	Johnny Kucks	10.00		155	Hector Lopez	6.50
88	Duke Snider	100.00		156	Dick Hyde	6.50
89	Billy Klaus	10.00		157	Dee Fondy	6.50
90	Robin Roberts	30.00		158	Indians Team/Checklist 177-264	12.50
91	Chuck Tanner	10.00		159	Taylor Phillips	6.50
92a	Clint Courtney (yellow name)	50.00		160	Don Hoak	6.50
92b	Clint Courtney (white name)	10.00		161	Don Larsen	9.00
93	Sandy Amoros	10.00		162	Gil Hodges	35.00
94	Bob Skinner	10.00		163	Jim Wilson	6.50

164	Bob Taylor	6.50
165	Bob Nieman	6.50
166	Danny O'Connell	6.50
167	Frank Baumann	6.50
168	Joe Cunningham	6.50
169	Ralph Terry	6.50
170	Vic Wertz	6.50
171	Harry Anderson	6.50
172	Don Gross	6.50
173	Eddie Yost	6.50
174	A's Team/Checklist 89-176	12.00
175	*Marv Throneberry*	12.00
176	Bob Buhl	6.50
177	Al Smith	6.50
178	Ted Kluszewski	9.00
179	Willy Miranda	6.50
180	Lindy McDaniel	6.50
181	Willie Jones	6.50
182	Joe Caffie	6.50
183	Dave Jolly	6.50
184	Elvin Tappe	6.50
185	Ray Boone	6.50
186	Jack Meyer	6.50
187	Sandy Koufax	250.00
188	Milt Bolling (photo actually Lou Berberet)	6.50
189	George Susce	6.50
190	Red Schoendienst	17.50
191	Art Ceccarelli	6.50
192	Milt Graff	6.50
193	*Jerry Lumpe*	7.00
194	Roger Craig	8.00
195	Whitey Lockman	6.50
196	Mike Garcia	6.50
197	Haywood Sullivan	6.50
198	Bill Virdon	6.50
199	Don Blasingame	5.50
200	Bob Keegan	5.50
201	Jim Bolger	5.50
202	*Woody Held*	5.50
203	Al Walker	5.50
204	Leo Kiely	5.50
205	Johnny Temple	5.50
206	Bob Shaw	5.50
207	Solly Hemus	5.50
208	Cal McLish	5.50
209	Bob Anderson	5.50
210	Wally Moon	5.50
211	Pete Burnside	5.50
212	Bubba Phillips	5.50
213	Red Wilson	5.50
214	Willard Schmidt	5.50
215	Jim Gilliam	7.50
216	Cards Team/Checklist 177-264	13.50
217	Jack Harshman	5.50
218	Dick Rand	5.50
219	Camilo Pascual	5.50
220	Tom Brewer	5.50
221	Jerry Kindall	5.50
222	Bud Daley	5.50
223	Andy Pafko	5.50
224	Bob Grim	8.00
225	Billy Goodman	5.50
226	Bob Smith (photo actually Bobby Gene Smith)	5.50
227	Gene Stephens	5.50
228	Duke Maas	5.50
229	Frank Zupo	5.50
230	Richie Ashburn	20.00
231	Lloyd Merritt	5.50
232	Reno Bertoia	5.50
233	Mickey Vernon	5.50
234	Carl Sawatski	5.50
235	Tom Gorman	5.50
236	Ed Fitz Gerald	5.50
237	Bill Wight	5.50
238	Bill Mazeroski	25.00
239	Chuck Stobbs	5.50
240	Moose Skowron	10.00
241	Dick Littlefield	5.50
242	Johnny Klippstein	5.50
243	Larry Raines	5.50
244	*Don Demeter*	5.50
245	*Frank Lary*	5.50
246	Yankees Team	75.00
247	Casey Wise	5.50
248	Herm Wehmeier	5.50
249	Ray Moore	5.50
250	Roy Sievers	5.50
251	Warren Hacker	5.50
252	Bob Trowbridge	5.50
253	Don Mueller	5.50
254	Alex Grammas	5.50
255	Bob Turley	7.00
256	White Sox Team/Checklist 265-352	12.00
257	Hal Smith	5.50
258	Carl Erskine	7.00
259	Al Pilarcik	5.50
260	Frank Malzone	5.50
261	Turk Lown	5.50
262	Johnny Groth	5.50
263	Eddie Bressoud	5.50
264	Jack Sanford	5.50
265	Pete Runnels	5.50
266	Connie Johnson	5.50
267	Sherm Lollar	5.50
268	Granny Hamner	5.50
269	Paul Smith	5.50
270	Warren Spahn	55.00
271	Billy Martin	12.00
272	Ray Crone	5.50
273	Hal Smith	5.50
274	Rocky Bridges	5.50
275	Elston Howard	8.00
276	Bobby Avila	5.50
277	Virgil Trucks	5.50
278	Mack Burk	5.50
279	Bob Boyd	5.50
280	Jim Piersall	6.00
281	Sam Taylor	5.50
282	Paul Foytack	5.50
283	Ray Shearer	5.50
284	Ray Katt	5.50
285	Frank Robinson	100.00
286	Gino Cimoli	5.50
287	Sam Jones	5.50
288	Harmon Killebrew	100.00
289	Series Hurling Rivals (Lou Burdette, Bobby Shantz)	8.00
290	Dick Donovan	5.50
291	Don Landrum	5.50
292	Ned Garver	5.50
293	Gene Freese	5.50
294	Hal Jeffcoat	5.50
295	Minnie Minoso	7.00
296	*Ryne Duren*	12.00
297	Don Buddin	5.50
298	Jim Hearn	5.50
299	Harry Simpson	7.00
300	League Presidents (Warren Giles, William Harridge)	9.00
301	Randy Jackson	5.50
302	Mike Baxes	5.50
303	Neil Chrisley	5.50
304	Tigers' Big Bats (Al Kaline, Harvey Kuenn)	17.50
305	Clem Labine	7.00
306	Whammy Douglas	5.50
307	Brooks Robinson	150.00
308	Paul Giel	5.50
309	Gail Harris	5.50
310	Ernie Banks	100.00
311	Bob Purkey	5.50

312	Red Sox Team	12.00
313	Bob Rush	5.50
314	Dodgers' Boss & Power (Duke Snider, Walter Alston)	25.00
315	Bob Friend	5.50
316	Tito Francona	5.50
317	*Albie Pearson*	6.00
318	Frank House	5.50
319	Lou Skizas	5.50
320	Whitey Ford	50.00
321	Sluggers Supreme (Ted Kluszewski, Ted Williams)	75.00
322	Harding Peterson	5.50
323	Elmer Valo	5.50
324	Hoyt Wilhelm	15.00
325	Joe Adcock	5.50
326	Bob Miller	5.50
327	Cubs Team/Checklist 265-352	12.50
328	Ike Delock	5.50
329	Bob Cerv	5.50
330	Ed Bailey	5.50
331	Pedro Ramos	5.50
332	Jim King	5.50
333	Andy Carey	7.50
334	Mound Aces (Bob Friend, Billy Pierce)	9.00
335	Ruben Gomez	5.50
336	Bert Hamric	5.50
337	Hank Aguirre	5.50
338	Walt Dropo	5.50
339	Fred Hatfield	5.50
340	Don Newcombe	7.50
341	Pirates Team/Checklist 265-352	12.50
342	Jim Brosnan	5.50
343	*Orlando Cepeda*	150.00
344	Bob Porterfield	5.50
345	Jim Hegan	5.50
346	Steve Bilko	5.50
347	Don Rudolph	5.50
348	Chico Fernandez	5.50
349	Murry Dickson	5.50
350	Ken Boyer	5.50
351	Braves' Fence Busters (Hank Aaron, Joe Adcock, Del Crandall, Eddie Mathews)	50.00
352	Herb Score	5.50
353	Stan Lopata	4.00
354	Art Ditmar	7.50
355	Bill Bruton	4.00
356	Bob Malkmus	4.00
357	Danny McDevitt	4.00
358	Gene Baker	4.00
359	Billy Loes	4.00
360	Roy McMillan	4.00
361	Mike Fornieles	4.00
362	Ray Jablonski	4.00
363	Don Elston	4.00
364	Earl Battey	4.00
365	Tom Morgan	4.00
366	Gene Green	4.00
367	Jack Urban	4.00
368	Rocky Colavito	50.00
369	Ralph Lumenti	4.00
370	Yogi Berra	125.00
371	Marty Keough	4.00
372	Don Cardwell	4.00
373	Joe Pignatano	4.00
374	Brooks Lawrence	4.00
375	Pee Wee Reese	75.00
376	Charley Rabe	4.00
377a	Braves Team (alphabetical checklist on back)	15.00
377b	Braves Team (numerical checklist on back)	125.00
377b	Braves Team	125.00
378	Hank Sauer	4.00
379	Ray Herbert	4.00
380	Charley Maxwell	4.00
381	Hal Brown	4.00
382	Al Cicotte	7.00
383	Lou Berberet	4.00
384	John Goryl	4.00
385	Wilmer Mizell	4.00
386	Birdie's Young Sluggers (Ed Bailey, Frank Robinson, Birdie Tebbetts)	12.00
387	Wally Post	4.00
388	Billy Moran	4.00
389	Bill Taylor	4.00
390	Del Crandall	6.00
391	Dave Melton	4.00
392	Bennie Daniels	4.00
393	Tony Kubek	15.00
394	*Jim Grant*	6.00
395	Willard Nixon	4.00
396	Dutch Dotterer	4.00
397a	Tigers Team (alphabetical checklist on back)	15.00
397b	Tigers Team (checklist on back)	125.00
397b	Tigers Team (numerical)	125.00
398	Gene Woodling	4.00
399	Marv Grissom	4.00
400	Nellie Fox	15.00
401	Don Bessent	4.00
402	Bobby Gene Smith	4.00
403	Steve Korcheck	4.00
404	Curt Simmons	4.00
405	Ken Aspromonte	4.00
406	Vic Power	4.00
407	Carlton Willey	4.00
408a	Orioles Team (alphabetical checklist on back)	12.00
408b	Orioles Team (checklist on back)	125.00
408b	Orioles Team (numerical)	125.00
409	Frank J. Thomas	4.00
410	Murray Wall	4.00
411	*Tony Taylor*	4.00
412	Jerry Staley	4.00
413	*Jim Davenport*	4.00
414	Sammy White	4.00
415	Bob Bowman	4.00
416	Foster Castleman	4.00
417	Carl Furillo	9.00
418	World Series Foes (Hank Aaron, Mickey Mantle)	250.00
419	Bobby Shantz	5.50
420	*Vada Pinson*	5.50
421	Dixie Howell	5.50
422	Norm Zauchin	5.50
423	Phil Clark	5.50
424	Larry Doby	5.50
425	Sam Esposito	5.50
426	Johnny O'Brien	5.50
427	Al Worthington	5.50
428a	Redlegs Team	13.50
428b	Redlegs Team (numerical checklist on back)	125.00
429	Gus Triandos	5.50
430	Bobby Thomson	6.00
431	Gene Conley	5.50
432	John Powers	5.50
433	Pancho Herrera	5.50
434	Harvey Kuenn	6.00
435	Ed Roebuck	5.50
436	Rival Fence Busters (Willie Mays, Duke Snider)	75.00
437	Bob Speake	5.50
438	Whitey Herzog	7.50
439	Ray Narleski	5.50
440	Eddie Mathews	40.00
441	Jim Marshall	4.00
442	Phil Paine	4.00
443	Billy Harrell	7.50
444	Danny Kravitz	4.00
445	Bob Smith	4.00
446	Carroll Hardy	7.50
447	Ray Monzant	4.00
448	*Charlie Lau*	5.50
449	Gene Fodge	4.00
450	Preston Ward	7.50
451	Joe Taylor	4.00
452	Roman Mejias	4.00

453	Tom Qualters	4.00
454	Harry Hanebrink	4.00
455	Hal Griggs	4.00
456	Dick Brown	4.00
457	*Milt Pappas*	5.50
458	Julio Becquer	4.00
459	Ron Blackburn	4.00
460	Chuck Essegian	4.00
461	Ed Mayer	4.00
462	Gary Geiger	7.50
463	Vito Valentinetti	4.00
464	*Curt Flood*	28.00
465	Arnie Portocarrero	4.00
466	Pete Whisenant	4.00
467	Glen Hobbie	4.00
468	Bob Schmidt	4.00
469	Don Ferrarese	4.00
470	R.C. Stevens	4.00
471	Lenny Green	4.00
472	Joe Jay	4.00
473	Bill Renna	4.00
474	Roman Semproch	4.00
475	All-Star Managers (Fred Haney, Casey Stengel)	18.00
476	Stan Musial (All-Star)	35.00
477	Bill Skowron (All-Star)	6.00
478	Johnny Temple (All-Star)	7.00
479	Nellie Fox (All-Star)	10.00
480	Eddie Mathews (All-Star)	13.50
481	Frank Malzone (All-Star)	7.00
482	Ernie Banks (All-Star)	25.00
483	Luis Aparicio (All-Star)	12.00
484	Frank Robinson (All-Star)	25.00
485	Ted Williams (All-Star)	65.00
486	Willie Mays (All-Star)	50.00
487	Mickey Mantle (All-Star)	115.00
488	Hank Aaron (All-Star)	50.00
489	Jackie Jensen (All-Star)	7.00
490	Ed Bailey (All-Star)	7.00
491	Sherm Lollar (All-Star)	7.00
492	Bob Friend (All-Star)	7.00
493	Bob Turley (All-Star)	7.50
494	Warren Spahn (All-Star)	17.50
495	Herb Score (All-Star)	7.50
----	Contest Card (All-Star Game, July 8)	15.00
----	Felt Emblems Insert Card	15.00

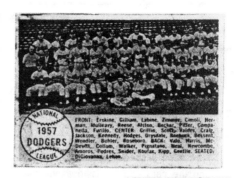

1959 Topps

These 2-1/2" by 3-1/2" cards have a round photograph at the center of the front with a solid-color background and white border. A facsimile autograph is found across the photo. The 572-card set marks the largest set issued to that time. Card numbers below 507 have red and green printing with the card number in white in a green box. On high number cards beginning with #507, the printing is black and red and the card number is in a black box. Specialty cards include multiple-player cards, team cards with checklists, "All-Star" cards, highlights from previous season, and 31 "Rookie Stars." There is also a card of the commissioner, Ford Frick, and one of Roy Campanella in a wheelchair. A handful of cards can be found with and without lines added to the biographies on back indicating trades or demotions; those without the added lines are considerably more rare and valuable and are not included in the complete set price. Card numbers 199-286 can be found with either white or grey backs, with the grey stock being the less common.

Mr. Mint Says - This was the first year of the presentation sets. A popular year, it is still available but tough to find in mint condition. Numbers 1-110 and the high numbers are extremely difficult, and most of the high numbers seem to come off-center. Though this would seem to defy conventional wisdom, I think 1959s are the toughest high numbers in the era from 1959 to 1963.

Similarly, the 1959 Mantle card is harder to find in top shape than 1958, 1960 or 1961. It is rarely found centered with four razor sharp corners, except in the Dan Wells purchase when he had 75 to 100 sets.

The variations without the traded/optioned designations are very hard to find and much in demand in mint condition. I do not think that many collectors care about whether the backs are white or gray in the middle numbers.

		MT
Complete Set (572):		6700.
Common Player (1-110):		8.00
Common Player (111-506):		4.00
Common Player (507-572):		20.00
1	Ford Frick	100.00
2	Eddie Yost	8.00
3	Don McMahon	8.00
4	Albie Pearson	8.00
5	Dick Donovan	8.00
6	Alex Grammas	8.00
7	Al Pilarcik	8.00
8	Phillies Team	75.00
9	Paul Giel	8.00
10	Mickey Mantle	750.00
11	Billy Hunter	8.00
12	Vern Law	8.00
13	Dick Gernert	8.00
14	Pete Whisenant	8.00
15	Dick Drott	8.00
16	Joe Pignatano	8.00
17	Danny's All-Stars	
	(Ted Kluszewski, Danny Murtaugh, Frank J. Thomas)	9.00
18	Jack Urban	8.00
19	Ed Bressoud	8.00
20	Duke Snider	75.00
21	Connie Johnson	8.00
22	Al Smith	8.00
23	Murry Dickson	8.00
24	Red Wilson	8.00
25	Don Hoak	8.00
26	Chuck Stobbs	8.00
27	Andy Pafko	8.00
28	Red Worthington	8.00
29	Jim Bolger	8.00
30	Nellie Fox	20.00
31	Ken Lehman	8.00
32	Don Buddin	8.00
33	Ed Fitz Gerald	8.00
34	Pitchers Beware (Al Kaline, Charlie Maxwell)	15.00
35	Ted Kluszewski	10.00
36	Hank Aguirre	8.00
37	Gene Green	8.00
38	Morrie Martin	8.00
39	Ed Bouchee	8.00
40	Warren Spahn	65.00
41	Bob Martyn	8.00
42	Murray Wall	8.00
43	Steve Bilko	8.00
44	Vito Valentinetti	8.00

No.	Player	Price		No.	Player	Price
45	Andy Carey	8.00		118	John Buzhardt	4.00
46	Bill Henry	8.00		119	*John Callison*	6.00
47	Jim Finigan	8.00		120	Chuck Coles	4.00
48	Orioles Team/Checklist 1-88	20.00		121	Bob Conley	4.00
49	Bill Hall	8.00		122	Bennie Daniels	4.00
50	Willie Mays	175.00		123	Don Dillard	4.00
51	Rip Coleman	8.00		124	Dan Dobbek	4.00
52	Coot Veal	8.00		125	*Ron Fairly*	5.00
53	Stan Williams	8.00		126	Eddie Haas	4.00
54	Mel Roach	8.00		127	Kent Hadley	4.00
55	Tom Brewer	8.00		128	Bob Hartman	4.00
56	Carl Sawatski	8.00		129	Frank Herrera	4.00
57	Al Cicotte	8.00		130	Lou Jackson	4.00
58	Eddie Miksis	8.00		131	*Deron Johnson*	5.00
59	Irv Noren	8.00		132	Don Lee	4.00
60	Bob Turley	8.00		133	*Bob Lillis*	5.00
61	Dick Brown	8.00		134	Jim McDaniel	4.00
62	Tony Taylor	8.00		135	Gene Oliver	4.00
63	Jim Hearn	8.00		136	*Jim O'Toole*	5.00
64	Joe DeMaestri	8.00		137	Dick Ricketts	4.00
65	Frank Torre	8.00		138	John Romano	4.00
66	Joe Ginsberg	8.00		139	Ed Sadowski	4.00
67	Brooks Lawrence	8.00		140	Charlie Secrest	4.00
68	Dick Schofield	8.00		141	Joe Shipley	4.00
69	Giants Team/Checklist 89-176	25.00		142	Dick Stigman	4.00
70	Harvey Kuenn	8.00		143	Willie Tasby	4.00
71	Don Bessent	8.00		144	Jerry Walker	4.00
72	Bill Renna	8.00		145	Dom Zanni	4.00
73	Ron Jackson	8.00		146	Jerry Zimmerman	4.00
74	Directing the Power (Cookie Lavagetto, Jim Lemon, Roy Sievers)	8.00		147	Cubs' Clubbers (Ernie Banks, Dale Long, Walt Moryn)	12.00
75	Sam Jones	8.00		148	Mike McCormick	4.00
76	Bobby Richardson	30.00		149	Jim Bunning	15.00
77	John Goryl	8.00		150	Stan Musial	175.00
78	Pedro Ramos	8.00		151	Bob Malkmus	4.00
79	Harry Chiti	8.00		152	Johnny Klippstein	4.00
80	Minnie Minoso	8.00		153	Jim Marshall	4.00
81	Hal Jeffcoat	8.00		154	Ray Herbert	4.00
82	Bob Boyd	8.00		155	Enos Slaughter	18.00
83	Bob Smith	8.00		156	Ace Hurlers (Billy Pierce, Robin Roberts)	5.00
84	Reno Bertoia	8.00		157	Felix Mantilla	4.00
85	Harry Anderson	8.00		158	Walt Dropo	4.00
86	Bob Keegan	8.00		159	Bob Shaw	4.00
87	Danny O'Connell	8.00		160	Dick Groat	4.00
88	Herb Score	8.00		161	Frank Baumann	4.00
89	Billy Gardner	8.00		162	Bobby G. Smith	4.00
90	Bill Skowron	20.00		163	Sandy Koufax	175.00
91	Herb Moford	8.00		164	Johnny Groth	4.00
92	Dave Philley	8.00		165	Bill Bruton	4.00
93	Julio Becquer	8.00		166	Destruction Crew (Rocky Colavito, Larry Doby, Minnie Minoso)	5.00
94	W. Sox Team	20.00		167	Duke Maas	5.00
95	Carl Willey	8.00		168	Carroll Hardy	4.00
96	Lou Berberet	8.00		169	Ted Abernathy	4.00
97	Jerry Lynch	8.00		170	Gene Woodling	4.00
98	Arnie Portocarrero	8.00		171	Willard Schmidt	4.00
99	Ted Kazanski	8.00		172	A's Team/Checklist 177-242	12.00
100	Bob Cerv	8.00		173	*Bill Monbouquette*	4.00
101	Alex Kellner	8.00		174	Jim Pendleton	4.00
102	*Felipe Alou*	40.00		175	Dick Farrell	4.00
103	Billy Goodman	8.00		176	Preston Ward	4.00
104	Del Rice	8.00		177	Johnny Briggs	4.00
105	Lee Walls	8.00		178	Ruben Amaro	4.00
106	Hal Woodeshick	8.00		179	Don Rudolph	4.00
107	Norm Larker	8.00		180	Yogi Berra	100.00
108	Zack Monroe	8.00		181	Bob Porterfield	4.00
109	Bob Schmidt	8.00		182	Milt Graff	4.00
110	George Witt	8.00		183	Stu Miller	4.00
111	Redlegs Team,	17.50		184	Harvey Haddix	4.00
112	Billy Consolo	4.00		185	Jim Busby	4.00
113	Taylor Phillips	4.00		186	Mudcat Grant	4.00
114	Earl Battey	4.00		187	Bubba Phillips	4.00
115	Mickey Vernon	4.00		188	Juan Pizarro	4.00
116	*Bob Allison*	7.00		189	Neil Chrisley	4.00
117	*John Blanchard*	5.00				

190	Bill Virdon	4.00
191	Russ Kemmerer	4.00
192	Charley Beamon	4.00
193	Sammy Taylor	4.00
194	Jim Brosnan	4.00
195	Rip Repulski	4.00
196	Billy Moran	4.00
197	Ray Semproch	4.00
198	Jim Davenport	4.00
199	Leo Kiely	4.00
200	Warren Giles	5.00
201	Tom Acker	4.00
202	Roger Maris	150.00
203	Ozzie Virgil	4.00
204	Casey Wise	4.00
205	Don Larsen	7.00
206	Carl Furillo	7.00
207	George Strickland	4.00
208	Willie Jones	4.00
209	Lenny Green	4.00
210	Ed Bailey	4.00
211	Bob Blaylock	4.00
212	Fence Busters (Hank Aaron, Eddie Mathews)	75.00
213	Jim Rivera	4.00
214	Marcelino Solis	4.00
215	Jim Lemon	4.00
216	Andre Rodgers	4.00
217	Carl Erskine	6.00
218	Roman Mejias	4.00
219	George Zuverink	4.00
220	Frank Malzone	4.00
221	Bob Bowman	4.00
222	Bobby Shantz	6.00
223	Cards Team/Checklist 265-352	12.00
224	*Claude Osteen*	4.00
225	Johnny Logan	4.00
226	Art Ceccarelli	4.00
227	Hal Smith	4.00
228	Don Gross	4.00
229	Vic Power	4.00
230	Bill Fischer	4.00
231	Ellis Burton	4.00
232	Eddie Kasko	4.00
233	Paul Foytack	4.00
234	Chuck Tanner	4.00
235	Valmy Thomas	4.00
236	Ted Bowsfield	4.00
237	Run Preventers (Gil McDougald, Bobby Richardson, Bob Turley)	9.00
238	Gene Baker	4.00
239	Bob Trowbridge	4.00
240	Hank Bauer	7.00
241	Billy Muffett	7.00
242	Ron Samford	4.00
243	Marv Grissom	4.00
244	Dick Gray	4.00
245	Ned Garver	4.00
246	J.W. Porter	4.00
247	Don Ferrarese	4.00
248	Red Sox Team/Checklist 177-264	12.50
249	Bobby Adams	4.00
250	Billy O'Dell	4.00
251	Cletis Boyer	6.00
252	Ray Boone	4.00
253	Seth Morehead	4.00
254	Zeke Bella	4.00
255	Del Ennis	4.00
256	Jerry Davie	4.00
257	*Leon Wagner*	4.00
258	Fred Kipp	4.00
259	Jim Pisoni	4.00
260	Early Wynn	15.00
261	Gene Stephens	4.00
262	Hitters' Foes (Don Drysdale, Clem Labine, Johnny Podres)	12.00
263	Buddy Daley	4.00
264	Chico Carrasquel	4.00
265	Ron Kline	4.00
266	Woody Held	4.00
267	John Romonosky	4.00
268	Tito Francona	4.00
269	Jack Meyer	4.00
270	Gil Hodges	25.00
271	*Orlando Pena*	4.00
272	Jerry Lumpe	5.00
273	Joe Jay	4.00
274	Jerry Kindall	4.00
275	Jack Sanford	4.00
276	Pete Daley	4.00
277	Turk Lown	4.00
278	Chuck Essegian	4.00
279	Ernie Johnson	4.00
280	Frank Bolling	4.00
281	Walt Craddock	4.00
282	R.C. Stevens	4.00
283	Russ Heman	4.00
284	Steve Korcheck	4.00
285	Joe Cunningham	4.00
286	Dean Stone	4.00
287	Don Zimmer	5.00
288	Dutch Dotterer	4.00
289	Johnny Kucks	5.00
290	Wes Covington	4.00
291	Pitching Partners (Camilo Pascual, Pedro Ramos)	5.00
292	Dick Williams	4.00
293	Ray Moore	4.00
294	Hank Foiles	4.00
295	Billy Martin	12.50
296	*Ernie Broglio*	4.00
297	*Jackie Brandt*	4.00
298	Tex Clevenger	4.00
299	Billy Klaus	4.00
300	Richie Ashburn	25.00
301	Earl Averill	4.00
302	Don Mossi	4.00
303	Marty Keough	4.00
304	Cubs Team/Checklist 265-352	12.00
305	Curt Raydon	4.00
306	Jim Gilliam	6.00
307	Curt Barclay	4.00
308	Norm Siebern	5.00
309	Sal Maglie	4.00
310	Luis Aparicio	20.00
311	Norm Zauchin	4.00
312	Don Newcombe	6.00
313	Frank House	4.00
314	Don Cardwell	4.00
315	Joe Adcock	4.00
316a	Ralph Lumenti (no optioned statement)	100.00
316b	Ralph Lumenti (optioned statement)	40.00
317	N.L. Hitting Kings (Richie Ashburn, Willie Mays)	45.00
318	Rocky Bridges	4.00
319	Dave Hillman	4.00
320	Bob Skinner	4.00
321a	Bob Giallombardo (no optioned statement)	100.00
321b	Bob Giallombardo (optioned statement)	4.00
322a	Harry Hanebrink (no trade statement)	100.00
322b	Harry Hanebrink (trade statement)	4.00
323	Frank Sullivan	4.00
324	Don Demeter	4.00
325	Ken Boyer	5.00
326	Marv Throneberry	6.00
327	*Gary Bell*	4.00
328	Lou Skizas	4.00
329	Tigers Team/Checklist 353-429	12.50
330	Gus Triandos	4.00
331	Steve Boros	4.00

32	Ray Monzant	4.00
33	Harry Simpson	4.00
34	Glen Hobbie	4.00
35	Johnny Temple	4.00
36a	Billy Loes (no trade statement)	100.00
36b	Billy Loes (trade statement)	4.00
37	George Crowe	4.00
38	*Sparky Anderson*	100.00
39	Roy Face	4.00
40	Roy Sievers	4.00
41	Tom Qualters	4.00
42	Ray Jablonski	4.00
43	Billy Hoeft	4.00
44	Russ Nixon	4.00
45	Gil McDougald	7.00
46	Batter Bafflers (Tom Brewer, Dave Sisler)	5.00
47	Bob Buhl	5.00
48	Ted Lepcio	4.00
49	Hoyt Wilhelm	25.00
50	Ernie Banks	100.00
51	Earl Torgeson	4.00
52	Robin Roberts	15.00
53	Curt Flood	4.00
54	Pete Burnside	4.00
55	Jim Piersall	4.00
56	Bob Mabe	4.00
57	*Dick Stuart*	6.00
58	Ralph Terry	4.00
59	*Bill White*	30.00
60	Al Kaline	75.00
61	Willard Nixon	4.00
62a	Dolan Nichols (no optioned statement)	100.00
62b	Dolan Nichols (optioned statement)	4.00
63	Bobby Avila	4.00
64	Danny McDevitt	4.00
65	Gus Bell	4.00
66	Humberto Robinson	4.00
67	Cal Neeman	4.00
68	Don Mueller	4.00
69	Dick Tomanek	4.00
70	Pete Runnels	4.00
71	Dick Brodowski	4.00
72	Jim Hegan	4.00
73	Herb Plews	4.00
74	Art Ditmar	4.00
75	Bob Nieman	4.00
76	Hal Naragon	4.00
77	Johnny Antonelli	4.00
78	Gail Harris	4.00
79	Bob Miller	4.00
80	Hank Aaron	175.00
81	Mike Baxes	4.00
82	Curt Simmons	4.00
83	Words of Wisdom (Don Larsen, Casey Stengel)	9.00
84	Dave Sisler	4.00
85	Sherm Lollar	4.00
86	Jim Delsing	4.00
87	Don Drysdale	50.00
88	Bob Will	4.00
89	Joe Nuxhall	4.00
90	Orlando Cepeda	25.00
91	Milt Pappas	4.00
92	Whitey Herzog	6.00
93	Frank Lary	4.00
94	Randy Jackson	4.00
95	Elston Howard	7.00
96	Bob Rush	4.00
97	Senators Team/Checklist 430-495	12.00
98	Wally Post	4.00
99	Larry Jackson	4.00
00	Jackie Jensen	4.00
01	Ron Blackburn	4.00
02	Hector Lopez	4.00

403	Clem Labine	4.00
404	Hank Sauer	4.00
405	Roy McMillan	4.00
406	Solly Drake	4.00
407	Moe Drabowsky	4.00
408	Keystone Combo (Luis Aparicio, Nellie Fox)	12.00
409	Gus Zernial	4.00
410	Billy Pierce	4.00
411	Whitey Lockman	4.00
412	Stan Lopata	4.00
413	Camillo (Camilo) Pascual	4.00
414	Dale Long	4.00
415	Bill Mazeroski	5.00
416	Haywood Sullivan	4.00
417	Virgil Trucks	4.00
418	Gino Cimoli	4.00
419	Braves Team/Checklist 353-429	12.50
420	Rocky Colavito	30.00
421	Herm Wehmeier	4.00
422	Hobie Landrith	4.00
423	Bob Grim	4.00
424	Ken Aspromonte	4.00
425	Del Crandall	4.00
426	Jerry Staley	4.00
427	Charlie Neal	4.00
428	Buc Hill Aces (Roy Face, Bob Friend, Ron Kline, Vern Law)	5.00
429	Bobby Thomson	4.00
430	Whitey Ford	50.00
431	Whammy Douglas	4.00
432	Smoky Burgess	4.00
433	Billy Harrell	4.00
434	Hal Griggs	4.00
435	Frank Robinson	60.00
436	Granny Hamner	4.00
437	Ike Delock	4.00
438	Sam Esposito	4.00
439	Brooks Robinson	60.00
440	Lou Burdette	6.00
441	John Roseboro	4.00
442	Ray Narleski	4.00
443	Daryl Spencer	4.00
444	*Ronnie Hansen*	5.00
445	Cal McLish	4.00
446	Rocky Nelson	4.00
447	Bob Anderson	4.00
448	Vada Pinson	6.00
449	Tom Gorman	4.00
450	Eddie Mathews	35.00
451	Jimmy Constable	4.00
452	Chico Fernandez	4.00
453	Les Moss	4.00
454	Phil Clark	4.00
455	Larry Doby	4.00
456	Jerry Casale	4.00
457	Dodgers Team	20.00
458	Gordon Jones	4.00
459	Bill Tuttle	4.00
460	Bob Friend	4.00
461	Mantle Hits 42nd Homer For Crown (Mickey Mantle)	75.00
462	Colavito's Great Catch Saves Game (RockyColavito)	10.00
463	Kaline Becomes Youngest Batting Champ (Al Kaline)	20.00
464	Mays' Catch Makes Series History (Willie Mays)	30.00
465	Sievers Sets Homer Mark (Roy Sievers)	5.00
466	Pierce All-Star Starter (Billy Pierce)	5.00
467	Aaron Clubs World Series Homer (Hank Aaron)	25.00
468	Snider's Play Brings L.A. Victory (Duke Snider)	12.50
469	Hustler Banks Wins M.V.P. Award (Ernie Banks)	10.00
470	Musial Raps Out 3,000th Hit (Stan Musial)	25.00
471	Tom Sturdivant	5.00
472	Gene Freese	4.00
473	Mike Fornieles	4.00
474	Moe Thacker	4.00

475	Jack Harshman	4.00
476	Indians Team/Checklist 496-572	12.00
477	Barry Latman	4.00
478	Roberto Clemente	150.00
479	Lindy McDaniel	4.00
480	Red Schoendienst	15.00
481	Charley Maxwell	4.00
482	Russ Meyer	4.00
483	Clint Courtney	4.00
484	Willie Kirkland	4.00
485	Ryne Duren	6.00
486	Sammy White	4.00
487	Hal Brown	4.00
488	Walt Moryn	4.00
489	John C. Powers	4.00
490	Frank J. Thomas	4.00
491	Don Blasingame	4.00
492	Gene Conley	4.00
493	Jim Landis	4.00
494	Don Pavletich	4.00
495	Johnny Podres	6.00
496	Wayne Terwilliger	4.00
497	Hal R. Smith	4.00
498	Dick Hyde	4.00
499	Johnny O'Brien	4.00
500	Vic Wertz	4.00
501	Bobby Tiefenauer	4.00
502	Al Dark	4.00
503	Jim Owens	4.00
504	Ossie Alvarez	4.00
505	Tony Kubek	8.00
506	Bob Purkey	4.00
507	Bob Hale	20.00
508	Art Fowler	20.00
509	*Norm Cash*	100.00
510	Yankees Team	100.00
511	George Susce	20.00
512	George Altman	20.00
513	Tom Carroll	20.00
514	*Bob Gibson*	500.00
515	Harmon Killebrew	200.00
516	Mike Garcia	20.00
517	Joe Koppe	20.00
518	*Mike Cueller*	20.00
519	Infield Power (Dick Gernert, Frank Malzone, Pete Runnels)	20.00
520	Don Elston	20.00
521	Gary Geiger	20.00
522	Gene Snyder	20.00
523	Harry Bright	20.00
524	Larry Osborne	20.00
525	Jim Coates	20.00
526	Bob Speake	20.00
527	Solly Hemus	20.00
528	Pirates Team	60.00
529	*George Bamberger*	20.00
530	Wally Moon	20.00
531	Ray Webster	20.00
532	Mark Freeman	20.00
533	Darrell Johnson	20.00
534	Faye Throneberry	20.00
535	Ruben Gomez	20.00
536	Dan Kravitz	20.00
537	Rodolfo Arias	20.00
538	Chick King	20.00
539	Gary Blaylock	20.00
540	Willy Miranda	20.00
541	Bob Thurman	20.00
542	*Jim Perry*	40.00
543	Corsair Outfield Trio (Roberto Clemente, Bob Skinner, Bill Virdon)	100.00
544	Lee Tate	20.00
545	Tom Morgan	20.00
546	Al Schroll	20.00
547	Jim Baxes	20.00
548	Elmer Singleton	20.00
549	Howie Nunn	20.00
550	Roy Campanella	200.00
551	Fred Haney (All-Star)	25.00
552	Casey Stengel (All-Star)	50.00
553	Orlando Cepeda (All-Star)	29.00
554	Bill Skowron (All-Star)	25.00
555	Bill Mazeroski (All-Star)	29.00
556	Nellie Fox (All-Star)	25.00
557	Ken Boyer (All-Star)	25.00
558	Frank Malzone (All-Star)	23.00
559	Ernie Banks (All-Star)	75.00
560	Luis Aparicio (All-Star)	25.00
561	Hank Aaron (All-Star)	150.00
562	Al Kaline (All-Star)	75.00
563	Willie Mays (All-Star)	175.00
564	Mickey Mantle (All-Star)	450.00
565	Wes Covington (All-Star)	23.00
566	Roy Sievers (All-Star)	23.00
567	Del Crandall (All-Star)	23.00
568	Gus Triandos (All-Star)	23.00
569	Bob Friend (All-Star)	23.00
570	Bob Turley (All-Star)	25.00
571	Warren Spahn (All-Star)	35.00
572	Billy Pierce (All-Star)	75.00
----	Elect Your Favorite Rookie Insert (paper stock, September 29 date on back)	15.00
----	Felt Pennants Insert (paper stock)	15.00

1960 Topps

In 1960, Topps returned to a horizontal format (3-1/2" by 2-1/2") with a color portrait and a black and white "action" photograph on the front. The backs returned to the use of just the previous year and lifetime statistics along with a cartoon and short career summary or previous season highlights. Specialty cards in the 572-card set are multi-player cards, managers and coaches cards, and highlights of the 1959 World Series. Two groups of rookie cards are included. The first are numbers 117-148, which are the Sport Magazine rookies. The second group is called "Topps All-Star Rookies." Finally, there is a continuation of the All-Star cards to close out the set in the scarcer high numbers. Card #'s 375-440 can be found with backs printed on either white or grey cardboard, with the white stock being the less common.

PITTSBURGH PIRATES   OUTFIELD

Mr. Mint Says - With 1960, we are getting into cards now that are more available in mint condition. This is not a particularly tough set, and both the Yaz and the Mantle are easy as are, for the most part, all of the high numbers.

These are the easiest high numbers in the early 60s to obtain, and also the least in demand from that 1959-63 era, though the all-stars are quite popular.

By 1960 the little print dots started to appear on the panels at the bottom of the card, and most noticeably on the orange rookie cards, like the Yaz rookie. On these cards they are black dots and they can make the cards hard to sell. The rookie cards in the 300 series often come off-center, leaving the McCovey rookie a tough item.

		MT
Complete Set (572):		5500.
Common Player (1-110):		4.00
Common Player (111-286):		4.00
Common Player (287-440):		4.00
Common Player (441-506):		5.50
Common Player (507-572):		15.00
1	Early Wynn	40.00
2	Roman Mejias	4.00
3	Joe Adcock	4.00
4	Bob Purkey	4.00
5	Wally Moon	4.00
6	Lou Berberet	4.00
7	Master and Mentor (Willie Mays, Bill Rigney)	25.00
8	Bud Daley	4.00
9	Faye Throneberry	4.00
10	Ernie Banks	50.00
11	Norm Siebern	4.00
12	Milt Pappas	4.00
13	Wally Post	4.00
14	Jim Grant	4.00
15	Pete Runnels	4.00
16	Ernie Broglio	4.00
17	Johnny Callison	4.00
18	Dodgers Team/Checklist 1-88	25.00
19	Felix Mantilla	4.00
20	Roy Face	4.00
21	Dutch Dotterer	4.00
22	Rocky Bridges	4.00
23	Eddie Fisher	4.00
24	Dick Gray	4.00
25	Roy Sievers	4.00
26	Wayne Terwilliger	4.00
27	Dick Drott	4.00
28	Brooks Robinson	55.00
29	Clem Labine	4.00
30	Tito Francona	4.00
31	Sammy Esposito	4.00
32	Sophomore Stalwarts (Jim O'Toole, Vada Pinson)	6.00
33	Tom Morgan	4.00
34	Sparky Anderson	25.00
35	Whitey Ford	45.00
36	Russ Nixon	4.00
37	Bill Bruton	4.00
38	Jerry Casale	4.00
39	Earl Averill	4.00
40	Joe Cunningham	4.00
41	Barry Latman	4.00
42	Hobie Landrith	4.00
43	Senators Team/Checklist 1-88	10.00
44	Bobby Locke	4.00
45	Roy McMillan	4.00
46	Jack Fisher	4.00
47	Don Zimmer	4.00
48	Hal Smith	4.00
49	Curt Raydon	4.00
50	Al Kaline	55.00
51	Jim Coates	4.00
52	Dave Philley	4.00
53	Jackie Brandt	4.00
54	Mike Fornieles	4.00
55	Bill Mazeroski	5.00
56	Steve Korcheck	4.00
57	Win-Savers (Turk Lown, Gerry Staley)	4.50
58	Gino Cimoli	4.00
59	Juan Pizarro	4.00
60	Gus Triandos	4.00
61	Eddie Kasko	4.00

No.	Player	Price		No.	Player	Price
62	Roger Craig	4.00		135	Ken Johnson	3.00
63	George Strickland	4.00		136	*Jim Kaat*	40.00
64	Jack Meyer	4.00		137	Lou Klimchock	3.00
65	Elston Howard	6.00		138	*Art Mahaffey*	3.00
66	Bob Trowbridge	4.00		139	Carl Mathias	3.00
67	*Jose Pagan*	4.00		140	Julio Navarro	3.00
68	Dave Hillman	4.00		141	Jim Proctor	3.00
69	Billy Goodman	4.00		142	Bill Short	5.00
70	Lou Burdette	4.00		143	Al Spangler	3.00
71	Marty Keough	4.00		144	Al Stieglitz	3.00
72	Tigers Team/Checklist 89-176	12.00		145	Jim Umbricht	3.00
73	Bob Gibson	60.00		146	Ted Wieand	3.00
74	Walt Moryn	4.00		147	Bob Will	3.00
75	Vic Power	4.00		148	*Carl Yastrzemski*	300.00
76	Bill Fischer	4.00		149	Bob Nieman	3.00
77	Hank Foiles	4.00		150	Billy Pierce	3.00
78	Bob Grim	4.00		151	Giants Team/Checklist 177-264	9.00
79	Walt Dropo	4.00		152	Gail Harris	3.00
80	Johnny Antonelli	4.00		153	Bobby Thomson	3.00
81	Russ Snyder	4.00		154	Jim Davenport	3.00
82	Ruben Gomez	4.00		155	Charlie Neal	3.00
83	Tony Kubek	4.50		156	Art Ceccarelli	3.00
84	Hal Smith	4.00		157	Rocky Nelson	3.00
85	Frank Lary	4.00		158	Wes Covington	3.00
86	Dick Gernert	4.00		159	Jim Piersall	3.00
87	John Romonosky	4.00		160	Rival All-Stars (Ken Boyer, Mickey Mantle)	75.00
88	John Roseboro	4.00		161	Ray Narleski	3.00
89	Hal Brown	4.00		162	Sammy Taylor	3.00
90	Bobby Avila	4.00		163	Hector Lopez	3.00
91	Bennie Daniels	4.00		164	Reds Team/Checklist 89-176	9.00
92	Whitey Herzog	4.50		165	Jack Sanford	3.00
93	Art Schult	4.00		166	Chuck Essegian	3.00
94	Leo Kiely	4.00		167	Valmy Thomas	3.00
95	Frank J. Thomas	4.00		168	Alex Grammas	3.00
96	Ralph Terry	4.00		169	Jake Striker	3.00
97	Ted Lepcio	4.00		170	Del Crandall	3.00
98	Gordon Jones	4.00		171	Johnny Groth	3.00
99	Lenny Green	4.00		172	Willie Kirkland	3.00
100	Nellie Fox	7.00		173	Billy Martin	10.00
101	Bob Miller	4.00		174	Indians Team/Checklist 89-176	9.00
102	Kent Hadley	4.00		175	Pedro Ramos	3.00
103	Dick Farrell	4.00		176	Vada Pinson	3.00
104	Dick Schofield	4.00		177	Johnny Kucks	3.00
105	Larry Sherry	4.00		178	Woody Held	3.00
106	Billy Gardner	4.00		179	Rip Coleman	3.00
107	Carl Willey	4.00		180	Harry Simpson	3.00
108	Pete Daley	4.00		181	Billy Loes	3.00
109	Cletis Boyer	4.00		182	Glen Hobbie	3.00
110	Cal McLish	4.00		183	Eli Grba	3.00
111	Vic Wertz	3.00		184	Gary Geiger	3.00
112	Jack Harshman	3.00		185	Jim Owens	3.00
113	Bob Skinner	3.00		186	Dave Sisler	3.00
114	Ken Aspromonte	3.00		187	Jay Hook	3.00
115	Fork and Knuckler (Roy Face, Hoyt Wilhelm)	6.00		188	Dick Williams	3.00
116	Jim Rivera	3.00		189	Don McMahon	3.00
117	Tom Borland	3.00		190	Gene Woodling	3.00
118	Bob Bruce	3.00		191	Johnny Klippstein	3.00
119	*Chico Cardenas*	3.00		192	Danny O'Connell	3.00
120	Duke Carmel	3.00		193	Dick Hyde	3.00
121	Camilo Carreon	3.00		194	Bobby Gene Smith	3.00
122	Don Dillard	3.00		195	Lindy McDaniel	3.00
123	Dan Dobbek	3.00		196	Andy Carey	3.00
124	Jim Donohue	3.00		197	Ron Kline	3.00
125	*Dick Ellsworth*	3.00		198	Jerry Lynch	3.00
126	*Chuck Estrada*	3.00		199	Dick Donovan	3.00
127	Ronnie Hansen	3.00		200	Willie Mays	150.00
128	Bill Harris	3.00		201	Larry Osborne	3.00
129	Bob Hartman	3.00		202	Fred Kipp	3.00
130	Frank Herrera	3.00		203	Sammy White	3.00
131	Ed Hobaugh	3.00		204	Ryne Duren	4.50
132	*Frank Howard*	30.00		205	Johnny Logan	3.00
133	*Manuel Javier*	3.00		206	Claude Osteen	3.00
134	Deron Johnson	5.00		207	Bob Boyd	3.00

No.	Player	Price
208	White Sox Team/Checklist 177-264	9.00
209	Ron Blackburn	3.00
210	Harmon Killebrew	35.00
211	Taylor Phillips	3.00
212	Walt Alston	9.00
213	Chuck Dressen	3.00
214	Jimmie Dykes	3.00
215	Bob Elliott	3.00
216	Joe Gordon	3.00
217	Charley Grimm	3.00
218	Solly Hemus	3.00
219	Fred Hutchinson	3.00
220	Billy Jurges	3.00
221	Cookie Lavagetto	3.00
222	Al Lopez	5.50
223	Danny Murtaugh	3.00
224	Paul Richards	3.00
225	Bill Rigney	3.00
226	Eddie Sawyer	3.00
227	Casey Stengel	20.00
228	Ernie Johnson	3.00
229	Joe M. Morgan	3.00
230	Mound Magicians (Bob Buhl, Lou Burdette, Warren Spahn)	9.00
231	Hal Naragon	3.00
232	Jim Busby	3.00
233	Don Elston	3.00
234	Don Demeter	3.00
235	Gus Bell	3.00
236	Dick Ricketts	3.00
237	Elmer Valo	3.00
238	Danny Kravitz	3.00
239	Joe Shipley	3.00
240	Luis Aparicio	15.00
241	Albie Pearson	3.00
242	Cards Team/Checklist 265-352	9.00
243	Bubba Phillips	3.00
244	Hal Griggs	3.00
245	Eddie Yost	3.00
246	Lee Maye	3.00
247	Gil McDougald	5.00
248	Del Rice	3.00
249	*Earl Wilson*	3.00
250	Stan Musial	125.00
251	Bobby Malkmus	3.00
252	Ray Herbert	3.00
253	Eddie Bressoud	3.00
254	Arnie Portocarrero	3.00
255	Jim Gilliam	5.00
256	Dick Brown	3.00
257	Gordy Coleman	3.00
258	Dick Groat	4.50
259	George Altman	3.00
260	Power Plus (Rocky Colavito, Tito Francona)	6.00
261	Pete Burnside	3.00
262	Hank Bauer	3.00
263	Darrell Johnson	3.00
264	Robin Roberts	15.00
265	Rip Repulski	3.00
266	Joe Jay	3.00
267	Jim Marshall	3.00
268	Al Worthington	3.00
269	Gene Green	3.00
270	Bob Turley	4.50
271	Julio Becquer	3.00
272	Fred Green	3.00
273	Neil Chrisley	3.00
274	Tom Acker	3.00
275	Curt Flood	3.00
276	Ken McBride	3.00
277	Harry Bright	3.00
278	Stan Williams	3.00
279	Chuck Tanner	3.00
280	Frank Sullivan	3.00
281	Ray Boone	3.00
282	Joe Nuxhall	3.00
283	John Blanchard	4.50
284	Don Gross	3.00
285	Harry Anderson	3.00
286	Ray Semproch	3.00
287	Felipe Alou	6.00
288	Bob Mabe	4.00
289	Willie Jones	4.00
290	Jerry Lumpe	4.00
291	Bob Keegan	4.00
292	Dodger Backstops (Joe Pignatano, John Roseboro)	6.00
293	Gene Conley	4.00
294	Tony Taylor	4.00
295	Gil Hodges	25.00
296	Nelson Chittum	4.00
297	Reno Bertoia	4.00
298	George Witt	4.00
299	Earl Torgeson	4.00
300	Hank Aaron	150.00
301	Jerry Davie	4.00
302	Phillies Team/Checklist 353-429	10.00
303	Billy O'Dell	4.00
304	Joe Ginsberg	4.00
305	Richie Ashburn	15.00
306	Frank Baumann	4.00
307	Gene Oliver	4.00
308	Dick Hall	4.00
309	Bob Hale	4.00
310	Frank Malzone	4.00
311	Raul Sanchez	4.00
312	Charlie Lau	4.50
313	Turk Lown	4.00
314	Chico Fernandez	4.00
315	Bobby Shantz	5.00
316	*Willie McCovey*	300.00
317	Pumpsie Green	4.00
318	Jim Baxes	4.00
319	Joe Koppe	4.00
320	Bob Allison	4.00
321	Ron Fairly	4.00
322	Willie Tasby	4.00
323	Johnny Romano	4.00
324	Jim Perry	4.00
325	Jim O'Toole	4.00
326	Roberto Clemente	150.00
327	*Ray Sadecki*	4.00
328	Earl Battey	4.00
329	Zack Monroe	4.00
330	Harvey Kuenn	4.50
331	Henry Mason	4.00
332	Yankees Team/Checklist 265-352	50.00
333	Danny McDevitt	4.00
334	Ted Abernathy	4.00
335	Red Schoendienst	12.50
336	Ike Delock	4.00
337	Cal Neeman	4.00
338	Ray Monzant	4.00
339	Harry Chiti	4.00
340	Harvey Haddix	4.00
341	Carroll Hardy	4.00
342	Casey Wise	4.00
343	Sandy Koufax	150.00
344	Clint Courtney	4.00
345	Don Newcombe	4.00
346	J.C. Martin (photo actually Gary Peters)	4.00
347	Ed Bouchee	4.00
348	Barry Shetrone	4.00
349	Moe Drabowsky	4.00
350	Mickey Mantle	600.00
351	Don Nottebart	4.00
352	Cincy Clouters (Gus Bell, Jerry Lynch, Frank Robinson)	9.00
353	Don Larsen	4.50

354	Bob Lillis	4.00
355	Bill White	4.50
356	Joe Amalfitano	4.00
357	Al Schroll	4.00
358	Joe DeMaestri	4.00
359	Buddy Gilbert	4.00
360	Herb Score	4.00
361	Bob Oldis	4.00
362	Russ Kemmerer	4.00
363	Gene Stephens	4.00
364	Paul Foytack	4.00
365	Minnie Minoso	4.50
366	*Dallas Green*	4.50
367	Bill Tuttle	4.00
368	Daryl Spencer	4.00
369	Billy Hoeft	4.00
370	Bill Skowron	6.00
371	Bud Byerly	4.00
372	Frank House	4.00
373	Don Hoak	4.00
374	Bob Buhl	4.00
375	Dale Long	4.00
376	Johnny Briggs	4.00
377	Roger Maris	150.00
378	Stu Miller	4.00
379	Red Wilson	4.00
380	Bob Shaw	4.00
381	Braves Team/Checklist 353-429	10.00
382	Ted Bowsfield	4.00
383	Leon Wagner	4.00
384	Don Cardwell	4.00
385	World Series Game 1 Neal Steals Second	6.00
386	World Series Game 2 Neal Belts 2nd Homer	6.00
387	World Series Game 3 Furillo Breaks Up Game	8.00
388	World Series Game 4 Hodges' Winning Homer	8.00
389	World Series Game 5 Luis Swipes Base	8.00
390	World Series Game 6 Scrambling After Ball	6.00
391	World Series Summary The Champs Celebrate	7.00
392	Tex Clevenger	4.00
393	Smoky Burgess	4.00
394	Norm Larker	4.00
395	Hoyt Wilhelm	15.00
396	Steve Bilko	4.00
397	Don Blasingame	4.00
398	Mike Cuellar	4.00
399	Young Hill Stars (Jack Fisher, Milt Pappas, Jerry Walker)	5.00
400	Rocky Colavito	20.00
401	Bob Duliba	4.00
402	Dick Stuart	4.50
403	Ed Sadowski	4.00
404	Bob Rush	4.00
405	Bobby Richardson	10.00
406	Billy Klaus	4.00
407	*Gary Peters* (photo actually J.C. Martin)	4.00
408	Carl Furillo	7.50
409	Ron Samford	4.00
410	Sam Jones	4.00
411	Ed Bailey	4.00
412	Bob Anderson	4.00
413	A's Team/Checklist 430-495	10.00
414	Don Williams	4.00
415	Bob Cerv	4.00
416	Humberto Robinson	4.00
417	Chuck Cottier	4.00
418	Don Mossi	4.00
419	George Crowe	4.00
420	Eddie Mathews	35.00
421	Duke Maas	4.00
422	Johnny Powers	4.00
423	Ed Fitz Gerald	4.00
424	Pete Whisenant	4.00
425	Johnny Podres	4.50
426	Ron Jackson	4.00

427	Al Grunwald	4.00
428	Al Smith	4.00
429	American League Kings (Nellie Fox, Harvey Kuenn)	6.00
430	Art Ditmar	4.00
431	Andre Rodgers	4.00
432	Chuck Stobbs	4.00
433	Irv Noren	4.00
434	Brooks Lawrence	4.00
435	Gene Freese	4.00
436	Marv Throneberry	4.00
437	Bob Friend	4.00
438	Jim Coker	4.00
439	Tom Brewer	4.00
440	Jim Lemon	4.00
441	Gary Bell	5.50
442	Joe Pignatano	5.50
443	Charlie Maxwell	5.50
444	Jerry Kindall	5.50
445	Warren Spahn	60.00
446	Ellis Burton	5.50
447	Ray Moore	5.50
448	*Jim Gentile*	5.50
449	Jim Brosnan	5.50
450	Orlando Cepeda	15.00
451	Curt Simmons	5.50
452	Ray Webster	5.50
453	Vern Law	5.50
454	Hal Woodeshick	5.50
455	Orioles Coaches (Harry Brecheen, Lum Harris, Eddie Robinson)	5.50
456	Red Sox Coaches (Del Baker, Billy Herman, Sal Maglie, Rudy York)	5.50
457	Cubs Coaches (Lou Klein, Charlie Root, Elvin Tappe)	5.50
458	White Sox Coaches (Ray Berres, Johnny Cooney, Tony Cuccinello, Don Gutteridge)	5.50
459	Reds Coaches (Cot Deal, Wally Moses, Reggie Otero)	5.50
460	Indians Coaches (Mel Harder, Red Kress, Bob Lemon, Jo-Jo White)	6.50
461	Tigers Coaches (Luke Appling, Tom Ferrick, Billy Hitchcock)	6.50
462	A's Coaches (Walker Cooper, Fred Fitzsimmons, Don Heffner)	5.50
463	Dodgers Coaches (Joe Becker, Bobby Bragan, Greg Mulleavy, Pete Reiser)	5.50
464	Braves Coaches (George Myatt, Andy Pafko, Bob Scheffing, Whitlow Wyatt)	5.50
465	Yankees Coaches (Frank Crosetti, Bill Dickey, Ralph Houk, Ed Lopat,)	12.00
466	Phillies Coaches (Dick Carter, Andy Cohen, Ken Silvestri)	5.50
467	Pirates Coaches (Bill Burwell, Sam Narron, Frank Oceak, Mickey Vernon)	5.50
468	Cardinals Coaches (Ray Katt, Johnny Keane, HowiePollet, Harry Walker)	5.50
469	Giants Coaches (Salty Parker, Bill Posedel, Wes Westrum)	5.50
470	Senators Coaches (Ellis Clary, Sam Mele, Bob Swift)	5.50
471	Ned Garver	5.50
472	Al Dark	5.50
473	Al Cicotte	5.50
474	Haywood Sullivan	5.50
475	Don Drysdale	60.00
476	Lou Johnson	5.50
477	Don Ferrarese	5.50
478	Frank Torre	5.50
479	Georges Maranda	5.50
480	Yogi Berra	100.00
481	Wes Stock	5.50
482	Frank Bolling	5.50
483	Camilo Pascual	5.50
484	Pirates Team/Checklist 430-495	25.00
485	Ken Boyer	8.00
486	Bobby Del Greco	5.50
487	Tom Sturdivant	5.50

488	Norm Cash	6.00
489	Steve Ridzik	5.50
490	Frank Robinson	75.00
491	Mel Roach	5.50
492	Larry Jackson	5.50
493	Duke Snider	60.00
494	Orioles Team/Checklist 496-572	10.00
495	Sherm Lollar	5.50
496	Bill Virdon	5.50
497	John Tsitouris	5.50
498	Al Pilarcik	5.50
499	Johnny James	5.50
500	Johnny Temple	5.50
501	Bob Schmidt	5.50
502	Jim Bunning	12.00
503	Don Lee	5.50
504	Seth Morehead	5.50
505	Ted Kluszewski	9.00
506	Lee Walls	5.50
507	Dick Stigman	15.00
508	Billy Consolo	15.00
509	*Tommy Davis*	35.00
510	Jerry Staley	15.00
511	Ken Walters	15.00
512	Joe Gibbon	15.00
513	Cubs Team/Checklist 496-572	50.00
514	*Steve Barber*	15.00
515	Stan Lopata	15.00
516	Marty Kutyna	15.00
517	Charley James	15.00
518	*Tony Gonzalez*	15.00
519	Ed Roebuck	15.00
520	Don Buddin	15.00
521	Mike Lee	15.00
522	Ken Hunt	15.00
523	*Clay Dalrymple*	15.00
524	Bill Henry	15.00
525	Marv Breeding	15.00
526	Paul Giel	15.00
527	Jose Valdivielso	15.00
528	Ben Johnson	15.00
529	Norm Sherry	15.00
530	Mike McCormick	15.00
531	Sandy Amoros	15.00

532	Mike Garcia	15.00
533	Lu Clinton	15.00
534	Ken MacKenzie	15.00
535	Whitey Lockman	15.00
536	Wynn Hawkins	15.00
537	Red Sox Team/Checklist 496-572	50.00
538	Frank Barnes	15.00
539	Gene Baker	15.00
540	Jerry Walker	15.00
541	Tony Curry	15.00
542	Ken Hamlin	15.00
543	Elio Chacon	15.00
544	Bill Monbouquette	15.00
545	Carl Sawatski	15.00
546	Hank Aguirre	15.00
547	*Bob Aspromonte*	15.00
548	*Don Mincher*	15.00
549	John Buzhardt	15.00
550	Jim Landis	15.00
551	Ed Rakow	15.00
552	Walt Bond	15.00
553	Bill Skowron (All-Star)	20.00
554	Willie McCovey (All-Star)	60.00
555	Nellie Fox (All-Star)	25.00
556	Charlie Neal (All-Star)	20.00
557	Frank Malzone (All-Star)	20.00
558	Eddie Mathews (All-Star)	35.00
559	Luis Aparicio (All-Star)	25.00
560	Ernie Banks (All-Star)	75.00
561	Al Kaline (All-Star)	75.00
562	Joe Cunningham (All-Star)	20.00
563	Mickey Mantle (All-Star)	350.00
564	Willie Mays (All-Star)	150.00
565	Roger Maris (All-Star)	150.00
566	Hank Aaron (All-Star)	150.00
567	Sherm Lollar (All-Star)	20.00
568	Del Crandall (All-Star)	20.00
569	Camilo Pascual (All-Star)	20.00
570	Don Drysdale (All-Star)	50.00
571	Billy Pierce (All-Star)	20.00
572	Johnny Antonelli (All-Star)	30.00
----	Elect Your Favorite Rookie Insert (paper stock, no date on back)	15.00
----	Hot Iron Transfer Insert (paper stock)	15.00

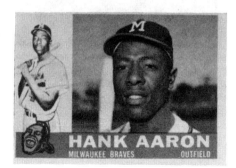

1961 Topps

Except for some of the specialty cards, Topps returned to a vertical format with their 1961 cards. The set is numbered through 598, however only 587 cards were printed. No numbers 426, 587 and 588 were issued. Two cards numbered 463 exist (one a Braves team card and one a player card of Jack Fisher). Actually, the Braves team card is checklisted as #426. Designs for 1961 are basically large color portraits; the backs return to extensive statistics. A three-panel cartoon highlighting the player's career appears on the card backs. Innovations include numbered checklists, cards for statistical leaders, and 10 "Baseball Thrills" cards. The scarce high numbers are card numbers 523-589.

BOB GIBSON
Pitcher — St. Louis Cardinals

Mr. Mint Says - One of the most popular sets of the 60s, this has a very challenging and expensive high number series. Nice collectable set, easily available in mint condition and easy to put together. The Maris card is tough to get and a high demand piece, and the Mantle card is hard to find centered and often comes with a tiny print line down the righthand side.

The MVP cards can be tricky, and the background reds and blues often have the little white dots that drive collectors crazy. There is also a lot of swing in the color intensity of the reds and blues; the darker color produces the more attractive card, but it also yields the more pronounced print dots.

		MT
Complete Set (587):		7500.
Common Player (1-446):		2.50
Common Player (447-522):		4.50
Common Player (523-589):		35.00
1	Dick Groat	50.00
2	Roger Maris	250.00
3	John Buzhardt	2.50
4	Lenny Green	2.50
5	Johnny Romano	2.50
6	Ed Roebuck	2.50
7	White Sox Team	6.00
8	Dick Williams	4.50
9	Bob Purkey	2.50
10	Brooks Robinson	40.00
11	Curt Simmons	2.50
12	Moe Thacker	2.50
13	Chuck Cottier	2.50
14	Don Mossi	2.50
15	Willie Kirkland	2.50
16	Billy Muffett	2.50
17	Checklist 1-88	5.00
18	Jim Grant	2.50
19	Cletis Boyer	2.50
20	Robin Roberts	10.00
21	*Zorro Versalles*	3.50
22	Clem Labine	2.50
23	Don Demeter	2.50
24	Ken Johnson	2.50
25	Reds' Heavy Artillery (Gus Bell, Vada Pinson, Frank Robinson)	8.00
26	Wes Stock	2.50
27	Jerry Kindall	2.50
28	Hector Lopez	2.50
29	Don Nottebart	2.50
30	Nellie Fox	6.00
31	Bob Schmidt	2.50
32	Ray Sadecki	2.50
33	Gary Geiger	2.50
34	Wynn Hawkins	2.50
35	*Ron Santo*	70.00
36	Jack Kralick	2.50
37	Charlie Maxwell	2.50
38	Bob Lillis	2.50
39	Leo Posada	2.50
40	Bob Turley	3.00
41	N.L. Batting Leaders (Roberto Clemente, Dick Groat, Norm Larker, Willie Mays)	8.00
42	A.L. Batting Leaders (Minnie Minoso, Pete Runnels, Bill Skowron, Al Smith)	6.00
43	N.L. Home Run Leaders (Hank Aaron, Ernie Banks, Ken Boyer, Eddie Mathews)	8.00
44	A.L. Home Run Leaders (Rocky Colavito, Jim Lemon, Mickey Mantle, Roger Maris)	60.00
45	N.L. E.R.A. Leaders (Ernie Broglio, Don Drysdale, Bob Friend, Mike McCormick, Stan Williams)	6.00
46	A.L. E.R.A. Leaders (Frank Baumann, Hal Brown, Jim Bunning, Art Ditmar)	6.00
47	N.L. Pitching Leaders (Ernie Broglio, Lou Burdette, Vern Law, Warren Spahn)	6.00
48	A.L. Pitching Leaders (Bud Daley, Art Ditmar, Chuck Estrada, Frank Lary, Milt Pappas, Jim Perry)	6.00
49	N.L. Strikeout Leaders (Ernie Broglio, Don Drysdale, Sam Jones, Sandy Koufax)	8.00

#	Player	Price
50	A.L. Strikeout Leaders (Jim Bunning, Frank Lary, Pedro Ramos, Early Wynn)	6.00
51	Tigers Team	7.50
52	George Crowe	2.50
53	Russ Nixon	2.50
54	Earl Francis	2.50
55	Jim Davenport	2.50
56	Russ Kemmerer	2.50
57	Marv Throneberry	2.50
58	Joe Schaffernoth	2.50
59	Jim Woods	2.50
60	Woodie Held	2.50
61	Ron Piche	2.50
62	Al Pilarcik	2.50
63	Jim Kaat	7.50
64	Alex Grammas	2.50
65	Ted Kluszewski	7.50
66	Bill Henry	2.50
67	Ossie Virgil	2.50
68	Deron Johnson	2.50
69	Earl Wilson	2.50
70	Bill Virdon	2.50
71	Jerry Adair	2.50
72	Stu Miller	2.50
73	Al Spangler	2.50
74	Joe Pignatano	2.50
75	Lindy Shows Larry (Larry Jackson, Lindy McDaniel)	5.00
76	Harry Anderson	2.50
77	Dick Stigman	2.50
78	Lee Walls	2.50
79	Joe Ginsberg	2.50
80	Harmon Killebrew	30.00
81	Tracy Stallard	2.50
82	Joe Christopher	2.50
83	Bob Bruce	2.50
84	Lee Maye	2.50
85	Jerry Walker	2.50
86	Dodgers Team	7.50
87	Joe Amalfitano	2.50
88	Richie Ashburn	12.00
89	Billy Martin	12.00
90	Jerry Staley	2.50
91	Walt Moryn	2.50
92	Hal Naragon	2.50
93	Tony Gonzalez	2.50
94	Johnny Kucks	2.50
95	Norm Cash	3.50
96	Billy O'Dell	2.50
97	Jerry Lynch	2.50
98a	Checklist 89-176 (word "Checklist" in red on front)	7.00
98b	Checklist 89-176 ("Checklist" in yellow, 98 on back in black)	5.00
98c	Checklist 89-176 ("Checklist" in yellow, 98 on back in white)	7.00
99	Don Buddin	2.50
100	Harvey Haddix	2.50
101	Bubba Phillips	2.50
102	Gene Stephens	2.50
103	Ruben Amaro	2.50
104	John Blanchard	2.50
105	Carl Willey	2.50
106	Whitey Herzog	4.00
107	Seth Morehead	2.50
108	Dan Dobbek	2.50
109	Johnny Podres	3.50
110	Vada Pinson	6.00
111	Jack Meyer	2.50
112	Chico Fernandez	2.50
113	Mike Fornieles	2.50
14	Hobie Landrith	2.50
15	Johnny Antonelli	2.50
16	Joe DeMaestri	2.50
17	Dale Long	2.50
18	Chris Cannizzaro	2.50
119	A's Big Armor (Hank Bauer, Jerry Lumpe, Norm Siebern)	5.00
120	Eddie Mathews	35.00
121	Eli Grba	2.50
122	Cubs Team	6.00
123	Billy Gardner	2.50
124	J.C. Martin	2.50
125	Steve Barber	2.50
126	Dick Stuart	3.00
127	Ron Kline	2.50
128	Rip Repulski	2.50
129	Ed Hobaugh	2.50
130	Norm Larker	2.50
131	Paul Richards	2.50
132	Al Lopez	5.00
133	Ralph Houk	5.00
134	Mickey Vernon	2.50
135	Fred Hutchinson	2.50
136	Walt Alston	5.00
137	Chuck Dressen	2.50
138	Danny Murtaugh	2.50
139	Solly Hemus	2.50
140	Gus Triandos	2.50
141	*Billy Williams*	100.00
142	Luis Arroyo	2.50
143	Russ Snyder	2.50
144	Jim Coker	2.50
145	Bob Buhl	2.50
146	Marty Keough	2.50
147	Ed Rakow	2.50
148	Julian Javier	2.50
149	Bob Oldis	2.50
150	Willie Mays	135.00
151	Jim Donohue	2.50
152	Earl Torgeson	2.50
153	Don Lee	2.50
154	Bobby Del Greco	2.50
155	Johnny Temple	2.50
156	Ken Hunt	2.50
157	Cal McLish	2.50
158	Pete Daley	2.50
159	Orioles Team	6.00
160	Whitey Ford	50.00
161	Sherman Jones (photo actually Eddie Fisher)	2.50
162	Jay Hook	2.50
163	Ed Sadowski	2.50
164	Felix Mantilla	2.50
165	Gino Cimoli	2.50
166	Danny Kravitz	2.50
167	Giants Team	6.00
168	Tommy Davis	5.00
169	Don Elston	2.50
170	Al Smith	2.50
171	Paul Foytack	2.50
172	Don Dillard	2.50
173	Beantown Bombers (Jackie Jensen, Frank Malzone, Vic Wertz)	6.00
174	Ray Semproch	2.50
175	Gene Freese	2.50
176	Ken Aspromonte	2.50
177	Don Larsen	2.50
178	Bob Nieman	2.50
179	Joe Koppe	2.50
180	Bobby Richardson	6.00
181	Fred Green	2.50
182	Dave Nicholson	2.50
183	Andre Rodgers	2.50
184	Steve Bilko	2.50
185	Herb Score	2.50
186	Elmer Valo	2.50
187	Billy Klaus	2.50
188	Jim Marshall	2.50
189	Checklist 177-264	5.00
190	Stan Williams	2.50

191	Mike de la Hoz	2.50		264	Glen Hobbie	2.50
192	Dick Brown	2.50		265	Tony Kubek	15.00
193	Gene Conley	2.50		266	Lindy McDaniel	2.50
194	Gordy Coleman	2.50		267	Norm Siebern	2.50
195	Jerry Casale	2.50		268	Ike DeLock (Delock)	2.50
196	Ed Bouchee	2.50		269	Harry Chiti	2.50
197	Dick Hall	2.50		270	Bob Friend	2.50
198	Carl Sawatski	2.50		271	Jim Landis	2.50
199	Bob Boyd	2.50		272	Tom Morgan	2.50
200	Warren Spahn	30.00		273	Checklist 265-352	5.00
201	Pete Whisenant	2.50		274	Gary Bell	2.50
202	Al Neiger	2.50		275	Gene Woodling	2.50
203	Eddie Bressoud	2.50		276	Ray Rippelmeyer	2.50
204	Bob Skinner	2.50		277	Hank Foiles	2.50
205	Bill Pierce	2.50		278	Don McMahon	2.50
206	Gene Green	2.50		279	Jose Pagan	2.50
207	Dodger Southpaws (Sandy Koufax, Johnny Podres)	30.00		280	Frank Howard	4.00
208	Larry Osborne	2.50		281	Frank Sullivan	2.50
209	Ken McBride	2.50		282	Faye Throneberry	2.50
210	Pete Runnels	2.50		283	Bob Anderson	2.50
211	Bob Gibson	40.00		284	Dick Gernert	2.50
212	Haywood Sullivan	2.50		285	Sherm Lollar	2.50
213	*Bill Stafford*	4.50		286	George Witt	2.50
214	Danny Murphy	2.50		287	Carl Yastrzemski	90.00
215	Gus Bell	2.50		288	Albie Pearson	2.50
216	Ted Bowsfield	2.50		289	Ray Moore	2.50
217	Mel Roach	2.50		290	Stan Musial	125.00
218	Hal Brown	2.50		291	Tex Clevenger	2.50
219	Gene Mauch	2.50		292	Jim Baumer	2.50
220	Al Dark	2.50		293	Tom Sturdivant	2.50
221	Mike Higgins	2.50		294	Don Blasingame	2.50
222	Jimmie Dykes	2.50		295	Milt Pappas	2.50
223	Bob Scheffing	2.50		296	Wes Covington	2.50
224	Joe Gordon	2.50		297	Athletics Team	6.00
225	Bill Rigney	2.50		298	Jim Golden	2.50
226	Harry Lavagetto	2.50		299	Clay Dalrymple	2.50
227	Juan Pizarro	2.50		300	Mickey Mantle	550.00
228	Yankees Team	50.00		301	Chet Nichols	2.50
229	Rudy Hernandez	2.50		302	Al Heist	2.50
230	Don Hoak	2.50		303	Gary Peters	2.50
231	Dick Drott	2.50		304	Rocky Nelson	2.50
232	Bill White	4.50		305	Mike McCormick	2.50
233	Joe Jay	2.50		306	World Series Game 1 Virdon Saves Game	7.50
234	Ted Lepcio	2.50		307	World Series Game 2 Mantle Slams 2 Homers	60.00
235	Camilo Pascual	2.50		308	World Series Game 3 Richardson is Hero	7.50
236	Don Gile	2.50		309	World Series Game 4 Cimoli is Safe in Crucial Play	7.50
237	Billy Loes	2.50		310	World Series Game 5 Face Saves the Day	7.50
238	Jim Gilliam	4.50		311	World Series Game 6 Ford Pitches Second Shutout	7.50
239	Dave Sisler	2.50		312	World Series Game 7 Mazeroski's Homer Wins It!	12.00
240	Ron Hansen	2.50		313	World Series Summary The Winners Celebrate	7.50
241	Al Cicotte	2.50		314	Bob Miller	2.50
242	Hal W. Smith	2.50		315	Earl Battey	2.50
243	Frank Lary	2.50		316	Bobby Gene Smith	2.50
244	Chico Cardenas	2.50		317	*Jim Brewer*	2.50
245	Joe Adcock	2.50		318	Danny O'Connell	2.50
246	Bob Davis	2.50		319	Valmy Thomas	2.50
247	Billy Goodman	2.50		320	Lou Burdette	2.50
248	Ed Keegan	2.50		321	Marv Breeding	2.50
249	Reds Team	6.00		322	Bill Kunkel	2.50
250	Buc Hill Aces (Roy Face, Vern Law)	6.00		323	Sammy Esposito	2.50
251	Bill Bruton	2.50		324	Hank Aguirre	2.50
252	Bill Short	2.50		325	Wally Moon	2.50
253	Sammy Taylor	2.50		326	Dave Hillman	2.50
254	Ted Sadowski	2.50		327	*Matty Alou*	4.00
255	Vic Power	2.50		328	Jim O'Toole	2.50
256	Billy Hoeft	2.50		329	Julio Becquer	2.50
257	Carroll Hardy	2.50		330	Rocky Colavito	10.00
258	Jack Sanford	2.50		331	Ned Garver	2.50
259	John Schaive	2.50		332	Dutch Dotterer (photo actually Tommy Dotterer)	2.50
260	Don Drysdale	40.00		333	Fritz Brickell	3.00
261	Charlie Lau	2.50		334	Walt Bond	2.50
262	Tony Curry	2.50		335	Frank Bolling	2.50
263	Ken Hamlin	2.50		336	Don Mincher	2.50

337	Al's Aces (Al Lopez, Herb Score, Early Wynn)	7.50
338	Don Landrum	2.50
339	Gene Baker	2.50
340	Vic Wertz	2.50
341	Jim Owens	2.50
342	Clint Courtney	2.50
343	Earl Robinson	2.50
344	Sandy Koufax	100.00
345	Jim Piersall	2.50
346	Howie Nunn	2.50
347	Cardinals Team	6.00
348	Steve Boros	2.50
349	Danny McDevitt	2.50
350	Ernie Banks	50.00
351	Jim King	2.50
352	Bob Shaw	2.50
353	Howie Bedell	2.50
354	Billy Harrell	2.50
355	Bob Allison	2.50
356	Ryne Duren	3.50
357	Daryl Spencer	2.50
358	Earl Averill	2.50
359	Dallas Green	3.50
360	Frank Robinson	50.00
361a	Checklist 353-429 ("Topps Baseball" in black on front)	5.00
361b	Checklist 353-429 ("Topps Baseball" in yellow)	6.00
362	Frank Funk	2.50
363	John Roseboro	2.50
364	Moe Drabowsky	2.50
365	Jerry Lumpe	2.50
366	Eddie Fisher	2.50
367	Jim Rivera	2.50
368	Bennie Daniels	2.50
369	Dave Philley	2.50
370	Roy Face	2.50
371	Bill Skowron (SP)	5.00
372	Bob Hendley	2.50
373	Red Sox Team	8.00
374	Paul Giel	2.50
375	Ken Boyer	6.00
376	Mike Roarke	2.50
377	Ruben Gomez	2.50
378	Wally Post	2.50
379	Bobby Shantz	5.00
380	Minnie Minoso	6.00
381	Dave Wickersham	2.50
382	Frank J. Thomas	2.50
383	Frisco First Liners (Mike McCormick, Billy O'Dell, Jack Sanford)	6.00
384	Chuck Essegian	2.50
385	Jim Perry	2.50
386	Joe Hicks	2.50
387	Duke Maas	2.50
388	Roberto Clemente	125.00
389	Ralph Terry	5.00
390	Del Crandall	2.50
391	Winston Brown	2.50
392	Reno Bertoia	2.50
393	Batter Bafflers (Don Cardwell, Glen Hobbie)	2.50
394	Ken Walters	2.50
395	Chuck Estrada	2.50
396	Bob Aspromonte	2.50
397	Hal Woodeshick	2.50
398	Hank Bauer	2.50
399	Cliff Cook	2.50
400	Vern Law	2.50
401	Babe Ruth Hits 60th Homer	50.00
402	Larsen Pitches Perfect Game	25.00
403	Brooklyn-Boston Play 26-Inning Tie	2.50
404	Hornsby Tops N.L. with .424 Average	5.00
405	(After 2,130 Games, Gehrig Benched)	35.00
406	Mantle Blasts 565 ft. Home Run	55.00
407	Jack Chesbro Wins 41st Game	2.50
408	Mathewson Strikes Out 267 Batters	6.00
409	Johnson Hurls 3rd Shutout in 4 Days	5.00
410	Haddix Pitches 12 Perfect Innings	6.00
411	Tony Taylor	2.50
412	Larry Sherry	2.50
413	Eddie Yost	2.50
414	Dick Donovan	2.50
415	Hank Aaron	150.00
416	*Dick Howser*	6.00
417	*Juan Marichal*	150.00
418	Ed Bailey	2.50
419	Tom Borland	2.50
420	Ernie Broglio	2.50
421	Ty Cline (SP)	2.50
422	Bud Daley	2.50
423	Charlie Neal	2.50
424	Turk Lown	2.50
425	Yogi Berra	100.00
426	Not Issued	
427	Dick Ellsworth	2.50
428	Ray Barker (SP)	2.50
429	Al Kaline	50.00
430	Bill Mazeroski	50.00
431	Chuck Stobbs	2.50
432	Coot Veal	2.50
433	Art Mahaffey	2.50
434	Tom Brewer	2.50
435	Orlando Cepeda	15.00
436	*Jim Maloney*	10.00
437a	Checklist 430-506 (#440 is Louis Aparicio)	8.00
437b	Checklist 430-506 (#440 is Luis Aparicio)	8.00
438	Curt Flood	2.50
439	*Phil Regan*	2.50
440	Luis Aparicio	14.00
441	Dick Bertell	2.50
442	Gordon Jones	2.50
443	Duke Snider	50.00
444	Joe Nuxhall	2.50
445	Frank Malzone	2.50
446	Bob "Hawk" Taylor	2.50
447	Harry Bright	4.50
448	Del Rice	4.50
449	*Bobby Bolin*	4.50
450	Jim Lemon	4.50
451	Power For Ernie (Ernie Broglio, Daryl Spencer, Bill White)	5.00
452	Bob Allen	4.50
453	Dick Schofield	4.50
454	Pumpsie Green	4.50
455	Early Wynn	15.00
456	Hal Bevan	4.50
457	Johnny James	4.50
458	Willie Tasby	4.50
459	Terry Fox	4.50
460	Gil Hodges	20.00
461	Smoky Burgess	4.50
462	Lou Klimchock	4.50
463a	Braves Team (should be card #426)	8.00
463b	Jack Fisher	4.50
464	*Leroy Thomas*	4.50
465	Roy McMillan	4.50
466	Ron Moeller	4.50
467	Indians Team	8.00
468	Johnny Callison	4.50
469	Ralph Lumenti	4.50
470	Roy Sievers	4.50
471	Phil Rizzuto (MVP)	25.00
472	Yogi Berra (MVP)	100.00
473	Bobby Shantz (MVP)	7.50
474	Al Rosen (MVP)	7.50
475	Mickey Mantle (MVP)	200.00
476	Jackie Jensen (MVP)	7.50
477	Nellie Fox (MVP)	9.00
478	Roger Maris (MVP)	50.00
479	Jim Konstanty	7.50

480	Roy Campanella (MVP)	50.00
481	Hank Sauer	7.50
482	Willie Mays	50.00
483	Don Newcombe (MVP)	9.00
484	Hank Aaron (MVP)	50.00
485	Ernie Banks (MVP)	35.00
486	Dick Groat (MVP)	7.50
487	Gene Oliver	4.50
488	Joe McClain	4.50
489	Walt Dropo	4.50
490	Jim Bunning	8.00
491	Phillies Team	9.00
492	Ron Fairly	4.50
493	Don Zimmer	4.50
494	Tom Cheney	4.50
495	Elston Howard	6.00
496	Ken MacKenzie	4.50
497	Willie Jones	4.50
498	Ray Herbert	4.50
499	Chuck Schilling	4.50
500	Harvey Kuenn	5.00
501	John DeMerit	4.50
502	Clarence Coleman	4.50
503	Tito Francona	4.50
504	Billy Consolo	4.50
505	Red Schoendienst	12.50
506	*Willie Davis*	12.00
507	Pete Burnside	4.50
508	Rocky Bridges	4.50
509	Camilo Carreon	4.50
510	Art Ditmar	4.50
511	Joe M. Morgan	4.50
512	Bob Will	4.50
513	Jim Brosnan	4.50
514	Jake Wood	4.50
515	Jackie Brandt	4.50
516	Checklist 507-587	10.00
517	Willie McCovey	55.00
518	Andy Carey	4.50
519	Jim Pagliaroni	4.50
520	Joe Cunningham	4.50
521	Brother Battery (Larry Sherry, Norm Sherry)	6.00
522	Dick Farrell	35.00
523	Joe Gibbon	35.00
524	Johnny Logan	50.00
525	*Ron Perranoski*	15.00
526	R.C. Stevens	35.00
527	Gene Leek	35.00
528	Pedro Ramos	35.00
529	Bob Roselli	35.00
530	Bobby Malkmus	35.00
531	Jim Coates	35.00
532	Bob Hale	35.00
533	Jack Curtis	35.00
534	Eddie Kasko	35.00
535	Larry Jackson	35.00
536	Bill Tuttle	35.00
537	Bobby Locke	35.00
538	Chuck Hiller	35.00
539	Johnny Klippstein	35.00
540	Jackie Jensen	35.00
541	Roland Sheldon	50.00
542	Twins Team	75.00
543	Roger Craig	40.00
544	George Thomas	35.00
545	Hoyt Wilhelm	75.00
546	Marty Kutyna	35.00
547	Leon Wagner	35.00
548	Ted Wills	35.00
549	Hal R. Smith	35.00
550	Frank Baumann	35.00
551	George Altman	35.00
552	Jim Archer	35.00
553	Bill Fischer	35.00
554	Pirates Team	100.00
555	Sam Jones	35.00
556	Ken R. Hunt	35.00
557	Jose Valdivielso	35.00
558	Don Ferrarese	35.00
559	Jim Gentile	50.00
560	Barry Latman	35.00
561	Charley James	35.00
562	Bill Monbouquette	35.00
563	Bob Cerv	75.00
564	Don Cardwell	35.00
565	Felipe Alou	55.00
566	Paul Richards (All-Star)	35.00
567	Danny Murtaugh (All-Star)	35.00
568	Bill Skowron (All-Star)	45.00
569	Frank Herrera (All-Star)	35.00
570	Nellie Fox (All-Star)	50.00
571	Bill Mazeroski (All-Star)	45.00
572	Brooks Robinson (All-Star)	100.00
573	Ken Boyer (All-Star)	40.00
574	Luis Aparicio (All-Star)	50.00
575	Ernie Banks (All-Star)	100.00
576	Roger Maris (All-Star)	200.00
577	Hank Aaron (All-Star)	225.00
578	Mickey Mantle (All-Star)	500.00
579	Willie Mays (All-Star)	225.00
580	Al Kaline (All-Star)	100.00
581	Frank Robinson (All-Star)	100.00
582	Earl Battey (All-Star)	35.00
583	Del Crandall (All-Star)	35.00
584	Jim Perry (All-Star)	35.00
585	Bob Friend (All-Star)	35.00
586	Whitey Ford (All-Star)	100.00
587	Not Issued	
588	Not Issued	
589	Warren Spahn (All-Star)	150.00

CHARLIE LAU
Catcher   Milwaukee Braves

1962 Topps

The 1962 Topps set established another plateau for set size with 598 cards. The 2-1/2" by 3-1/2" cards feature a photograph set against a wood grain background. The lower righthand corner has been made to look like it is curling away. Many established specialty cards dot the set including statistical leaders, multi-player cards, team cards, checklists, World Series cards and All-Stars. Of note is that 1962 was the first year of the multi-player rookie card. There is a 9-card "In Action" sub-set and a 10-card run of special Babe Ruth cards. Photo variations of several cards in the 2nd Series (#'s 110-196) exist. All cards in the 2nd Series can be found with two distinct printing variations, an early printing with the cards containing a very noticeable greenish tint, having been corrected to clear photos in subsequent print runs. The complete set price in the checklist that follows does not include the higher-priced variations. Among the high numbers (#523-598) certain cards were "short-printed," produced in lesser quantities. These cards carry a higher value and are indicated in the checklist by the notation (SP) after the player name.

set, in my opinion, that is strictly mint, through and through, every card. It does not exist.

The green tint variation cards are a waste of money, ugly and disgusting and nobody cares. I get a lot more calls for the "with emblems" variation on the Buhl and Tasby cards than without, and I think the various guides ought to be changed to reflect that.

The high numbers are not as rare as many people think, and they often come in a nice, dark brown and shiny card when found in high-quality bricks. The Maris card is almost impossible to find mint, centered and all brown, and I've sold the Mantle card for $1,000 or more when available in full brown.

Like the 1955 Bowmans and the 1971 Topps, even if a 1962 card is close to being mint, or even near-mint, it shows the wear because of those borders. The same wear on a card with white borders might be hardly visible.

		MT
Complete Set (598):		8000.
Common Player (1-370):		5.00
Common Player (371-446):		7.00
Common Player (447-522):		10.00
Common Player (523-598):		25.00
1	Roger Maris	300.00
2	Jim Brosnan	5.00
3	Pete Runnels	5.00
4	John DeMerit	5.00
5	Sandy Koufax	200.00
6	Marv Breeding	5.00
7	Frank J. Thomas	5.00
8	Ray Herbert	5.00
9	Jim Davenport	5.00
10	Roberto Clemente	150.00
11	Tom Morgan	5.00
12	Harry Craft	5.00
13	Dick Howser	5.00
14	Bill White	5.00
15	Dick Donovan	5.00
16	Darrell Johnson	5.00
17	Johnny Callison	5.00
18	Managers' Dream (Mickey Mantle, Willie Mays)	200.00
19	*Ray Washburn*	5.00
20	Rocky Colavito	20.00
21	Jim Kaat	5.00
22a	Checklist 1-88 (numbers 121-176 on back)	5.00
22b	Checklist 1-88 (numbers 33-88 on back)	5.00
23	Norm Larker	5.00
24	Tigers Team	10.00
25	Ernie Banks	50.00
26	Chris Cannizzaro	5.00
27	Chuck Cottier	5.00
28	Minnie Minoso	5.00
29	Casey Stengel	30.00
30	Eddie Mathews	30.00
31	*Tom Tresh*	20.00
32	John Roseboro	5.00

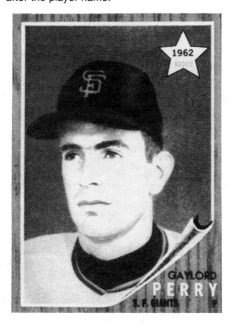

Mr. Mint Says - This is one of the toughest sets in the world to complete because of the wood grain borders. The cards are very hard to find in full brown. There is no

#	Player	Price
33	Don Larsen	5.00
34	Johnny Temple	5.00
35	*Don Schwall*	5.00
36	Don Leppert	5.00
37	Tribe Hill Trio (Barry Latman, Jim Perry, Dick Stigman)	5.00
38	Gene Stephens	5.00
39	Joe Koppe	5.00
40	Orlando Cepeda	15.00
41	Cliff Cook	5.00
42	Jim King	5.00
43	Dodgers Team	10.00
44	Don Taussig	5.00
45	Brooks Robinson	50.00
46	*Jack Baldschun*	5.00
47	Bob Will	5.00
48	Ralph Terry	5.00
49	Hal Jones	5.00
50	Stan Musial	150.00
51	A.L. Batting Leaders (Norm Cash, Elston Howard, Al Kaline, Jim Piersall)	10.00
52	N.L. Batting Leaders (Ken Boyer, Bob Clemente, Wally Moon, Vada Pinson)	10.00
53	A.L. Home Run Leaders (Jim Gentile, Harmon Killebrew, Mickey Mantle, Roger Maris)	100.00
54	N.L. Home Run Leaders (Orlando Cepeda, Willie Mays, Frank Robinson)	15.00
55	A.L. E.R.A. Leaders (Dick Donovan, Don Mossi, Milt Pappas, Bill Stafford)	10.00
56	N.L. E.R.A. Leaders (Mike McCormick, Jim O'Toole, Curt Simmons, Warren Spahn)	10.00
57	A.L. Win Leaders (Steve Barber, Jim Bunning, Whitey Ford, Frank Lary)	10.00
58	N.L. Win Leaders (Joe Jay, Jim O'Toole, Warren Spahn)	10.00
59	A.L. Strikeout Leaders (Jim Bunning, Whitey Ford, Camilo Pascual, Juan Pizzaro)	10.00
60	N.L. Strikeout Leaders (Don Drysdale, Sandy Koufax, Jim O'Toole, Stan Williams)	15.00
61	Cardinals Team	10.00
62	Steve Boros	5.00
63	*Tony Cloninger*	5.00
64	Russ Snyder	5.00
65	Bobby Richardson	5.00
66	Cuno Barragon (Barragan)	5.00
67	Harvey Haddix	5.00
68	Ken L. Hunt	5.00
69	Phil Ortega	5.00
70	Harmon Killebrew	25.00
71	Dick LeMay	5.00
72	Bob's Pupils (Steve Boros, Bob Scheffing, Jake Wood)	5.00
73	Nellie Fox	15.00
74	Bob Lillis	5.00
75	Milt Pappas	5.00
76	Howie Bedell	5.00
77	Tony Taylor	5.00
78	Gene Green	5.00
79	Ed Hobaugh	5.00
80	Vada Pinson	5.00
81	Jim Pagliaroni	5.00
82	Deron Johnson	5.00
83	Larry Jackson	5.00
84	Lenny Green	5.00
85	Gil Hodges	20.00
86	*Donn Clendenon*	5.00
87	Mike Roarke	5.00
88	Ralph Houk	5.00
89	Barney Schultz	5.00
90	Jim Piersall	5.00
91	J.C. Martin	5.00
92	Sam Jones	5.00
93	John Blanchard	5.00
94	Jay Hook	5.00
95	Don Hoak	5.00
96	Eli Grba	5.00
97	Tito Francona	5.00
98	Checklist 89-176	8.00
99	*Boog Powell*	30.00
100	Warren Spahn	35.00
101	Carroll Hardy	5.00
102	Al Schroll	5.00
103	Don Blasingame	5.00
104	Ted Savage	5.00
105	Don Mossi	5.00
106	Carl Sawatski	5.00
107	Mike McCormick	5.00
108	Willie Davis	5.00
109	Bob Shaw	5.00
110	Bill Skowron	5.00
111	Dallas Green	5.00
112	Hank Foiles	5.00
113	White Sox Team	10.00
114	Howie Koplitz	5.00
115	Bob Skinner	5.00
116	Herb Score	5.00
117	Gary Geiger	5.00
118	Julian Javier	5.00
119	Danny Murphy	5.00
120	Bob Purkey	5.00
121	Billy Hitchcock	5.00
122	Norm Bass	5.00
123	Mike de la Hoz	5.00
124	Bill Pleis	5.00
125	Gene Woodling	5.00
126	Al Cicotte	5.00
127	Pride of the A's (Hank Bauer, Jerry Lumpe, Norm Siebern)	5.00
128	Art Fowler	5.00
129a	Lee Walls (facing left)	35.00
129b	Lee Walls (facing right)	5.00
130	*Frank Bolling*	5.00
131	*Pete Richert*	5.00
132a	Angels Team (with inset photos)	35.00
132b	Angels Team (no inset photos)	10.00
133	Felipe Alou	7.00
134a	Billy Hoeft (green sky)	35.00
134b	Billy Hoeft (blue sky)	5.00
135	Babe As A Boy	20.00
136	Babe Joins Yanks	20.00
137	Babe and Mgr. Huggins	20.00
138	The Famous Slugger	20.00
139a	Hal Reniff (pitching)	75.00
139b	Hal Reniff (portrait)	25.00
139c	Babe Hits 60	.25
140	Gehrig and Ruth	40.00
141	Twilight Years	20.00
142	Coaching for the Dodgers	20.00
143	Greatest Sports Hero	20.00
144	Farewell Speech	20.00
145	Barry Latman	5.00
146	Don Demeter	5.00
147a	Bill Kunkel (pitching)	35.00
147b	Bill Kunkel (portrait)	5.00
148	Wally Post	5.00
149	Bob Duliba	5.00
150	Al Kaline	40.00
151	Johnny Klippstein	5.00
152	Mickey Vernon	5.00
153	Pumpsie Green	5.00
154	Lee Thomas	5.00
155	Stu Miller	5.00
156	Merritt Ranew	5.00
157	Wes Covington	5.00
158	Braves Team	10.00
159	Hal Reniff	5.00
160	Dick Stuart	5.00
161	Frank Baumann	5.00
162	Sammy Drake	5.00

163 Hot Corner Guardians (Cletis Boyer, Billy Gardner)	5.00
164 Hal Naragon	5.00
165 Jackie Brandt	5.00
166 Don Lee	5.00
167 *Tim McCarver*	40.00
168 Leo Posada	5.00
169 Bob Cerv	5.00
170 Ron Santo	20.00
171 Dave Sisler	5.00
172 Fred Hutchinson	5.00
173 Chico Fernandez	5.00
174a Carl Willey (with cap)	35.00
174b Carl Willey (no cap)	5.00
175 Frank Howard	5.00
176a Eddie Yost (batting)	35.00
176b Eddie Yost (portrait)	5.00
177 Bobby Shantz	5.00
178 Camilo Carreon	5.00
179 Tom Sturdivant	5.00
180 Bob Allison	5.00
181 Paul Brown	5.00
182 Bob Nieman	5.00
183 Roger Craig	5.00
184 Haywood Sullivan	5.00
185 Roland Sheldon	5.00
186 *Mack Jones*	5.00
187 Gene Conley	5.00
188 Chuck Hiller	5.00
189 Dick Hall	5.00
190a Wally Moon (with cap)	35.00
190b Wally Moon (no cap)	5.00
191 Jim Brewer	5.00
192a Checklist 177-264 (192 is Check List, 3)	8.00
192b Checklist 177-264 (192 is Check List 3)	8.00
193 Eddie Kasko	5.00
194 *Dean Chance*	5.00
195 Joe Cunningham	5.00
196 Terry Fox	5.00
197 Daryl Spencer	5.00
198 Johnny Keane	5.00
199 *Gaylord Perry*	175.00
200 Mickey Mantle	750.00
201 Ike Delock	5.00
202 Carl Warwick	5.00
203 Jack Fisher	5.00
204 Johnny Weekly	5.00
205 Gene Freese	5.00
206 Senators Team	10.00
207 Pete Burnside	5.00
208 Billy Martin	10.00
209 *Jim Fregosi*	10.00
210 Roy Face	5.00
211 Midway Masters (Frank Bolling, Roy McMillan)	5.00
212 Jim Owens	5.00
213 Richie Ashburn	15.00
214 Dom Zanni	5.00
215 Woody Held	5.00
216 Ron Kline	5.00
217 Walt Alston	5.00
218 *Joe Torre*	35.00
219 *Al Downing*	5.00
220 Roy Sievers	5.00
221 Bill Short	5.00
222 Jerry Zimmerman	5.00
223 Alex Grammas	5.00
224 Don Rudolph	5.00
225 Frank Malzone	5.00
226 Giants Team	10.00
227 Bobby Tiefenauer	5.00
228 Dale Long	5.00
229 Jesus McFarlane	5.00
230 Camlio Pascual	5.00
231 Ernie Bowman	5.00

232 World Series Game 1 Yanks Win Opener	10.00
233 World Series Game 2 Jay Ties It Up	10.00
234 World Series Game 3 Maris Wins It In The 9th	20.00
235 World Series Game 4 Ford Sets New Mark	10.00
236 World Series Game 5 Yanks Crush Reds In Finale	10.00
237 World Series Summary The Winners Celebrate	10.00
238 Norm Sherry	5.00
239 Cecil Butler	5.00
240 George Altman	5.00
241 Johnny Kucks	5.00
242 Mel McGaha	5.00
243 Robin Roberts	20.00
244 Don Gile	5.00
245 Ron Hansen	5.00
246 Art Ditmar	5.00
247 Joe Pignatano	5.00
248 Bob Aspromonte	5.00
249 Ed Keegan	5.00
250 Norm Cash	5.00
251 Yankees Team	40.00
252 Earl Francis	5.00
253 Harry Chiti	5.00
254 Gordon Windhorn	5.00
255 Juan Pizarro	5.00
256 Elio Chacon	5.00
257 Jack Spring	5.00
258 Marty Keough	5.00
259 Lou Klimchock	5.00
260 Bill Pierce	5.00
261 George Alusik	5.00
262 Bob Schmidt	5.00
263 The Right Pitch (Joe Jay, Bob Purkey, Jim Turner)	5.00
264 Dick Ellsworth	5.00
265 Joe Adcock	5.00
266 John Anderson	5.00
267 Dan Dobbek	5.00
268 Ken McBride	5.00
269 Bob Oldis	5.00
270 Dick Groat	5.00
271 Ray Rippelmeyer	5.00
272 Earl Robinson	5.00
273 Gary Bell	5.00
274 Sammy Taylor	5.00
275 Norm Siebern	5.00
276 Hal Kostad	5.00
277 Checklist 265-352	7.00
278 Ken Johnson	5.00
279 Hobie Landrith	5.00
280 Johnny Podres	5.00
281 *Jake Gibbs*	5.00
282 Dave Hillman	5.00
283 Charlie Smith	5.00
284 Ruben Amaro	5.00
285 Curt Simmons	5.00
286 Al Lopez	5.00
287 George Witt	5.00
288 Billy Williams	40.00
289 Mike Krsnich	5.00
290 Jim Gentile	5.00
291 Hal Stowe	5.00
292 Jerry Kindall	5.00
293 Bob Miller	5.00
294 Phillies Team	10.00
295 Vern Law	5.00
296 Ken Hamlin	5.00
297 Ron Perranoski	5.00
298 Bill Tuttle	5.00
299 *Don Wert*	5.00
300 Willie Mays	200.00
301 Galen Cisco	5.00
302 *John Edwards*	5.00
303 Frank Torre	5.00
304 Dick Farrell	5.00

305	Jerry Lumpe	5.00
306	Redbird Rippers (Larry Jackson, Lindy McDaniel)	5.00
307	Jim Grant	5.00
308	Neil Chrisley	5.00
309	Moe Morhardt	5.00
310	Whitey Ford	50.00
311	Kubek Makes The Double Play	10.00
312	Spahn Show No-Hit Form	15.00
313	Maris Blasts 61st	30.00
314	Colavito's Power	10.00
315	Ford Tosses a Curve	10.00
316	Killebrew Send One into Orbit	20.00
317	Musial Plays 21st Season	30.00
318	The Switch Hitter Connects, Mickey Mantle	100.00
319	McCormick Shows His Stuff	5.00
320	Hank Aaron	200.00
321	Lee Stange	5.00
322	Al Dark	5.00
323	Don Landrum	5.00
324	Joe McClain	5.00
325	Luis Aparicio	20.00
326	Tom Parsons	5.00
327	Ozzie Virgil	5.00
328	Ken Walters	5.00
329	Bob Bolin	5.00
330	Johnny Romano	5.00
331	Moe Drabowsky	5.00
332	Don Buddin	5.00
333	Frank Cipriani	5.00
334	Red Sox Team	10.00
335	Bill Bruton	5.00
336	Billy Muffett	5.00
337	Jim Marshall	5.00
338	Billy Gardner	5.00
339	Jose Valdivielso	5.00
340	Don Drysdale	60.00
341	Mike Hershberger	5.00
342	Ed Rakow	5.00
343	Albie Pearson	5.00
344	Ed Bauta	5.00
345	Chuck Schilling	5.00
346	Jack Kralick	5.00
347	Chuck Hinton	5.00
348	Larry Burright	5.00
349	Paul Foytack	5.00
350	Frank Robinson	75.00
351	Braves' Backstops (Del Crandall, Joe Torre)	5.00
352	Frank Sullivan	5.00
353	Bill Mazeroski	10.00
354	Roman Mejias	5.00
355	Steve Barber	5.00
356	Tom Haller	5.00
357	Jerry Walker	5.00
358	Tommy Davis	5.00
359	Bobby Locke	5.00
360	Yogi Berra	100.00
361	Bob Hendley	5.00
362	Ty Cline	5.00
363	Bob Roselli	5.00
364	Ken Hunt	5.00
365	Charley Neal	5.00
366	Phil Regan	5.00
367	Checklist 353-429	5.00
368	Bob Tillman	5.00
369	Ted Bowsfield	5.00
370	Ken Boyer	10.00
371	Earl Battey	7.00
372	Jack Curtis	7.00
373	Al Heist	7.00
374	Gene Mauch	7.00
375	Ron Fairly	7.00
376	Bud Daley	7.00
377	Johnny Orsino	7.00

378	Bennie Daniels	7.00
379	Chuck Essegian	7.00
380	Lou Burdette	7.00
381	Chico Cardenas	7.00
382	Dick Williams	7.00
383	Ray Sadecki	7.00
384	Athletics Team	10.00
385	Early Wynn	25.00
386	Don Mincher	5.00
387	*Lou Brock*	275.00
388	Ryne Duren	5.00
389	Smoky Burgess	5.00
390	Orlando Cepeda (All-Star)	10.00
391	Bill Mazeroski (All-Star)	10.00
392	Ken Boyer (All-Star)	10.00
393	Roy McMillan (All-Star)	6.00
394	Hank Aaron (All-Star)	50.00
395	Willie Mays (All-Star)	50.00
396	Frank Robinson (All-Star)	25.00
397	John Roseboro (All-Star)	6.00
398	Don Drysdale (All-Star)	25.00
399	Warren Spahn (All-Star)	25.00
400	Elston Howard	15.00
401	AL & NL Homer Kings (Roger Maris, Orlando Cepeda)	75.00
402	Gino Cimoli	7.00
403	Chet Nichols	7.00
404	Tim Harkness	7.00
405	Jim Perry	7.00
406	Bob Taylor	7.00
407	Hank Aguirre	7.00
408	Gus Bell	7.00
409	Pirates Team	12.00
410	Al Smith	7.00
411	Danny O'Connell	7.00
412	Charlie James	7.00
413	Matty Alou	7.00
414	Joe Gaines	7.00
415	Bill Virdon	7.00
416	Bob Scheffing	7.00
417	Joe Azcue	7.00
418	Andy Carey	7.00
419	Bob Bruce	7.00
420	Gus Triandos	7.00
421	Ken MacKenzie	7.00
422	Steve Bilko	7.00
423	Rival League Relief Aces (Roy Face, Hoyt Wilhelm)	10.00
424	Al McBean	7.00
425	Carl Yastrzemski	175.00
426	Bob Farley	7.00
427	Jake Wood	7.00
428	Joe Hicks	7.00
429	Bill O'Dell	7.00
430	Tony Kubek	10.00
431	*Bob Rodgers*	7.00
432	Jim Pendleton	7.00
433	Jim Archer	7.00
434	Clay Dalrymple	7.00
435	Larry Sherry	7.00
436	Felix Mantilla	7.00
437	Ray Moore	7.00
438	Dick Brown	7.00
439	Jerry Buchek	7.00
440	Joe Jay	7.00
441	Checklist 430-506	10.00
442	Wes Stock	7.00
443	Del Crandall	7.00
444	Ted Wills	7.00
445	Vic Power	7.00
446	Don Elston	7.00
447	Willie Kirkland	10.00
448	Joe Gibbon	10.00
449	Jerry Adair	10.00
450	Jim O'Toole	10.00

451	*Jose Tartabull*	10.00
452	Earl Averill	10.00
453	Cal McLish	10.00
454	Floyd Robinson	10.00
455	Luis Arroyo	10.00
456	Joe Amalfitano	10.00
457	Lou Clinton	10.00
458a	Bob Buhl ("M" on cap)	75.00
458b	Bob Buhl (plain cap)	10.00
459	Ed Bailey	10.00
460	Jim Bunning	12.00
461	*Ken Hubbs*	40.00
462a	Willie Tasby ("W" on cap)	75.00
462b	Willie Tasby (plain cap)	10.00
463	Hank Bauer	10.00
464	*Al Jackson*	10.00
465	Reds Team	10.00
466	Norm Cash (All-Star)	10.00
467	Chuck Schilling (All-Star)	10.00
468	Brooks Robinson (All-Star)	25.00
469	Luis Aparicio (All-Star)	15.00
470	Al Kaline (All-Star)	25.00
471	Mickey Mantle (All-Star)	200.00
472	Rocky Colavito (All-Star)	15.00
473	Elston Howard (All-Star)	10.00
474	Frank Lary (All-Star)	10.00
475	Whitey Ford (All-Star)	20.00
476	Orioles Team	12.00
477	Andre Rodgers	10.00
478	Don Zimmer	10.00
479	*Joel Horlen*	10.00
480	Harvey Kuenn	10.00
481	Vic Wertz	10.00
482	Sam Mele	10.00
483	Don McMahon	10.00
484	Dick Schofield	10.00
485	Pedro Ramos	10.00
486	Jim Gilliam	10.00
487	Jerry Lynch	10.00
488	Hal Brown	10.00
489	Julio Gotay	10.00
490	Clete Boyer	10.00
491	Leon Wagner	10.00
492	Hal Smith	10.00
493	Danny McDevitt	10.00
494	Sammy White	10.00
495	Don Cardwell	10.00
496	Wayne Causey	10.00
497	Ed Bouchee	10.00
498	Jim Donohue	10.00
499	Zoilo Versalles	10.00
500	Duke Snider	75.00
501	Claude Osteen	10.00
502	Hector Lopez	10.00
503	Danny Murtaugh	10.00
504	Eddie Bressoud	10.00
505	Juan Marichal	50.00
506	Charley Maxwell	10.00
507	Ernie Broglio	10.00
508	Gordy Coleman	10.00
509	*Dave Giusti*	10.00
510	Jim Lemon	10.00
511	Bubba Phillips	10.00
512	Mike Fornieles	10.00
513	Whitey Herzog	10.00
514	Sherm Lollar	10.00
515	Stan Williams	10.00
516	Checklist 507-598	10.00
517	Dave Wickersham	10.00
518	Lee Maye	10.00
519	Bob Johnson	10.00
520	Bob Friend	10.00
521	Jacke Davis	10.00
522	Lindy McDaniel	10.00
523	Russ Nixon (SP)	30.00
524	Howie Nunn (SP)	30.00
525	George Thomas	25.00
526	Hal Woodeshick (SP)	30.00
527	*Dick McAuliffe*	25.00
528	Turk Lown	25.00
529	John Schaive (SP)	30.00
530	Bob Gibson	200.00
531	Bobby G. Smith	25.00
532	Dick Stigman	25.00
533	Charley Lau (SP)	30.00
534	Tony Gonzalez (SP)	30.00
535	Ed Roebuck	25.00
536	Dick Gernert	25.00
537	Indians Team	50.00
538	Jack Sanford	25.00
539	Billy Moran	25.00
540	Jim Landis (SP)	30.00
541	Don Nottebart (SP)	30.00
542	Dave Philley	25.00
543	Bob Allen (SP)	30.00
544	Willie McCovey (SP)	200.00
545	Hoyt Wilhelm (SP)	75.00
546	Moe Thacker (SP)	30.00
547	Don Ferrarese	25.00
548	Bobby Del Greco	25.00
549	Bill Rigney (SP)	30.00
550	Art Mahaffey (SP)	30.00
551	Harry Bright	25.00
552	Cubs Team	50.00
553	Jim Coates	25.00
554	Bubba Morton (SP)	30.00
555	John Buzhardt (SP)	30.00
556	Al Spangler	25.00
557	Bob Anderson (SP)	30.00
558	John Goryl	25.00
559	Mike Higgins	25.00
560	Chuck Estrada (SP)	30.00
561	Gene Oliver (SP)	30.00
562	Bill Henry	25.00
563	Ken Aspromonte	25.00
564	Bob Grim	25.00
565	Jose Pagan	25.00
566	Marty Kutyna (SP)	30.00
567	Tracy Stallard (SP)	30.00
568	Jim Golden	25.00
569	Ed Sadowski (SP)	30.00
570	Bill Stafford	25.00
571	Billy Klaus (SP)	30.00
572	Bob Miller	40.00
573	Johnny Logan	25.00
574	Dean Stone	25.00
575	Red Schoendienst	40.00
576	Russ Kemmerer (SP)	30.00
577	Dave Nicholson (SP)	30.00
578	Jim Duffalo	25.00
579	Jim Schaffer (SP)	30.00
580	Bill Monbouquette	25.00
581	Mel Roach	25.00
582	Ron Piche	25.00
583	Larry Osborne	25.00
584	Twins Team	50.00
585	Glen Hobbie (SP)	30.00
586	Sammy Esposito (SP)	30.00
587	Frank Funk (SP)	30.00
588	Birdie Tebbetts	25.00
589	Bob Turley	25.00
590	Curt Flood	25.00
591	Rookie Parade Pitchers (*Sam McDowell*, Ron Nischwitz, Art Quirk, Dick Radatz, Ron Taylor)	100.00
592	Rookie Parade Pitchers (*Bo Belinsky*, Jim Bouton, Joe Bonikowski, Dan Pfister, Dave Stenhouse)	100.00

593   Rookie Parade Pitchers (Craig Anderson, Jack
      Hamilton, Jack Lamabe, Bob Moorhead, Bob Veale)   50.00
594   Rookie Parade Catchers (Doug Camilli, Doc
      Edwards, Don Pavletich, Ken Retzer, Bob Uecker)   150.00
595   Rookie Parade Infielders (*Ed Charles*,
      Marlin Coughtry, Bob Sadowski, Felix Torres)   50.00
596   Rookie Parade Infielders (*Bernie Allen*,
      Phil Linz, Joe Pepitone, Rich Rollins)   100.00
597   Rookie Parade Infielders (Rod Kanehl, Jim
      McKnight, Denis Menke, Amado Samuel)   50.00
598   Rookie Parade Outfielders (Howie Goss, Jim
      Hickman, Manny Jimenez, Al Luplow, Ed Olivares)   100.00

1963 Topps

Although the number of cards dropped to 576, the 1963 Topps set is among the most popular of the 1960s. A color photo dominates the 2-1/2" by 3-1/2" card, but a colored circle at the bottom carries a black and white portrait as well. A colored band gives the player's name, team and position. The backs again feature career statistics and a cartoon, career summary and brief biographical details. The set is somewhat unlike those immediately preceding it in that there are fewer specialty cards. The major groupings are statistical leaders, World Series highlights and rookies. It is one rookie which makes the set special - Pete Rose. As one of most avidly sought cards in history and a high-numbered card at that, the Rose rookie card accounts for much of the value of a complete set.

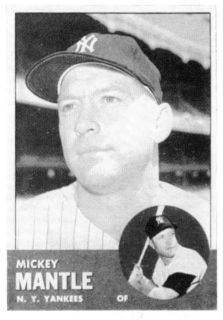

Mr. Mint Says - Mint condition cards in this year are virtually impossible because of the colored borders on the bottom. I have never seen a mint set of 1963s, though a guy did once sell me 100 mint Roses for $3 each. They were all full blue, and I turned around and blew them out for $4.50 each. We are not talking about last week here. This is a very popular set, with Rose and Stargell rookies and the ususal pile of Hall of Famers.

The set has a long high number run from 507 through 576 that is very difficult, but the mid-range of 447-506 is actually tougher than the higher numbers. Centering can also be a thorn with the highs.

Printing dots are also a problem, like the little white "bubbles" on the top of the Rose card.

		MT
Complete Set (576):		8000.
Common Player (1-283):		5.00
Common Player (284-446):		6.00
Common Player (447-522):		20.00
Common Player (523-576):		12.00
1	N.L. Batting Leaders (Hank Aaron, Bill White, Frank Robinson, Tommy Davis, Stan Musial)	50.00
2	A.L. Batting Leaders (Chuck Hinton, Mickey Mantle, Floyd Robinson, Pete Runnels, Norm Siebern)	40.00
3	N.L. Home Run Leaders (Hank Aaron, Ernie Banks, Orlando Cepeda, Willie Mays, Frank Robinson)	35.00
4	A.L. Home Run Leaders (Norm Cash, Rocky Colavito, Harmon Killebrew, Roger Maris, Leon Wagner)	15.00
5	N.L. E.R.A. Leaders (Don Drysdale, Bob Gibson, Sandy Koufax)	15.00
6	A.L. E.R.A. Leaders (Whitey Ford, Hank Aguirre, Eddie Fisher, Robin Roberts)	10.00
7	N.L. Pitching Leaders (Don Drysdale, Joe Jay, Art Mahaffey, Billy O'Dell, Bob Purkey, Jack Sanford)	10.00
8	A.L. Pitching Leaders (Jim Bunning, Dick Donovan, Ray Herbert, Camilo Pascual, Ralph Terry)	10.00
9	N.L. Strikeout Leaders (Don Drysdale, Dick Farrell, Bob Gibson, Sandy Koufax, Billy O'Dell)	15.00
10	A.L. Strikeout Leaders (Jim Bunning, Jim Kaat, Camilo Pascual, Ralph Terry)	6.00
11	Lee Walls	5.00
12	Steve Barber	5.00
13	Phillies Team	7.00
14	Pedro Ramos	5.00
15	Ken Hubbs	5.00
16	Al Smith	5.00
17	Ryne Duren	5.00
18	Buc Blasters (Smoky Burgess, Roberto Clemente, Bob Skinner, Dick Stuart)	30.00
19	Pete Burnside	5.00
20	Tony Kubek	10.00
21	Marty Keough	5.00
22	Curt Simmons	5.00
23	Ed Lopat	5.00
24	Bob Bruce	5.00
25	Al Kaline	40.00
26	Ray Moore	5.00
27	Choo Choo Coleman	5.00
28	Mike Fornieles	5.00
29a	1962 Rookie Stars (Sammy Ellis)	10.00
29a	1962 Rookie Stars (Ray Culp)	10.00
29a	1962 Rookie Stars (*John Boozer*)	10.00
29a	1962 Rookie Stars (Jesse Gonder)	10.00
29b	1963 Rookie Stars (Sammy Ellis)	5.00
29b	1963 Rookie Stars (*Ray Culp*)	5.00
29b	1963 Rookie Stars (John Boozer)	5.00
29b	1963 Rookie Stars (Jesse Gonder)	5.00
30	Harvey Kuenn	5.00
31	Cal Koonce	5.00
32	Tony Gonzalez	5.00
33	Bo Belinsky	5.00
34	Dick Schofield	5.00
35	John Buzhardt	5.00
36	Jerry Kindall	5.00

37	Jerry Lynch	5.00	
38	Bud Daley	5.00	
39	Angels Team	5.00	
40	Vic Power	5.00	
41	Charlie Lau	5.00	
42	Stan Williams	5.00	
43	Veteran Masters (Casey Stengel, Gene Woodling)	8.00	
44	Terry Fox	5.00	
45	Bob Aspromonte	5.00	
46	*Tommie Aaron*	5.00	
47	Don Lock	5.00	
48	Birdie Tebbetts	5.00	
49	*Dal Maxvill*	5.00	
50	Bill Pierce	5.00	
51	George Alusik	5.00	
52	Chuck Schilling	5.00	
53	Joe Moeller	5.00	
54a	1962 Rookie Stars (*Nelson Mathews*)	20.00	
54a	1962 Rookie Stars (*Harry Fanok*)	20.00	
54a	1962 Rookie Stars (*Jack Cullen*)	20.00	
54a	1962 Rookie Stars (*Dave DeBusschere*)	20.00	
54b	1963 Rookie Stars (*Jack Cullen*)	8.00	
54b	1962 Rookie Stars (*Dave DeBusschere*) (1963)	8.00	
54b	1963 Rookie Stars (Harry Fanok)	8.00	
54b	1963 Rookie Stars (Nelson Mathews)	8.00	
55	Bill Virdon	5.00	
56	Dennis Bennett	5.00	
57	Billy Moran	5.00	
58	Bob Will	5.00	
59	Craig Anderson	5.00	
60	Elston Howard	8.00	
61	Ernie Bowman	5.00	
62	Bob Hendley	5.00	
63	Reds Team	7.00	
64	Dick McAuliffe	5.00	
65	Jackie Brandt	5.00	
66	Mike Joyce	5.00	
67	Ed Charles	5.00	
68	Friendly Foes (Gil Hodges, Duke Snider)	20.00	
69	Bud Zipfel	5.00	
70	Jim O'Toole	5.00	
71	*Bobby Wine*	5.00	
72	Johnny Romano	5.00	
73	Bobby Bragan	5.00	
74	*Denver Lemaster*	5.00	
75	Bob Allison	5.00	
76	Earl Wilson	5.00	
77	Al Spangler	5.00	
78	Marv Throneberry	5.00	
79	Checklist 1-88	7.00	
80	Jim Gilliam	5.00	
81	Jimmie Schaffer	5.00	
82	Ed Rakow	5.00	
83	Charley James	5.00	
84	Ron Kline	5.00	
85	Tom Haller	5.00	
86	Charley Maxwell	5.00	
87	Bob Veale	5.00	
88	Ron Hansen	5.00	
89	Dick Stigman	5.00	
90	Gordy Coleman	5.00	
91	Dallas Green	5.00	
92	Hector Lopez	5.00	
93	Galen Cisco	5.00	
94	Bob Schmidt	5.00	
95	Larry Jackson	5.00	
96	Lou Clinton	5.00	
97	Bob Duliba	5.00	
98	George Thomas	5.00	
99	Jim Umbricht	5.00	
100	Joe Cunningham	5.00	
101	Joe Gibbon	5.00	
102a	Checklist 89-176 ("Checklist" in red on front)	7.00	
102b	Checklist 89-176 ("Checklist" in white)	12.00	
103	Chuck Essegian	5.00	
104	Lew Krausse	5.00	
105	Ron Fairly	5.00	
106	Bob Bolin	5.00	
107	Jim Hickman	5.00	
108	Hoyt Wilhelm	10.00	
109	Lee Maye	5.00	
110	Rich Rollins	5.00	
111	Al Jackson	5.00	
112	Dick Brown	5.00	
113	Don Landrum (photo actally Ron Santo)	5.00	
114	Dan Osinski	5.00	
115	Carl Yastrzemski	75.00	
116	Jim Brosnan	5.00	
117	Jacke Davis	5.00	
118	Sherm Lollar	5.00	
119	Bob Lillis	5.00	
120	Roger Maris	75.00	
121	Jim Hannan	5.00	
122	Julio Gotay	5.00	
123	Frank Howard	5.00	
124	Dick Howser	5.00	
125	Robin Roberts	15.00	
126	Bob Uecker	25.00	
127	Bill Tuttle	5.00	
128	Matty Alou	5.00	
129	Gary Bell	5.00	
130	Dick Groat	5.00	
131	Senators Team	7.00	
132	Jack Hamilton	5.00	
133	Gene Freese	5.00	
134	Bob Scheffing	5.00	
135	Richie Ashburn	5.00	
136	Ike Delock	15.00	
137	Mack Jones	5.00	
138	Pride of N.L. (Willie Mays, Stan Musial,)	5.00	
139	Earl Averill	5.00	
140	Frank Lary	5.00	
141	*Manny Mota*	7.00	
142	World Series Game 1 Yanks' Ford Wins Series Opener	10.00	
143	World Series Game 2 Sanford Flashes Shutout Magic	7.00	
144	World Series Game 3 Maris Sparks Yankee Rally	15.00	
145	World Series Game 4 Hiller Blasts Grand Slammer	7.00	
146	World Series Game 5 Tresh's Homer Defeats Giants	7.00	
147	World Series Game 6 Pierce Stars In 3-Hit Victory	7.00	
148	World Series Game 7 Yanks Celebrate As Terry Wins	7.00	
149	Marv Breeding	5.00	
150	Johnny Podres	5.00	
151	Pirates Team	7.00	
152	Ron Nischwitz	5.00	
153	Hal Smith	5.00	
154	Walt Alston	7.00	
155	Bill Stafford	5.00	
156	Roy McMillan	5.00	
157	*Diego Segui*	5.00	
158	1963 Rookie Stars (Rogelio Alvarez, Tommy Harper, Dave Roberts, Bob Saverine)	5.00	
159	Jim Pagliaroni	5.00	
160	Juan Pizarro	5.00	
161	Frank Torre	5.00	
162	Twins Team	7.00	
163	Don Larsen	5.00	
164	Bubba Morton	5.00	
165	Jim Kaat	10.00	
166	Johnny Keane	5.00	
167	Jim Fregosi	5.00	
168	Russ Nixon	5.00	
169	1963 Rookie Stars (Dick Egan, Julio Navarro, Gaylord Perry, Tommie Sisk)	35.00	
170	Joe Adcock	5.00	
171	Steve Hamilton	5.00	
172	Gene Oliver	5.00	

173	Bombers' Best (Tom Tresh, Mickey Mantle, Bobby Richardson)	100.00
174	Larry Burright	5.00
175	Bob Buhl	5.00
176	Jim King	5.00
177	Bubba Phillips	5.00
178	Johnny Edwards	5.00
179	Ron Piche	5.00
180	Bill Skowron	5.00
181	Sammy Esposito	5.00
182	Albie Pearson	5.00
183	Joe Pepitone	5.00
184	Vern Law	5.00
185	Chuck Hiller	5.00
186	Jerry Zimmerman	5.00
187	Willie Kirkland	5.00
188	Eddie Bressoud	5.00
189	Dave Giusti	5.00
190	Minnie Minoso	5.00
191	Checklist 177-264	5.00
192	Clay Dalrymple	5.00
193	Andre Rodgers	5.00
194	Joe Nuxhall	5.00
195	Manny Jimenez	5.00
196	Doug Camilli	5.00
197	Roger Craig	5.00
198	Lenny Green	5.00
199	Joe Amalfitano	5.00
200	Mickey Mantle	750.00
201	Cecil Butler	5.00
202	Red Sox Team	7.00
203	Chico Cardenas	5.00
204	Don Nottebart	5.00
205	Luis Aparicio	20.00
206	Ray Washburn	5.00
207	Ken Hunt	5.00
208	1963 Rookie Stars (Ron Herbel, John Miller, Ron Taylor, Wally Wolf)	5.00
209	Hobie Landrith	5.00
210	Sandy Koufax	200.00
211	Fred Whitfield	5.00
212	Glen Hobbie	5.00
213	Billy Hitchcock	5.00
214	Orlando Pena	5.00
215	Bob Skinner	5.00
216	Gene Conley	5.00
217	Joe Christopher	5.00
218	Tiger Twirlers (Jim Bunning, Frank Lary, Don Mossi)	5.00
219	Chuck Cottier	5.00
220	Camilo Pascual	5.00
221	*Cookie Rojas*	5.00
222	Cubs Team	7.00
223	Eddie Fisher	5.00
224	Mike Roarke	5.00
225	Joe Jay	5.00
226	Julian Javier	5.00
227	Jim Grant	5.00
228	1963 Rookie Stars (Max Alvis, Bob Bailey, Ed Kranepool, Tony Oliva)	50.00
229	Willie Davis	5.00
230	Pete Runnels	5.00
231	Eli Grba (photo actually Ryne Duren)	5.00
232	Frank Malzone	5.00
233	Casey Stengel	25.00
234	Dave Nicholson	5.00
235	Billy O'Dell	5.00
236	Bill Bryan	5.00
237	Jim Coates	5.00
238	Lou Johnson	5.00
239	Harvey Haddix	5.00
240	Rocky Colavito	20.00
241	Billy Smith	5.00
242	Power Plus (Hank Aaron, Ernie Banks)	75.00
243	Don Leppert	5.00
244	John Tsitouris	5.00
245	Gil Hodges	20.00
246	Lee Stange	5.00
247	Yankees Team	25.00
248	Tito Francona	5.00
249	Leo Burke	5.00
250	Stan Musial	125.00
251	Jack Lamabe	5.00
252	Ron Santo	10.00
253	1963 Rookie Stars (Len Gabrielson, Pete Jernigan, Deacon Jones, John Wojcik)	5.00
254	Mike Hershberger	5.00
255	Bob Shaw	5.00
256	Jerry Lumpe	5.00
257	Hank Aguirre	5.00
258	Alvin Dark	5.00
259	Johnny Logan	5.00
260	Jim Gentile	5.00
261	Bob Miller	5.00
262	Ellis Burton	5.00
263	Dave Stenhouse	5.00
264	Phil Linz	5.00
265	Vada Pinson	5.00
266	Bob Allen	5.00
267	Carl Sawatski	5.00
268	Don Demeter	5.00
269	Don Mincher	5.00
270	Felipe Alou	7.00
271	Dean Stone	5.00
272	Danny Murphy	5.00
273	Sammy Taylor	5.00
274	Checklist 265-352	5.00
275	Eddie Mathews	25.00
276	Barry Shetrone	5.00
277	Dick Farrell	5.00
278	Chico Fernandez	5.00
279	Wally Moon	5.00
280	Bob Rodgers	5.00
281	Tom Sturdivant	5.00
282	Bob Del Greco	5.00
283	Roy Sievers	5.00
284	Dave Sisler	6.00
285	Dick Stuart	6.00
286	Stu Miller	6.00
287	Dick Bertell	6.00
288	White Sox Team	7.00
289	Hal Brown	6.00
290	Bill White	7.00
291	Don Rudolph	6.00
292	Pumpsie Green	6.00
293	Bill Pleis	6.00
294	Bill Rigney	6.00
295	Ed Roebuck	6.00
296	Doc Edwards	6.00
297	Jim Golden	6.00
298	Don Dillard	6.00
299	1963 Rookie Stars (Tom Butters, Bob Dustal, Dave Morehead, Dan Schneider)	6.00
300	Willie Mays	200.00
301	Bill Fischer	6.00
302	Whitey Herzog	6.00
303	Earl Francis	6.00
304	Harry Bright	6.00
305	Don Hoak	6.00
306	Star Receivers (Earl Battey, Elston Howard)	6.00
307	Chet Nichols	6.00
308	Camilo Carreon	6.00
309	Jim Brewer	6.00
310	Tommy Davis	6.00
311	Joe McClain	6.00
312	Colt .45s Team	25.00
313	Ernie Broglio	6.00
314	John Goryl	6.00
315	Ralph Terry	6.00

#	Player	Price
316	Norm Sherry	6.00
317	Sam McDowell	6.00
318	Gene Mauch	6.00
319	Joe Gaines	6.00
320	Warren Spahn	50.00
321	Gino Cimoli	6.00
322	Bob Turley	6.00
323	Bill Mazeroski	8.00
324	1963 Rookie Stars (Vic Davalillo, Phil Roof, Pete Ward, George Williams)	6.00
325	Jack Sanford	6.00
326	Hank Foiles	6.00
327	Paul Foytack	6.00
328	Dick Williams	6.00
329	Lindy McDaniel	6.00
330	Chuck Hinton	6.00
331	Series Foes (Bill Pierce, Bill Stafford)	6.00
332	Joel Horlen	6.00
333	Carl Warwick	6.00
334	Wynn Hawkins	6.00
335	Leon Wagner	6.00
336	Ed Bauta	6.00
337	Dodgers Team	20.00
338	Russ Kemmerer	6.00
339	Ted Bowsfield	6.00
340	Yogi Berra	125.00
341	Jack Baldschun	6.00
342	Gene Woodling	6.00
343	Johnny Pesky	6.00
344	Don Schwall	6.00
345	Brooks Robinson	75.00
346	Billy Hoeft	6.00
347	Joe Torre	8.00
348	Vic Wertz	6.00
349	Zoilo Versalles	6.00
350	Bob Purkey	6.00
351	Al Luplow	6.00
352	Ken Johnson	6.00
353	Billy Williams	30.00
354	Dom Zanni	6.00
355	Dean Chance	6.00
356	John Schaive	6.00
357	George Altman	6.00
358	Milt Pappas	6.00
359	Haywood Sullivan	6.00
360	Don Drysdale	60.00
361	Clete Boyer	6.00
362	Checklist 353-429	8.00
363	Dick Radatz	6.00
364	Howie Goss	6.00
365	Jim Bunning	15.00
366	Tony Taylor	6.00
367	Tony Cloninger	6.00
368	Ed Bailey	6.00
369	Jim Lemon	6.00
370	Dick Donovan	6.00
371	Rod Kanehl	6.00
372	Don Lee	6.00
373	Jim Campbell	6.00
374	Claude Osteen	6.00
375	Ken Boyer	8.00
376	Johnnie Wyatt	6.00
377	Orioles Team	10.00
378	Bill Henry	6.00
379	Bob Anderson	6.00
380	Ernie Banks	100.00
381	Frank Baumann	6.00
382	Ralph Houk	6.00
383	Pete Richert	6.00
384	Bob Tillman	6.00
385	Art Mahaffey	6.00
386	1963 Rookie Stars (John Bateman, Larry Bearnarth, Ed Kirkpatrick, Garry Roggenburk)	6.00
387	Al McBean	6.00
388	Jim Davenport	6.00
389	Frank Sullivan	6.00
390	Hank Aaron	200.00
391	Bill Dailey	6.00
392	Tribe Thumpers (Tito Francona, Johnny Romano)	6.00
393	Ken MacKenzie	6.00
394	Tim McCarver	6.00
395	Don McMahon	6.00
396	Joe Koppe	6.00
397	Athletics Team	10.00
398	Boog Powell	15.00
399	Dick Ellsworth	6.00
400	Frank Robinson	75.00
401	Jim Bouton	20.00
402	Mickey Vernon	6.00
403	Ron Perranoski	6.00
404	Bob Oldis	6.00
405	Floyd Robinson	6.00
406	Howie Koplitz	6.00
407	1963 Rookie Stars (Larry Elliot, Frank Kostro, Chico Ruiz, Dick Simpson)	6.00
408	Billy Gardner	6.00
409	Roy Face	6.00
410	Earl Battey	6.00
411	Jim Constable	6.00
412	Dodgers' Big Three (Johnny Podres, Don Drysdale, Sandy Koufax)	75.00
413	Jerry Walker	6.00
414	Ty Cline	6.00
415	Bob Gibson	75.00
416	Alex Grammas	6.00
417	Giants Team	10.00
418	Johnny Orsino	6.00
419	Tracy Stallard	6.00
420	Bobby Richardson	20.00
421	Tom Morgan	6.00
422	Fred Hutchinson	6.00
423	Ed Hobaugh	6.00
424	Charley Smith	6.00
425	Smoky Burgess	6.00
426	Barry Latman	6.00
427	Bernie Allen	6.00
428	Carl Boles	6.00
429	Lou Burdette	6.00
430	Norm Siebern	6.00
431a	Checklist 430-506 ("Checklist" in black on front)	7.00
431b	Checklist 430-506 ("Checklist" in white)	10.00
432	Roman Mejias	6.00
433	Denis Menke	6.00
434	Johnny Callison	6.00
435	Woody Held	6.00
436	Tim Harkness	6.00
437	Bill Bruton	6.00
438	Wes Stock	6.00
439	Don Zimmer	6.00
440	Juan Marichal	40.00
441	Lee Thomas	6.00
442	J.C. Hartman	6.00
443	Jim Piersall	6.00
444	Jim Maloney	6.00
445	Norm Cash	6.00
446	Whitey Ford	50.00
447	Felix Mantilla	20.00
448	Jack Kralick	20.00
449	Jose Tartabull	20.00
450	Bob Friend	20.00
451	Indians Team	35.00
452	Barney Schultz	20.00
453	Jake Wood	20.00
454a	Art Fowler (card # on orange background)	20.00
454b	Art Fowler (card # on white background)	20.00
455	Ruben Amaro	20.00
456	Jim Coker	20.00
457	Tex Clevenger	20.00

458	Al Lopez	20.00
459	Dick LeMay	20.00
460	Del Crandall	20.00
461	Norm Bass	20.00
462	Wally Post	20.00
463	Joe Schaffernoth	20.00
464	Ken Aspromonte	20.00
465	Chuck Estrada	20.00
466	1963 Rookie Stars (*Bill Freehan*, Tony Martinez, Nate Oliver, Jerry Robinson)	75.00
467	Phil Ortega	20.00
468	Carroll Hardy	20.00
469	Jay Hook	20.00
470	Tom Tresh	75.00
471	Ken Retzer	20.00
472	Lou Brock	150.00
473	Mets Team	125.00
474	Jack Fisher	20.00
475	Gus Triandos	20.00
476	Frank Funk	20.00
477	Donn Clendenon	20.00
478	Paul Brown	20.00
479	*Ed Brinkman*	20.00
480	Bill Monbouquette	20.00
481	Bob Taylor	20.00
482	Felix Torres	20.00
483	Jim Owens	20.00
484	Dale Long	20.00
485	Jim Landis	20.00
486	Ray Sadecki	20.00
487	John Roseboro	20.00
488	Jerry Adair	20.00
489	Paul Toth	20.00
490	Willie McCovey	125.00
491	Harry Craft	20.00
492	Dave Wickersham	20.00
493	Walt Bond	20.00
494	Phil Regan	20.00
495	Frank J. Thomas	20.00
496	1963 Rookie Stars (Carl Bouldin, Steve Dalkowski, Fred Newman, Jack Smith)	20.00
497	Bennie Daniels	20.00
498	Eddie Kasko	20.00
499	J.C. Martin	20.00
500	Harmon Killebrew	150.00
501	Joe Azcue	20.00
502	Daryl Spencer	20.00
503	Braves Team	35.00
504	Bob Johnson	20.00
505	Curt Flood	20.00
506	Gene Green	20.00
507	Roland Sheldon	20.00
508	Ted Savage	20.00
509a	Checklist 507-576 (copyright centered)	20.00
509b	Checklist 509-576 (copyright to right)	20.00
510	Ken McBride	20.00
511	Charlie Neal	20.00
512	Cal McLish	20.00
513	Gary Geiger	20.00
514	Larry Osborne	20.00
515	Don Elston	20.00
516	Purnal Goldy	20.00
517	Hal Woodeshick	20.00
518	Don Blasingame	20.00
519	Claude Raymond	20.00
520	Orlando Cepeda	35.00
521	Dan Pfister	20.00
522	1963 Rookie Stars (Mel Nelson, Gary Peters, Art Quirk, Jim Roland)	20.00
523	Bill Kunkel	12.00
524	Cardinals Team	25.00
525	Nellie Fox	25.00
526	Dick Hall	12.00
527	Ed Sadowski	12.00
528	Carl Willey	12.00
529	Wes Covington	12.00
530	Don Mossi	12.00
531	Sam Mele	12.00
532	Steve Boros	12.00
533	Bobby Shantz	12.00
534	Ken Walters	12.00
535	Jim Perry	12.00
536	Norm Larker	12.00
537	1963 Rookie Stars (Pedro Gonzalez, Ken McMullen, Pete Rose, Al Weis)	1200.00
538	George Brunet	12.00
539	Wayne Causey	12.00
540	Roberto Clemente	300.00
541	Ron Moeller	12.00
542	Lou Klimchock	12.00
543	Russ Snyder	12.00
544	1963 Rookie Stars (Duke Carmel, Bill Haas, Dick Phillips, Rusty Staub)	50.00
545	Jose Pagan	12.00
546	Hal Reniff	12.00
547	Gus Bell	12.00
548	Tom Satriano	12.00
549	1963 Rookie Stars (*Marcelino Lopez*, Pete Lovrich, Elmo Plaskett, Paul Ratliff)	12.00
550	Duke Snider	85.00
551	Billy Klaus	12.00
552	Tigers Team	40.00
553	1963 Rookie Stars (Brock Davis, Jim Gosger, John Herrnstein, Willie Stargell)	250.00
554	Hank Fischer	12.00
555	John Blanchard	12.00
556	Al Worthington	12.00
557	Cuno Barragan	12.00
558	1963 Rookie Stars (Bill Faul, Ron Hunt, Bob Lipski, Al Moran)	12.00
559	Danny Murtaugh	12.00
560	Ray Herbert	12.00
561	Mike de la Hoz	12.00
562	1963 Rookie Stars (Randy Cardinal, Dave McNally, Don Rowe, Ken Rowe)	40.00
563	Mike McCormick	12.00
564	George Banks	12.00
565	Larry Sherry	12.00
566	Cliff Cook	12.00
567	Jim Duffalo	12.00
568	Bob Sadowski	12.00
569	Luis Arroyo	12.00
570	Frank Bolling	12.00
571	Johnny Klippstein	12.00
572	Jack Spring	12.00
573	Coot Veal	12.00
574	Hal Kolstad	12.00
575	Don Cardwell	12.00
576	Johnny Temple	20.00

1964 Topps

The 1964 Topps set is a 587-card issue of 2-1/2" by 3-1/2" cards which is considered by many as being among the company's best efforts. Card fronts feature a large color photo which blends into a top panel which contains the team name, while a panel below the picture carries the player's name and position. An interesting innovation on the back is a baseball quiz question which required the rubbing of a white panel to reveal the answer. As in 1963, specialty cards remained modest in number with a 12-card set of statistical leaders, a few multi-player cards, rookies and World Series highlights. An interesting card is an "In Memoriam" card for Ken Hubbs who was killed in an airplane crash.

Mr. Mint Says - One of the least interesting sets of this period, with no great rookie cards to speak of. Simple design, no pizzazz, but obviously still desirable as a set. These are easy to obtain in mint, easier than any of the earlier years.

Centering is not bad, and the card stock was sturdy and held up pretty well, but the black boxes sometimes suffer from those print "bubbles."

The AL Bombers card is a real popular item, as is the Clemente card in centered, mint

condition. A centered one went for $500 at auction even though the guides currently list it at much less than that.

If the comic on the back of the card has been scratched off it can't be considered mint, since it didn't come from the factory that way.

		MT
Complete Set (587):		4000.
Common Player (1-370):		2.50
Common Player (371-522):		5.00
Common Player (523-587):		15.00

1	N.L. E.R.A. Leaders (Dick Ellsworth, Bob Friend, Sandy Koufax)	25.00
2	A.L. E.R.A. Leaders (Camilo Pascual, Gary Peters, Juan Pizarro)	7.00
3	N.L. Pitching Leaders (Sandy Koufax, Jim Maloney, Juan Marichal, Warren Spahn)	20.00
4a	A.L. Pitching Leaders (Jim Bouton) (apostrophe after "Pitching" on back)	12.00
4a	A.L. Pitching Leaders (Whitey Ford) (apostrophe after "Pitching" on back)	12.00
4a	A.L. Pitching Leaders (Camilo Pascual) (apostrophe after "Pitching" on back)	12.00
4b	A.L. Pitching Leaders (Jim Bouton) (no apostrophe)	7.00
4b	A.L. Pitching Leaders (Whitey Ford) (no apostrophe)	7.00
4b	A.L. Pitching Leaders (Camilo Pascual) (no apostrophe)	7.00
5	N.L. Strikeout Leaders (Don Drysdale, Sandy Koufax, Jim Maloney)	15.00
6	A.L. Strikeout Leaders (Jim Bunning, Camilo Pascual, Dick Stigman)	7.00
7	N.L. Batting Leaders (Hank Aaron, Roberto Clemente, Tommy Davis, Dick Groat)	15.00
8	A.L. Batting Leaders (Al Kaline, Rich Rollins, Carl Yastrzemski)	12.00
9	N.L. Home Run Leaders (Hank Aaron, Orlando Cepeda, Willie Mays, Willie McCovey)	25.00
10	A.L. Home Run Leaders (Bob Allison, Harmon Killebrew, Dick Stuart)	10.00
11	N.L. R.B.I. Leaders (Hank Aaron, Ken Boyer, Bill White)	10.00
12	A.L. R.B.I. Leaders (Al Kaline, Harmon Killebrew, Dick Stuart)	10.00
13	Hoyt Wilhelm	10.00
14	Dodgers Rookies (Dick Nen, Nick Willhite)	2.50
15	Zoilo Versalles	2.50
16	John Boozer	2.50
17	Willie Kirkland	2.50
18	Billy O'Dell	2.50
19	Don Wert	2.50
20	Bob Friend	2.50
21	Yogi Berra	40.00
22	Jerry Adair	2.50
23	Chris Zachary	2.50
24	Carl Sawatski	2.50
25	Bill Monbouquette	2.50
26	Gino Cimoli	2.50
27	Mets Team	5.00
28	Claude Osteen	2.50
29	Lou Brock	40.00
30	Ron Perranoski	2.50
31	Dave Nicholson	2.50
32	Dean Chance	3.00
33	Reds Rookies (Sammy Ellis, Mel Queen)	2.50
34	Jim Perry	2.50
35	Eddie Mathews	25.00
36	Hal Reniff	2.50

37	Smoky Burgess	2.50
38	*Jim Wynn*	5.00
39	Hank Aguirre	2.50
40	Dick Groat	3.00
41	Friendly Foes (Willie McCovey, Leon Wagner)	5.00
42	Moe Drabowsky	2.50
43	Roy Sievers	2.50
44	Duke Carmel	2.50
45	Milt Pappas	2.50
46	Ed Brinkman	2.50
47	Giants Rookies (*Jesus Alou*, Ron Herbel)	3.50
48	Bob Perry	2.50
49	Bill Henry	2.50
50	Mickey Mantle	350.00
51	Pete Richert	2.50
52	Chuck Hinton	2.50
53	Denis Menke	2.50
54	Sam Mele	2.50
55	Ernie Banks	40.00
56	Hal Brown	2.50
57	Tim Harkness	2.50
58	Don Demeter	2.50
59	Ernie Broglio	2.50
60	Frank Malzone	2.50
61	Angel Backstops (Bob Rodgers, Ed Sadowski)	3.50
62	Ted Savage	2.50
63	Johnny Orsino	2.50
64	Ted Abernathy	2.50
65	Felipe Alou	6.50
66	Eddie Fisher	2.50
67	Tigers Team	5.00
68	Willie Davis	3.50
69	Clete Boyer	3.50
70	Joe Torre	2.50
71	Jack Spring	2.50
72	Chico Cardenas	2.50
73	*Jimmie Hall*	2.50
74	Pirates Rookies (Tom Butters, Bob Priddy)	2.50
75	Wayne Causey	2.50
76	Checklist 1-88	5.00
77	Jerry Walker	2.50
78	Merritt Ranew	2.50
79	Bob Heffner	2.50
80	Vada Pinson	3.50
81	All-Star Vets (Nellie Fox, Harmon Killebrew)	9.50
82	Jim Davenport	2.50
83	Gus Triandos	2.50
84	Carl Willey	2.50
85	Pete Ward	2.50
86	Al Downing	3.00
87	Cardinals Team	9.50
88	John Roseboro	2.50
89	Boog Powell	5.00
90	Earl Battey	2.50
91	Bob Bailey	2.50
92	Steve Ridzik	2.50
93	Gary Geiger	2.50
94	Braves Rookies (Jim Britton, Larry Maxie)	2.50
95	George Altman	2.50
96	Bob Buhl	2.50
97	Jim Fregosi	3.00
98	Bill Bruton	2.50
99	Al Stanek	2.50
100	Elston Howard	4.50
101	Walt Alston	5.00
102	Checklist 89-176	5.00
103	Curt Flood	3.50
104	Art Mahaffey	2.50
105	Woody Held	2.50
106	Joe Nuxhall	2.50
107	White Sox Rookies (Bruce Howard, Frank Kreutzer)	2.50
108	John Wyatt	2.50
109	Rusty Staub	9.00
110	Albie Pearson	2.50
111	Don Elston	2.50
112	Bob Tillman	2.50
113	Grover Powell	2.50
114	Don Lock	2.50
115	Frank Bolling	2.50
116	Twins Rookies (Tony Oliva, Jay Ward)	20.00
117	Earl Francis	2.50
118	John Blanchard	2.50
119	Gary Kolb	30.00
120	Don Drysdale	30.00
121	Pete Runnels	2.50
122	Don McMahon	2.50
123	Jose Pagan	2.50
124	Orlando Pena	2.50
125	Pete Rose	200.00
126	Russ Snyder	2.50
127	Angels Rookies (Aubrey Gatewood, Dick Simpson)	2.50
128	*Mickey Lolich*	25.00
129	Amado Samuel	2.50
130	Gary Peters	2.50
131	Steve Boros	2.50
132	Braves Team	5.50
133	Jim Grant	2.50
134	Don Zimmer	3.50
135	Johnny Callison	2.50
136	World Series Game 1 (Koufax Strikes Out 15)	20.00
137	World Series Game 2 (Davis Sparks Rally)	3.50
138	World Series Game 3 (L.A. Takes 3rd Straight)	3.50
139	World Series Game 4 (Sealing Yanks' Doom)	3.50
140	World Series Summary (The Dodgers Celebrate)	3.50
141	Danny Murtaugh	2.50
142	John Bateman	2.50
143	Bubba Phillips	2.50
144	Al Worthington	2.50
145	Norm Siebern	2.50
146	Indians Rookies (Bob Chance, Tommy John)	65.00
147	Ray Sadecki	2.50
148	J.C. Martin	2.50
149	Paul Foytack	2.50
150	Willie Mays	125.00
151	Athletics Team	5.50
152	Denver Lemaster	2.50
153	Dick Williams	3.00
154	Dick Tracewski	2.50
155	Duke Snider	35.00
156	Bill Dailey	2.50
157	Gene Mauch	2.50
158	Ken Johnson	2.50
159	Charlie Dees	2.50
160	Ken Boyer	10.00
161	Dave McNally	2.50
162	Hitting Area (Vada Pinson, Dick Sisler)	3.50
163	Donn Clendenon	2.50
164	Bud Daley	2.50
165	Jerry Lumpe	2.50
166	Marty Keough	2.50
167	Senators Rookies (Mike Brumley, Lou Piniella)	40.00
168	Al Weis	2.50
169	Del Crandall	2.50
170	Dick Radatz	2.50
171	Ty Cline	2.50
172	Indians Team	5.50
173	Ryne Duren	2.50
174	Doc Edwards	2.50
175	Billy Williams	20.00
176	Tracy Stallard	2.50
177	Harmon Killebrew	30.00
178	Hank Bauer	2.50
179	Carl Warwick	2.50
180	Tommy Davis	5.00
181	Dave Wickersham	2.50
182	Sox Sockers (Chuck Schilling, Carl Yastrzemski)	15.00

183	Ron Taylor	2.50	256	Johnny Weekly	2.50
184	Al Luplow	2.50	257	Giants Team	5.50
185	Jim O'Toole	2.50	258	Garry Roggenburk	2.50
186	Roman Mejias	2.50	259	Harry Bright	2.50
187	Ed Roebuck	2.50	260	Frank Robinson	40.00
188	Checklist 177-264	5.00	261	Jim Hannan	2.50
189	Bob Hendley	2.50	262	Cardinals Rookies (Harry Fanok, Mike Shannon)	10.00
190	Bobby Richardson	10.00	263	Chuck Estrada	2.50
191	Clay Dalrymple	2.50	264	Jim Landis	2.50
192	Cubs Rookies (John Boccabella, Billy Cowan)	2.50	265	Jim Bunning	10.00
193	Jerry Lynch	2.50	266	Gene Freese	2.50
194	John Goryl	2.50	267	*Wilbur Wood*	5.00
195	Floyd Robinson	2.50	268	Bill's Got It (Danny Murtaugh, Bill Virdon)	3.00
196	Jim Gentile	2.50	269	Ellis Burton	2.50
197	Frank Lary	2.50	270	Rich Rollins	2.50
198	Len Gabrielson	2.50	271	Bob Sadowski	2.50
199	Joe Azcue	2.50	272	Jake Wood	2.50
200	Sandy Koufax	125.00	273	Mel Nelson	2.50
201	Orioles Rookies (Sam Bowens, Wally Bunker)	2.50	274	Checklist 265-352	5.00
202	Galen Cisco	2.50	275	John Tsitouris	2.50
203	John Kennedy	2.50	276	Jose Tartabull	2.50
204	Matty Alou	2.50	277	Ken Retzer	2.50
205	Nellie Fox	7.00	278	Bobby Shantz	3.00
206	Steve Hamilton	2.50	279	Joe Koppe	2.50
207	Fred Hutchinson	2.50	280	Juan Marichal	20.00
208	Wes Covington	2.50	281	Yankees Rookies (Jake Gibbs, Tom Metcalf)	5.00
209	Bob Allen	2.50	282	Bob Bruce	2.50
210	Carl Yastrzemski	60.00	283	*Tommy McCraw*	2.50
211	Jim Coker	2.50	284	Dick Schofield	2.50
212	Pete Lovrich	2.50	285	Robin Roberts	15.00
213	Angels Team	5.50	286	Don Landrum	2.50
214	Ken McMullen	2.50	287	Red Sox Rookies (*Tony Conigliaro*, Bill Spanswick)	50.00
215	Ray Herbert	2.50	288	Al Moran	2.50
216	Mike de la Hoz	2.50	289	Frank Funk	2.50
217	Jim King	2.50	290	Bob Allison	2.50
218	Hank Fischer	2.50	291	Phil Ortega	2.50
219	Young Aces (Jim Bouton, Al Downing)	5.00	292	Mike Roarke	2.50
220	Dick Ellsworth	2.50	293	Phillies Team	5.50
221	Bob Saverine	2.50	294	Ken Hunt	2.50
222	Bill Pierce	2.50	295	Roger Craig	3.50
223	George Banks	2.50	296	Ed Kirkpatrick	2.50
224	Tommie Sisk	2.50	297	Ken MacKenzie	2.50
225	Roger Maris	75.00	298	Harry Craft	2.50
226	Colts Rookies (*Gerald Grote*, Larry Yellen)	3.50	299	Bill Stafford	2.50
227	Barry Latman	2.50	300	Hank Aaron	135.00
228	Felix Mantilla	2.50	301	Larry Brown	2.50
229	Charley Lau	2.50	302	Dan Pfister	2.50
230	Brooks Robinson	40.00	303	Jim Campbell	2.50
231	Dick Calmus	2.50	304	Bob Johnson	2.50
232	Al Lopez	5.00	305	Jack Lamabe	2.50
233	Hal Smith	2.50	306	Giant Gunners (Orlando Cepeda, Willie Mays)	40.00
234	Gary Bell	2.50	307	Joe Gibbon	2.50
235	Ron Hunt	2.50	308	Gene Stephens	2.50
236	Bill Faul	2.50	309	Paul Toth	2.50
237	Cubs Team	5.50	310	Jim Gilliam	3.50
238	Roy McMillan	2.50	311	Tom Brown	2.50
239	Herm Starrette	2.50	312	Tigers Rookies (Fritz Fisher, Fred Gladding)	2.50
240	Bill White	3.50	313	Chuck Hiller	2.50
241	Jim Owens	2.50	314	Jerry Buchek	2.50
242	Harvey Kuenn	3.50	315	Bo Belinsky	2.50
243	Phillies Rookies (*Richie Allen*, John Herrnstein)	40.00	316	Gene Oliver	2.50
244	*Tony LaRussa*	22.50	317	Al Smith	2.50
245	Dick Stigman	2.50	318	Twins Team	5.50
246	Manny Mota	3.00	319	Paul Brown	2.50
247	Dave DeBusschere	5.00	320	Rocky Colavito	10.00
248	Johnny Pesky	2.50	321	Bob Lillis	2.50
249	Doug Camilli	2.50	322	George Brunet	2.50
250	Al Kaline	40.00	323	John Buzhardt	2.50
251	Choo Choo Coleman	2.50	324	Casey Stengel	20.00
252	Ken Aspromonte	2.50	325	Hector Lopez	2.50
253	Wally Post	2.50	326	Ron Brand	2.50
254	Don Hoak	2.50	327	Don Blasingame	2.50
255	Lee Thomas	2.50	328	Bob Shaw	2.50

329	Russ Nixon	2.50		401	Charlie Maxwell	5.00
330	Tommy Harper	2.50		402	Tom Sturdivant	5.00
331	A.L. Bombers (Norm Cash, Al Kaline, Mickey Mantle, Roger Maris)	200.00		403	Reds Team	9.00
				404	Tony Martinez	5.00
332	Ray Washburn	2.50		405	Ken McBride	5.00
333	Billy Moran	2.50		406	Al Spangler	5.00
334	Lew Krausse	2.50		407	Bill Freehan	5.00
335	Don Mossi	2.50		408	Cubs Rookies (Fred Burdette, Jim Stewart)	5.00
336	Andre Rodgers	2.50		409	Bill Fischer	5.00
337	Dodgers Rookies (*Al Ferrara*, Jeff Torborg)	3.50		410	Dick Stuart	5.50
338	Jack Kralick	2.50		411	Lee Walls	5.00
339	Walt Bond	2.50		412	Ray Culp	5.00
340	Joe Cunningham	2.50		413	Johnny Keane	5.00
341	Jim Roland	2.50		414	Jack Sanford	5.00
342	Willie Stargell	50.00		415	Tony Kubek	10.00
343	Senators Team	5.50		416	Lee Maye	5.00
344	Phil Linz	3.00		417	Don Cardwell	5.00
345	Frank J. Thomas	2.50		418	Orioles Rookies (*Darold Knowles*, Les Narum)	5.50
346	Joe Jay	2.50		419	*Ken Harrelson*	7.00
347	Bobby Wine	2.50		420	Jim Maloney	5.00
348	Ed Lopat	2.50		421	Camilo Carreon	5.00
349	Art Fowler	2.50		422	Jack Fisher	5.00
350	Willie McCovey	30.00		423	Tops in N.L. (Hank Aaron, Willie Mays)	175.00
351	Dan Schneider	2.50		424	Dick Bertell	5.00
352	Eddie Bressoud	2.50		425	Norm Cash	6.00
353	Wally Moon	2.50		426	Bob Rodgers	5.00
354	Dave Giusti	2.50		427	Don Rudolph	5.00
355	Vic Power	2.50		428	Red Sox Rookies (Archie Skeen, Pete Smith)	5.00
356	Reds Rookies (Bill McCool, Chico Ruiz)	2.50		429	Tim McCarver	6.00
357	Charley James	2.50		430	Juan Pizarro	5.00
358	Ron Kline	2.50		431	George Alusik	5.00
359	Jim Schaffer	2.50		432	Ruben Amaro	5.00
360	Joe Pepitone	3.00		433	Yankees Team	20.00
361	Jay Hook	2.50		434	Don Nottebart	5.00
362	Checklist 353-429	5.00		435	Vic Davalillo	5.00
363	Dick McAuliffe	2.50		436	Charlie Neal	5.00
364	Joe Gaines	2.50		437	Ed Bailey	5.00
365	Cal McLish	2.50		438	Checklist 430-506	9.50
366	Nelson Mathews	2.50		439	Harvey Haddix	5.00
367	Fred Whitfield	2.50		440	Roberto Clemente	250.00
368	White Sox Rookies (Fritz Ackley, Don Buford)	2.50		441	Bob Duliba	5.00
369	Jerry Zimmerman	2.50		442	Pumpsie Green	5.00
370	Hal Woodeshick	2.50		443	Chuck Dressen	5.00
371	Frank Howard	6.00		444	Larry Jackson	5.00
372	Howie Koplitz	5.00		445	Bill Skowron	6.00
373	Pirates Team	9.00		446	Julián Javier	5.00
374	Bobby Bolin	5.00		447	Ted Bowsfield	5.00
375	Ron Santo	7.00		448	Cookie Rojas	5.00
376	Dave Morehead	5.00		449	Deron Johnson	5.00
377	Bob Skinner	5.00		450	Steve Barber	5.00
378	Braves Rookies (Jack Smith, Woody Woodward)	5.00		451	Joe Amalfitano	5.00
379	Tony Gonzalez	5.00		452	Giants Rookies (Gil Garrido, Jim Hart)	5.50
380	Whitey Ford	40.00		453	Frank Baumann	5.00
381	Bob Taylor	5.00		454	Tommie Aaron	5.50
382	Wes Stock	5.00		455	Bernie Allen	5.00
383	Bill Rigney	5.00		456	Dodgers Rookies (*Wes Parker*, John Werhas)	5.00
384	Ron Hansen	5.00		457	Jesse Gonder	5.00
385	Curt Simmons	5.00		458	Ralph Terry	5.00
386	Lenny Green	5.00		459	Red Sox Rookies (Pete Charton, Dalton Jones)	5.00
387	Terry Fox	5.00		460	Bob Gibson	40.00
388	Athletics Rookies (John O'Donoghue, George Williams)	5.00		461	George Thomas	5.00
				462	Birdie Tebbetts	5.00
389	Jim Umbricht	5.00		463	Don Leppert	5.00
390	Orlando Cepeda	12.00		464	Dallas Green	5.50
391	Sam McDowell	6.00		465	Mike Hershberger	5.00
392	Jim Pagliaroni	5.00		466	Athletics Rookies (*Dick Green*, Aurelio Monteagudo)	5.50
393	Casey Teaches (Ed Kranepool, Casey Stengel,)	12.00		467	Bob Aspromonte	5.00
394	Bob Miller	5.00		468	Gaylord Perry	45.00
395	Tom Tresh	6.00		469	Cubs Rookies (Fred Norman, Sterling Slaughter)	5.00
396	Dennis Bennett	5.00		470	Jim Bouton	6.00
397	Chuck Cottier	5.00		471	*Gates Brown*	5.50
398	Mets Rookies (Bill Haas, Dick Smith)	5.00		472	Vern Law	5.00
399	Jackie Brandt	40.00		473	Orioles Team	9.00
400	Warren Spahn	50.00				

474	Larry Sherry	5.00
475	Ed Charles	5.00
476	Braves Rookies (*Rico Carty*, Dick Kelley)	9.50
477	Mike Joyce	5.00
478	Dick Howser	5.00
479	Cardinals Rookies (Dave Bakenhaster, Johnny Lewis)	5.00
480	Bob Purkey	5.00
481	Chuck Schilling	5.00
482	Phillies Rookies (*John Briggs*, Danny Cater)	5.00
483	Fred Valentine	5.00
484	Bill Pleis	5.00
485	Tom Haller	5.00
486	Bob Kennedy	5.00
487	Mike McCormick	5.00
488	Yankees Rookies (Bob Meyer, Pete Mikkelsen)	5.00
489	Julio Navarro	5.00
490	Ron Fairly	5.00
491	Ed Rakow	5.00
492	Colts Rookies (Jim Beauchamp, Mike White)	5.00
493	Don Lee	5.00
494	Al Jackson	5.00
495	Bill Virdon	5.00
496	White Sox Team	9.00
497	Jeoff Long	5.00
498	Dave Stenhouse	5.00
499	Indians Rookies (Chico Salmon, Gordon Seyfried)	5.00
500	Camilo Pascual	5.00
501	Bob Veale	5.00
502	Angels Rookies (*Bobby Knoop*, Bob Lee)	5.50
503	Earl Wilson	5.00
504	Claude Raymond	5.00
505	Stan Williams	5.00
506	Bobby Bragan	5.00
507	John Edwards	5.00
508	Diego Segui	5.00
509	Pirates Rookies (*Gene Alley*, Orlando McFarlane)	5.50
510	Lindy McDaniel	5.00
511	Lou Jackson	5.00
512	*Willie Horton*, (Joe Sparma)	12.00
513	Don Larsen	5.00
514	Jim Hickman	5.00
515	Johnny Romano	5.00
516	Twins Rookies (Jerry Arrigo, Dwight Siebler)	5.00
517a	Checklist 507-587 (wrong numbering on back)	9.50
517b	Checklist 507-587 (correct numbering on back)	9.50
518	Carl Bouldin	5.00
519	Charlie Smith	5.00
520	Jack Baldschun	5.00
521	Tom Satriano	5.00
522	Bobby Tiefenauer	5.00
523	Lou Burdette	15.00
524	Reds Rookies (Jim Dickson, Bobby Klaus)	15.00
525	Al McBean	15.00
526	Lou Clinton	15.00
527	Larry Bearnarth	15.00
528	Athletics Rookies (*Dave Duncan*, Tom Reynolds)	15.00
529	Al Dark	15.00
530	Leon Wagner	15.00
531	Dodgers Team	30.00
532	Twins Rookies (Bud Bloomfield, Joe Nossek)	15.00
533	Johnny Klippstein	15.00
534	Gus Bell	15.00
535	Phil Regan	15.00
536	Mets Rookies (Larry Elliot, John Stephenson)	15.00
537	Dan Osinski	15.00
538	Minnie Minoso	17.00
539	Roy Face	15.00
540	Luis Aparicio	20.00
541	Braves Rookies (*Phil Niekro*, Phil Roof)	200.00
542	Don Mincher	15.00
543	Bob Uecker	40.00
544	Colts Rookies (Steve Hertz, Joe Hoerner)	15.00
545	Max Alvis	15.00
546	Joe Christopher	15.00
547	Gil Hodges	20.00
548	N.L. Rookies (Wayne Schurr, Paul Speckenbach)	15.00
549	Joe Moeller	15.00
550	Ken Hubbs	35.00
551	Billy Hoeft	15.00
552	Indians Rookies (Tom Kelley, Sonny Siebert)	15.00
553	Jim Brewer	15.00
554	Hank Foiles	15.00
555	Lee Stange	15.00
556	Mets Rookies (Steve Dillon, Ron Locke)	15.00
557	Leo Burke	15.00
558	Don Schwall	15.00
559	Dick Phillips	15.00
560	Dick Farrell	15.00
561	Phillies Rookies (Dave Bennett, Rick Wise)	15.00
562	Pedro Ramos	15.00
563	Dal Maxvill	15.00
564	A.L. Rookies (Joe McCabe, Jerry McNertney)	15.00
565	Stu Miller	15.00
566	Ed Kranepool	15.00
567	Jim Kaat	17.00
568	N.L. Rookies (Phil Gagliano, Cap Peterson)	15.00
569	Fred Newman	15.00
570	Bill Mazeroski	20.00
571	Gene Conley	15.00
572	A.L. Rookies (Dick Egan, Dave Gray)	15.00
573	Jim Duffalo	15.00
574	Manny Jimenez	15.00
575	Tony Cloninger	15.00
576	Mets Rookies (Jerry Hinsley, Bill Wakefield)	15.00
577	Gordy Coleman	15.00
578	Glen Hobbie	15.00
579	Red Sox Team	25.00
580	Johnny Podres	15.00
581	Yankees Rookies (Pedro Gonzalez, Archie Moore)	15.00
582	Rod Kanehl	15.00
583	Tito Francona	15.00
584	Joel Horlen	15.00
585	Tony Taylor	15.00
586	Jim Piersall	15.00
587	Bennie Daniels	20.00

YOUNG ACES

AL DOWNING • JIM BOUTON

1964 Topps Stand-Ups

These 2-1/2" by 3-1/2" cards were the first since the All-Star sets of 1951 to be die cut. This made it possible for a folded card to stand on display. The 77 cards in the set feature color photographs of the player with yellow and green backgrounds. Directions for folding are on the yellow top background, and when folded only the green background remains. Of the 77 cards, 55 were double-printed while 22 were single-printed, making them twice as scarce. Included in the single-printed group are Warren Spahn, Don Drysdale, Juan Marichal, Willie McCovey and Carl Yastrzemski.

Mr. Mint Says - It is a good trick to find this entire set all green with no nicks or dings on the corners. I have only seen one set totally green. With only 77 cards in the set it is obtainable, the cards are out there and they are attractive. Sometimes you find the green washed out on the bottom half of the card. The Hall of Famers sell well, and the single prints are much in demand and obviously a lot tougher to find.

Drysdale and Clemente are difficult cards, as are Yaz and Mantle. The Clendenon is listed as a single print, but I don't believe it, and the Frank Robinson is listed as a double print, yet I think it is one of the toughest cards in the set.

Watch for cards that have the Topps Chewing Gum tag line on the bottom of the card; it is important that the printing be visible. If the card has been "stood up" it is not mint. The cards come flat and must be kept that way.

		MT
Complete Set:		3600.
Common Player:		10.00
(1)	Hank Aaron	150.00
(2)	Hank Aguirre	10.00
(3)	George Altman	10.00
(4)	Max Alvis	10.00
(5)	Bob Aspromonte	10.00
(6)	Jack Baldschun (SP)	40.00
(7)	Ernie Banks	100.00
(8)	Steve Barber	10.00
(9)	Earl Battey	10.00
(10)	Ken Boyer	15.00
(11)	Ernie Broglio	10.00
(12)	Johnny Callison	10.00
(13)	Norm Cash (SP)	50.00
(14)	Wayne Causey	10.00
(15)	Orlando Cepeda	15.00
(16)	Ed Charles	10.00
(17)	Roberto Clemente	150.00
(18)	Donn Clendenon (SP)	40.00
(19)	Rocky Colavito	20.00
(20)	Ray Culp (SP)	40.00
(21)	Tommy Davis	12.00
(22)	Don Drysdale (SP)	150.00
(23)	Dick Ellsworth	10.00
(24)	Dick Farrell	10.00
(25)	Jim Fregosi	10.00
(26)	Bob Friend	10.00
(27)	Jim Gentile	10.00
(28)	Jesse Gonder (SP)	40.00
(29)	Tony Gonzalez (SP)	40.00
(30)	Dick Groat	12.00
(31)	Woody Held	10.00
(32)	Chuck Hinton	10.00
(33)	Elston Howard	12.00
(34)	Frank Howard (SP)	50.00
(35)	Ron Hunt	10.00
(36)	Al Jackson	10.00
(37)	Ken Johnson	10.00
(38)	Al Kaline	100.00
(39)	Harmon Killebrew	100.00
(40)	Sandy Koufax	150.00
(41)	Don Lock (SP)	40.00
(42)	Jerry Lumpe (SP)	40.00
(43)	Jim Maloney	10.00
(44)	Frank Malzone	10.00
(45)	Mickey Mantle	500.00
(46)	Juan Marichal (SP)	150.00
(47)	Ed Mathews (SP)	150.00
(48)	Willie Mays	150.00
(49)	Bill Mazeroski	12.00
(50)	Ken McBride	10.00
(51)	Willie McCovey (SP)	150.00
(52)	Claude Osteen	10.00
(53)	Jim O'Toole	10.00
(54)	Camilo Pascual	10.00
(55)	Albie Pearson (SP)	40.00
(56)	Gary Peters	10.00
(57)	Vada Pinson	15.00

(58)	Juan Pizarro	10.00
(59)	Boog Powell	15.00
(60)	Bobby Richardson	15.00
(61)	Brooks Robinson	100.00
(62)	Floyd Robinson	10.00
(63)	Frank Robinson	100.00
(64)	Ed Roebuck (SP)	40.00
(65)	Rich Rollins	10.00
(66)	Johnny Romano	10.00
(67)	Ron Santo (SP)	50.00
(68)	Norm Siebern	10.00
(69)	Warren Spahn (SP)	150.00
(70)	Dick Stuart (SP)	40.00
(71)	Lee Thomas	10.00
(72)	Joe Torre	10.00
(73)	Pete Ward	10.00
(74)	Bill White (SP)	50.00
(75)	Billy Williams (SP)	125.00
(76)	Hal Woodeshick (SP)	40.00
(77)	Carl Yastrzemski (SP)	500.00

1965 Topps

The 1965 Topps set features a large color photograph of the player which was surrounded by a colored, round-cornered frame and a white border. The bottom of the 2-1/2" by 3-1/2" cards include a pennant with a color team logo and name over the left side of a rectangle which features the player's name and position. Backs feature statistics and, if space allowed, a cartoon and headline about the player. There are no multi-player cards in the 1965 set other than the usual team cards and World Series highlights. Rookie cards include team, as well as league groupings from two to four players per card. Also present in the 598-card set are statistical leaders. Certain cards in the high-number series (#523-598) were produced in lesser quantities than the rest of the series. Known as "short-prints," and valued somewhat higher than the other high numbers, they are indicated in the checklist by an (SP) after the player name.

FRITZ ACKLEY   pitcher   STEVE CARLTON   pitcher

Mr. Mint Says - A nice, popular set, with good availability in mint condition and uncirculated vendor sets still available.

Mantle and the high numbers are tricky to find centered (frequently off-center to the right), and this is the hardest Mantle to find in top grades in the 60s except for 1962. Carlton is another key, and there are plenty of mint Carltons out there. Numbers 523-598 are a little tougher, but not the usual kind of high number difficulty.

		MT
Complete Set (598):		4750.
Common Player (1-283):		3.00
Common Player (284-370):		3.00
Common Player (371-522):		7.00

1	A.L. Batting Leaders (Elston Howard, Tony Oliva, Brooks Robinson)	25.00
2	N.L. Batting Leaders (Hank Aaron, Rico Carty, Roberto Clemente)	20.00
3	A.L. Home Run Leaders (Harmon Killebrew, Mickey Mantle, Boog Powell)	35.00
4	N.L. Home Run Leaders (Johnny Callison, Orlando Cepeda, Jim Hart, Willie Mays, Billy Williams)	15.00
5	A.L. RBI Leaders (Harmon Killebrew, Mickey Mantle, Brooks Robinson, Dick Stuart)	35.00
6	N.L. RBI Leaders (Ken Boyer, Willie Mays, Ron Santo)	12.00
7	A.L. ERA Leaders (Dean Chance, Joel Horlen)	5.00
8	N.L. ERA Leaders (Don Drysdale, Sandy Koufax)	20.00
9	A.L. Pitching Leaders (Wally Bunker, Dean Chance, Gary Peters, Juan Pizarro, Dave Wickersham)	5.00
10	N.L. Pitching Leaders (Larry Jackson, Juan Marichal, Ray Sadecki)	5.00
11	A.L. Strikeout Leaders (Dean Chance, Al Downing, Camilo Pascual)	5.00
12	N.L. Strikeout Leaders (Don Drysdale, Bob Gibson, Bob Veale)	10.00
13	Pedro Ramos	3.00
14	Len Gabrielson	3.00
15	Robin Roberts	10.00
16	Astros Rookies (*Sonny Jackson*, Joe Morgan)	125.00
17	Johnny Romano	3.00
18	Bill McCool	3.00
19	Gates Brown	3.00
20	Jim Bunning	5.00
21	Don Blasingame	3.00
22	Charlie Smith	3.00
23	Bob Tiefenauer	3.00
24	Twins Team	5.00
25	Al McBean	3.00
26	Bobby Knoop	3.00
27	Dick Bertell	3.00
28	Barney Schultz	3.00
29	Felix Mantilla	3.00
30	Jim Bouton	5.00
31	Mike White	3.00
32	Herman Franks	3.00
33	Jackie Brandt	3.00
34	Cal Koonce	3.00
35	Ed Charles	3.00
36	Bobby Wine	3.00
37	Fred Gladding	3.00
38	Jim King	3.00
39	Gerry Arrigo	3.00
40	Frank Howard	5.00
41	White Sox Rookies (Bruce Howard, Marv Staehle)	3.00
42	Earl Wilson	3.00
43	Mike Shannon	3.00
44	Wade Blasingame	3.00
45	Roy McMillan	3.00
46	Bob Lee	3.00
47	Tommy Harper	3.00
48	Claude Raymond	3.00
49	Orioles Rookies (*Curt Blefary*, John Miller)	5.00
50	Juan Marichal	15.00
51	Billy Bryan	3.00
52	Ed Roebuck	3.00
53	Dick McAuliffe	3.00
54	Joe Gibbon	3.00
55	Tony Conigliaro	10.00
56	Ron Kline	3.00
57	Cardinals Team	5.00
58	Fred Talbot	3.00
59	Nate Oliver	3.00
60	Jim O'Toole	3.00
61	Chris Cannizzaro	3.00
62	Jim Katt (Kaat)	7.00
63	Ty Cline	3.00
64	Lou Burdette	3.00
65	Tony Kubek	6.00

66	Bill Rigney	3.00	
67	Harvey Haddix	3.00	
68	Del Crandall	3.00	
69	Bill Virdon	3.00	
70	Bill Skowron	3.00	
71	John O'Donoghue	3.00	
72	Tony Gonzalez	3.00	
73	Dennis Ribant	3.00	
74	Red Sox Rookies (*Rico Petrocelli*, Jerry Stephenson)	10.00	
75	Deron Johnson	3.00	
76	Sam McDowell	3.00	
77	Doug Camilli	3.00	
78	Dal Maxvill	3.00	
79a	Checklist 1-88 (61 is C. Cannizzaro)	6.00	
79b	Checklist 1-88 (61 is Cannizzaro)	8.00	
80	Turk Farrell	3.00	
81	Don Buford	3.00	
82	Braves Rookies (*Santos Alomar*, John Braun)	3.00	
83	George Thomas	3.00	
84	Ron Herbel	3.00	
85	Willie Smith	3.00	
86	Les Narum	3.00	
87	Nelson Mathews	3.00	
88	Jack Lamabe	3.00	
89	Mike Hershberger	3.00	
90	Rich Rollins	3.00	
91	Cubs Team	5.00	
92	Dick Howser	3.00	
93	Jack Fisher	3.00	
94	Charlie Lau	3.00	
95	Bill Mazeroski	8.00	
96	Sonny Siebert	3.00	
97	Pedro Gonzalez	3.00	
98	Bob Miller	3.00	
99	Gil Hodges	10.00	
100	Ken Boyer	5.00	
101	Fred Newman	3.00	
102	Steve Boros	3.00	
103	Harvey Kuenn	4.00	
104	Checklist 89-176	5.00	
105	Chico Salmon	3.00	
106	Gene Oliver	3.00	
107	Phillies Rookies (*Pat Corrales*, Costen Shockley)	5.00	
108	Don Mincher	3.00	
109	Walt Bond	3.00	
110	Ron Santo	6.00	
111	Lee Thomas	3.00	
112	Derrell Griffith	3.00	
113	Steve Barber	3.00	
114	Jim Hickman	3.00	
115	Bobby Richardson	7.00	
116	Cardinals Rookies (Dave Dowling, Bob Tolan)	3.00	
117	Wes Stock	3.00	
118	*Hal Lanier*	3.00	
119	John Kennedy	3.00	
120	Frank Robinson	35.00	
121	Gene Alley	3.00	
122	Bill Pleis	3.00	
123	Frank J. Thomas	3.00	
124	Tom Satriano	3.00	
125	Juan Pizarro	3.00	
126	Dodgers Team	7.00	
127	Frank Lary	3.00	
128	Vic Davalillo	3.00	
129	Bennie Daniels	3.00	
130	Al Kaline	35.00	
131	Johnny Keane	3.00	
132	World Series Game 1 Cards Take Opener	6.00	
133	World Series Game 2 Stottlemyre Wins	6.00	
134	World Series Game 3 Mantle's Clutch HR	60.00	
135	World Series Game 4 Boyer's Grand-Slam	6.00	
136	World Series Game 5 10th Inning Triumph	6.00	
137	World Series Game 6 Bouton Wins Again	6.00	
138	World Series Game 7 Gibson Wins Finale	6.00	
139	World Series Summary The Cards Celebrate	6.00	
140	Dean Chance	3.00	
141	Charlie James	3.00	
142	Bill Monbouquette	3.00	
143	Pirates Rookies (John Gelnar, Jerry May)	3.00	
144	Ed Kranepool	3.00	
145	*Luis Tiant*	25.00	
146	Ron Hansen	3.00	
147	Dennis Bennett	3.00	
148	Willie Kirkland	3.00	
149	Wayne Schurr	3.00	
150	Brooks Robinson	35.00	
151	Athletics Team	6.00	
152	Phil Ortega	3.00	
153	Norm Cash	5.00	
154	Bob Humphreys	3.00	
155	Roger Maris	75.00	
156	Bob Sadowski	3.00	
157	Zoilo Versalles	3.00	
158	Dick Sisler	3.00	
159	Jim Duffalo	3.00	
160	Roberto Clemente	95.00	
161	Frank Baumann	3.00	
162	Russ Nixon	3.00	
163	John Briggs	3.00	
164	Al Spangler	3.00	
165	Dick Ellsworth	3.00	
166	Indians Rookies (*Tommie Agee*, George Culver)	5.00	
167	Bill Wakefield	3.00	
168	Dick Green	3.00	
169	Dave Vineyard	3.00	
170	Hank Aaron	100.00	
171	Jim Roland	3.00	
172	Jim Piersall	3.00	
173	Tigers Team	6.00	
174	Joe Jay	3.00	
175	Bob Aspromonte	3.00	
176	Willie McCovey	25.00	
177	Pete Mikkelsen	3.00	
178	Dalton Jones	3.00	
179	Hal Woodeshick	3.00	
180	Bob Allison	3.00	
181	Senators Rookies (Don Loun, Joe McCabe)	3.00	
182	Mike de la Hoz	3.00	
183	Dave Nicholson	3.00	
184	John Boozer	3.00	
185	Max Alvis	3.00	
186	Billy Cowan	3.00	
187	Casey Stengel	20.00	
188	Sam Bowens	3.00	
189	Checklist 177-264	6.00	
190	Bill White	5.00	
191	Phil Regan	3.00	
192	Jim Coker	3.00	
193	Gaylord Perry	25.00	
194	Angels Rookies (Bill Kelso, Rick Reichardt)	3.00	
195	Bob Veale	3.00	
196	Ron Fairly	3.00	
197	Diego Segui	3.00	
198	Smoky Burgess	3.00	
199	Bob Heffner	3.00	
200	Joe Torre	5.00	
201	Twins Rookies (*Cesar Tovar*, Sandy Valdespino)	3.00	
202	Leo Burke	3.00	
203	Dallas Green	5.00	
204	Russ Snyder	3.00	
205	Warren Spahn	35.00	
206	Willie Horton	3.00	
207	Pete Rose	200.00	
208	Tommy John	15.00	
209	Pirates Team	6.00	
210	Jim Fregosi	3.00	

211	Steve Ridzik	3.00
212	Ron Brand	3.00
213	Jim Davenport	3.00
214	Bob Purkey	3.00
215	Pete Ward	3.00
216	Al Worthington	3.00
217	Walt Alston	5.00
218	Dick Schofield	3.00
219	Bob Meyer	3.00
220	Billy Williams	15.00
221	John Tsitouris	3.00
222	Bob Tillman	3.00
223	Dan Osinski	3.00
224	Bob Chance	3.00
225	Bo Belinsky	3.00
226	Yankees Rookies (Jake Gibbs, Elvio Jimenez)	3.00
227	Bobby Klaus	3.00
228	Jack Sanford	3.00
229	Lou Clinton	3.00
230	Ray Sadecki	3.00
231	Jerry Adair	3.00
232	Steve Blass	3.00
233	Don Zimmer	3.00
234	White Sox Team	6.00
235	Chuck Hinton	3.00
236	Dennis McLain	35.00
237	Bernie Allen	3.00
238	Joe Moeller	3.00
239	Doc Edwards	3.00
240	Bob Bruce	3.00
241	Mack Jones	3.00
242	George Brunet	3.00
243	Reds Rookies (Ted Davidson, Tommy Helms)	3.00
244	Lindy McDaniel	3.00
245	Joe Pepitone	3.00
246	Tom Butters	3.00
247	Wally Moon	3.00
248	Gus Triandos	3.00
249	Dave McNally	3.00
250	Willie Mays	150.00
251	Billy Herman	5.00
252	Pete Richert	3.00
253	Danny Cater	3.00
254	Roland Sheldon	3.00
255	Camilo Pascual	3.00
256	Tito Francona	3.00
257	Jim Wynn	3.00
258	Larry Bearnarth	3.00
259	Tigers Rookies (Jim Northrup, Ray Oyler)	3.00
260	Don Drysdale	25.00
261	Duke Carmel	3.00
262	Bud Daley	3.00
263	Marty Keough	3.00
264	Bob Buhl	3.00
265	Jim Pagliaroni	3.00
266	Bert Campaneris	10.00
267	Senators Team	6.00
268	Ken McBride	3.00
269	Frank Bolling	3.00
270	Milt Pappas	3.00
271	Don Wert	3.00
272	Chuck Schilling	3.00
273	Checklist 265-352	4.00
274	Lum Harris	3.00
275	Dick Groat	3.00
276	Hoyt Wilhelm	10.00
277	Johnny Lewis	3.00
278	Ken Retzer	3.00
279	Dick Tracewski	3.00
280	Dick Stuart	3.00
281	Bill Stafford	3.00
282	Giants Rookies (Dick Estelle, Masanori Murakami)	5.00
283	Fred Whitfield	3.00
284	Nick Willhite	3.00
285	Ron Hunt	3.00
286	Athletic Rookies (Jim Dickson, Aurelio Monteagudo)	3.00
287	Gary Kolb	3.00
288	Jack Hamilton	3.00
289	Gordy Coleman	3.00
290	Wally Bunker	3.00
291	Jerry Lynch	3.00
292	Larry Yellen	3.00
293	Angels Team	6.00
294	Tim McCarver	6.00
295	Dick Radatz	3.00
296	Tony Taylor	3.00
297	Dave DeBusschere	6.00
298	Jim Stewart	3.00
299	Jerry Zimmerman	3.00
300	Sandy Koufax	125.00
301	Birdie Tebbetts	3.00
302	Al Stanek	3.00
303	Johnny Orsino	3.00
304	Dave Stenhouse	3.00
305	Rico Carty	3.00
306	Bubba Phillips	3.00
307	Barry Latman	3.00
308	Mets Rookies (Cleon Jones, Tom Parsons)	3.00
309	Steve Hamilton	3.00
310	Johnny Callison	3.00
311	Orlando Pena	3.00
312	Joe Nuxhall	3.00
313	Jimmie Schaffer	3.00
314	Sterling Slaughter	3.00
315	Frank Malzone	3.00
316	Reds Team	6.00
317	Don McMahon	3.00
318	Matty Alou	3.00
319	Ken McMullen	3.00
320	Bob Gibson	40.00
321	Rusty Staub	6.00
322	Rick Wise	3.00
323	Hank Bauer	3.00
324	Bobby Locke	3.00
325	Donn Clendenon	3.00
326	Dwight Siebler	3.00
327	Denis Menke	3.00
328	Eddie Fisher	3.00
329	Hawk Taylor	3.00
330	Whitey Ford	40.00
331	Dodgers Rookies (Al Ferrara, John Purdin)	3.00
332	Ted Abernathy	3.00
333	Tommie Reynolds	3.00
334	Vic Roznovsky	3.00
335	Mickey Lolich	3.00
336	Woody Held	3.00
337	Mike Cuellar	3.00
338	Phillies Team	6.00
339	Ryne Duren	3.00
340	Tony Oliva	8.00
341	Bobby Bolin	3.00
342	Bob Rodgers	3.00
343	Mike McCormick	3.00
344	Wes Parker	3.00
345	Floyd Robinson	3.00
346	Bobby Bragan	3.00
347	Roy Face	3.00
348	George Banks	3.00
349	Larry Miller	3.00
350	Mickey Mantle	750.00
351	Jim Perry	3.00
352	Alex Johnson	3.00
353	Jerry Lumpe	3.00
354	Cubs Rookies (Billy Ott, Jack Warner)	3.00
355	Vada Pinson	10.00
356	Bill Spanswick	3.00

357	Carl Warwick	3.00	430	Gary Peters	7.00
358	Albie Pearson	3.00	431	Cardinals Rookies (*Nelson Briles*, Wayne Spiezio)	7.00
359	Ken Johnson	3.00	432	Jim Grant	7.00
360	Orlando Cepeda	10.00	433	John Bateman	7.00
361	Checklist 353-429	6.00	434	Dave Morehead	7.00
362	Don Schwall	3.00	435	Willie Davis	7.00
363	Bob Johnson	3.00	436	Don Elston	7.00
364	Galen Cisco	3.00	437	Chico Cardenas	7.00
365	Jim Gentile	3.00	438	Harry Walker	7.00
366	Dan Schneider	3.00	439	Moe Drabowsky	7.00
367	Leon Wagner	3.00	440	Tom Tresh	7.00
368	White Sox Rookies (*Ken Berry*, Joel Gibson)	3.00	441	Denver Lemaster	7.00
369	Phil Linz	3.00	442	Vic Power	7.00
370	Tommy Davis	5.00	443	Checklist 430-506	8.00
371	Frank Kreutzer	7.00	444	Bob Hendley	7.00
372	Clay Dalrymple	7.00	445	Don Lock	7.00
373	Curt Simmons	7.00	446	Art Mahaffey	7.00
374	Angels Rookies (*Jose Cardenal*, Dick Simpson)	7.00	447	Julian Javier	7.00
375	Dave Wickersham	7.00	448	Lee Stange	7.00
376	Jim Landis	7.00	449	Mets Rookies (Jerry Hinsley, Gary Kroll)	7.00
377	Willie Stargell	35.00	450	Elston Howard	10.00
378	Chuck Estrada	7.00	451	Jim Owens	7.00
379	Giants Team	8.00	452	Gary Geiger	7.00
380	Rocky Colavito	10.00	453	Dodgers Rookies (*Willie Crawford*, John Werhas)	7.00
381	Al Jackson	7.00	454	Ed Rakow	7.00
382	J.C. Martin	7.00	455	Norm Siebern	7.00
383	Felipe Alou	7.00	456	Bill Henry	7.00
384	Johnny Klippstein	7.00	457	Bob Kennedy	7.00
385	Carl Yastrzemski	50.00	458	John Buzhardt	7.00
386	Cubs Rookies (Paul Jaeckel, Fred Norman)	7.00	459	Frank Kostro	7.00
387	Johnny Podres	7.00	460	Richie Allen	20.00
388	John Blanchard	7.00	461	Braves Rookies (*Clay Carroll*, Phil Niekro)	50.00
389	Don Larsen	7.00	462	Lew Krausse (photo actually Pete Lovrich)	7.00
390	Bill Freehan	7.00	463	Manny Mota	7.00
391	Mel McGaha	7.00	464	Ron Piche	7.00
392	Bob Friend	7.00	465	Tom Haller	7.00
393	Ed Kirkpatrick	7.00	466	Senators Rookies (Pete Craig, Dick Nen)	7.00
394	Jim Hannan	7.00	467	Ray Washburn	7.00
395	Jim Hart	7.00	468	Larry Brown	7.00
396	Frank Bertaina	7.00	469	Don Nottebart	7.00
397	Jerry Buchek	7.00	470	Yogi Berra	65.00
398	Reds Rookies (Dan Neville, Art Shamsky)	7.00	471	Billy Hoeft	7.00
399	Ray Herbert	7.00	472	Don Pavletich	7.00
400	Harmon Killebrew	40.00	473	Orioles Rookies (*Paul Blair*, Dave Johnson)	20.00
401	Carl Willey	7.00	474	Cookie Rojas	7.00
402	Joe Amalfitano	7.00	475	Clete Boyer	7.00
403	Red Sox Team	9.00	476	Billy O'Dell	7.00
404	Stan Williams	7.00	477	Cardinals Rookies (Fritz Ackley, Steve Carlton)	500.00
405	John Roseboro	7.00	478	Wilbur Wood	7.00
406	Ralph Terry	7.00	479	Ken Harrelson	7.00
407	Lee Maye	7.00	480	Joel Horlen	7.00
408	Larry Sherry	7.00	481	Indians Team	9.00
409	Astros Rookies (Jim Beauchamp, Larry Dierker)	7.00	482	Bob Priddy	7.00
410	Luis Aparicio	10.00	483	George Smith	7.00
411	Roger Craig	7.00	484	Ron Perranoski	7.00
412	Bob Bailey	7.00	485	Nellie Fox	11.00
413	Hal Reniff	7.00	486	Angels Rookies (Tom Egan, Pat Rogan)	7.00
414	Al Lopez	7.00	487	Woody Woodward	7.00
415	Curt Flood	7.00	488	Ted Wills	7.00
416	Jim Brewer	7.00	489	Gene Mauch	7.00
417	Ed Brinkman	7.00	490	Earl Battey	7.00
418	Johnny Edwards	7.00	491	Tracy Stallard	7.00
419	Ruben Amaro	7.00	492	Gene Freese	7.00
420	Larry Jackson	7.00	493	Tigers Rookies (Bruce Brubaker, Bill Roman)	7.00
421	Twins Rookies (Gary Dotter, Jay Ward)	7.00	494	Jay Ritchie	7.00
422	Aubrey Gatewood	7.00	495	Joe Christopher	7.00
423	Jesse Gonder	7.00	496	Joe Cunningham	7.00
424	Gary Bell	7.00	497	Giants Rookies (*Ken Henderson*, Jack Hiatt)	7.00
425	Wayne Causey	7.00	498	Gene Stephens	7.00
426	Braves Team	8.00	499	Stu Miller	7.00
427	Bob Saverine	7.00	500	Eddie Mathews	40.00
428	Bob Shaw	7.00	501	Indians Rookies (Ralph Gagliano, Jim Rittwage)	7.00
429	Don Demeter	7.00	502	Don Cardwell	7.00

503	Phil Gagliano	7.00
504	Jerry Grote	7.00
505	Ray Culp	7.00
506	Sam Mele	7.00
507	Sammy Ellis	7.00
508a	Checklist 507-598 (large print on front)	9.00
508b	Checklist 507-598 (small print on front)	9.00
509	Red Sox Rookies (Bob Guindon, Gerry Vezendy)	7.00
510	Ernie Banks	85.00
511	Ron Locke	7.00
512	Cap Peterson	7.00
513	Yankees Team	25.00
514	Joe Azcue	7.00
515	Vern Law	7.00
516	Al Weis	7.00
517	Angels Rookies (Paul Schaal, Jack Warner)	7.00
518	Ken Rowe	7.00
519	Bob Uecker	25.00
520	Tony Cloninger	7.00
521	Phillies Rookies (Dave Bennett, Morrie Stevens)	7.00
522	Hank Aguirre	7.00
523	Mike Brumley (SP)	10.00
524	Dave Giusti (SP)	10.00
525	Eddie Bressoud	10.00
526	Athletics Rookies (*Catfish Hunter*, Rene Lachemann, Skip Lockwood, Johnny Odom)	100.00
527	Jeff Torborg	10.00
528	George Altman	10.00
529	Jerry Fosnow (SP)	10.00
530	Jim Maloney	10.00
531	Chuck Hiller	10.00
532	Hector Lopez	10.00
533	Mets Rookies (Jim Bethke, Tug McGraw, Dan Napolean, Ron Swoboda)	30.00
534	John Herrnstein	10.00
535	Jack Kralick (SP)	10.00
536	Andre Rodgers (SP)	10.00
537	Angels Rookies (Marcelino Lopez, Rudy May, Phil Roof)	10.00
538	Chuck Dressen (SP)	10.00
539	Herm Starrette	10.00
540	Lou Brock	50.00
541	White Sox Rookies (Greg Bollo, Bob Locker)	10.00
542	Lou Klimchock	10.00
543	Ed Connolly (SP)	10.00
544	Howie Reed	10.00
545	Jesus Alou (SP)	10.00
546	Indians Rookies (Ray Barker, Bill Davis, Mike Hedlund, Floyd Weaver)	10.00
547	Jake Wood (SP)	10.00
548	Dick Stigman	10.00
549	Cubs Rookies (*Glenn Beckert*, Roberto Pena)	20.00
550	*Mel Stottlemyre*	30.00
551	Mets Team	25.00
552	Julio Gotay	10.00
553	Houston Rookies (Dan Coombs, Jack McClure, Gene Ratliff)	10.00
554	Chico Ruiz (SP)	10.00
555	Jack Baldschun (SP)	10.00
556	Red Schoendienst	20.00
557	Jose Santiago	10.00
558	Tommie Sisk	10.00
559	Ed Bailey (SP)	10.00
560	Boog Powell	25.00
561	Dodgers Rookies (Dennis Daboll, Mike Kekich, Jim Lefebvre, Hector Valle)	10.00
562	Billy Moran	10.00
563	Julio Navarro	10.00
564	Mel Nelson	10.00
565	Ernie Broglio (SP)	10.00

566	Yankees Rookies (Gil Blanco, Art Lopez, Ross Moschitto) (SP)	10.00
567	Tommie Aaron	10.00
568	Ron Taylor (SP)	10.00
569	Gino Cimoli (SP)	10.00
570	Claude Osteen (SP)	10.00
571	Ossie Virgil (SP)	10.00
572	Orioles Team	20.00
573	Red Sox Rookies (*Jim Lonborg*, Gerry Moses, Mike Ryan, Bill Schlesinger)	20.00
574	Roy Sievers	10.00
575	Jose Pagan	10.00
576	Terry Fox (SP)	10.00
577	A.L. Rookies (Jim Buschhorn, Darold Knowles, Richie Scheinblum) (SP)	10.00
578	Camilo Carreon (SP)	10.00
579	Dick Smith (SP)	10.00
580	Jimmie Hall (SP)	10.00
581	N.L. Rookies (Kevin Collins, Tony Perez, Dave Ricketts)	125.00
582	Bob Schmidt (SP)	10.00
583	Wes Covington (SP)	10.00
584	Harry Bright	10.00
585	Hank Fischer	10.00
586	Tommy McCraw (SP)	10.00
587	Joe Sparma	10.00
588	Lenny Green	10.00
589	Giants Rookies (Frank Linzy, Bob Schroder) (SP)	10.00
590	Johnnie Wyatt	10.00
591	Bob Skinner (SP)	10.00
592	Frank Bork (SP)	10.00
593	Tigers Rookies (Jackie Moore, John Sullivan)	10.00
594	Joe Gaines	10.00
595	Don Lee	10.00
596	Don Landrum (SP)	10.00
597	Twins Rookies (Joe Nossek, Dick Reese, John Sevcik)	10.00
598	Al Downing	20.00

HANK AARON

TONY CLONINGER

ROGER MARIS

AL KALINE

1966 Topps

In 1966, Topps produced another 598-card set. The 2-1/2" by 3-1/2" cards feature the almost traditional color photograph with a diagonal strip in the upper left-hand corner carrying the team name. A band at the bottom carries the player's name and position. Multi-player cards returned in 1966 after having had a year's hiatus. The statistical leader cards feature the categorical leader and two runners-up. Most team managers have cards as well. The 1966 set features a handful of cards found with or without a notice of the player's sale or trade to another team. Cards without the notice bring higher prices not included in the complete set prices below. Some cards in the high series (#523-598) were short-printed - produced in lesser quantities than the rest of the series. They are valued somewhat higher than the others and are indicated in the checklist by a (SP) notation following the player name.

JIM PALMER   pitcher

Mr. Mint Says - This set is still obtainable in mint condition. Topps printing runs apparently kept going up through the 1960s. This year has more expensive high numbers, including many that are single printed. Centering was not really a problem this year. The high numbers are much harder to find than the 67s.

The #1 Mays card is expensive and hard to find centered and mint, as are cards from the next-to-the-last series of 458-533. Baby Boomers are still piecing together these sets from the mid-60s sets, which I think will increase the most, percentage-wise, over the coming years as 2000 approaches, and rise dramatically once it actually gets here.

		MT
Complete Set (598):		5500.
Common Player (1-196):		1.50
Common Player (197-370):		2.00
Common Player (371-446):		3.50
Common Player (447-522):		6.00
Common Player (523-598):		21.00
1	Willie Mays	250.00
2	Ted Abernathy	1.50
3	Sam Mele	1.50
4	Ray Culp	1.50
5	Jim Fregosi	1.50
6	Chuck Schilling	1.50
7	Tracy Stallard	1.50
8	Floyd Robinson	1.50
9	Clete Boyer	2.00
10	Tony Cloninger	1.50
11	Senators Rookies (Brant Alyea, Pete Craig)	1.50
12	John Tsitouris	1.50
13	Lou Johnson	1.50
14	Norm Siebern	1.50
15	Vern Law	1.50
16	Larry Brown	1.50
17	Johnny Stephenson	1.50
18	Roland Sheldon	1.50
19	Giants Team	5.00
20	Willie Horton	1.50
21	Don Nottebart	1.50
22	Joe Nossek	1.50
23	Jack Sanford	1.50
24	*Don Kessinger*	2.00
25	Pete Ward	1.50
26	Ray Sadecki	1.50
27	Orioles Rookies (*Andy Etchebarren*, Darold Knowles)	2.00
28	Phil Niekro	15.00
29	Mike Brumley	1.50
30	Pete Rose	40.00
31	Jack Cullen	1.50
32	Adolfo Phillips	1.50
33	Jim Pagliaroni	1.50
34	Checklist 1-88	5.00
35	Ron Swoboda	1.50
36	Catfish Hunter	25.00
37	Billy Herman	5.00
38	Ron Nischwitz	1.50
39	Ken Henderson	1.50
40	Jim Grant	1.50
41	Don LeJohn	1.50
42	Aubrey Gatewood	1.50
43	Don Landrum	1.50
44	Indians Rookies (Bill Davis, Tom Kelley)	1.50
45	Jim Gentile	1.50
46	Howie Koplitz	1.50
47	J.C. Martin	1.50
48	Paul Blair	1.50
49	Woody Woodward	1.50
50	Mickey Mantle	350.00
51	Gordon Richardson	1.50

No.	Player	Price
52	Power Plus (Johnny Callison, Wes Covington)	2.50
53	Bob Duliba	1.50
54	Jose Pagan	1.50
55	Ken Harrelson	1.50
56	Sandy Valdespino	1.50
57	Jim Lefebvre	2.00
58	Dave Wickersham	1.50
59	Reds Team	5.00
60	Curt Flood	1.50
61	Bob Bolin	1.50
62a	Merritt Ranew (no sold statement)	21.00
62b	Merritt Ranew (with sold statement)	1.50
63	Jim Stewart	1.50
64	Bob Bruce	1.50
65	Leon Wagner	1.50
66	Al Weis	1.50
67	Mets Rookies (Cleon Jones, Dick Selma)	1.50
68	Hal Reniff	1.50
69	Ken Hamlin	1.50
70	Carl Yastrzemski	40.00
71	Frank Carpin	1.50
72	Tony Perez	35.00
73	Jerry Zimmerman	1.50
74	Don Mossi	1.50
75	Tommy Davis	2.50
76	Red Schoendienst	5.00
77	Johnny Orsino	1.50
78	Frank Linzy	1.50
79	Joe Pepitone	2.00
80	Richie Allen	2.50
81	Ray Oyler	1.50
82	Bob Hendley	1.50
83	Albie Pearson	1.50
84	Braves Rookies (Jim Beauchamp, Dick Kelley)	1.50
85	Eddie Fisher	1.50
86	John Bateman	1.50
87	Dan Napoleon	1.50
88	Fred Whitfield	1.50
89	Ted Davidson	1.50
90	Luis Aparicio	7.50
91a	Bob Uecker (no trade statement)	75.00
91b	Bob Uecker (with trade statement)	20.00
92	Yankees Team	7.50
93	Jim Lonborg	1.50
94	Matty Alou	1.50
95	Pete Richert	1.50
96	Felipe Alou	2.50
97	Jim Merritt	1.50
98	Don Demeter	1.50
99	Buc Belters (Donn Clendenon, Willie Stargell)	5.00
100	Sandy Koufax	100.00
101a	Checklist 89-176 (115 is Spahn)	9.00
101b	Checklist 89-176 (115 is Henry)	4.00
102	Ed Kirkpatrick	1.50
103a	Dick Groat (no trade statement)	20.00
103b	Dick Groat (with trade statement)	3.00
104a	Alex Johnson (no trade statement)	20.00
104b	Alex Johnson (with trade statement)	1.50
105	Milt Pappas	1.50
106	Rusty Staub	2.50
107	Athletics Rookies (Larry Stahl, Ron Tompkins)	1.50
108	Bobby Klaus	1.50
109	Ralph Terry	1.50
110	Ernie Banks	30.00
111	Gary Peters	2.00
112	Manny Mota	2.00
113	Hank Aguirre	2.00
114	Jim Gosger	2.00
115	Bill Henry	2.00
116	Walt Alston	5.00
117	Jake Gibbs	2.00
118	Mike McCormick	2.00
119	Art Shamsky	2.00
120	Harmon Killebrew	25.00
121	Ray Herbert	2.00
122	Joe Gaines	2.00
123	Pirates Rookies (Frank Bork, Jerry May)	2.00
124	Tug McGraw	2.00
125	Lou Brock	25.00
126	*Jim Palmer*	200.00
127	Ken Berry	2.00
128	Jim Landis	2.00
129	Jack Kralick	2.00
130	Joe Torre	2.25
131	Angels Team	2.25
132	Orlando Cepeda	6.00
133	Don McMahon	2.00
134	Wes Parker	2.00
135	Dave Morehead	2.00
136	Woody Held	2.00
137	Pat Corrales	2.00
138	Roger Repoz	2.00
139	Cubs Rookies (Byron Browne, Don Young)	2.00
140	Jim Maloney	2.00
141	Tom McCraw	2.00
142	Don Dennis	2.00
143	Jose Tartabull	2.00
144	Don Schwall	2.00
145	Bill Freehan	2.00
146	George Altman	2.00
147	Lum Harris	2.00
148	Bob Johnson	2.00
149	Dick Nen	2.00
150	Rocky Colavito	4.00
151	Gary Wagner	2.00
152	Frank Malzone	2.00
153	Rico Carty	2.50
154	Chuck Hiller	2.00
155	Marcelino Lopez	2.00
156	D P Combo (Hal Lanier, Dick Schofield)	2.50
157	Rene Lachemann	2.00
158	Jim Brewer	2.00
159	Chico Ruiz	2.00
160	Whitey Ford	25.00
161	Jerry Lumpe	2.00
162	Lee Maye	2.00
163	Tito Francona	2.00
164	White Sox Rookies (Tommie Agee, Marv Staehle)	2.00
165	Don Lock	2.00
166	Chris Krug	2.00
167	Boog Powell	2.50
168	Dan Osinski	2.00
169	Duke Sims	2.00
170	Cookie Rojas	2.00
171	Nick Willhite	2.00
172	Mets Team	7.00
173	Al Spangler	2.00
174	Ron Taylor	2.00
175	Bert Campaneris	3.00
176	Jim Davenport	2.00
177	Hector Lopez	2.00
178	Bob Tillman	2.00
179	Cardinals Rookies (Dennis Aust, Bob Tolan)	2.00
180	Vada Pinson	2.50
181	Al Worthington	2.00
182	Jerry Lynch	2.00
183a	Checklist 177-264 (large print on front)	4.00
183b	Checklist 177-264 (small print on front)	6.00
184	Denis Menke	2.00
185	Bob Buhl	2.00
186	Ruben Amaro	2.00
187	Chuck Dressen	2.00
188	Al Luplow	2.00
189	John Roseboro	2.00
190	Jimmie Hall	2.00
191	Darrell Sutherland	2.00

192	Vic Power	2.00
193	Dave McNally	2.00
194	Senators Team	6.00
195	Joe Morgan	36.00
196	Don Pavletich	2.00
197	Sonny Siebert	2.00
198	*Mickey Stanley*	2.00
199	Chisox Clubbers (Floyd Robinson, Johnny Romano, Bill Skowron)	2.50
200	Eddie Mathews	20.00
201	Jim Dickson	2.00
202	Clay Dalrymple	2.00
203	Jose Santiago	2.00
204	Cubs Team	6.00
205	Tom Tresh	5.00
206	Alvin Jackson	2.00
207	Frank Quilici	2.00
208	Bob Miller	2.00
209	Tigers Rookies (Fritz Fisher, John Hiller)	2.00
210	Bill Mazeroski	3.50
211	Frank Kreutzer	2.00
212	Ed Kranepool	2.00
213	Fred Newman	2.00
214	Tommy Harper	2.00
215	N.L. Batting Leaders (Hank Aaron, Roberto Clemente, Willie Mays)	35.00
216	A.L. Batting Leaders (Vic Davalillo, Tony Oliva, Carl Yastrzemski)	6.00
217	N.L. Home Run Leaders (Willie Mays, Willie McCovey, Billy Williams)	7.50
218	A.L. Home Run Leaders (Norm Cash, Tony Conigliaro, Willie Horton)	3.50
219	N.L. RBI Leaders (Deron Johnson, Willie Mays, Frank Robinson)	7.00
220	A.L. RBI Leaders (Rocky Colavito, Willie Horton, Tony Oliva)	3.50
221	N.L. ERA Leaders (Sandy Koufax, Vern Law, Juan Marichal)	6.00
222	A.L. ERA Leaders (Eddie Fisher, Sam McDowell, Sonny Siebert)	3.50
223	N.L. Pitching Leaders (Tony Cloninger, Don Drysdale, Sandy Koufax)	6.00
224	A.L. Pitching Leaders (Jim Grant, Jim Kaat, Mel Stottlemyre)	3.50
225	N.L. Strikeout Leaders (Bob Gibson, Sandy Koufax, Bob Veale)	6.00
226	A.L. Strikeout Leaders (Mickey Lolich, Sam McDowell, Denny McLain, Sonny Siebert)	3.50
227	Russ Nixon	2.00
228	Larry Dierker	2.00
229	Hank Bauer	2.00
230	Johnny Callison	2.00
231	Floyd Weaver	2.00
232	Glenn Beckert	2.00
233	Dom Zanni	2.00
234	Yankees Rookies (Rich Beck, Roy White)	7.50
235	Don Cardwell	2.00
236	Mike Hershberger	2.00
237	Billy O'Dell	2.00
238	Dodgers Team	6.00
239	Orlando Pena	2.00
240	Earl Battey	2.00
241	Dennis Ribant	2.00
242	Jesus Alou	2.00
243	Nelson Briles	2.00
244	Astros Rookies (Chuck Harrison, Sonny Jackson)	2.00
245	John Buzhardt	2.00
246	Ed Bailey	2.00
247	Carl Warwick	2.00
248	Pete Mikkelsen	2.00
249	Bill Rigney	2.00
250	Sam Ellis	2.00
251	Ed Brinkman	2.00
252	Denver Lemaster	2.00
253	Don Wert	2.00
254	Phillies Rookies (*Fergie Jenkins*, Bill Sorrell)	135.00
255	Willie Stargell	18.00
256	Lew Krausse	2.00
257	Jeff Torborg	2.00
258	Dave Giusti	2.00
259	Red Sox Team	6.00
260	Bob Shaw	2.00
261	Ron Hansen	2.00
262	Jack Hamilton	2.00
263	Tom Egan	2.00
264	Twins Rookies (Andy Kosco, Ted Uhlaender)	2.00
265	Stu Miller	2.00
266	Pedro Gonzalez	2.00
267	Joe Sparma	2.00
268	John Blanchard	2.00
269	Don Heffner	2.00
270	Claude Osteen	2.00
271	Hal Lanier	2.00
272	Jack Baldschun	2.00
273	Astro Aces (Bob Aspromonte, Rusty Staub)	4.50
274	Buster Narum	2.00
275	Tim McCarver	2.50
276	Jim Bouton	2.50
277	George Thomas	2.00
278	Calvin Koonce	2.00
279a	Checklist 265-352 (player's cap black)	6.00
279b	Checklist 265-352 (player's cap red)	4.00
280	Bobby Knoop	2.00
281	Bruce Howard	2.00
282	Johnny Lewis	2.00
283	Jim Perry	2.00
284	Bobby Wine	2.00
285	Luis Tiant	2.50
286	Gary Geiger	2.00
287	Jack Aker	2.00
288	Dodgers Rookies (*Bill Singer*, Don Sutton)	100.00
289	Larry Sherry	2.00
290	Ron Santo	4.50
291	Moe Drabowsky	2.00
292	Jim Coker	2.00
293	Mike Shannon	2.00
294	Steve Ridzik	2.00
295	Jim Hart	2.00
296	Johnny Keane	2.00
297	Jim Owens	2.00
298	Rico Petrocelli	2.00
299	Lou Burdette	2.00
300	Roberto Clemente	125.00
301	Greg Bollo	2.00
302	Ernie Bowman	2.00
303	Indians Team	6.00
304	John Herrnstein	2.00
305	Camilo Pascual	2.00
306	Ty Cline	2.00
307	Clay Carroll	2.00
308	Tom Haller	2.00
309	Diego Segui	2.00
310	Frank Robinson	40.00
311	Reds Rookies (Tommy Helms, Dick Simpson)	2.00
312	Bob Saverine	2.00
313	Chris Zachary	2.00
314	Hector Valle	2.00
315	Norm Cash	4.00
316	Jack Fisher	2.00
317	Dalton Jones	2.00
318	Harry Walker	2.00
319	Gene Freese	2.00
320	Bob Gibson	35.00
321	Rick Reichardt	2.00
322	Bill Faul	2.00
323	Ray Barker	2.00
324	John Boozer	2.00
325	Vic Davalillo	2.00

326	Braves Team	6.00
327	Bernie Allen	2.00
328	Jerry Grote	2.00
329	Pete Charton	2.00
330	Ron Fairly	2.00
331	Ron Herbel	2.00
332	Billy Bryan	2.00
333	Senators Rookies (*Joe Coleman*, Jim French)	2.00
334	Marty Keough	2.00
335	Juan Pizarro	2.00
336	Gene Alley	2.00
337	Fred Gladding	2.00
338	Dal Maxvill	2.00
339	Del Crandall	2.00
340	Dean Chance	2.00
341	Wes Westrum	2.00
342	Bob Humphreys	2.00
343	Joe Christopher	2.00
344	Steve Blass	2.00
345	Bob Allison	2.00
346	Mike de la Hoz	2.00
347	Phil Regan	2.00
348	Orioles Team	6.00
349	Cap Peterson	2.00
350	Mel Stottlemyre	2.50
351	Fred Valentine	2.00
352	Bob Aspromonte	2.00
353	Al McBean	2.00
354	Smoky Burgess	2.00
355	Wade Blasingame	2.00
356	Red Sox Rookies (Owen Johnson, Ken Sanders)	2.00
357	Gerry Arrigo	2.00
358	Charlie Smith	2.00
359	Johnny Briggs	2.00
360	Ron Hunt	2.00
361	Tom Satriano	2.00
362	Gates Brown	2.00
363	Checklist 353-429	4.00
364	Nate Oliver	2.00
365	Roger Maris	75.00
366	Wayne Causey	2.00
367	Mel Nelson	2.00
368	Charlie Lau	2.00
369	Jim King	2.00
370	Chico Cardenas	2.00
371	Lee Stange	3.50
372	Harvey Kuenn	3.50
373	Giants Rookies (Dick Estelle, Jack Hiatt)	3.50
374	Bob Locker	3.50
375	Donn Clendenon	3.50
376	Paul Schaal	3.50
377	Turk Farrell	3.50
378	Dick Tracewski	3.50
379	Cardinals Team	6.00
380	Tony Conigliaro	4.50
381	Hank Fischer	3.50
382	Phil Roof	3.50
383	Jackie Brandt	3.50
384	Al Downing	3.50
385	Ken Boyer	3.50
386	Gil Hodges	6.00
387	Howie Reed	3.50
388	Don Mincher	3.50
389	Jim O'Toole	3.50
390	Brooks Robinson	35.00
391	Chuck Hinton	3.50
392	Cubs Rookies (*Bill Hands*, Randy Hundley)	3.50
393	George Brunet	3.50
394	Ron Brand	3.50
395	Len Gabrielson	3.50
396	Jerry Stephenson	3.50
397	Bill White	3.50
398	Danny Cater	3.50
399	Ray Washburn	3.50
400	Zoilo Versalles	3.50
401	Ken McMullen	3.50
402	Jim Hickman	3.50
403	Fred Talbot	3.50
404	Pirates Team	6.00
405	Elston Howard	6.00
406	Joe Jay	3.50
407	John Kennedy	3.50
408	Lee Thomas	3.50
409	Billy Hoeft	3.50
410	Al Kaline	25.00
411	Gene Mauch	3.50
412	Sam Bowens	3.50
413	John Romano	3.50
414	Dan Coombs	3.50
415	Max Alvis	3.50
416	Phil Ortega	3.50
417	Angels Rookies (Jim McGlothlin, Ed Sukla)	3.50
418	Phil Gagliano	3.50
419	Mike Ryan	3.50
420	Juan Marichal	8.00
421	Roy McMillan	3.50
422	Ed Charles	3.50
423	Ernie Broglio	3.50
424	Reds Rookies (*Lee May*, Darrell Osteen)	8.50
425	Bob Veale	3.50
426	White Sox Team	6.00
427	John Miller	3.50
428	Sandy Alomar	3.50
429	Bill Monbouquette	3.50
430	Don Drysdale	25.00
431	Walt Bond	3.50
432	Bob Heffner	3.50
433	Alvin Dark	3.50
434	Willie Kirkland	3.50
435	Jim Bunning	6.00
436	Julian Javier	3.50
437	Al Stanek	3.50
438	Willie Smith	3.50
439	Pedro Ramos	3.50
440	Deron Johnson	3.50
441	Tommie Sisk	3.50
442	Orioles Rookies (Ed Barnowski, Eddie Watt)	3.50
443	Bill Wakefield	3.50
444a	Checklist 430-506 (456 is R. Sox Rookies)	4.00
444b	Checklist 430-506 (456 is Red Sox Rookies)	6.00
445	Jim Kaat	6.00
446	Mack Jones	3.50
447	Dick Ellsworth (photo actually Ken Hubbs)	7.50
448	Eddie Stanky	7.50
449	Joe Moeller	7.50
450	Tony Oliva	9.00
451	Barry Latman	7.50
452	Joe Azcue	7.50
453	Ron Kline	7.50
454	Jerry Buchek	7.50
455	Mickey Lolich	9.00
456	Red Sox Rookies (Darrell Brandon, Joe Foy)	7.50
457	Joe Gibbon	7.50
458	Manny Jiminez (Jimenez)	7.50
459	Bill McCool	7.50
460	Curt Blefary	7.50
461	Roy Face	7.50
462	Bob Rodgers	7.50
463	Phillies Team	11.00
464	Larry Bearnarth	7.50
465	Don Buford	7.50
466	Ken Johnson	7.50
467	Vic Roznovsky	7.50
468	Johnny Podres	8.00
469	Yankees Rookies (*Bobby Murcer*, Dooley Womack)	30.00
470	Sam McDowell	7.50

471	Bob Skinner	7.50
472	Terry Fox	7.50
473	Rich Rollins	7.50
474	Dick Schofield	7.50
475	Dick Radatz	7.50
476	Bobby Bragan	7.50
477	Steve Barber	7.50
478	Tony Gonzalez	7.50
479	Jim Hannan	7.50
480	Dick Stuart	7.50
481	Bob Lee	7.50
482	Cubs Rookies (John Boccabella, Dave Dowling)	7.50
483	Joe Nuxhall	7.50
484	Wes Covington	7.50
485	Bob Bailey	7.50
486	Tommy John	15.00
487	Al Ferrara	7.50
488	George Banks	7.50
489	Curt Simmons	7.50
490	Bobby Richardson	15.00
491	Dennis Bennett	7.50
492	Athletics Team	11.00
493	Johnny Klippstein	7.50
494	Gordon Coleman	7.50
495	Dick McAuliffe	7.50
496	Lindy McDaniel	7.50
497	Chris Cannizzaro	7.50
498	Pirates Rookies (*Woody Fryman*, Luke Walker)	7.50
499	Wally Bunker	7.50
500	Hank Aaron	125.00
501	John O'Donoghue	7.50
502	Lenny Green	7.50
503	Steve Hamilton	7.50
504	Grady Hatton	7.50
505	Jose Cardenal	7.50
506	Bo Belinsky	7.50
507	John Edwards	7.50
508	*Steve Hargan*	7.50
509	Jake Wood	7.50
510	Hoyt Wilhelm	15.00
511	Giants Rookies (Bob Barton, Tito Fuentes)	7.50
512	Dick Stigman	7.50
513	Camilo Carreon	7.50
514	Hal Woodeshick	7.50
515	Frank Howard	9.00
516	Eddie Bressoud	7.50
517a	Checklist 507-598 (529 is W. Sox Rookies)	9.00
517b	Checklist 506-598 (529 is White Sox Rookies)	10.00
518	Braves Rookies (Herb Hippauf, Arnie Umbach)	7.50
519	Bob Friend	7.50
520	Jim Wynn	7.50
521	John Wyatt	7.50
522	Phil Linz	7.50
523	Bob Sadowski	19.00
524	Giants Rookies (Ollie Brown, Don Mason) (SP)	24.00
525	Gary Bell (SP)	24.00
526	Twins Team	65.00
527	Julio Navarro	19.00
528	Jesse Gonder (SP)	24.00
529	White Sox Rookies (*Lee Elia*, Dennis Higgins, Bill Voss)	19.00
530	Robin Roberts	45.00
531	Joe Cunningham	19.00
532	Aurelio Monteagudo (SP)	24.00
533	Jerry Adair (SP)	24.00
534	Mets Rookies (Dave Eilers, Rob Gardner)	19.00
535	Willie Davis	40.00
536	Dick Egan	19.00
537	Herman Franks	19.00
538	Bob Allen (SP)	24.00
539	Astros Rookies (Bill Heath, Carroll Sembera)	19.00
540	Denny McLain	65.00
541	Gene Oliver (SP)	24.00

542	George Smith	19.00
543	Roger Craig	50.00
544	Cardinals Rookies (Joe Hoerner, George Kernek, Jimmy Williams) (SP)	24.00
545	Dick Green (SP)	24.00
546	Dwight Siebler	19.00
547	*Horace Clarke* (SP)	45.00
548	Gary Kroll (SP)	24.00
549	Senators Rookies (Al Closter, Casey Cox)	19.00
550	Willie McCovey	125.00
551	Bob Purkey (SP)	24.00
552	Birdie Tebbetts (SP)	24.00
553	Major League Rookies (Pat Garrett, Jackie Warner)	19.00
554	Jim Northrup (SP)	24.00
555	Ron Perranoski (SP)	24.00
556	Mel Queen (SP)	24.00
557	Felix Mantilla (SP)	24.00
558	Red Sox Rookies (Guido Grilli, Pete Magrini, George Scott)	30.00
559	Roberto Pena (SP)	24.00
560	Joel Horlen	19.00
561	Choo Choo Coleman	40.00
562	Russ Snyder	19.00
563	Twins Rookies (Pete Cimino, Cesar Tovar)	19.00
564	Bob Chance (SP)	24.00
565	Jimmy Piersall	50.00
566	Mike Cuellar	40.00
567	Dick Howser	19.00
568	Athletics Rookies (Paul Lindblad, Ron Stone)	19.00
569	Orlando McFarlane (SP)	24.00
570	Art Mahaffey (SP)	24.00
571	Dave Roberts (SP)	24.00
572	Bob Priddy	19.00
573	Derrell Griffith	19.00
574	Mets Rookies (Bill Hepler, Bill Murphy)	19.00
575	Earl Wilson	19.00
576	Dave Nicholson (SP)	24.00
577	Jack Lamabe (SP)	24.00
578	Chi Chi Olivo (SP)	24.00
579	Orioles Rookies (Frank Bertaina, Gene Brabender, Dave Johnson)	19.00
580	Billy Williams	100.00
581	Tony Martinez	19.00
582	Garry Roggenburk	19.00
583	Tigers Team	200.00
584	Yankees Rookies (Frank Fernandez, Fritz Peterson)	19.00
585	Tony Taylor	19.00
586	Claude Raymond (SP)	24.00
587	Dick Bertell	19.00
588	Athletics Rookies (Chuck Dobson, Ken Suarez)	19.00
589	Lou Klimchock	19.00
590	Bill Skowron	35.00
591	N.L. Rookies (*Grant Jackson*, Bart Shirley)	50.00
592	Andre Rodgers	19.00
593	Doug Camilli (SP)	24.00
594	Chico Salmon	19.00
595	Larry Jackson	19.00
596	Astros Rookies (*Nate Colbert*, Greg Sims)	19.00
597	John Sullivan	19.00
598	Gaylord Perry	300.00

1967 Topps

This 609-card set of 2-1/2" by 3-1/2" cards marked the largest set up to that time for Topps. Card fronts feature large color photographs bordered by white. The player's name and position are printed at the top with the team at the bottom. Across the front of the card with the exception of #254 (Milt Pappas) there is a facsimile autograph. The backs were the first to be done vertically, although they continued to carry familiar statistical and biographical information. The only subsets are statistical leaders and World Series highlights. Rookie cards are done by team or league with two players per card. The high numbers (#'s 534-609) in '67 are quite scarce, and while it is known that some are even scarcer, by virtue of having been short-printed in relation to the rest of the series, there is no general agreement on which cards are involved. Cards in the high series which are generally believed to have been double-printed - and thus worth somewhat less than the other cards in the series - and indicated in the checklist by a (DP) notation following the player name.

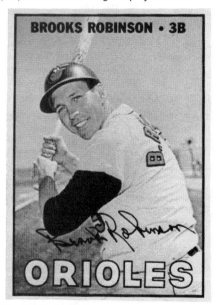

Mr. Mint Says - There is more availability in mint condition as we go up in years, and more than the 66s. There is always considerable interest in the superstars, rookie cards and the high numbers. From 1957 to 1967, Hall of Fame superstar cards sell well, since they are reasonable and not out of range like the early 50s stuff.

The high numbers are the key to the set, and they have a tendency to be off-center. When Seaver, Carew, Wills, Robinson and John are sharp and centered, they sell great. Cards of Mike Shannon, Rocky Colavito and the Red Sox team card are highly sought, and the Wills card, his first Topps offering, was very undervalued.

		MT
Complete Set (609):		6300.
Common Player (1-196):		1.50
Common Player (197-370):		2.00
Common Player (371-457):		3.00
Common Player (458-533):		7.00
Common Player (534-609):		12.00
1	The Champs (Hank Bauer, Brooks Robinson, Frank Robinson)	25.00
2	Jack Hamilton	1.50
3	Duke Sims	1.50
4	Hal Lanier	1.50
5	Whitey Ford	20.00
6	Dick Simpson	1.50
7	Don McMahon	1.50
8	Chuck Harrison	1.50
9	Ron Hansen	1.50
10	Matty Alou	1.50
11	Barry Moore	1.50
12	Dodgers Rookies (Jimmy Campanis, Bill Singer)	2.50
13	Joe Sparma	1.50
14	Phil Linz	1.50
15	Earl Battey	1.50
16	Bill Hands	1.50
17	Jim Gosger	1.50
18	Gene Oliver	1.50
19	Jim McGlothlin	1.50
20	Orlando Cepeda	10.00
21	Dave Bristol	1.50
22	Gene Brabender	1.50
23	Larry Elliot	1.50
24	Bob Allen	1.50
25	Elston Howard	4.00
26a	Bob Priddy (no trade statement)	15.00
26b	Bob Priddy (with trade statement)	1.50
27	Bob Saverine	1.50
28	Barry Latman	1.50
29	Tommy McCraw	1.50
30	Al Kaline	17.50
31	Jim Brewer	1.50
32	Bob Bailey	1.50
33	Athletics Rookies (*Sal Bando*, Randy Schwartz)	2.00
34	Pete Cimino	1.50
35	Rico Carty	1.50
36	Bob Tillman	1.50
37	Rick Wise	1.50
38	Bob Johnson	1.50
39	Curt Simmons	1.50
40	Rick Reichardt	1.50
41	Joe Hoerner	1.50
42	Mets Team	5.00
43	Chico Salmon	1.50
44	Joe Nuxhall	1.50
45a	Roger Maris (Cards on front)	45.00
45b	Roger Maris (Yankees on front, blank-back proof)	800.00
46	Lindy McDaniel	1.50
47	Ken McMullen	1.50
48	Bill Freehan	1.50

49	Roy Face	1.50
50	Tony Oliva	4.00
51	Astros Rookies (Dave Adlesh, Wes Bales)	1.50
52	Dennis Higgins	1.50
53	Clay Dalrymple	1.50
54	Dick Green	1.50
55	Don Drysdale	20.00
56	Jose Tartabull	1.50
57	*Pat Jarvis*	1.50
58	Paul Schaal	1.50
59	Ralph Terry	1.50
60	Luis Aparicio	7.50
61	Gordy Coleman	1.50
62	Checklist 1-109 (Frank Robinson)	5.00
63	Cards Clubbers (Lou Brock, Curt Flood)	13.00
64	Fred Valentine	1.50
65	Tom Haller	1.50
66	Manny Mota	1.50
67	Ken Berry	1.50
68	Bob Buhl	1.50
69	Vic Davalillo	1.50
70	Ron Santo	2.00
71	Camilo Pascual	1.50
72	Tigers Rookies (George Korince, John Matchick)	1.50
73	Rusty Staub	2.50
74	Wes Stock	1.50
75	George Scott	2.50
76	Jim Barbieri	1.50
77	Dooley Womack	1.50
78	Pat Corrales	1.50
79	Bubba Morton	1.50
80	Jim Maloney	1.50
81	Eddie Stanky	1.50
82	Steve Barber	1.50
83	Ollie Brown	1.50
84	Tommie Sisk	1.50
85	Johnny Callison	1.50
86a	Mike McCormick (no trade statement)	17.50
86b	Mike McCormick (with trade statement)	1.50
87	George Altman	1.50
88	Mickey Lolich	2.25
89	*Felix Millan*	1.50
90	Jim Nash	1.50
91	Johnny Lewis	1.50
92	Ray Washburn	1.50
93	Yankees Rookies (*Stan Bahnsen*, Bobby Murcer)	2.50
94	Ron Fairly	1.50
95	Sonny Siebert	1.50
96	Art Shamsky	1.50
97	Mike Cuellar	1.50
98	Rich Rollins	1.50
99	Lee Stange	1.50
100	Frank Robinson	17.50
101	Ken Johnson	1.50
102	Phillies Team	5.00
103a	Checklist 110-196 (Mickey Mantle) (170 is D McAuliffe)	15.00
103b	Checklist 110-196 (Mickey Mantle) (170 is D. McAuliffe)	10.00
104	Minnie Rojas	1.50
105	Ken Boyer	2.00
106	Randy Hundley	1.50
107	Joel Horlen	1.50
108	Alex Johnson	1.50
109	Tribe Thumpers (Rocky Colavito, Leon Wagner)	2.50
110	Jack Aker	2.50
111	John Kennedy	2.50
112	Dave Wickersham	2.50
113	Dave Nicholson	2.50
114	Jack Baldschun	2.50
115	Paul Casanova	2.50
116	Herman Franks	2.50
117	Darrell Brandon	2.50
118	Bernie Allen	2.50
119	Wade Blasingame	2.50
120	Floyd Robinson	2.50
121	Ed Bressoud	2.50
122	George Brunet	2.50
123	Pirates Rookies (Jim Price, Luke Walker)	2.50
124	Jim Stewart	2.50
125	Moe Drabowsky	2.50
126	Tony Taylor	2.50
127	John O'Donoghue	2.50
128	Ed Spiezio	2.50
129	Phil Roof	2.50
130	Phil Regan	2.50
131	Yankees Team	7.50
132	Ozzie Virgil	2.50
133	Ron Kline	2.50
134	Gates Brown	2.50
135	Deron Johnson	2.50
136	Carroll Sembera	2.50
137	Twins Rookies (Ron Clark, Jim Ollom)	2.50
138	Dick Kelley	2.50
139	Dalton Jones	2.50
140	Willie Stargell	20.00
141	John Miller	2.50
142	Jackie Brandt	2.50
143	Sox Sockers (Don Buford, Pete Ward)	3.00
144	Bill Hepler	2.50
145	Larry Brown	2.50
146	Steve Carlton	125.00
147	Tom Egan	2.50
148	Adolfo Phillips	2.50
149	Joe Moeller	2.50
150	Mickey Mantle	325.00
151	World Series Game 1 Moe Mows Down 11	3.50
152	World Series Game 2 Palmer Blanks Dodgers	5.00
153	World Series Game 3 Blair's Homer Defeats L.A.	3.50
154	World Series Game 4 Orioles Win 4th Straight	3.50
155	World Series Summary The Winners Celebrate	3.50
156	Ron Herbel	2.50
157	Danny Cater	2.50
158	Jimmy Coker	2.50
159	Bruce Howard	2.50
160	Willie Davis	2.50
161	Dick Williams	2.50
162	Billy O'Dell	2.50
163	Vic Roznovsky	2.50
164	Dwight Siebler	2.50
165	Cleon Jones	2.50
166	Eddie Mathews	15.00
167	Senators Rookies (Joe Coleman, Tim Cullen)	2.50
168	Ray Culp	2.50
169	Horace Clarke	2.50
170	Dick McAuliffe	2.50
171	Calvin Koonce	2.50
172	Bill Heath	2.50
173	Cardinals Team	5.00
174	Dick Radatz	2.50
175	Bobby Knoop	2.50
176	Sammy Ellis	2.50
177	Tito Fuentes	2.50
178	John Buzhardt	2.50
179	Braves Rookies (Cecil Upshaw, Chas. Vaughn)	2.50
180	Curt Blefary	2.50
181	Terry Fox	2.50
182	Ed Charles	2.50
183	Jim Pagliaroni	2.50
184	George Thomas	2.50
185	*Ken Holtzman*	2.50
186	Mets Maulers (Ed Kranepool, Ron Swoboda)	3.00
187	Pedro Ramos	2.50
188	Ken Harrelson	2.50
189	Chuck Hinton	2.50
190	Turk Farrell	2.50
191a	Checklist 197-283 (Willie Mays) (214 is Dick Kelley)	12.00

191b	Checklist 197-283 (Willie Mays) (214 is Tom Kelley)	12.00
192	Fred Gladding	2.50
193	Jose Cardenal	2.50
194	Bob Allison	2.50
195	Al Jackson	2.50
196	Johnny Romano	2.50
197	Ron Perranoski	2.50
198	Chuck Hiller	2.50
199	Billy Hitchcock	2.50
200	Willie Mays	100.00
201	Hal Reniff	2.50
202	Johnny Edwards	2.50
203	Al McBean	2.50
204	Orioles Rookies (*Mike Epstein*, Tom Phoebus)	2.50
205	Dick Groat	2.50
206	Dennis Bennett	2.50
207	John Orsino	2.50
208	Jack Lamabe	2.50
209	Joe Nossek	2.50
210	Bob Gibson	20.00
211	Twins Team	5.00
212	Chris Zachary	2.50
213	*Jay Johnstone*	2.00
214	Tom Kelley	3.00
215	Ernie Banks	25.00
216	Bengal Belters (Norm Cash, Al Kaline)	7.50
217	Rob Gardner	2.50
218	Wes Parker	2.50
219	Clay Carroll	2.50
220	Jim Hart	2.50
221	Woody Fryman	2.50
222	Reds Rookies (Lee May, Darrell Osteen)	2.50
223	Mike Ryan	2.50
224	Walt Bond	2.50
225	Mel Stottlemyre	2.50
226	Julian Javier	2.50
227	Paul Lindblad	2.50
228	Gil Hodges	5.00
229	Larry Jackson	2.50
230	Boog Powell	2.50
231	John Bateman	2.50
232	Don Buford	2.50
233	A.L. ERA Leaders (Steve Hargan, Joel Horlen, Gary Peters)	3.00
234	N.L. ERA Leaders (Mike Cuellar, Sandy Koufax, Juan Marichal)	12.00
235	A.L. Pitching Leaders (Jim Kaat, Denny McLain, Earl Wilson)	3.00
236	N.L. Pitching Leaders (Bob Gibson, Sandy Koufax, Juan Marichal, Gaylord Perry)	25.00
237	A.L. Strikeout Leaders (Jim Kaat, Sam McDowell, Earl Wilson)	3.00
238	N.L. Strikeout Leaders (Jim Bunning, Sandy Koufax, Bob Veale)	12.00
239	A.L. Batting Leaders (Al Kaline, Tony Oliva, Frank Robinson)	12.00
240	N.L. Batting Leaders (Felipe Alou, Matty Alou, Rico Carty)	3.00
241	A.L. RBI Leaders (Harmon Killebrew, Boog Powell, Frank Robinson)	4.50
242	N.L. RBI Leaders (Hank Aaron, Richie Allen, Bob Clemente)	12.00
243	A.L. Home Run Leaders (Harmon Killebrew, Boog Powell, Frank Robinson)	6.00
244	N.L. Home Run Leaders (Hank Aaron, Richie Allen, Willie Mays)	12.00
245	Curt Flood	2.50
246	Jim Perry	2.50
247	Jerry Lumpe	2.50
248	Gene Mauch	2.50
249	Nick Willhite	2.50
250	Hank Aaron	100.00
251	Woody Held	2.50
252	Bob Bolin	2.50
253	Indians Rookies (Bill Davis, Gus Gil)	2.50
254	Milt Pappas	2.50
255	Frank Howard	3.00
256	Bob Hendley	2.50
257	Charley Smith	2.50
258	Lee Maye	2.50
259	Don Dennis	2.50
260	Jim Lefebvre	2.50
261	John Wyatt	2.50
262	Athletics Team	5.00
263	Hank Aguirre	2.50
264	Ron Swoboda	2.50
265	Lou Burdette	2.50
266	Pitt Power (Donn Clendenon, Willie Stargell)	5.00
267	Don Schwall	2.50
268	John Briggs	2.50
269	Don Nottebart	2.50
270	Zoilo Versalles	2.50
271	Eddie Watt	2.50
272	Cubs Rookies (Bill Connors, Dave Dowling)	2.50
273	Dick Lines	2.50
274	Bob Aspromonte	2.50
275	Fred Whitfield	2.50
276	Bruce Brubaker	2.50
277	Steve Whitaker	2.50
278	Checklist 284-370 (Jim Kaat)	5.00
279	Frank Linzy	2.50
280	Tony Conigliaro	3.50
281	Bob Rodgers	2.50
282	Johnny Odom	2.50
283	Gene Alley	2.50
284	Johnny Podres	3.50
285	Lou Brock	25.00
286	Wayne Causey	2.50
287	Mets Rookies (Greg Goossen, Bart Shirley)	2.50
288	Denver Lemaster	2.50
289	Tom Tresh	3.50
290	Bill White	2.50
291	Jim Hannan	2.50
292	Don Pavletich	2.50
293	Ed Kirkpatrick	2.50
294	Walt Alston	5.00
295	Sam McDowell	2.50
296	Glenn Beckert	2.50
297	Dave Morehead	2.50
298	Ron Davis	2.50
299	Norm Siebern	2.50
300	Jim Kaat	9.00
301	Jesse Gonder	2.50
302	Orioles Team	5.00
303	Gil Blanco	2.50
304	Phil Gagliano	2.50
305	Earl Wilson	2.50
306	*Bud Harrelson*	2.50
307	Jim Beauchamp	2.50
308	Al Downing	2.50
309	Hurlers Beware (Richie Allen, Johnny Callison)	2.00
310	Gary Peters	2.50
311	Ed Brinkman	2.50
312	Don Mincher	2.50
313	Bob Lee	2.50
314	Red Sox Rookies (*Mike Andrews*, Reggie Smith)	7.50
315	Billy Williams	15.00
316	Jack Kralick	2.50
317	Cesar Tovar	2.50
318	Dave Giusti	2.50
319	Paul Blair	2.50
320	Gaylord Perry	15.00
321	Mayo Smith	2.50
322	Jose Pagan	2.50
323	Mike Hershberger	2.50
324	Hal Woodeshick	2.50
325	Chico Cardenas	2.50
326	Bob Uecker	20.00

327	Angels Team	5.00		400	Roberto Clemente	100.00
328	Clete Boyer	2.50		401	Jim Coates	3.00
329	Charlie Lau	2.50		402	Phillies Rookies (Grant Jackson, Billy Wilson)	3.00
330	Claude Osteen	2.50		403	Dick Nen	3.00
331	Joe Foy	2.50		404	Nelson Briles	3.00
332	Jesus Alou	2.50		405	Russ Snyder	3.00
333	Fergie Jenkins	25.00		406	Lee Elia	3.00
334	Twin Terrors (Bob Allison, Harmon Killebrew)	4.50		407	Reds Team	5.00
335	Bob Veale	2.50		408	Jim Northrup	3.00
336	Joe Azcue	2.50		409	Ray Sadecki	3.00
337	Joe Morgan	22.00		410	Lou Johnson	3.00
338	Bob Locker	2.50		411	Dick Howser	3.00
339	Chico Ruiz	2.50		412	Astros Rookies (Norm Miller, Doug Rader)	3.00
340	Joe Pepitone	2.50		413	Jerry Grote	3.00
341	Giants Rookies (*Dick Dietz*, Bill Sorrell)	2.50		414	Casey Cox	3.00
342	Hank Fischer	2.50		415	Sonny Jackson	3.00
343	Tom Satriano	2.50		416	Roger Repoz	3.00
344	Ossie Chavarria	2.50		417a	Bob Bruce (RBAVES on back)	18.00
345	Stu Miller	2.50		417b	Bob Bruce (corrected)	3.00
346	Jim Hickman	2.50		418	Sam Mele	3.00
347	Grady Hatton	2.50		419	Don Kessinger	3.00
348	Tug McGraw	2.50		420	Denny McLain	5.00
349	Bob Chance	2.50		421	Dal Maxvill	3.00
350	Joe Torre	2.50		422	Hoyt Wilhelm	15.00
351	Vern Law	2.50		423	Fence Busters (Willie Mays, Willie McCovey)	35.00
352	Ray Oyler	2.50		424	Pedro Gonzalez	3.00
353	Bill McCool	2.50		425	Pete Mikkelsen	3.00
354	Cubs Team	5.00		426	Lou Clinton	3.00
355	Carl Yastrzemski	75.00		427	Ruben Gomez	3.00
356	Larry Jaster	2.50		428	Dodgers Rookies (Tom Hutton, Gene Michael)	3.00
357	Bill Skowron	3.50		429	Garry Roggenburk	3.00
358	Ruben Amaro	2.50		430	Pete Rose	75.00
359	Dick Ellsworth	2.50		431	Ted Uhlaender	3.00
360	Leon Wagner	2.50		432	Jimmie Hall	3.00
361	Checklist 371-457 (Roberto Clemente)	13.00		433	Al Luplow	3.00
362	Darold Knowles	2.50		434	Eddie Fisher	3.00
363	Dave Johnson	2.50		435	Mack Jones	3.00
364	Claude Raymond	2.50		436	Pete Ward	3.00
365	John Roseboro	2.50		437	Senators Team	5.00
366	Andy Kosco	2.50		438	Chuck Dobson	3.00
367	Angels Rookies (Bill Kelso, Don Wallace)	2.50		439	Byron Browne	3.00
368	Jack Hiatt	2.50		440	Steve Hargan	3.00
369	Catfish Hunter	18.00		441	Jim Davenport	3.00
370	Tommy Davis	2.50		442	Yankees Rookies (*Bill Robinson*, Joe Verbanic)	3.00
371	Jim Lonborg	3.00		443	Tito Francona	3.00
372	Mike de la Hoz	3.00		444	George Smith	3.00
373	White Sox Rookies (Duane Josephson, Fred Klages)	3.00		445	Don Sutton	35.00
374	Mel Queen	3.00		446	Russ Nixon	3.00
375	Jake Gibbs	3.00		447	Bo Belinsky	3.00
376	Don Lock	3.00		448	Harry Walker	3.00
377	Luis Tiant	3.00		449	Orlando Pena	3.00
378	Tigers Team	5.00		450	Richie Allen	5.00
379	Jerry May	3.00		451	Fred Newman	3.00
380	Dean Chance	3.00		452	Ed Kranepool	3.00
381	Dick Schofield	3.00		453	Aurelio Monteagudo	3.00
382	Dave McNally	3.00		454a	Checklist 458-533 (Juan Marichal) (left ear shows)	12.00
383	Ken Henderson	3.00		454b	Checklist 458-533 (Juan Marichal) (no left ear)	12.00
384	Cardinals Rookies (Jim Cosman, Dick Hughes)	3.00		455	Tommie Agee	3.00
385	Jim Fregosi	3.00		456	Phil Niekro	15.00
386	Dick Selma	3.00		457	Andy Etchebarren	3.00
387	Cap Peterson	3.00		458	Lee Thomas	7.00
388	Arnold Earley	3.00		459	Senators Rookies (*Dick Bosman*, Pete Craig)	7.00
389	Al Dark	3.00		460	Harmon Killebrew	60.00
390	Jim Wynn	3.00		461	Bob Miller	7.00
391	Wilbur Wood	3.00		462	Bob Barton	7.00
392	Tommy Harper	3.00		463	Hill Aces (Sam McDowell, Sonny Siebert)	11.00
393	Jim Bouton	3.00		464	Dan Coombs	7.00
394	Jake Wood	3.00		465	Willie Horton	9.00
395	Chris Short	3.00		466	Bobby Wine	7.00
396	Atlanta Aces (Tony Cloninger, Denis Menke)	3.00		467	Jim O'Toole	7.00
397	Willie Smith	3.00		468	Ralph Houk	9.00
398	Jeff Torborg	3.00		469	Len Gabrielson	7.00
399	Al Worthington	3.00		470	Bob Shaw	7.00

471	Rene Lachemann	7.00
472	Pirates Rookies (John Gelnar, George Spriggs)	7.00
473	Jose Santiago	7.00
474	Bob Tolan	7.00
475	Jim Palmer	100.00
476	Tony Perez	100.00
477	Braves Team	12.00
478	Bob Humphreys	7.00
479	Gary Bell	7.00
480	Willie McCovey	35.00
481	Leo Durocher	13.00
482	Bill Monbouquette	7.00
483	Jim Landis	7.00
484	Jerry Adair	7.00
485	Tim McCarver	25.00
486	Twins Rookies (Rich Reese, Bill Whitby)	7.00
487	Tom Reynolds	7.00
488	Gerry Arrigo	7.00
489	Doug Clemens	7.00
490	Tony Cloninger	7.00
491	Sam Bowens	7.00
492	Pirates Team	12.00
493	Phil Ortega	7.00
494	Bill Rigney	7.00
495	Fritz Peterson	9.00
496	Orlando McFarlane	7.00
497	Ron Campbell	7.00
498	Larry Dierker	7.00
499	Indians Rookies (George Culver, Jose Vidal)	7.00
500	Juan Marichal	24.00
501	Jerry Zimmerman	7.00
502	Derrell Griffith	7.00
503	Dodgers Team	13.00
504	Orlando Martinez	7.00
505	Tommy Helms	7.00
506	Smoky Burgess	8.00
507	Orioles Rookies (Ed Barnowski, Larry Haney)	7.00
508	Dick Hall	7.00
509	Jim King	7.00
510	Bill Mazeroski	13.00
511	Don Wert	7.00
512	Red Schoendienst	15.00
513	Marcelino Lopez	7.00
514	John Werhas	7.00
515	Bert Campaneris	9.00
516	Giants Team	12.00
517	Fred Talbot	7.00
518	Denis Menke	7.00
519	Ted Davidson	7.00
520	Max Alvis	7.00
521	Bird Bombers (Curt Blefary, Boog Powell)	13.00
522	John Stephenson	7.00
523	Jim Merritt	7.00
524	Felix Mantilla	7.00
525	Ron Hunt	7.00
526	Tigers Rookies (*Pat Dobson*, George Korince)	9.00
527	Dennis Ribant	7.00
528	Rico Petrocelli	12.00
529	Gary Wagner	7.00
530	Felipe Alou	12.00
531	Checklist 534-609 (Brooks Robinson)	12.00
532	Jim Hicks	7.00
533	Jack Fisher	7.00
534	Hank Bauer	12.00
535	Donn Clendenon	15.00
536	Cubs Rookies (*Joe Niekro*, Paul Popovich)	45.00
537	Chuck Estrada	12.00
538	J.C. Martin	15.00
539	Dick Egan	12.00
540	Norm Cash	50.00
541	Joe Gibbon	15.00
542	Athletics Rookies (*Rick Monday*, Tony Pierce)	15.00
543	Dan Schneider	15.00
544	Indians Team	22.00
545	Jim Grant	15.00
546	Woody Woodward	15.00
547	Red Sox Rookies (Russ Gibson, Bill Rohr)	12.00
548	Tony Gonzalez	12.00
549	Jack Sanford	15.00
550	Vada Pinson	18.00
551	Doug Camilli	12.00
552	Ted Savage	15.00
553	Yankees Rookies (Mike Hegan, Thad Tillotson)	18.00
554	Andre Rodgers	12.00
555	Don Cardwell	15.00
556	Al Weis	12.00
557	Al Ferrara	15.00
558	Orioles Rookies (*Mark Belanger*, Bill Dillman)	55.00
559	Dick Tracewski	12.00
560	Jim Bunning	75.00
561	Sandy Alomar	15.00
562	Steve Blass	12.00
563	Joe Adcock	20.00
564	Astros Rookies (Alonzo Harris, Aaron Pointer)	12.00
565	Lew Krausse	15.00
566	Gary Geiger	12.00
567	Steve Hamilton	15.00
568	John Sullivan	15.00
569	A.L. Rookies (Hank Allen, Rod Carew)	375.00
570	Maury Wills	125.00
571	Larry Sherry	15.00
572	Don Demeter	15.00
573	White Sox Team	22.00
574	Jerry Buchek	15.00
575	*Dave Boswell*	15.00
576	N.L. Rookies (Norm Gigon, Ramon Hernandez)	15.00
577	Bill Short	15.00
578	John Boccabella	15.00
579	Bill Henry	15.00
580	Rocky Colavito	100.00
581	Mets Rookies (Bill Denehy, Tom Seaver)	1400.00
582	Jim Owens	12.00
583	Ray Barker	15.00
584	Jim Piersall	20.00
585	Wally Bunker	15.00
586	Manny Jimenez	15.00
587	N.L. Rookies (Don Shaw, Gary Sutherland)	15.00
588	Johnny Klippstein	12.00
589	Dave Ricketts	12.00
590	Pete Richert	15.00
591	Ty Cline	15.00
592	N.L. Rookies (Jim Shellenback, Ron Willis)	15.00
593	Wes Westrum	15.00
594	Dan Osinski	15.00
595	Cookie Rojas	15.00
596	Galen Cisco	12.00
597	Ted Abernathy	15.00
598	White Sox Rookies (Ed Stroud, Walt Williams)	15.00
599	Bob Duliba	12.00
600	Brooks Robinson	250.00
601	Bill Bryan	12.00
602	Juan Pizarro	15.00
603	Athletics Rookies (Tim Talton, Ramon Webster)	15.00
604	Red Sox Team	150.00
605	Mike Shannon	60.00
606	Ron Taylor	15.00
607	Mickey Stanley	35.00
608	Cubs Rookies (Rich Nye, John Upham)	12.00
609	Tommy John	100.00

1968 Topps

In 1968, Topps returned to a 598-card set of 2-1/2" by 3-1/2" cards. It is not, however, more of the same by way of appearance as the cards feature a color photograph on a background of what appears to be a burlap fabric. The player's name is below the photo but on the unusual background. A colored circle on the lower right carries the team and position. Backs were also changed while retaining the vertical format introduced the previous year, with stats in the middle and cartoon at the bottom. The set features many of the old favorite subsets, including statistical leaders, World Series highlights, multi-player cards, checklists, rookie cards and the return of All-Star cards.

Mr. Mint Says - Ah, the burlap set. Oh, how I hate this set! This year is available in mint condition, and the high numbers are a little harder than the lows, but nothing compared to the gap in previous years. Most of the cards are centered pretty well.

The Ryan rookie is more than half of the set. I often get between $2,000 and $2,500 for mint, centered examples. All Bench cards are very weak, including this one. Superstar cards, like Mantle, Mays and Killebrew, are popular, along with some of the all-star cards, and once again, the Tigers team card is a toughie.

I grade this set from the backs of the cards. The gold backs are much more useful in illustrating wear on the card, and it is very difficult to tell sometimes from the front.

		MT
Complete Set (598):		4550.
Common Player (1-457):		1.50
Common Player (458-533):		2.50
Common Player (534-598):		4.00

1	N.L. Batting Leaders (Matty Alou, Roberto Clemente, Tony Gonzalez)	25.00
2	A.L. Batting Leaders (Al Kaline, Frank Robinson, Carl Yastrzemski)	10.00
3	N.L. RBI Leaders (Hank Aaron, Orlando Cepeda, Roberto Clemente)	10.00
4	A.L. RBI Leaders (Harmon Killebrew, Frank Robinson, Carl Yastrzemski)	10.00
5	N.L. Home Run Leaders (Hank Aaron, Willie McCovey, Ron Santo, Jim Wynn)	10.00
6	A.L. Home Run Leaders (Frank Howard, Harmon Killebrew, Carl Yastrzemski)	10.00
7	N.L. ERA Leaders (Jim Bunning, Phil Niekro, Chris Short)	3.50
8	A.L. ERA Leaders (Joe Horlen, Gary Peters, Sonny Siebert)	3.00
9	N.L. Pitching Leaders (Jim Bunning, Fergie Jenkins, Mike McCormick, Claude Osteen)	3.50
10a	A.L. Pitching Leaders (Dean Chance) ("Lonberg" on back)	3.50
10a	A.L. Pitching Leaders (Jim Lonborg) ("Lonberg" on back)	3.50
10a	A.L. Pitching Leaders (Earl Wilson) ("Lonberg" on back)	3.50
10b	A.L. Pitching Leaders (Dean Chance) ("Lonborg" on back)	3.00
10b	A.L. Pitching Leaders (Jim Lonborg) ("Lonborg" on back)	3.00
10b	A.L. Pitching Leaders (Earl Wilson) ("Lonborg" on back)	3.00
11	N.L. Strikeout Leaders (Jim Bunning, Fergie Jenkins, Gaylord Perry)	4.50
12	A.L. Strikeout Leaders (Dean Chance, Jim Lonborg, Sam McDowell)	3.00
13	Chuck Hartenstein	1.50
14	Jerry McNertney	1.50
15	Ron Hunt	1.50
16	Indians Rookies (*Lou Piniella*, Richie Scheinblum)	2.50
17	Dick Hall	1.50
18	Mike Hershberger	1.50
19	Juan Pizarro	1.50
20	Brooks Robinson	25.00
21	Ron Davis	1.50
22	Pat Dobson	1.50
23	Chico Cardenas	1.50
24	Bobby Locke	1.50
25	Julian Javier	1.50
26	Darrell Brandon	1.50
27	Gil Hodges	10.00
28	Ted Uhlaender	1.50
29	Joe Verbanic	1.50
30	Joe Torre	1.50
31	Ed Stroud	1.50
32	Joe Gibbon	1.50
33	Pete Ward	1.50
34	Al Ferrara	1.50
35	Steve Hargan	1.50
36	Pirates Rookies (Bob Moose, Bob Robertson)	1.50
37	Billy Williams	10.00

38	Tony Pierce	1.50	
39	Cookie Rojas	1.50	
40	Denny McLain	5.00	
41	Julio Gotay	1.50	
42	Larry Haney	1.50	
43	Gary Bell	1.50	
44	Frank Kostro	1.50	
45	Tom Seaver	125.00	
46	Dave Ricketts	1.50	
47	Ralph Houk	1.50	
48	Ted Davidson	1.50	
49a	Ed Brinkman (yellow team)	60.00	
49b	Ed Brinkman (white team)	1.50	
50	Willie Mays	100.00	
51	Bob Locker	1.50	
52	Hawk Taylor	1.50	
53	Gene Alley	1.50	
54	Stan Williams	1.50	
55	Felipe Alou	2.50	
56	Orioles Rookies (Dave Leonhard, Dave May)	1.50	
57	Dan Schneider	1.50	
58	Eddie Mathews	15.00	
59	Don Lock	1.50	
60	Ken Holtzman	1.50	
61	Reggie Smith	2.50	
62	Chuck Dobson	1.50	
63	Dick Kenworthy	1.50	
64	Jim Merritt	1.50	
65	John Roseboro	1.50	
66a	Casey Cox (yellow team)	60.00	
66b	Casey Cox (white team)	1.50	
67	Checklist 1-109 (Jim Kaat)	3.00	
68	Ron Willis	1.50	
69	Tom Tresh	2.50	
70	Bob Veale	1.50	
71	Vern Fuller	1.50	
72	Tommy John	5.00	
73	Jim Hart	1.50	
74	Milt Pappas	1.50	
75	Don Mincher	1.50	
76	Braves Rookies (Jim Britton, Ron Reed)	2.50	
77	*Don Wilson*	1.50	
78	Jim Northrup	1.50	
79	Ted Kubiak	1.50	
80	Rod Carew	75.00	
81	Larry Jackson	1.50	
82	Sam Bowens	1.50	
83	John Stephenson	1.50	
84	Bob Tolan	1.50	
85	Gaylord Perry	12.00	
86	Willie Stargell	12.00	
87	Dick Williams	2.00	
88	Phil Regan	1.50	
89	Jake Gibbs	1.50	
90	Vada Pinson	3.00	
91	Jim Ollom	1.50	
92	Ed Kranepool	1.50	
93	Tony Cloninger	1.50	
94	Lee Maye	1.50	
95	Bob Aspromonte	1.50	
96	Senators Rookies (Frank Coggins, Dick Nold)	1.50	
97	Tom Phoebus	1.50	
98	Gary Sutherland	1.50	
99	Rocky Colavito	10.00	
100	Bob Gibson	20.00	
101	Glenn Beckert	1.50	
102	Jose Cardenal	1.50	
103	Don Sutton	8.00	
104	Dick Dietz	1.50	
105	Al Downing	2.00	
106	Dalton Jones	1.50	
107	Checklist 110-196 (Juan Marichal)	3.50	
108	Don Pavletich	1.50	
109	Bert Campaneris	2.00	
110	Hank Aaron	100.00	
111	Rich Reese	1.50	
112	Woody Fryman	1.50	
113	Tigers Rookies (Tom Matchick, Daryl Patterson)	1.50	
114	Ron Swoboda	1.50	
115	Sam McDowell	1.50	
116	Ken McMullen	1.50	
117	Larry Jaster	1.50	
118	Mark Belanger	2.00	
119	Ted Savage	1.50	
120	Mel Stottlemyre	2.00	
121	Jimmie Hall	1.50	
122	Gene Mauch	1.50	
123	Jose Santiago	1.50	
124	Nate Oliver	1.50	
125	Joe Horlen	1.50	
126	Bobby Etheridge	1.50	
127	Paul Lindblad	1.50	
128	Astros Rookies (Tom Dukes, Alonzo Harris)	1.50	
129	Mickey Stanley	1.50	
130	Tony Perez	15.00	
131	Frank Bertaina	1.50	
132	Bud Harrelson	1.50	
133	Fred Whitfield	1.50	
134	Pat Jarvis	1.50	
135	Paul Blair	1.50	
136	Randy Hundley	1.50	
137	Twins Team	4.00	
138	Ruben Amaro	1.50	
139	Chris Short	1.50	
140	Tony Conigliaro	3.00	
141	Dal Maxvill	1.50	
142	White Sox Rookies (Buddy Bradford, Bill Voss)	1.50	
143	Pete Cimino	1.50	
144	Joe Morgan	15.00	
145	Don Drysdale	15.00	
146	Sal Bando	1.50	
147	Frank Linzy	1.50	
148	Dave Bristol	1.50	
149	Bob Saverine	1.50	
150	Roberto Clemente	75.00	
151	World Series Game 1 Brock Socks 4-Hits in Opener	4.00	
152	World Series Game 2 Yaz Smashes Two Homers	6.00	
153	World Series Game 3 Briles Cools Off Boston	3.00	
154	World Series Game 4 Gibson Hurls Shutout!	8.00	
155	World Series Game 5 Lonborg Wins Again!	3.00	
156	World Series Game 6 Petrocelli Socks Two Homers	3.00	
157	World Series Game 7 St. Louis Wins It!	3.00	
158	World Series Summary The Cardinals Celebrate!	3.00	
159	Don Kessinger	1.50	
160	Earl Wilson	1.50	
161	Norm Miller	1.50	
162	Cardinals Rookies (Hal Gilson, Mike Torrez)	2.00	
163	Gene Brabender	1.50	
164	Ramon Webster	1.50	
165	Tony Oliva	2.50	
166	Claude Raymond	1.50	
167	Elston Howard	2.50	
168	Dodgers Team	4.00	
169	Bob Bolin	1.50	
170	Jim Fregosi	2.00	
171	Don Nottebart	1.50	
172	Walt Williams	1.50	
173	John Boozer	1.50	
174	Bob Tillman	1.50	
175	Maury Wills	2.50	
176	Bob Allen	1.50	
177	Mets Rookies (*Jerry Koosman*, Nolan Ryan)	2300.00	
178	Don Wert	1.50	
179	Bill Stoneman	1.50	
180	Curt Flood	1.50	
181	Jerry Zimmerman	1.50	

182	Dave Giusti	1.50
183	Bob Kennedy	1.50
184	Lou Johnson	1.50
185	Tom Haller	1.50
186	Eddie Watt	1.50
187	Sonny Jackson	1.50
188	Cap Peterson	1.50
189	Bill Landis	1.50
190	Bill White	2.50
191	Dan Frisella	1.50
192a	Checklist 197-283 (Carl Yastrzemski) ("To increase the..." on back)	4.50
192b	Checklist 197-283 (Carl Yastrzemski) ("To increase your..." on back)	6.00
193	Jack Hamilton	1.50
194	Don Buford	1.50
195	Joe Pepitone	1.50
196	Gary Nolan	1.50
197	Larry Brown	1.50
198	Roy Face	1.50
199	A's Rookies (Darrell Osteen, Roberto Rodriguez)	1.50
200	Orlando Cepeda	4.00
201	*Mike Marshall*	3.00
202	Adolfo Phillips	1.50
203	Dick Kelley	1.50
204	Andy Etchebarren	1.50
205	Juan Marichal	8.00
206	Cal Ermer	1.50
207	Carroll Sembera	1.50
208	Willie Davis	1.50
209	Tim Cullen	1.50
210	Gary Peters	1.50
211	J.C. Martin	1.50
212	Dave Morehead	1.50
213	Chico Ruiz	1.50
214	Yankees Rookies (Stan Bahnsen, Frank Fernandez)	2.00
215	Jim Bunning	4.00
216	Bubba Morton	1.50
217	Turk Farrell	1.50
218	Ken Suarez	1.50
219	Rob Gardner	1.50
220	Harmon Killebrew	15.00
221	Braves Team	4.00
222	Jim Hardin	1.50
223	Ollie Brown	1.50
224	Jack Aker	1.50
225	Richie Allen	2.50
226	Jimmie Price	1.50
227	Joe Hoerner	1.50
228	Dodgers Rookies (*Jack Billingham*, Jim Fairey)	1.50
229	Fred Klages	1.50
230	Pete Rose	50.00
231	Dave Baldwin	1.50
232	Denis Menke	1.50
233	George Scott	1.50
234	Bill Monbouquette	1.50
235	Ron Santo	2.50
236	Tug McGraw	1.50
237	Alvin Dark	1.50
238	Tom Satriano	1.50
239	Bill Henry	1.50
240	Al Kaline	25.00
241	Felix Millan	1.50
242	Moe Drabowsky	1.50
243	Rich Rollins	1.50
244	John Donaldson	1.50
245	Tony Gonzalez	1.50
246	Fritz Peterson	1.50
247	Reds Rookies (*Johnny Bench*, Ron Tompkins)	250.00
248	Fred Valentine	1.50
249	Bill Singer	1.50
250	Carl Yastrzemski	30.00
251	*Manny Sanguillen*	1.50
252	Angels Team	4.00
253	Dick Hughes	1.50
254	Cleon Jones	1.50
255	Dean Chance	1.50
256	Norm Cash	3.00
257	Phil Niekro	5.00
258	Cubs Rookies (Jose Arcia, Bill Schlesinger)	2.50
259	Ken Boyer	3.00
260	Jim Wynn	1.50
261	Dave Duncan	1.50
262	Rick Wise	1.50
263	Horace Clarke	1.50
264	Ted Abernathy	1.50
265	Tommy Davis	1.50
266	Paul Popovich	1.50
267	Herman Franks	1.50
268	Bob Humphreys	1.50
269	Bob Tiefenauer	1.50
270	Matty Alou	1.50
271	Bobby Knoop	1.50
272	Ray Culp	1.50
273	Dave Johnson	1.50
274	Mike Cuellar	1.50
275	Tim McCarver	2.50
276	Jim Roland	1.50
277	Jerry Buchek	1.50
278a	Checklist 284-370 (Orlando Cepeda) (copyright at right)	3.00
278b	Checklist 284-370 (Orlando Cepeda) (copyright at left)	5.00
279	Bill Hands	1.50
280	Mickey Mantle	300.00
281	Jim Campanis	1.50
282	Rick Monday	1.50
283	Mel Queen	1.50
284	John Briggs	1.50
285	Dick McAuliffe	1.50
286	Cecil Upshaw	1.50
287	White Sox Rookies (Mickey Abarbanel, Cisco Carlos)	1.50
288	Dave Wickersham	1.50
289	Woody Held	1.50
290	Willie McCovey	15.00
291	Dick Lines	1.50
292	Art Shamsky	1.50
293	Bruce Howard	1.50
294	Red Schoendienst	4.00
295	Sonny Siebert	1.50
296	Byron Browne	1.50
297	Russ Gibson	1.50
298	Jim Brewer	1.50
299	Gene Michael	1.50
300	Rusty Staub	2.00
301	Twins Rookies (George Mitterwald, Rick Renick)	1.50
302	Gerry Arrigo	1.50
303	Dick Green	1.50
304	Sandy Valdespino	1.50
305	Minnie Rojas	1.50
306	Mike Ryan	1.50
307	John Hiller	1.50
308	Pirates Team	4.00
309	Ken Henderson	1.50
310	Luis Aparicio	5.00
311	Jack Lamabe	1.50
312	Curt Blefary	1.50
313	Al Weis	1.50
314	Red Sox Rookies (Bill Rohr, George Spriggs)	1.50
315	Zoilo Versalles	1.50
316	Steve Barber	1.50
317	Ron Brand	1.50
318	Chico Salmon	1.50
319	George Culver	1.50
320	Frank Howard	2.50
321	Leo Durocher	2.25
322	Dave Boswell	1.50
323	Deron Johnson	1.50

324	Jim Nash	1.50		397	Vic Davalillo	1.50
325	Manny Mota	1.50		398	Jim Grant	1.50
326	Dennis Ribant	1.50		399	Ray Oyler	1.50
327	Tony Taylor	1.50		400a	Mike McCormick (white team)	40.00
328	Angels Rookies (Chuck Vinson, Jim Weaver)	1.50		400b	Mike McCormick (yellow team)	1.50
329	Duane Josephson	1.50		401	Mets Team	4.50
330	Roger Maris	40.00		402	Mike Hegan	1.50
331	Dan Osinski	1.50		403	John Buzhardt	1.50
332	Doug Rader	1.50		404	Floyd Robinson	1.50
333	Ron Herbel	1.50		405	Tommy Helms	1.50
334	Orioles Team	4.00		406	Dick Ellsworth	1.50
335	Bob Allison	1.50		407	Gary Kolb	1.50
336	John Purdin	1.50		408	Steve Carlton	50.00
337	Bill Robinson	1.50		409	Orioles Rookies (Frank Peters, Ron Stone)	1.50
338	Bob Johnson	1.50		410	Fergie Jenkins	20.00
339	Rich Nye	1.50		411	Ron Hansen	1.50
340	Max Alvis	1.50		412	Clay Carroll	1.50
341	Jim Lemon	1.50		413	Tommy McCraw	1.50
342	Ken Johnson	1.50		414	Mickey Lolich	2.75
343	Jim Gosger	1.50		415	Johnny Callison	1.50
344	Donn Clendenon	1.50		416	Bill Rigney	1.50
345	Bob Hendley	1.50		417	Willie Crawford	1.50
346	Jerry Adair	1.50		418	Eddie Fisher	1.50
347	George Brunet	1.50		419	Jack Hiatt	1.50
348	Phillies Rookies (Larry Colton, Dick Thoenen)	1.50		420	Cesar Tovar	1.50
349	Ed Spiezio	1.50		421	Ron Taylor	1.50
350	Hoyt Wilhelm	6.00		422	Rene Lachemann	1.50
351	Bob Barton	1.50		423	Fred Gladding	1.50
352	Jackie Hernandez	1.50		424	White Sox Team	4.00
353	Mack Jones	1.50		425	Jim Maloney	1.50
354	Pete Richert	1.50		426	Hank Allen	1.50
355	Ernie Banks	30.00		427	Dick Calmus	1.50
356	Checklist 371-457 (Ken Holtzman)	3.00		428	Vic Roznovsky	1.50
357	Len Gabrielson	1.50		429	Tommie Sisk	1.50
358	Mike Epstein	1.50		430	Rico Petrocelli	1.50
359	Joe Moeller	1.50		431	Dooley Womack	1.50
360	Willie Horton	1.50		432	Indians Rookies (Bill Davis, Jose Vidal)	1.50
361	Harmon Killebrew (All-Star)	10.00		433	Bob Rodgers	1.50
362	Orlando Cepeda (All-Star)	4.00		434	Ricardo Joseph	1.50
363	Rod Carew (All-Star)	10.00		435	Ron Perranoski	1.50
364	Joe Morgan (All-Star)	7.00		436	Hal Lanier	1.50
365	Brooks Robinson (All-Star)	10.00		437	Don Cardwell	1.50
366	Ron Santo (All-Star)	4.00		438	Lee Thomas	1.50
367	Jim Fregosi (All-Star)	4.00		439	Luman Harris	1.50
368	Gene Alley (All-Star)	4.00		440	Claude Osteen	1.50
369	Carl Yastrzemski (All-Star)	10.00		441	Alex Johnson	1.50
370	Hank Aaron (All-Star)	17.00		442	Dick Bosman	1.50
371	Tony Oliva (All-Star)	4.00		443	Joe Azcue	1.50
372	Lou Brock (All-Star)	10.00		444	Jack Fisher	1.50
373	Frank Robinson (All-Star)	10.00		445	Mike Shannon	1.50
374	Roberto Clemente (All-Star)	20.00		446	Ron Kline	1.50
375	Bill Freehan (All-Star)	4.00		447	Tigers Rookies (George Korince, Fred Lasher)	1.50
376	Tim McCarver (All-Star)	4.00		448	Gary Wagner	1.50
377	Joe Horlen (All-Star)	4.00		449	Gene Oliver	1.50
378	Bob Gibson (All-Star)	10.00		450	Jim Kaat	6.00
379	Gary Peters (All-Star)	4.00		451	Al Spangler	1.50
380	Ken Holtzman (All-Star)	4.00		452	Jesus Alou	1.50
381	Boog Powell	4.00		453	Sammy Ellis	1.50
382	Ramon Hernandez	1.50		454	Checklist 458-533 (Frank Robinson)	4.00
383	Steve Whitaker	1.50		455	Rico Carty	1.50
384	Red Rookies (Bill Henry, Hal McRae)	18.00		456	John O'Donoghue	1.50
385	Catfish Hunter	15.00		457	Jim Lefebvre	1.50
386	Greg Goossen	1.50		458	Lew Krausse	2.50
387	Joe Foy	1.50		459	Dick Simpson	2.50
388	Ray Washburn	1.50		460	Jim Lonborg	2.50
389	Jay Johnstone	1.50		461	Chuck Hiller	2.50
390	Bill Mazeroski	4.00		462	Barry Moore	2.50
391	Bob Priddy	1.50		463	Jimmie Schaffer	2.50
392	Grady Hatton	1.50		464	Don McMahon	2.50
393	Jim Perry	1.50		465	Tommie Agee	2.50
394	Tommie Aaron	1.50		466	Bill Dillman	2.50
395	Camilo Pascual	1.50		467	Dick Howser	2.50
396	Bobby Wine	1.50		468	Larry Sherry	2.50

469	Ty Cline	2.50
470	Bill Freehan	2.50
471	Orlando Pena	2.50
472	Walt Alston	4.00
473	Al Worthington	2.50
474	Paul Schaal	2.50
475	Joe Niekro	2.50
476	Woody Woodward	2.50
477	Phillies Team	4.00
478	Dave McNally	2.50
479	Phil Gagliano	2.50
480	Manager's Dream (Chico Cardenas, Roberto Clemente, Tony Oliva)	50.00
481	John Wyatt	2.50
482	Jose Pagan	2.50
483	Darold Knowles	2.50
484	Phil Roof	2.50
485	Ken Berry	2.50
486	Cal Koonce	2.50
487	Lee May	2.50
488	Dick Tracewski	2.50
489	Wally Bunker	2.50
490	Super Stars (Harmon Killebrew, Mickey Mantle, Willie Mays)	150.00
491	Denny Lemaster	2.50
492	Jeff Torborg	2.50
493	Jim McGlothlin	2.50
494	Ray Sadecki	2.50
495	Leon Wagner	2.50
496	Steve Hamilton	2.50
497	Cards Team	4.00
498	Bill Bryan	2.50
499	Steve Blass	2.50
500	Frank Robinson	30.00
501	John Odom	2.50
502	Mike Andrews	2.50
503	Al Jackson	2.50
504	Russ Snyder	2.50
505	Joe Sparma	2.50
506	Clarence Jones	2.50
507	Wade Blasingame	2.50
508	Duke Sims	2.50
509	Dennis Higgins	2.50
510	Ron Fairly	2.50
511	Bill Kelso	2.50
512	Grant Jackson	2.50
513	Hank Bauer	2.50
514	Al McBean	2.50
515	Russ Nixon	2.50
516	Pete Mikkelsen	2.50
517	Diego Segui	2.50
518a	Checklist 534-598 (Clete Boyer) (539 is Maj. L. Rookies)	3.00
518b	Checklist 534-598 (Clete Boyer) (539 is Amer. L.Rookies)	5.00
519	Jerry Stephenson	2.50
520	Lou Brock	30.00
521	Don Shaw	2.50
522	Wayne Causey	2.50
523	John Tsitouris	2.50
524	Andy Kosco	2.50
525	Jim Davenport	2.50
526	Bill Denehy	2.50
527	Tito Francona	2.50
528	Tigers Team	100.00
529	Bruce Von Hoff	2.50
530	Bird Belters (Brooks Robinson, Frank Robinson)	20.00
531	Chuck Hinton	2.50
532	Luis Tiant	2.50
533	Wes Parker	2.50
534	Bob Miller	4.00
535	Danny Cater	4.00
536	Bill Short	4.00
537	Norm Siebern	4.00

538	Manny Jimenez	4.00
539	Major League Rookies (Mike Ferraro, Jim Ray)	4.00
540	Nelson Briles	4.00
541	Sandy Alomar	4.00
542	John Boccabella	4.00
543	Bob Lee	4.00
544	Mayo Smith	4.00
545	Lindy McDaniel	4.00
546	Roy White	4.00
547	Dan Coombs	4.00
548	Bernie Allen	4.00
549	Orioles Rookies (Curt Motton, Roger Nelson)	4.00
550	Clete Boyer	4.00
551	Darrell Sutherland	4.00
552	Ed Kirkpatrick	4.00
553	Hank Aguirre	4.00
554	A's Team	8.00
555	Jose Tartabull	4.00
556	Dick Selma	4.00
557	Frank Quilici	4.00
558	John Edwards	4.00
559	Pirates Rookies (Carl Taylor, Luke Walker)	4.00
560	Paul Casanova	4.00
561	Lee Elia	4.00
562	Jim Bouton	4.00
563	Ed Charles	4.00
564	Eddie Stanky	4.00
565	Larry Dierker	4.00
566	Ken Harrelson	4.00
567	Clay Dalrymple	4.00
568	Willie Smith	4.00
569	N.L. Rookies (Ivan Murrell, Les Rohr)	4.00
570	Rick Reichardt	4.00
571	Tony LaRussa	4.00
572	Don Bosch	4.00
573	Joe Coleman	4.00
574	Reds Team	8.00
575	Jim Palmer	55.00
576	Dave Adlesh	4.00
577	Fred Talbot	4.00
578	Orlando Martinez	4.00
579	N.L. Rookies (*Larry Hisle*, Mike Lum)	4.00
580	Bob Bailey	4.00
581	Garry Roggenburk	4.00
582	Jerry Grote	4.00
583	Gates Brown	4.00
584	Larry Shepard	4.00
585	Wilbur Wood	4.00
586	Jim Pagliaroni	4.00
587	Roger Repoz	4.00
588	Dick Schofield	4.00
589	Twins Rookies (Ron Clark, Moe Ogier)	4.00
590	Tommy Harper	4.00
591	Dick Nen	4.00
592	John Bateman	4.00
593	Lee Stange	4.00
594	Phil Linz	4.00
595	Phil Ortega	4.00
596	Charlie Smith	4.00
597	Bill McCool	4.00
598	Jerry May	15.00

1969 Topps

The 1969 Topps set broke yet another record for quantity as the issue is officially a whopping 664 cards. With substantial numbers of variations, the number of possible cards runs closer to 700. The design of the 2-1/2" by 3-1/2" cards in the set feature a color photo with the team name printed in block letters underneath. A circle contains the player's name and position. Card backs returned to a horizontal format. Despite the size of the set, it contains no team cards. It does, however, have multi-player cards, All-Stars, statistical leaders, and World Series highlights. Most significant among the varieties are white and yellow letter cards from the run of #'s 440-511. The complete set prices below do not include the scarcer and more expensive "white letter" variations.

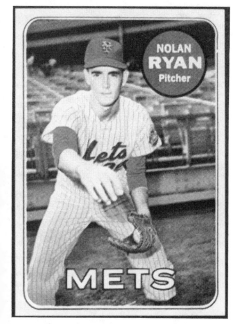

Mr. Mint Says - A lot of people buy the 69s. It is a relatively popular set, with some nice rookie cards and the last Mantle card. I have purchased large amounts of vendor cases from 1969, and the cards are easy to obtain in mint condition, but you must watch the centering.

I don't really believe in 1969 Topps high numbers and many guides agree with that assessment.

The last Mantle card is really neat, though it often turns up with a little printing flaw in the lefthand border. Turn it over and it has every year of his statistics. I think it is a good card, very affordable and a good investment. Eventually, that will be a $500 card.

Most, but not all, of the other stars in this set are slightly overpriced. Still, the Brock is virtually impossible and is the toughest card in the set to find centered, and the Carlton and Mays cards are sneaky tough. The Mantle and the Jackson rookie are the keys, and the Jackson card is now a $500 item, at best. Reggie's rookie is only rarely found with perfect centering. Ryan always sells between $600 and $800, and Bobby Bonds always attracts a lot of attention as well. The white-letter variations are interesting, and one of the most collectable variations from this period. I have consistently been getting between $800 to $1,000 for the white-letter Mantle.

		MT
Complete Set (664):		3500.
Common Player (1-218):		1.00
Common Player (219-327):		1.50
Common Player (328-512):		1.00
Common Player (513-588):		1.50
Common Player (589-664):		2.50
1	A.L. Batting Leaders (Danny Cater, Tony Oliva, Carl Yastrzemski)	10.00
2	N.L. Batting Leaders (Felipe Alou, Matty Alou, Pete Rose)	6.00
3	A.L. RBI Leaders (Ken Harrelson, Frank Howard, Jim Northrup)	2.00
4	N.L. RBI Leaders (Willie McCovey, Ron Santo, Billy Williams)	4.00
5	A.L. Home Run Leaders (Ken Harrelson, Willie Horton, Frank Howard)	2.00
6	N.L. Home Run Leaders (Richie Allen, Ernie Banks, Willie McCovey)	4.00
7	A.L. ERA Leaders (Sam McDowell, Dave McNally, Luis Tiant)	2.00
8	N.L. ERA Leaders (Bobby Bolin, Bob Gibson, Bob Veale)	3.00
9	A.L. Pitching Leaders (Denny McLain, Dave McNally, Mel Stottlemyre, Luis Tiant)	2.50
10	N.L. Pitching Leaders (Bob Gibson, Fergie Jenkins, Juan Marichal)	3.50
11	A.L. Strikeout Leaders (Sam McDowell, Denny McLain, Luis Tiant)	2.50
12	N.L. Strikeout Leaders (Bob Gibson, Fergie Jenkins, Bill Singer)	3.00
13	Mickey Stanley	1.00
14	Al McBean	1.00
15	Boog Powell	2.00
16	Giants Rookies (Cesar Gutierrez, Rich Robertson)	1.00
17	Mike Marshall	1.00
18	Dick Schofield	1.00
19	Ken Suarez	1.00
20	Ernie Banks	20.00
21	Jose Santiago	1.00
22	Jesus Alou	1.00
23	Lew Krausse	1.00
24	Walt Alston	3.00

25	Roy White	1.00
26	Clay Carroll	1.00
27	Bernie Allen	1.00
28	Mike Ryan	1.00
29	Dave Morehead	1.00
30	Bob Allison	1.00
31	Mets Rookies (*Gary Gentry*, Amos Otis)	1.50
32	Sammy Ellis	1.00
33	Wayne Causey	1.00
34	Gary Peters	1.00
35	Joe Morgan	12.00
36	Luke Walker	1.00
37	Curt Motton	1.00
38	Zoilo Versalles	1.00
39	Dick Hughes	1.00
40	Mayo Smith	1.00
41	Bob Barton	1.00
42	Tommy Harper	1.00
43	Joe Niekro	1.50
44	Danny Cater	1.00
45	Maury Wills	2.00
46	Fritz Peterson	1.00
47a	Paul Popovich (emblem visible thru airbrush)	4.00
47b	Paul Popovich (helmet emblem completely airbrushed)	1.00
48	Brant Alyea	1.00
49a	Royals Rookies (Steve Jones) (Rodriquez on front)	6.00
49a	Royals Rookies (Eliseo Rodriquez) (Rodriquez on front)	6.00
49b	Royals Rookies (Steve Jones) (Rodriquez on front)	1.00
49b	Royals Rookies (Eliseo Rodriquez) (Rodriguez on front)	1.00
50	Roberto Clemente	45.00
51	Woody Fryman	1.00
52	Mike Andrews	1.00
53	Sonny Jackson	1.00
54	Cisco Carlos	1.00
55	Jerry Grote	1.00
56	Rich Reese	1.00
57	Checklist 1-109 (Denny McLain)	3.00
58	Fred Gladding	1.00
59	Jay Johnstone	1.00
60	Nelson Briles	1.00
61	Jimmie Hall	1.00
62	Chico Salmon	1.00
63	Jim Hickman	1.00
64	Bill Monbouquette	1.00
65	Willie Davis	1.00
66	Orioles Rookies (Mike Adamson, Merv Rettenmund)	1.00
67	Bill Stoneman	1.00
68	Dave Duncan	1.00
69	Steve Hamilton	1.00
70	Tommy Helms	1.00
71	Steve Whitaker	1.00
72	Ron Taylor	1.00
73	Johnny Briggs	1.00
74	Preston Gomez	1.00
75	Luis Aparicio	5.00
76	Norm Miller	1.00
77a	Ron Perranoski (LA visible thru airbrush)	4.50
77b	Ron Perranoski (cap emblem completely airbrushed)	1.00
78	Tom Satriano	1.00
79	Milt Pappas	1.00
80	Norm Cash	1.75
81	Mel Queen	1.00
82	Pirates Rookies (*Rich Hebner*, Al Oliver)	12.00
83	Mike Ferraro	1.00
84	Bob Humphreys	1.00
85	Lou Brock	50.00
86	Pete Richert	1.00
87	Horace Clarke	1.00
88	Rich Nye	1.00
89	Russ Gibson	1.00
90	Jerry Koosman	2.00
91	Al Dark	1.00
92	Jack Billingham	1.00
93	Joe Foy	1.00
94	Hank Aguirre	1.00
95	Johnny Bench	100.00
96	Denver Lemaster	1.00
97	Buddy Bradford	1.00
98	Dave Giusti	1.00
99a	Twins Rookies (Danny Morris) (black loop above "Twins")	20.00
99a	Twins Rookies (*Graig Nettles*) (black loop above "Twins")	20.00
99b	Twins Rookies (Danny Morris) (no black loop)	20.00
99b	*Graig Nettles*	20.00
100	Hank Aaron	65.00
101	Daryl Patterson	1.00
102	Jim Davenport	1.00
103	Roger Repoz	1.00
104	Steve Blass	1.00
105	Rick Monday	1.00
106	Jim Hannan	1.00
107a	Checklist 110-218 (Bob Gibson) (161 is Jim Purdin)	3.00
107b	Checklist 110-218 (Bob gibson) (161 is John Purdin)	6.00
108	Tony Taylor	1.00
109	Jim Lonborg	1.25
110	Mike Shannon	1.00
111	Johnny Morris	1.00
112	J.C. Martin	1.00
113	Dave May	1.00
114	Yankees Rookies (Alan Closter, John Cumberland)	1.00
115	Bill Hands	1.00
116	Chuck Harrison	1.00
117	Jim Fairey	1.00
118	Stan Williams	1.00
119	Doug Rader	1.00
120	Pete Rose	45.00
121	Joe Grzenda	1.00
122	Ron Fairly	1.00
123	Wilbur Wood	1.25
124	Hank Bauer	1.00
125	Ray Sadecki	1.00
126	Dick Tracewski	1.00
127	Kevin Collins	1.00
128	Tommie Aaron	1.00
129	Bill McCool	1.00
130	Carl Yastrzemski	35.00
131	Chris Cannizzaro	1.00
132	Dave Baldwin	1.00
133	Johnny Callison	1.00
134	Jim Weaver	1.00
135	Tommy Davis	1.00
136	Cards Rookies (Steve Huntz, Mike Torrez)	1.00
137	Wally Bunker	1.00
138	John Bateman	1.00
139	Andy Kosco	1.00
140	Jim Lefebvre	1.00
141	Bill Dillman	1.00
142	Woody Woodward	1.00
143	Joe Nossek	1.00
144	Bob Hendley	1.00
145	Max Alvis	1.00
146	Jim Perry	1.00
147	Leo Durocher	2.00
148	Lee Stange	1.00
149	Ollie Brown	1.00
150	Denny McLain	2.00
151a	Clay Dalrymple (Phillies)	9.00
151b	Clay Dalrymple (Orioles)	1.00
152	Tommie Sisk	1.00
153	Ed Brinkman	1.00
154	Jim Britton	1.00
155	Pete Ward	1.00
156	Astros Rookies (Hal Gilson, Leon McFadden)	1.00
157	Bob Rodgers	1.00

158	Joe Gibbon	1.00
159	Jerry Adair	1.00
160	Vada Pinson	2.00
161	John Purdin	1.00
162	World Series Game 1 (Gibson Fans 17; Sets New Record)	4.00
163	World Series Game 2 (Tiger Homers Deck The Cards)	3.00
164	World Series Game 3 (McCarver's Homer Puts St. Louis Ahead)	3.50
165	World Series Game 4 (Brock's Lead-Off HR Starts Cards' Romp)	3.50
166	World Series Game 5 (Kaline's Key Hit Sparks Tiger Rally)	4.00
167	World Series Game 6 (Tiger 10-Run Inning Ties Mark)	3.50
168	World Series Game 7 (Lolich Series Hero Outduels Gibson)	3.50
169	World Series Summary (Tigers Celebrate Their Victory)	3.50
170	Frank Howard	1.50
171	Glenn Beckert	1.00
172	Jerry Stephenson	1.00
173	White Sox Rookies (Bob Christian, Gerry Nyman)	1.00
174	Grant Jackson	1.00
175	Jim Bunning	4.00
176	Joe Azcue	1.00
177	Ron Reed	1.00
178	Ray Oyler	1.00
179	Don Pavletich	1.00
180	Willie Horton	1.00
181	Mel Nelson	1.00
182	Bill Rigney	1.00
183	Don Shaw	1.00
184	Roberto Pena	1.00
185	Tom Phoebus	1.00
186	John Edwards	1.00
187	Leon Wagner	1.00
188	Rick Wise	1.00
189	Red Sox Rookies (Joe Lahoud, John Thibdeau)	1.00
190	Willie Mays	75.00
191	Lindy McDaniel	1.00
192	Jose Pagan	1.00
193	Don Cardwell	1.00
194	Ted Uhlaender	1.00
195	John Odom	1.00
196	Lum Harris	1.00
197	Dick Selma	1.00
198	Willie Smith	1.00
199	Jim French	1.00
200	Bob Gibson	12.50
201	Russ Snyder	1.00
202	Don Wilson	1.00
203	Dave Johnson	
204	Jack Hiatt	
205	Rick Reichardt	1.00
206	Phillies Rookies (Larry Hisle, Barry Lersch)	1.00
207	Roy Face	1.00
208a	Donn Clendenon (Expos)	7.00
208b	Donn Clendenon (Houston)	1.00
209	Larry Haney (photo reversed)	1.00
210	Felix Millan	1.00
211	Galen Cisco	1.00
212	Tom Tresh	1.50
213	Gerry Arrigo	1.00
214	Checklist 219-327	2.50
215	Rico Petrocelli	1.25
216	Don Sutton	4.00
217	John Donaldson	1.00
218	John Roseboro	1.00
219	*Freddie Patek*	2.00
220	Sam McDowell	1.50
221	Art Shamsky	1.50
222	Duane Josephson	1.50
223	Tom Dukes	1.50
224	Angels Rookies (Bill Harrelson, Steve Kealey)	1.50
225	Don Kessinger	1.50
226	Bruce Howard	1.50
227	Frank Johnson	1.50
228	Dave Leonhard	1.50
229	Don Lock	1.50
230	Rusty Staub	2.50
231	Pat Dobson	1.50
232	Dave Ricketts	1.50
233	Steve Barber	1.50
234	Dave Bristol	1.50
235	Catfish Hunter	10.00
236	Manny Mota	1.50
237	*Bobby Cox*	1.50
238	Ken Johnson	1.50
239	Bob Taylor	1.50
240	Ken Harrelson	2.00
241	Jim Brewer	1.50
242	Frank Kostro	1.50
243	Ron Kline	1.50
244	Indians Rookies (*Ray Fosse*, George Woodson)	1.50
245	Ed Charles	1.50
246	Joe Coleman	1.50
247	Gene Oliver	1.50
248	Bob Priddy	1.50
249	Ed Spiezio	1.50
250	Frank Robinson	50.00
251	Ron Herbel	1.50
252	Chuck Cottier	1.50
253	Jerry Johnson	1.50
254	Joe Schultz	1.50
255	Steve Carlton	75.00
256	Gates Brown	1.50
257	Jim Ray	1.50
258	Jackie Hernandez	1.50
259	Bill Short	1.50
260	*Reggie Jackson*	500.00
261	Bob Johnson	1.50
262	Mike Kekich	1.50
263	Jerry May	1.50
264	Bill Landis	1.50
265	Chico Cardenas	1.50
266	Dodgers Rookies (Alan Foster, Tom Hutton)	1.50
267	Vicente Romo	1.50
268	Al Spangler	1.50
269	Al Weis	1.50
270	Mickey Lolich	3.50
271	Larry Stahl	1.50
272	Ed Stroud	1.50
273	Ron Willis	1.50
274	Clyde King	1.50
275	Vic Davalillo	1.50
276	Gary Wagner	1.50
277	*Rod Hendricks*	1.50
278	Gary Geiger	1.50
279	Roger Nelson	1.50
280	Alex Johnson	1.50
281	Ted Kubiak	1.50
282	Pat Jarvis	1.50
283	Sandy Alomar	1.50
284	Expos Rookies (Jerry Robertson, Mike Wegener)	1.50
285	Don Mincher	1.50
286	*Dock Ellis*	1.50
287	Jose Tartabull	1.50
288	Ken Holtzman	1.50
289	Bart Shirley	1.50
290	Jim Kaat	4.50
291	Vern Fuller	1.50
292	Al Downing	1.50
293	Dick Dietz	1.50
294	Jim Lemon	1.50
295	Tony Perez	10.00
296	*Andy Messersmith*	1.50

297	Deron Johnson	1.50
298	Dave Nicholson	1.50
299	Mark Belanger	1.50
300	Felipe Alou	2.50
301	Darrell Brandon	1.50
302	Jim Pagliaroni	1.50
303	Cal Koonce	1.50
304	Padres Rookies (Bill Davis, Cito Gaston	15.00
305	Dick McAuliffe	1.50
306	Jim Grant	1.50
307	Gary Kolb	1.50
308	Wade Blasingame	1.50
309	Walt Williams	1.50
310	Tom Haller	1.50
311	*Sparky Lyle*	10.00
312	Lee Elia	1.50
313	Bill Robinson	1.50
314	Checklist 328-425 (Don Drysdale)	3.50
315	Eddie Fisher	1.50
316	Hal Lanier	1.50
317	Bruce Look	1.50
318	Jack Fisher	1.50
319	Ken McMullen	1.50
320	Dal Maxvill	1.50
321	Jim McAndrew	1.50
322	Jose Vidal	1.50
323	Larry Miller	1.50
324	Tigers Rookies (Les Cain, Dave Campbell)	1.50
325	Jose Cardenal	1.50
326	Gary Sutherland	1.50
327	Willie Crawford	1.50
328	Joe Horlen	1.00
329	Rick Joseph	1.00
330	Tony Conigliaro	1.50
331	Braves Rookies (Gil Garrido, Tom House)	1.00
332	Fred Talbot	1.00
333	Ivan Murrell	1.00
334	Phil Roof	1.00
335	Bill Mazeroski	2.50
336	Jim Roland	1.00
337	Marty Martinez	1.00
338	*Del Unser*	1.00
339	Reds Rookies (Steve Mingori, Jose Pena)	1.00
340	Dave McNally	1.00
341	Dave Adlesh	1.00
342	Bubba Morton	1.00
343	Dan Frisella	1.00
344	Tom Matchick	1.00
345	Frank Linzy	1.00
346	Wayne Comer	1.00
347	Randy Hundley	1.00
348	Steve Hargan	1.00
349	Dick Williams	1.25
350	Richie Allen	2.00
351	Carroll Sembera	1.00
352	Paul Schaal	1.00
353	Jeff Torborg	1.00
354	Nate Oliver	1.00
355	Phil Niekro	7.00
356	Frank Quilici	1.00
357	Carl Taylor	1.00
358	Athletics Rookies (George Lauzerique, Roberto Rodriguez)	1.00
359	Dick Kelley	1.00
360	Jim Wynn	1.00
361	Gary Holman	1.00
362	Jim Maloney	1.00
363	Russ Nixon	1.00
364	Tommie Agee	1.00
365	Jim Fregosi	1.00
366	Bo Belinsky	1.00
367	Lou Johnson	1.00
368	Vic Roznovsky	1.00
369	Bob Skinner	1.00
370	Juan Marichal	7.00
371	Sal Bando	1.25
372	Adolfo Phillips	1.00
373	Fred Lasher	1.00
374	Bob Tillman	1.00
375	Harmon Killebrew	20.00
376	Royals Rookies (Mike Fiore, Jim Rooker)	1.00
377	Gary Bell	1.00
378	Jose Herrera	1.00
379	Ken Boyer	1.50
380	Stan Bahnsen	1.00
381	Ed Kranepool	1.00
382	Pat Corrales	1.00
383	Casey Cox	1.00
384	Larry Shepard	1.00
385	Orlando Cepeda	4.00
386	Jim McGlothlin	1.00
387	Bobby Klaus	1.00
388	Tom McCraw	1.00
389	Dan Coombs	1.00
390	Bill Freehan	1.00
391	Ray Culp	1.00
392	Bob Burda	1.00
393	Gene Brabender	1.00
394	Pilots Rookies (*Lou Piniella*, Marv Staehle)	2.00
395	Chris Short	1.00
396	Jim Campanis	1.00
397	Chuck Dobson	1.00
398	Tito Francona	1.00
399	Bob Bailey	1.00
400	Don Drysdale	10.00
401	Jake Gibbs	1.00
402	Ken Boswell	1.00
403	Bob Miller	1.00
404	Cubs Rookies (Vic LaRose, Gary Ross)	1.00
405	Lee May	1.00
406	Phil Ortega	1.00
407	Tom Egan	1.00
408	Nate Colbert	1.00
409	Bob Moose	1.00
410	Al Kaline	25.00
411	Larry Dierker	1.00
412	Checklist 426-512 (Mickey Mantle)	9.00
413	Roland Sheldon	1.00
414	Duke Sims	1.00
415	Ray Washburn	1.00
416	Willie McCovey (All-Star)	3.50
417	Ken Harrelson (All-Star)	1.00
418	Tommy Helms (All-Star)	1.00
419	Rod Carew (All-Star)	8.00
420	Ron Santo (All-Star)	1.50
421	Brooks Robinson (All-Star)	4.00
422	Don Kessinger (All-Star)	1.00
423	Bert Campaneris (All-Star)	1.00
424	Pete Rose (All-Star)	12.00
425	Carl Yastrzemski (All-Star)	10.00
426	Curt Flood (All-Star)	1.00
427	Tony Oliva (All-Star)	1.50
428	Lou Brock (All-Star)	5.00
429	Willie Horton (All-Star)	1.00
430	Johnny Bench (All-Star)	12.00
431	Bill Freehan (All-Star)	1.00
432	Bob Gibson (All-Star)	5.00
433	Denny McLain (All-Star)	1.50
434	Jerry Koosman (All-Star)	1.00
435	Sam McDowell (All-Star)	1.00
436	Gene Alley	1.00
437	Luis Alcaraz	1.00
438	Gary Waslewski	1.00
439	White Sox Rookies (Ed Herrmann, Dan Lazar)	1.00
440a	Willie McCovey (last name in white)	150.00
440b	Willie McCovey (last name in yellow)	18.00
441a	Dennis Higgins (last name in white)	35.00

441b Dennis Higgins (last name in yellow)	1.00
442 Ty Cline	1.00
443 Don Wert	1.00
444a Joe Moeller (last name in white)	35.00
444b Joe Moeller (last name in yellow)	1.00
445 Bobby Knoop	1.00
446 Claude Raymond	1.00
447a Ralph Houk (last name in white)	35.00
447b Ralph Houk (last name in yellow)	1.50
448 Bob Tolan	1.00
449 Paul Lindblad	1.00
450 Billy Williams	6.00
451a Rich Rollins (first name in white)	35.00
451b Rich Rollins (first name in yellow)	1.25
452a Al Ferrara (first name in white)	35.00
452b Al Ferrara (first name in yellow)	1.00
453 Mike Cuellar	1.00
454a Phillies Rookies (Larry Colton) (names in white)	35.00
454a Phillies Rookies (*Don Money*) (names in white)	35.00
454b Phillies Rookies (Larry Colton) (names in yellow)	1.25
454b Phillies Rookies (*Don Money*) (names in yellow)	1.25
455 Sonny Siebert	1.00
456 Bud Harrelson	1.00
457 Dalton Jones	1.00
458 Curt Blefary	1.00
459 Dave Boswell	1.00
460 Joe Torre	1.00
461a Mike Epstein (last name in white)	35.00
461b Mike Epstein (last name in yellow)	1.00
462 Red Schoendienst	3.00
463 Dennis Ribant	1.00
464a Dave Marshall (last name in white)	35.00
464b Dave Marshall (last name in yellow)	1.00
465 Tommy John	4.00
466 John Boccabella	1.00
467 Tom Reynolds	1.00
468a Pirates Rookies (Bruce Dal Canton) (names in white)	35.00
468a Pirates Rookies (Bob Robertson) (names in white)	35.00
468b Pirates Rookies (Bruce Dal Canton) (names in yellow)	1.00
468b Pirates Rookies (Bob Robertson) (names in yellow)	1.00
469 Chico Ruiz	1.00
470a Mel Stottlemyre (last name in white)	40.00
470b Mel Stottlemyre (last name in yellow)	1.50
471a Ted Savage (last name in white)	35.00
471b Ted Savage (last name in yellow)	1.00
472 Jim Price	1.00
473a Jose Arcia (first name in white)	35.00
473b Jose Arcia (first name in yellow)	1.00
474 Tom Murphy	1.00
475 Tim McCarver	1.50
476a Red Sox Rookies (*Ken Brett*) (names in white)	35.00
476a Red Sox Rookies (Gerry Moses) (names in white)	35.00
476b Red Sox Rookies (*Ken Brett*) (names in yellow)	1.00
476b Red Sox Rookies (Gerry Moses) (names in yellow)	1.00
477 Jeff James	1.00
478 Don Buford	1.00
479 Richie Scheinblum	1.00
480 Tom Seaver	95.00
481 *Bill Melton*	1.25
482a Jim Gosger (first name in white)	35.00
482b Jim Gosger (first name in yellow)	1.25
483 Ted Abernathy	1.00
484 Joe Gordon	1.00
485a Gaylord Perry (last name in white)	100.00
485b Gaylord Perry (last name in yellow)	10.00
486a Paul Casanova (last name in white)	35.00
486b Paul Casanova (last name in yellow)	1.00
487 Denis Menke	1.00
488 Joe Sparma	1.00
489 Clete Boyer	1.00
490 Matty Alou	1.00
491a Twins Rookies (Jerry Crider) (names in white)	35.00
491a Twins Rookies (George Mitterwald) (names in white)	35.00
491b Twins Rookies (Jerry Crider) (names in yellow)	1.00
491b Twins Rookies (George Mitterwald) (names in yellow)	1.00
492 Tony Cloninger	1.00
493a Wes Parker (last name in white)	35.00
493b Wes Parker (last name in yellow)	1.00
494 Ken Berry	1.00
495 Bert Campaneris	1.00
496 Larry Jaster	1.00
497 Julian Javier	1.00
498 Juan Pizarro	1.00
499 Astros Rookies (Don Bryant, Steve Shea)	1.00
500a Mickey Mantle (last name in white)	1000.00
500b Mickey Mantle (last name in yellow)	300.00
501a Tony Gonzalez (first name in white)	35.00
501b Tony Gonzalez (first name in yellow)	1.00
502 Minnie Rojas	1.00
503 Larry Brown	1.00
504 Checklist 513-588 (Brooks Robinson)	4.00
505a Bobby Bolin (last name in white)	10.00
505b Bobby Bolin (last name in yellow)	1.00
506 Paul Blair	1.00
507 Cookie Rojas	1.00
508 Moe Drabowsky	1.00
509 Manny Sanguillen	1.00
510 Rod Carew	60.00
511a Diego Segui (first name in white)	35.00
511b Diego Segui (first name in yellow)	1.00
512 Cleon Jones	1.00
513 Camilo Pascual	1.50
514 Mike Lum	1.50
515 Dick Green	1.50
516 Earl Weaver	5.00
517 Mike McCormick	1.50
518 Fred Whitfield	1.50
519 Yankees Rookies (Len Boehmer, Gerry Kenney)	1.50
520 Bob Veale	1.50
521 George Thomas	1.50
522 Joe Hoerner	1.50
523 Bob Chance	1.50
524 Expos Rookies (Jose Laboy, Floyd Wicker)	1.50
525 Earl Wilson	1.50
526 Hector Torres	1.50
527 Al Lopez	3.00
528 Claude Osteen	1.50
529 Ed Kirkpatrick	1.50
530 Cesar Tovar	1.50
531 Dick Farrell	1.50
532 Bird Hill Aces (Mike Cuellar, Jim Hardin, Dave McNally, Tom Phoebus)	3.00
533 Nolan Ryan	700.00
534 Jerry McNertney	1.50
535 Phil Regan	1.50
536 Padres Rookies (Danny Breeden, Dave Roberts)	1.50
537 Mike Paul	1.50
538 Charlie Smith	1.50
539 Ted Shows How (Mike Epstein, Ted Williams)	3.25
540 Curt Flood	2.00
541 Joe Verbanic	1.50
542 Bob Aspromonte	1.50
543 Fred Newman	1.50
544 Tigers Rookies (Mike Kilkenny, Ron Woods)	1.50
545 Willie Stargell	10.00
546 Jim Nash	1.50
547 Billy Martin	5.00
548 Bob Locker	1.50
549 Ron Brand	1.50
550 Brooks Robinson	15.00
551 Wayne Granger	1.50
552 Dodgers Rookies (*Ted Sizemore*, Bill Sudakis)	1.75
553 Ron Davis	1.50
554 Frank Bertaina	1.50
555 Jim Hart	1.50
556 A's Stars (Sal Bando, Bert Campaneris, Danny Cater)	2.50
557 Frank Fernandez	1.50

558	*Tom Burgmeier*	1.50
559	Cards Rookies (Joe Hague, Jim Hicks)	1.50
560	Luis Tiant	2.50
561	Ron Clark	1.50
562	*Bob Watson*	1.50
563	Marty Pattin	1.50
564	Gil Hodges	6.00
565	Hoyt Wilhelm	7.00
566	Ron Hansen	1.50
567	Pirates Rookies (Elvio Jimenez, Jim Shellenback)	1.50
568	Cecil Upshaw	1.50
569	Billy Harris	1.50
570	Ron Santo	2.00
571	Cap Peterson	1.50
572	Giants Heroes (Juan Marichal, Willie McCovey)	7.00
573	Jim Palmer	30.00
574	George Scott	1.50
575	Bill Singer	1.50
576	Phillies Rookies (Ron Stone, Bill Wilson)	1.50
577	Mike Hegan	1.50
578	Don Bosch	1.50
579	*Dave Nelson*	1.50
580	Jim Northrup	1.50
581	Gary Nolan	1.50
582a	Checklist 589-664 (Tony Oliva) (red circle on back)	3.50
582b	Checklist 589-664 (Tony oliva) (white circle on back)	2.50
583	*Clyde Wright*	1.50
584	Don Mason	1.50
585	Ron Swoboda	1.50
586	Tim Cullen	1.50
587	*Joe Rudi*	2.00
588	Bill White	2.50
589	Joe Pepitone	3.50
590	Rico Carty	2.50
591	Mike Hedlund	2.50
592	Padres Rookies (Rafael Robles, Al Santorini)	2.50
593	Don Nottebart	2.50
594	Dooley Womack	2.50
595	Lee Maye	2.50
596	Chuck Hartenstein	2.50
597	A.L. Rookies (Larry Burchart, Rollie Fingers, Bob Floyd)	75.00
598	Ruben Amaro	2.50
599	John Boozer	2.50
600	Tony Oliva	4.50
601	Tug McGraw	2.50
602	Cubs Rookies (Alec Distaso, Jim Qualls, Don Young)	2.50
603	Joe Keough	2.50
604	Bobby Etheridge	2.50
605	Dick Ellsworth	2.50
606	Gene Mauch	2.50
607	Dick Bosman	2.50
608	Dick Simpson	2.50
609	Phil Gagliano	2.50
610	Jim Hardin	2.50
611	Braves Rookies (Bob Didier, Walt Hriniak, Gary Neibauer)	2.50
612	Jack Aker	2.50
613	Jim Beauchamp	2.50
614	Astros Rookies (Tom Griffin, Skip Guinn)	2.50
615	Len Gabrielson	2.50
616	Don McMahon	2.50
617	Jesse Gonder	2.50
618	Ramon Webster	2.50
619	Royals Rookies (Bill Butler, Pat Kelly, Juan Rios)	2.50
620	Dean Chance	2.50
621	Bill Voss	2.50
622	Dan Osinski	2.50
623	Hank Allen	2.50
624	N.L. Rookies (Darrel Chaney, Duffy Dyer, Terry Harmon)	2.50
625	Mack Jones	2.50
626	Gene Michael	2.50
627	George Stone	2.50

628	Red Sox Rookies (*Bill Conigliaro*, Syd O'Brien, Fred Wenz)	2.50
629	Jack Hamilton	2.50
630	*Bobby Bonds*	50.00
631	John Kennedy	2.50
632	Jon Warden	2.50
633	Harry Walker	2.50
634	Andy Etchebarren	2.50
635	George Culver	2.50
636	Woodie Held	2.50
637	Padres Rookies (Jerry DaVanon, Clay Kirby, Frank Reberger)	2.50
638	Ed Sprague	2.50
639	Barry Moore	2.50
640	Fergie Jenkins	20.00
641	N.L. Rookies (Bobby Darwin, Tommy Dean, John Miller)	2.50
642	John Hiller	2.50
643	Billy Cowan	2.50
644	Chuck Hinton	2.50
645	George Brunet	2.50
646	Expos Rookies (Dan McGinn, Carl Morton)	2.50
647	Dave Wickersham	2.50
648	Bobby Wine	2.50
649	Al Jackson	2.50
650	Ted Williams	12.00
651	Gus Gil	2.50
652	Eddie Watt	2.50
653	*Aurelio Rodriguez* (photo actually batboy Leonard Garcia)	3.50
654	White Sox Rookies (*Carlos May*, Rich Morales, Don Secrist)	2.50
655	Mike Hershberger	2.50
656	Dan Schneider	2.50
657	Bobby Murcer	3.00
658	A.L. Rookies (Bill Burbach, Tom Hall, Jim Miles)	2.50
659	Johnny Podres	3.00
660	Reggie Smith	2.50
661	Jim Merritt	2.50
662	Royals Rookies (Dick Drago, Bob Oliver, George Spriggs)	2.50
663	Dick Radatz	2.50
664	Ron Hunt	2.50

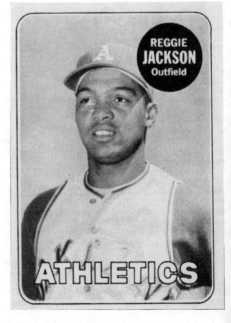

REGGIE JACKSON Outfield

ATHLETICS

1970 Topps

Topps established another set size record by coming out with 720 cards in 1970. The 2-1/2" by 3-1/2" cards have a color photo with a thin white frame. The photos have the player's team overprinted at the top, while the player's name in script and his position are at the bottom. A gray border surrounds the front. Card backs follow the normal design pattern, although they are more readable than some issues of the past.Team cards returned and were joined with many of the usual specialty cards.The World Series highlights were joined by cards with playoff highlights. Statistical leaders and All-Stars are also included in the set. High-numbered cards provide the most expensive cards in the set.

Mr. Mint Says - One of my least favorite sets of all time. Boring. Complete, original vendor sets command a premium, but pieced together sets would not. Still, a nice set, and the superstars have nowhere to go but up over the coming years. I believe that a mint, uncirculated vendor set would easily bring over $3,000.

I've had hundreds of boxes over the years, and bought over 200 boxes of high numbers in a span of six to eight months. They are available by the boat-load in mint, and really, no problem with centering, for the most part.

The second-year Ryan is highly sought after and the most popular card in the set, and Munson sells well. If you can't sell a 1968 Bench, how can you sell a 1970?

		MT
Complete Set (720):		3000.
Common Player (1-372):		.90
Common Player (373-546):		1.50
Common Player (547-633):		3.00
Common Player (634-720):		6.00
1	World Champions (Mets Team,)	12.00
2	Diego Segui	.90
3	Darrel Chaney	.90
4	Tom Egan	.90
5	Wes Parker	.90
6	Grant Jackson	.90
7	Indians Rookies (Gary Boyd, Russ Nagelson)	.90
8	Jose Martinez	.90
9	Checklist 1-132	3.50
10	Carl Yastrzemski	25.00
11	Nate Colbert	90.00
12	John Hiller	90.00
13	Jack Hiatt	90.00
14	Hank Allen	90.00
15	Larry Dierker	90.00
16	Charlie Metro	90.00
17	Hoyt Wilhelm	4.00
18	Carlos May	.90
19	John Boccabella	.90
20	Dave McNally	.90
21	Athletics Rookies (*Vida Blue*, Gene Tenace)	6.00
22	Ray Washburn	.90
23	Bill Robinson	.90
24	Dick Selma	.90
25	Cesar Tovar	.90
26	Tug McGraw	.90
27	Chuck Hinton	.90
28	Billy Wilson	.90
29	Sandy Alomar	.90
30	Matty Alou	.90
31	Marty Pattin	.90
32	Harry Walker	.90
33	Don Wert	.90
34	Willie Crawford	.90
35	Joe Horlen	.90
36	Reds Rookies (Danny Breeden, Bernie Carbo)	.90
37	Dick Drago	.90
38	Mack Jones	.90
39	Mike Nagy	.90
40	Rich Allen	2.00
41	George Lauzerique	.90
42	Tito Fuentes	.90
43	Jack Aker	.90
44	Roberto Pena	.90
45	Dave Johnson	.90
46	Ken Rudolph	.90
47	Bob Miller	.90
48	Gill Garrido (Gil)	.90
49	Tim Cullen	.90
50	Tommie Agee	.90
51	Bob Christian	.90
52	Bruce Dal Canton	.90
53	John Kennedy	.90
54	Jeff Torborg	.90
55	John Odom	.90
56	Phillies Rookies (Joe Lis, Scott Reid)	.90

57	Pat Kelly	.90		119	Chuck Taylor	.90
58	Dave Marshall	.90		120	Sal Bando	.90
59	Dick Ellsworth	.90		121	Orioles Rookies (Fred Beene, Terry Crowley)	.90
60	Jim Wynn	.90		122	George Stone	.90
61	N.L. Batting Leaders (Roberto Clemente, Cleon Jones, Pete Rose)	7.00		123	Don Gutteridge	.90
				124	Larry Jaster	.90
62	A.L. Batting Leaders (Rod Carew, Tony Oliva, Reggie Smith)	3.50		125	Deron Johnson	.90
				126	Marty Martinez	.90
63	N.L. RBI Leaders (Willie McCovey, Tony Perez, Ron Santo)	3.75		127	Joe Coleman	.90
				128a	Checklist 133-263 (226 is R Perranoski)	3.00
64	A.L. RBI Leaders (Reggie Jackson, Harmon Killebrew, Boog Powell)	5.00		128b	Checklist 133-263 (226 is R. Perranoski)	3.50
				129	Jimmie Price	.90
65	N.L. Home Run Leaders (Hank Aaron, Lee May, Willie McCovey)	5.00		130	Ollie Brown	.90
				131	Dodgers Rookies (Ray Lamb, Bob Stinson)	.90
66	A.L. Home Run Leaders (Frank Howard, Reggie Jackson, Harmon Killebrew)	5.00		132	Jim McGlothlin	.90
				133	Clay Carroll	.90
67	N.L. ERA Leaders (Steve Carlton, Bob Gibson, Juan Marichal)	4.00		134	Danny Walton, Mantle's Clutch HR,	.90
				135	Dick Dietz	.90
68	A.L. ERA Leaders (Dick Bosman, Mike Cuellar, Jim Palmer)	3.50		136	Steve Hargan	.90
				137	Art Shamsky	.90
69	N.L. Pitching Leaders (Fergie Jenkins, Juan Marichal, Phil Niekro, Tom Seaver)	5.00		138	Joe Foy	.90
				139	Rich Nye	.90
70	A.L. Pitching Leaders (Dave Boswell, Mike Cuellar, Dennis McLain, Dave McNally, Jim Perry, Mel Stottlemyre)	3.50		140	Reggie Jackson	175.00
				141	Pirates Rookies (*Dave Cash*, Johnny Jeter)	.90
71	N.L. Strikeout Leaders (Bob Gibson, Fergie Jenkins,Bill Singer)	4.00		142	Fritz Peterson	.90
				143	Phil Gagliano	.90
72	A.L. Strikeout Leaders (Mickey Lolich, Sam McDowell, Andy Messersmith)	3.50		144	Ray Culp	.90
				145	Rico Carty	.90
73	Wayne Granger	.90		146	Danny Murphy	.90
74	Angels Rookies (Greg Washburn, Wally Wolf)	.90		147	Angel Hermoso	.90
75	Jim Kaat	3.00		148	Earl Weaver	1.75
76	Carl Taylor	.90		149	Billy Champion	.90
77	Frank Linzy	.90		150	Harmon Killebrew	8.00
78	Joe Lahoud	.90		151	Dave Roberts	.90
79	Clay Kirby	.90		152	Ike Brown	.90
80	Don Kessinger	.90		153	Gary Gentry	.90
81	Dave May	.90		154	Senators Rookies (Jan Dukes, Jim Miles)	.90
82	Frank Fernandez	.90		155	Denis Menke	.90
83	Don Cardwell	.90		156	Eddie Fisher	.90
84	Paul Casanova	.90		157	Manny Mota	.90
85	Max Alvis	.90		158	Jerry McNertney	.90
86	Lum Harris	.90		159	Tommy Helms	.90
87	Steve Renko	.90		160	Phil Niekro	3.50
88	Pilots Rookies (Dick Baney, Miguel Fuentes)	.90		161	Richie Scheinblum	.90
89	Juan Rios	.90		162	Jerry Johnson	.90
90	Tim McCarver	1.00		163	Syd O'Brien	.90
91	Rich Morales	.90		164	Ty Cline	.90
92	George Culver	.90		165	Ed Kirkpatrick	.90
93	Rick Renick	.90		166	Al Oliver	2.50
94	Fred Patek	.90		167	Bill Burbach	.90
95	Earl Wilson	.90		168	Dave Watkins	.90
96	Cards Rookies (Leron Lee, Jerry Reuss)	3.00		169	Tom Hall	.90
97	Joe Moeller	.90		170	Billy Williams	6.00
98	Gates Brown	.90		171	Jim Nash	.90
99	Bobby Pfeil	.90		172	Braves Rookies (*Ralph Garr*, Garry Hill)	2.50
100	Mel Stottlemyre	.90		173	Jim Hicks	.90
101	Bobby Floyd	.90		174	Ted Sizemore	.90
102	Joe Rudi	.90		175	Dick Bosman	.90
103	Frank Reberger	.90		176	Jim Hart	.90
104	Gerry Moses	.90		177	Jim Northrup	.90
105	Tony Gonzalez	.90		178	Denny Lemaster	.90
106	Darold Knowles	.90		179	Ivan Murrell	.90
107	Bobby Etheridge	.90		180	Tommy John	3.00
108	Tom Burgmeier	.90		181	Sparky Anderson	3.00
109	Expos Rookies (Garry Jestadt, Carl Morton)	.90		182	Dick Hall	.90
110	Bob Moose	.90		183	Jerry Grote	.90
111	Mike Hegan	.90		184	Ray Fosse	.90
112	Dave Nelson	.90		185	Don Mincher	.90
113	Jim Ray	.90		186	Rick Joseph	.90
114	Gene Michael	.90		187	Mike Hedlund	.90
115	Alex Johnson	.90		188	Manny Sanguillen	.90
116	Sparky Lyle	1.50		189	Yankees Rookies (Dave McDonald, Thurman Munson)	90.00
117	Don Young	.90				
118	George Mitterwald	.90		190	Joe Torre	.90

191	Vicente Romo	.90
192	Jim Qualls	.90
193	Mike Wegener	.90
194	Chuck Manuel	.90
195	N.L.C.S. Game 1 (Seaver Wins Opener!)	12.00
196	N.L.C.S. Game 2 (Mets Show Muscle!)	4.00
197	N.L.C.S. Game 3 (Ryan Saves The Day!)	20.00
198	N.L. Playoffs Summary (We're Number One!)	4.00
199	A.L.C.S. Game 1 (Orioles Win A Squeaker!)	5.00
200	A.L.C.S. Game 2 (Powell Scores Winning Run!)	5.00
201	A.L.C.S. Game 3 (Birds Wrap It Up!)	5.00
202	A.L.C.S. Summary (Sweep Twins In Three!)	5.00
203	Rudy May	.90
204	Len Gabrielson	.90
205	Bert Campaneris	.90
206	Clete Boyer	.90
207	Tigers Rookies (Norman McRae, Bob Reed)	.90
208	Fred Gladding	.90
209	Ken Suarez	.90
210	Juan Marichal	8.00
211	Ted Williams	10.00
212	Al Santorini	.90
213	Andy Etchebarren	.90
214	Ken Boswell	.90
215	Reggie Smith	1.00
216	Chuck Hartenstein	.90
217	Ron Hansen	.90
218	Ron Stone	.90
219	Jerry Kenney	.90
220	Steve Carlton	32.50
221	Ron Brand	.90
222	Jim Rooker	.90
223	Nate Oliver	.90
224	Steve Barber	.90
225	Lee May	.90
226	Ron Perranoski	.90
227	Astros Rookies (*John Mayberry*, Bob Watkins)	1.50
228	Aurelio Rodriguez	.90
229	Rich Robertson	.90
230	Brooks Robinson	12.00
231	Luis Tiant	1.25
232	Bob Didier	.90
233	Lew Krausse	.90
234	Tommy Dean	.90
235	Mike Epstein	.90
236	Bob Veale	.90
237	Russ Gibson	.90
238	Jose Laboy	.90
239	Ken Berry	.90
240	Fergie Jenkins	8.00
241	Royals Rookies (Al Fitzmorris, Scott Northey)	.90
242	Walter Alston	3.50
243	Joe Sparma	.90
244a	Checklist 264-372 (red bat on front)	3.00
244b	Checklist 264-372 (brown bat on front)	3.50
245	Leo Cardenas	.90
246	Jim McAndrew	.90
247	Lou Klimchock	.90
248	Jesus Alou	.90
249	Bob Locker	.90
250	Willie McCovey	8.00
251	Dick Schofield	.90
252	Lowell Palmer	.90
253	Ron Woods	.90
254	Camilo Pascual	.90
255	*Jim Spencer*	.90
256	Vic Davalillo	.90
257	Dennis Higgins	.90
258	Paul Popovich	.90
259	Tommie Reynolds	.90
260	Claude Osteen	.90
261	Curt Motton	.90
262	Padres Rookies (Jerry Morales, Jim Williams)	.90

263	Duane Josephson	.90
264	Rich Hebner	.90
265	Randy Hundley	.90
266	Wally Bunker	.90
267	Twins Rookies (Herman Hill, Paul Ratliff)	.90
268	Claude Raymond	.90
269	Cesar Gutierrez	.90
270	Chris Short	.90
271	Greg Goossen	.90
272	Hector Torres	.90
273	Ralph Houk	1.00
274	Gerry Arrigo	.90
275	Duke Sims	.90
276	Ron Hunt	.90
277	Paul Doyle	.90
278	Tommie Aaron	.90
279	*Bill Lee*	.90
280	Donn Clendenon	.90
281	Casey Cox	.90
282	Steve Huntz	.90
283	Angel Bravo	.90
284	Jack Baldschun	.90
285	Paul Blair	.90
286	*Bill Buckner*, Jack Jenkins)	9.00
287	Fred Talbot	.90
288	Larry Hisle	.90
289	Gene Brabender	.90
290	Rod Carew	30.00
291	Leo Durocher	1.75
292	Eddie Leon	.90
293	Bob Bailey	.90
294	Jose Azcue	.90
295	Cecil Upshaw	.90
296	Woody Woodward	.90
297	Curt Blefary	.90
298	Ken Henderson	.90
299	Buddy Bradford	.90
300	Tom Seaver	90.00
301	Chico Salmon	.90
302	Jeff James	.90
303	Brant Alyea	.90
304	*Bill Russell*	3.00
305	World Series Game 1 (Buford Belts Leadoff Homer!)	4.00
306	World Series Game 2 (Clendenon's HR Breaks Ice!)	4.00
307	World Series Game 3 (Agee's Catch Saves The Day!)	4.00
308	World Series Game 4 (Martin's Bunt Ends Deadlock!)	4.00
309	World Series Game 5 (Koosman Shuts The Door!)	4.00
310	World Series Summary (Mets Whoop It Up!)	4.00
311	Dick Green	.90
312	Mike Torrez	.90
313	Mayo Smith	.90
314	Bill McCool	.90
315	Luis Aparicio	4.50
316	Skip Guinn	.90
317	Red Sox Rookies (Luis Alvarado, Billy Conigliaro)	.90
318	Willie Smith	.90
319	Clayton Dalrymple	.90
320	Jim Maloney	.90
321	Lou Piniella	1.50
322	Luke Walker	.90
323	Wayne Comer	.90
324	Tony Taylor	.90
325	Dave Boswell	.90
326	Bill Voss	.90
327	Hal King	.90
328	George Brunet	.90
329	Chris Cannizzaro	.90
330	Lou Brock	10.00
331	Chuck Dobson	.90
332	Bobby Wine	.90
333	Bobby Murcer	.90
334	Phil Regan	.90
335	Bill Freehan	.90

#	Player	Price
336	Del Unser	.90
337	Mike McCormick	.90
338	Paul Schaal	.90
339	Johnny Edwards	.90
340	Tony Conigliaro	1.75
341	Bill Sudakis	.90
342	Wilbur Wood	.90
343a	Checklist 373-459 (red bat on front)	3.50
343b	Checklist 373-459 (brown bat on front)	3.00
344	Marcelino Lopez	.90
345	Al Ferrara	.90
346	Red Schoendienst	1.75
347	Russ Snyder	.90
348	Mets Rookies (Jesse Hudson, Mike Jorgensen)	.90
349	Steve Hamilton	.90
350	Roberto Clemente	52.50
351	Tom Murphy	.90
352	Bob Barton	.90
353	Stan Williams	.90
354	Amos Otis	.90
355	Doug Rader	.90
356	Fred Lasher	.90
357	Bob Burda	.90
358	*Pedro Borbon*	1.00
359	Phil Roof	.90
360	Curt Flood	.90
361	Ray Jarvis	.90
362	Joe Hague	.90
363	Tom Shopay	.90
364	Dan McGinn	.90
365	Zoilo Versalles	.90
366	Barry Moore	.90
367	Mike Lum	.90
368	Ed Herrmann	.90
369	Alan Foster	.90
370	Tommy Harper	.90
371	Rod Gaspar	.90
372	Dave Giusti	.90
373	Roy White	1.50
374	Tommie Sisk	1.50
375	Johnny Callison	1.50
376	Lefty Phillips	1.50
377	Bill Butler	1.50
378	Jim Davenport	1.50
379	Tom Tischinski	1.50
380	Tony Perez	3.00
381	Athletics Rookies (Bobby Brooks, Mike Olivo)	1.50
382	Jack DiLauro	1.50
383	Mickey Stanley	1.50
384	Gary Neibauer	1.50
385	George Scott	1.50
386	Bill Dillman	1.50
387	Orioles Team	3.00
388	Byron Browne	1.50
389	Jim Shellenback	1.50
390	Willie Davis	1.75
391	Larry Brown	1.50
392	Walt Hriniak	1.50
393	John Gelnar	1.50
394	Gil Hodges	4.00
395	Walt Williams	1.50
396	Steve Blass	1.50
397	Roger Repoz	1.50
398	Bill Stoneman	1.50
399	Yankees Team	5.00
400	Denny McLain	2.50
401	Giants Rookies (John Harrell, Bernie Williams)	1.50
402	Ellie Rodriguez	1.50
403	Jim Bunning	3.25
404	Rich Reese	1.50
405	Bill Hands	1.50
406	Mike Andrews	1.50
407	Bob Watson	1.50
408	Paul Lindblad	1.50
409	Bob Tolan	1.50
410	Boog Powell	2.50
411	Dodgers Team	4.00
412	Larry Burchart	1.50
413	Sonny Jackson	1.50
414	Paul Edmondson	1.50
415	Julian Javier	1.50
416	Joe Verbanic	1.50
417	John Bateman	1.50
418	John Donaldson	1.50
419	Ron Taylor	1.50
420	Ken McMullen	1.50
421	Pat Dobson	1.50
422	Royals Team	3.00
423	Jerry May	1.50
424	Mike Kilkenny	1.50
425	Bobby Bonds	2.00
426	Bill Rigney	1.50
427	Fred Norman	1.50
428	Don Buford	1.50
429	Cubs Rookies (Randy Bobb, Jim Cosman)	1.50
430	Andy Messersmith	1.50
431	Ron Swoboda	1.50
432a	Checklist 460-546 ("Baseball" on front in yellow)	4.00
432b	Checklist 460-546 ("Baseball" on front in white)	3.50
433	Ron Bryant	1.50
434	Felipe Alou	2.50
435	Nelson Briles	1.50
436	Phillies Team	3.00
437	Danny Cater	1.50
438	Pat Jarvis	1.50
439	Lee Maye	1.50
440	Bill Mazeroski	3.00
441	John O'Donoghue	1.50
442	Gene Mauch	1.75
443	Al Jackson	1.50
444	White Sox Rookies (Bill Farmer, John Matias)	1.50
445	Vada Pinson	2.00
446	*Billy Grabarkewitz*	1.50
447	Lee Stange	1.50
448	Astros Team	3.00
449	Jim Palmer	20.00
450	Willie McCovey (All-Star)	5.00
451	Boog Powell (All-Star)	1.50
452	Felix Millan (All-Star)	1.50
453	Rod Carew (All-Star)	6.00
454	Ron Santo (All-Star)	1.50
455	Brooks Robinson (All-Star)	8.00
456	Don Kessinger (All-Star)	1.50
457	Rico Petrocelli (All-Star)	1.50
458	Pete Rose (All-Star)	12.00
459	Reggie Jackson (All-Star)	35.00
460	Matty Alou (All-Star)	1.50
461	Carl Yastrzemski (All-Star)	8.00
462	Hank Aaron (All-Star)	15.00
463	Frank Robinson (All-Star)	8.00
464	Johnny Bench (All-Star)	10.00
465	Bill Freehan (All-Star)	1.50
466	Juan Marichal (All-Star)	5.00
467	Denny McLain (All-Star)	1.50
468	Jerry Koosman (All-Star)	1.50
469	Sam McDowell (All-Star)	1.50
470	Willie Stargell	7.00
471	Chris Zachary	1.50
472	Braves Team	3.00
473	Don Bryant	1.50
474	Dick Kelley	1.50
475	Dick McAuliffe	1.50
476	Don Shaw	1.50
477	Orioles Rookies (Roger Freed, Al Severinsen)	1.50
478	Bob Heise	1.50
479	Dick Woodson	1.50

480	Glenn Beckert	1.50
481	Jose Tartabull	1.50
482	Tom Hilgendorf	1.50
483	Gail Hopkins	1.50
484	Gary Nolan	1.50
485	Jay Johnstone	1.50
486	Terry Harmon	1.50
487	Cisco Carlos	1.50
488	J.C. Martin	1.50
489	Eddie Kasko	1.50
490	Bill Singer	1.50
491	Graig Nettles	3.00
492	Astros Rookies (Keith Lampard, Scipio Spinks)	1.50
493	Lindy McDaniel	1.50
494	Larry Stahl	1.50
495	Dave Morehead	1.50
496	Steve Whitaker	1.50
497	Eddie Watt	1.50
498	Al Weis	1.50
499	Skip Lockwood	
500	Hank Aaron	60.00
501	White Sox Team	3.00
502	Rollie Fingers	30.00
503	Dal Maxvill	1.50
504	Don Pavletich	1.50
505	Ken Holtzman	1.50
506	Ed Stroud	1.50
507	Pat Corrales	1.50
508	Joe Niekro	2.00
509	Expos Team	3.00
510	Tony Oliva	2.50
511	Joe Hoerner	1.50
512	Billy Harris	1.50
513	Preston Gomez	1.50
514	Steve Hovley	1.50
515	Don Wilson	1.50
516	Yankees Rookies (John Ellis, Jim Lyttle)	1.50
517	Joe Gibbon	1.50
518	Bill Melton	1.50
519	Don McMahon	1.50
520	Willie Horton	1.75
521	Cal Koonce	1.50
522	Angels Team	3.00
523	Jose Pena	1.50
524	Alvin Dark	1.50
525	Jerry Adair	1.50
526	Ron Herbel	1.50
527	Don Bosch	1.50
528	Elrod Hendricks	1.50
529	Bob Aspromonte	1.50
530	Bob Gibson	10.00
531	Ron Clark	1.50
532	Danny Murtaugh	1.50
533	Buzz Stephen	1.50
534	Twins Team	3.00
535	Andy Kosco	1.50
536	Mike Kekich	1.50
537	Joe Morgan	10.00
538	Bob Humphreys	1.50
539	Phillies Rookies (*Larry Bowa*, Dennis Doyle)	3.00
540	Gary Peters	1.50
541	Bill Heath	1.50
542a	Checklist 547-633 (grey bat on front)	3.50
542b	Checklist 547-633 (brown bat on front)	3.50
543	Clyde Wright	1.50
544	Reds Team	3.00
545	Ken Harrelson	1.50
546	Ron Reed	1.50
547	Rick Monday	3.00
548	Howie Reed	3.00
549	Cardinals Team	7.00
550	Frank Howard	4.50
551	Dock Ellis	3.00

552	Royals Rookies (Don O'Riley, Dennis Paepke, Fred Rico)	3.00
553	Jim Lefebvre	3.50
554	Tom Timmermann	3.00
555	Orlando Cepeda	4.50
556	Dave Bristol	3.00
557	Ed Kranepool	3.00
558	Vern Fuller	3.00
559	Tommy Davis	4.00
560	Gaylord Perry	10.00
561	Tom McCraw	3.00
562	Ted Abernathy	3.00
563	Red Sox Team	7.00
564	Johnny Briggs	3.00
565	Catfish Hunter	11.00
566	Gene Alley	3.00
567	Bob Oliver	3.00
568	Stan Bahnsen	3.00
569	Cookie Rojas	3.00
570	Jim Fregosi	3.50
571	Jim Brewer	3.00
572	Frank Quilici	3.00
573	Padres Rookies (Mike Corkins, Rafael Robles, Ron Slocum)	3.00
574	Bobby Bolin	3.00
575	Cleon Jones	3.00
576	Milt Pappas	3.00
577	Bernie Allen	3.00
578	Tom Griffin	3.00
579	Tigers Team	7.00
580	Pete Rose	70.00
581	Tom Satriano	3.00
582	Mike Paul	3.00
583	Hal Lanier	3.00
584	Al Downing	3.00
585	Rusty Staub	4.50
586	Rickey Clark	3.00
587	Jose Arcia	3.00
588a	Checklist 634-720 (666 is Adolpho Phillips)	4.50
588b	Checklist 634-720 (666 is Adolfo Phillips)	4.00
589	Joe Keough	3.00
590	Mike Cuellar	3.50
591	Mike Ryan	3.00
592	Daryl Patterson	3.00
593	Cubs Team	7.00
594	Jake Gibbs	3.00
595	Maury Wills	4.00
596	Mike Hershberger	3.00
597	Sonny Siebert	3.00
598	Joe Pepitone	3.00
599	Senators Rookies (Gene Martin, Dick Stelmaszek, Dick Such)	3.00
600	Willie Mays	80.00
601	Pete Richert	3.00
602	Ted Savage	3.00
603	Ray Oyler	3.00
604	Cito Gaston	4.50
605	Rick Wise	3.00
606	Chico Ruiz	3.00
607	Gary Waslewski	3.00
608	Pirates Team	7.00
609	*Buck Martinez*	3.00
610	Jerry Koosman	3.00
611	Norm Cash	4.00
612	Jim Hickman	3.00
613	Dave Baldwin	3.00
614	Mike Shannon	3.00
615	Mark Belanger	3.00
616	Jim Merritt	3.00
617	Jim French	3.00
618	Billy Wynne	3.00
619	Norm Miller	3.00
620	Jim Perry	3.00

621	Braves Rookies (*Darrell Evans*, Rick Kester, Mike McQueen)	20.00
622	Don Sutton	7.00
623	Horace Clarke	3.00
624	Clyde King	3.00
625	Dean Chance	3.00
626	Dave Ricketts	3.00
627	Gary Wagner	3.00
628	Wayne Garrett	3.00
629	Merv Rettenmund	3.00
630	Ernie Banks	30.00
631	Athletics Team	7.00
632	Gary Sutherland	3.00
633	Roger Nelson	3.00
634	Bud Harrelson	7.00
635	Bob Allison	6.00
636	Jim Stewart	6.00
637	Indians Team	9.00
638	Frank Bertaina	6.00
639	Dave Campbell	6.00
640	Al Kaline	50.00
641	Al McBean	6.00
642	Angels Rookies (Greg Garrett, Gordon Lund, Jarvis Tatum)	6.00
643	Jose Pagan	6.00
644	Gerry Nyman	6.00
645	Don Money	6.00
646	Jim Britton	6.00
647	Tom Matchick	6.00
648	Larry Haney	6.00
649	Jimmie Hall	6.00
650	Sam McDowell	7.00
651	Jim Gosger	6.00
652	Rich Rollins	6.00
653	Moe Drabowsky	6.00
654	N.L. Rookies (Boots Day, Oscar Gamble, Angel Mangual)	6.00
655	John Roseboro	6.00
656	Jim Hardin	6.00
657	Padres Team	9.00
658	Ken Tatum	6.00
659	Pete Ward	6.00
660	Johnny Bench	150.00
661	Jerry Robertson	6.00
662	Frank Lucchesi	6.00
663	Tito Francona	6.00
664	Bob Robertson	6.00
665	Jim Lonborg	7.00
666	Adolfo Phillips	6.00
667	Bob Meyer	6.00
668	Bob Tillman	6.00
669	White Sox Rookies (Bart Johnson, Dan Lazar, Mickey Scott)	6.00
670	Ron Santo	7.50
671	Jim Campanis	6.00
672	Leon McFadden	6.00
673	Ted Uhlaender	6.00
674	Dave Leonhard	6.00
675	Jose Cardenal	6.00
676	Senators Team	9.00
677	Woodie Fryman	6.00
678	Dave Duncan	6.00
679	Ray Sadecki	6.00
680	Rico Petrocelli	7.00
681	Bob Garibaldi	6.00
682	Dalton Jones	6.00
683	Reds Rookies (Vern Geishert, Hal McRae, Wayne Simpson)	7.00
684	Jack Fisher	6.00
685	Tom Haller	6.00
686	Jackie Hernandez	6.00

687	Bob Priddy	6.00
688	Ted Kubiak	6.00
689	Frank Tepedino	6.00
690	Ron Fairly	6.00
691	Joe Grzenda	6.00
692	Duffy Dyer	6.00
693	Bob Johnson	6.00
694	Gary Ross	6.00
695	Bobby Knoop	6.00
696	Giants Team	9.00
697	Jim Hannan	6.00
698	Tom Tresh	7.00
699	Hank Aguirre	6.00
700	Frank Robinson	50.00
701	Jack Billingham	6.00
702	A.L. Rookies (Bob Johnson, Ron Klimkowski, Bill Zepp)	6.00
703	Lou Marone	6.00
704	Frank Baker	6.00
705	Tony Cloninger	6.00
706	John McNamara	6.00
707	Kevin Collins	6.00
708	Jose Santiago	6.00
709	Mike Fiore	6.00
710	Felix Millan	6.00
711	Ed Brinkman	6.00
712	Nolan Ryan	550.00
713	Pilots Team	25.00
714	Al Spangler	6.00
715	Mickey Lolich	7.00
716	Cards Rookies (Sal Campisi, Reggie Cleveland, Santiago Guzman)	6.00
717	Tom Phoebus	6.00
718	Ed Spiezio	6.00
719	Jim Roland	6.00
720	Rick Reichardt	6.00

1971 Topps

In 1971, Topps again increased the size of its set to 752 cards. These well-liked cards, measuring 2-1/2" by 3-1/2," feature a large color photo which has a thin white frame. Above the picture, in the card's overall black border, is the player's name, team and position. A facsimile autograph completes the front. Backs feature a major change as a black and white "snapshot" of the player appears. Abbreviated statistics, a line giving the player's first pro and major league games and a short biography complete the back of these innovative cards. Specialty cards in this issue are limited. There are statistical leaders as well as World Series and playoff highlights. High numbered cards #644-752 are scarce, with about half of the cards being short-printed.

still found little dings and nicks on the corners. There is not much unopened around anymore, as most from 1971 and back has disappeared, but there is still a good amount from 1972 and 1975.

The Munson card is pretty neat, and the Ryan card sells very well. The Blyleven card was once very hot, but not so much now, and people also like the Ted Williams manager card. All the Hall of Famers sell, but nobody seems to care much about the Garvey rookie.

		MT
Complete Set (752):		3000.
Common Player (1-393):		1.00
Common Player (394-523):		2.00
Common Player (524-643):		3.50
Common Player (644-752):		4.50

1	World Champions (Orioles Team)	12.00
2	Dock Ellis	1.00
3	Dick McAuliffe	1.00
4	Vic Davalillo	1.00
5	Thurman Munson	30.00
6	Ed Spiezio	1.00
7	Jim Holt	1.00
8	Mike McQueen	1.00
9	George Scott	1.00
10	Claude Osteen	1.00
11	*Elliott Maddox*	1.00
12	Johnny Callison	1.00
13	White Sox Rookies (Charlie Brinkman, Dick Moloney)	1.00
14	*Dave Concepcion*	20.00
15	Andy Messersmith	1.00
16	*Ken Singleton*	3.50
17	Billy Sorrell	1.00
18	Norm Miller	1.00
19	Skip Pitlock	1.00
20	Reggie Jackson	100.00
21	Dan McGinn	1.00
22	Phil Roof	1.00
23	Oscar Gamble	1.00
24	Rich Hand	1.00
25	Cito Gaston	2.50
26	*Bert Blyleven*	1.00
27	Pirates Rookies (Fred Cambria, Gene Clines)	1.00
28	Ron Klimkowski	1.00
29	Don Buford	1.00
30	Phil Niekro	3.25
31	Eddie Kasko	1.00
32	Jerry DaVanon	1.00
33	Del Unser	1.00
34	Sandy Vance	1.00
35	Lou Piniella	1.00
36	Dean Chance	1.00
37	Rich McKinney	1.00
38	*Jim Colborn*	1.00
39	Tigers Rookies (Gene Lamont, Lerrin LaGrow)	1.00
40	Lee May	1.00
41	Rick Austin	1.00
42	Boots Day	1.00
43	Steve Kealey	1.00
44	Johnny Edwards	1.00
45	Catfish Hunter	5.00
46	Dave Campbell	1.00
47	Johnny Jeter	1.00

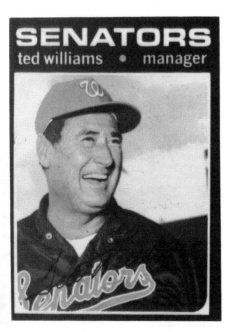

Mr. Mint Says - This is the toughest set in the world to complete in true mint condition. There is not a set on the face of the earth that is absolutely mint. I would say that an original vendor set could bring $3,000, if available. I've had lots of unopened, maybe 60-75 boxes, and even those when you open the packs there will be some wear showing. We bought 40,000 commons, all in vendor boxes, and as we went through the boxes we

#	Card	Price
48	Dave Baldwin	1.00
49	Don Money	1.00
50	Willie McCovey	7.00
51	Steve Kline	1.00
52	Braves Rookies (Oscar Brown, Earl Williams)	1.00
53	Paul Blair	1.00
54	Checklist 1-132	3.25
55	Steve Carlton	25.00
56	Duane Josephson	1.00
57	Von Joshua	1.00
58	Bill Lee	1.00
59	Gene Mauch	1.00
60	Dick Bosman	1.00
61	A.L. Batting Leaders (Alex Johnson, Tony Oliva, Carl Yastrzemski)	3.50
62	N.L. Batting Leaders (Rico Carty, Manny Sanguillen, Joe Torre)	1.50
63	A.L. RBI Leaders (Tony Conigliaro, Frank Howard, Boog Powell)	1.50
64	N.L. RBI Leaders (Johnny Bench, Tony Perez, Billy Williams)	3.50
65	A.L. Home Run Leaders (Frank Howard, Harmon Killebrew, Carl Yastrzemski)	3.50
66	N.L. Home Run Leaders (Johnny Bench, Tony Perez, Billy Williams)	3.50
67	A.L. ERA Leaders (Jim Palmer, Diego Segui, Clyde Wright)	1.50
68	N.L. ERA Leaders (Tom Seaver, Wayne Simpson, Luke Walker)	1.50
69	A.L. Pitching Leaders (Mike Cuellar, Dave McNally, Jim Perry)	1.50
70	N.L. Pitching Leaders (Bob Gibson, Fergie Jenkins, Gaylord Perry)	3.50
71	A.L. Strikeout Leaders (Bob Johnson, Mickey Lolich, Sam McDowell)	1.50
72	N.L. Strikeout Leaders (Bob Gibson, Fergie Jenkins, Tom Seaver)	3.50
73	George Brunet	1.00
74	Twins Rookies (Pete Hamm, Jim Nettles)	1.00
75	Gary Nolan	1.00
76	Ted Savage	1.00
77	Mike Compton	1.00
78	Jim Spencer	1.00
79	Wade Blasingame	1.00
80	Bill Melton	1.00
81	Felix Millan	1.00
82	Casey Cox	1.00
83	Mets Rookies (Randy Bobb, Tim Foli)	1.00
84	Marcel Lachemann	1.00
85	Billy Grabarkewitz	1.00
86	Mike Kilkenny	1.00
87	Jack Heidemann	1.00
88	Hal King	1.00
89	Ken Brett	1.00
90	Joe Pepitone	1.00
91	Bob Lemon	3.50
92	Fred Wenz	1.00
93	Senators Rookies (Norm McRae, Denny Riddleberger)	1.00
94	Don Hahn	1.50
95	Luis Tiant	1.00
96	Joe Hague	1.00
97	Floyd Wicker	1.00
98	Joe Decker	1.00
99	Mark Belanger	1.00
100	Pete Rose	35.00
101	Les Cain	1.00
102	Astros Rookies (Ken Forsch, Larry Howard)	1.00
103	Rich Severson	1.00
104	Dan Frisella	1.00
105	Tony Conigliaro	1.25
106	Tom Dukes	1.00
107	Roy Foster	1.00
108	John Cumberland	1.00
109	Steve Hovley	1.00
110	Bill Mazeroski	2.50
111	Yankees Rookies (Loyd Colson, Bobby Mitchell)	1.00
112	Manny Mota	1.00
113	Jerry Crider	1.00
114	Billy Conigliaro	1.00
115	Donn Clendenon	1.00
116	Ken Sanders	1.00
117	*Ted Simmons*	15.00
118	Cookie Rojas	1.00
119	Frank Lucchesi	1.00
120	Willie Horton	1.00
121	Cubs Rookies (Jim Dunegan, Roe Skidmore)	1.00
122	Eddie Watt	1.00
123a	Checklist 133-263 (card # on right, orange helmet)	3.25
123b	Checklist 133-263 (card # on right, red helmet)	3.25
123c	Checklist 133-263 (card # centered)	3.50
124	*Don Gullett*	1.00
125	Ray Fosse	1.00
126	Danny Coombs	1.00
127	*Danny Thompson*	1.00
128	Frank Johnson	1.00
129	Aurelio Monteagudo	1.00
130	Denis Menke	1.00
131	Curt Blefary	1.00
132	Jose Laboy	1.00
133	Mickey Lolich	1.25
134	Jose Arcia	1.00
135	Rick Monday	1.00
136	Duffy Dyer	1.00
137	Marcelino Lopez	1.00
138	Phillies Rookies (Joe Lis, Willie Montanez)	1.00
139	Paul Casanova	1.00
140	Gaylord Perry	6.00
141	Frank Quilici	1.00
142	Mack Jones	1.00
143	Steve Blass	1.00
144	Jackie Hernandez	1.00
145	Bill Singer	1.00
146	Ralph Houk	1.00
147	Bob Priddy	1.00
148	John Mayberry	1.00
149	Mike Hershberger	1.00
150	Sam McDowell	1.00
151	Tommy Davis	1.00
152	Angels Rookies (Lloyd Allen, Winston Llenas)	1.00
153	Gary Ross	1.00
154	Cesar Gutierrez	1.00
155	Ken Henderson	1.00
156	Bart Johnson	1.00
157	Bob Bailey	1.00
158	Jerry Reuss	1.00
159	Jarvis Tatum	1.00
160	Tom Seaver	45.00
161	Coins Checklist	3.25
162	Jack Billingham	1.00
163	Buck Martinez	1.00
164	Reds Rookies (Frank Duffy, Milt Wilcox)	1.00
165	Cesar Tovar	1.00
166	Joe Hoerner	1.00
167	Tom Grieve	1.00
168	Bruce Dal Canton	1.00
169	Ed Herrmann	1.00
170	Mike Cuellar	1.00
171	Bobby Wine	1.00
172	Duke Sims	1.00
173	Gil Garrido	1.00
174	*Dave LaRoche*	1.00
175	Jim Hickman	1.00
176	Red Sox Rookies (Doug Griffin, Bob Montgomery)	1.00
177	Hal McRae	2.00
178	Dave Duncan	1.00
179	Mike Corkins	1.00
180	Al Kaline (1.00)	15.00
181	Hal Lanier	1.00
182	Al Downing	1.00

183	Gil Hodges	4.00
184	Stan Bahnsen	1.00
185	Julian Javier	1.00
186	Bob Spence	1.00
187	Ted Abernathy	1.00
188	Dodgers Rookies (Mike Strahler, Bob Valentine)	3.50
189	George Mitterwald	1.00
190	Bob Tolan	1.00
191	Mike Andrews	1.00
192	Billy Wilson	1.00
193	*Bob Grich*	3.50
194	Mike Lum	1.00
195	A.L. Playoff Game 1 (Powell Muscles Twins!)	2.00
196	A.L. Playoff Game 2 (McNally Makes It Two Straight!)	2.00
197	A.L. Playoff Game 3 (Palmer Mows 'Em Down!)	3.50
198	A.L. Playoffs Summary (A Team Effort!)	2.00
199	N.L. Playoff Game 1 (Cline Pinch-Triple Decides It!)	2.00
200	N.L. Playoff Game 2 (Tolan Scores For Third Time!)	2.00
201	N.L. Playoff Game 3 (Cline Scores Winning Run!)	2.00
202	N.L. Playoffs Summary (World Series Bound!)	2.00
203	*Larry Gura*	1.00
204	Brewers Rookies (George Kopacz, Bernie Smith)	1.00
205	Gerry Moses	1.00
206a	Checklist 264-393 (orange helmet)	3.25
206b	Checklist 264-393 (red helmet)	3.25
207	Alan Foster	1.00
208	Billy Martin	3.50
209	Steve Renko	1.00
210	Rod Carew	30.00
211	Phil Hennigan	1.00
212	Rich Hebner	1.00
213	Frank Baker	1.00
214	Al Ferrara	1.00
215	Diego Segui	1.00
216	Cards Rookies (Reggie Cleveland, Luis Melendez)	1.00
217	Ed Stroud	1.00
218	Tony Cloninger	1.00
219	Elrod Hendricks	1.00
220	Ron Santo	2.50
221	Dave Morehead	1.00
222	Bob Watson	1.00
223	Cecil Upshaw	1.00
224	Alan Gallagher	1.00
225	Gary Peters	1.00
226	Bill Russell	2.00
227	Floyd Weaver	1.00
228	Wayne Garrett	1.00
229	Jim Hannan	1.00
230	Willie Stargell	8.00
231	Indians Rookies (Vince Colbert, John Lowenstein)	1.00
232	John Strohmayer	1.00
233	Larry Bowa	2.00
234	Jim Lyttle	1.00
235	Nate Colbert	1.00
236	Bob Humphreys	1.00
237	*Cesar Cedeno*	3.50
238	Chuck Dobson	1.00
239	Red Schoendienst	3.50
240	Clyde Wright	1.00
241	Dave Nelson	1.00
242	Jim Ray	1.00
243	Carlos May	1.00
244	Bob Tillman	1.00
245	Jim Kaat	2.50
246	Tony Taylor	1.00
247	Royals Rookies (Jerry Cram, Paul Splittorff)	1.00
248	Hoyt Wilhelm	3.75
249	Chico Salmon	1.00
250	Johnny Bench	35.00
251	Frank Reberger	1.00
252	Eddie Leon	1.00
253	Bill Sudakis	1.00
254	Cal Koonce	1.00
255	Bob Robertson	1.00
256	Tony Gonzalez	1.00
257	Nelson Briles	1.00
258	Dick Green	1.00
259	Dave Marshall	1.00
260	Tommy Harper	1.00
261	Darold Knowles	1.00
262	Padres Rookies (Dave Robinson, Jim Williams)	1.00
263	John Ellis	1.00
264	Joe Morgan	10.00
265	Jim Northrup	1.00
266	Bill Stoneman	1.00
267	Rich Morales	1.00
268	Phillies Team	3.50
269	Gail Hopkins	1.00
270	Rico Carty	1.00
271	Bill Zepp	1.00
272	Tommy Helms	1.00
273	Pete Richert	1.00
274	Ron Slocum	1.00
275	Vada Pinson	2.00
276	Giants Rookies (Mike Davison, George Foster)	6.00
277	Gary Waslewski	1.00
278	Jerry Grote	1.00
279	Lefty Phillips	1.00
280	Fergie Jenkins	8.00
281	Danny Walton	1.00
282	Jose Pagan	1.00
283	Dick Such	1.00
284	Jim Gosger	1.00
285	Sal Bando	1.00
286	Jerry McNertney	1.00
287	Mike Fiore	1.00
288	Joe Moeller	1.00
289	White Sox Team	3.50
290	Tony Oliva	1.50
291	George Culver	1.00
292	Jay Johnstone	1.00
293	Pat Corrales	1.00
294	Steve Dunning	1.00
295	Bobby Bonds	1.25
296	Tom Timmermann	1.00
297	Johnny Briggs	1.00
298	Jim Nelson	1.00
299	Ed Kirkpatrick	1.00
300	Brooks Robinson	20.00
301	Earl Wilson	1.00
302	Phil Gagliano	1.00
303	Lindy McDaniel	1.00
304	Ron Brand	1.00
305	Reggie Smith	1.50
306	Jim Nash	1.00
307	Don Wert	1.00
308	Cards Team	3.50
309	Dick Ellsworth	1.00
310	Tommie Agee	1.00
311	Lee Stange	1.00
312	Harry Walker	1.00
313	Tom Hall	1.00
314	Jeff Torborg	1.00
315	Ron Fairly	1.00
316	Fred Scherman	1.00
317	Athletics Rookies (Jim Driscoll, Angel Mangual)	1.00
318	Rudy May	1.00
319	Ty Cline	1.00
320	Dave McNally	1.00
321	Tom Matchick	1.00
322	Jim Beauchamp	1.00
323	Billy Champion	1.00
324	Graig Nettles	2.00
325	Juan Marichal	6.00
326	Richie Scheinblum	1.00
327	World Series Game 1 (Powell Homers To Opposite Field!)	3.50
328	World Series Game 2 (Buford Goes 2-For-4!)	2.00

No.	Name	Price	No.	Name	Price
329	World Series Game 3 (F. Robinson Shows Muscle!)	3.50	400	Hank Aaron	45.00
330	World Series Game 4 (Reds Stay Alive!)	2.00	401	Tom Murphy	2.00
331	World Series Game 5		402	Dodgers Team	3.50
	(B. Robinson Commits Robbery!)	3.50	403	Joe Coleman	2.00
332	World Series Summary (Convincing Performance!)	2.00	404	Astros Rookies (Buddy Harris, Roger Metzger)	2.00
333	Clay Kirby	1.00	405	Leo Cardenas	2.00
334	Roberto Pena	1.00	406	Ray Sadecki	2.00
335	Jerry Koosman	1.00	407	Joe Rudi	2.00
336	Tigers Team	3.50	408	Rafael Robles	2.00
337	Jesus Alou	1.00	409	Don Pavletich	2.00
338	Gene Tenace	1.00	410	Ken Holtzman	2.00
339	Wayne Simpson	1.00	411	George Spriggs	2.00
340	Rico Petrocelli	1.00	412	Jerry Johnson	2.00
341	*Steve Garvey*	55.00	413	Pat Kelly	2.00
342	Frank Tepedino		414	Woodie Fryman	2.00
343	Pirates Rookies (Ed Acosta, Milt May)	1.00	415	Mike Hegan	2.00
344	Ellie Rodriguez	1.00	416	Gene Alley	2.00
345	Joe Horlen	1.00	417	Dick Hall	2.00
346	Lum Harris	1.00	418	Adolfo Phillips	2.00
347	Ted Uhlaender	1.00	419	Ron Hansen	2.00
348	Fred Norman	1.00	420	Jim Merritt	2.00
349	Rich Reese	1.00	421	John Stephenson	2.00
350	Billy Williams	8.00	422	Frank Bertaina	2.00
351	Jim Shellenback	1.00	423	Tigers Rookies (Tim Marting, Dennis Saunders)	2.00
352	Denny Doyle	1.00	424	Roberto Rodriquez (Rodriguez)	2.00
353	Carl Taylor	1.00	425	Doug Rader	2.00
354	Don McMahon	1.00	426	Chris Cannizzaro	2.00
355	Bud Harrelson	1.00	427	Bernie Allen	2.00
356	Bob Locker	1.00	428	Jim McAndrew	2.00
357	Reds Team	3.50	429	Chuck Hinton	2.00
358	Danny Cater	1.00	430	Wes Parker	2.00
359	Ron Reed	1.00	431	Tom Burgmeier	2.00
360	Jim Fregosi	1.00	432	Bob Didier	2.00
361	Don Sutton	3.50	433	Skip Lockwood	2.00
362	Orioles Rookies (Mike Adamson, Roger Freed)	1.00	434	Gary Sutherland	2.00
363	Mike Nagy	1.00	435	Jose Cardenal	2.00
364	Tommy Dean	1.00	436	Wilbur Wood	2.00
365	Bob Johnson	1.00	437	Danny Murtaugh	2.00
366	Ron Stone	1.00	438	Mike McCormick	2.00
367	Dalton Jones	1.00	439	Phillies Rookies (*Greg Luzinski*, Scott Reid)	5.00
368	Bob Veale	1.00	440	Bert Campaneris	2.00
369a	Checklist 394-523 (orange helmet)	3.25	441	Milt Pappas	2.00
369b	Checklist 394-523 (red helmet, black line above ear)	3.25	442	Angels Team	3.50
369c	Checklist 394-523 (red helmet, no line)	3.25	443	Rich Robertson	2.00
370	Joe Torre	1.00	444	Jimmie Price	2.00
371	Jack Hiatt	1.00	445	Art Shamsky	2.00
372	Lew Krausse	1.00	446	Bobby Bolin	2.00
373	Tom McCraw	1.00	447	*Cesar Geronimo*	2.00
374	Clete Boyer	1.00	448	Dave Roberts	2.00
375	Steve Hargan	1.00	449	Brant Alyea	2.00
376	Expos Rookies (Clyde Mashore, Ernie McAnally)	1.00	450	Bob Gibson	10.00
377	Greg Garrett	1.00	451	Joe Keough	2.00
378	Tito Fuentes	1.00	452	John Boccabella	2.00
379	Wayne Granger	1.00	453	Terry Crowley	2.00
380	Ted Williams	10.00	454	Mike Paul	2.00
381	Fred Gladding	1.00	455	Don Kessinger	2.25
382	Jake Gibbs	1.00	456	Bob Meyer	2.00
383	Rod Gaspar	1.00	457	Willie Smith	2.00
384	Rollie Fingers	7.50	458	White Sox Rookies (Dave Lemonds, Ron Lolich)	2.00
385	Maury Wills	1.25	459	Jim Lefebvre	2.50
386	Red Sox Team	3.50	460	Fritz Peterson	2.00
387	Ron Herbel	1.00	461	Jim Hart	2.00
388	Al Oliver	1.50	462	Senators Team	3.50
389	Ed Brinkman	1.00	463	Tom Kelley	2.00
390	Glenn Beckert	1.00	464	Aurelio Rodriguez	2.00
391	Twins Rookies (Steve Brye, Cotton Nash)	1.00	465	Tim McCarver	2.50
392	Grant Jackson	1.00	466	Ken Berry	2.00
393	Merv Rettenmund	1.00	467	Al Santorini	2.00
394	Clay Carroll	2.00	468	Frank Fernandez	2.00
395	Roy White	2.00	469	Bob Aspromonte	2.00
396	Dick Schofield	2.00	470	Bob Oliver	2.00
397	Alvin Dark	2.00	471	Tom Griffin	2.00
398	Howie Reed	2.00	472	Ken Rudolph	2.00
399	Jim French	2.00	473	Gary Wagner	2.00

474	Jim Fairey	2.00	
475	Ron Perranoski	2.00	
476	Dal Maxvill	2.00	
477	Earl Weaver	4.00	
478	Bernie Carbo	2.00	
479	Dennis Higgins	2.00	
480	Manny Sanguillen	2.00	
481	Daryl Patterson	2.00	
482	Padres Team	3.50	
483	Gene Michael	2.00	
484	Don Wilson	2.00	
485	Ken McMullen	2.00	
486	Steve Huntz	2.00	
487	Paul Schaal	2.00	
488	Jerry Stephenson	2.00	
489	Luis Alvarado	2.00	
490	Deron Johnson	2.00	
491	Jim Hardin	2.00	
492	Ken Boswell	2.00	
493	Dave May	2.00	
494	Braves Rookies (Ralph Garr, Rick Kester)	2.00	
495	Felipe Alou	3.50	
496	Woody Woodward	2.00	
497	Horacio Pina	2.00	
498	John Kennedy	2.00	
499	Checklist 524-643	3.25	
500	Jim Perry	2.00	
501	Andy Etchebarren	2.00	
502	Cubs Team	3.50	
503	Gates Brown	2.00	
504	Ken Wright	2.00	
505	Ollie Brown	2.00	
506	Bobby Knoop	2.00	
507	George Stone	2.00	
508	Roger Repoz	2.00	
509	Jim Grant	2.00	
510	Ken Harrelson	2.00	
511	Chris Short	2.00	
512	Red Sox Rookies (Mike Garman, Dick Mills)	2.00	
513	Nolan Ryan	250.00	
514	Ron Woods	2.00	
515	Carl Morton	2.00	
516	Ted Kubiak	2.00	
517	Charlie Fox	2.00	
518	Joe Grzenda	2.00	
519	Willie Crawford	2.00	
520	Tommy John	4.00	
521	Leron Lee	2.00	
522	Twins Team	3.50	
523	John Odom	2.00	
524	Mickey Stanley	3.50	
525	Ernie Banks	30.00	
526	Ray Jarvis	3.50	
527	Cleon Jones	3.50	
528	Wally Bunker	3.50	
529	N.L. Rookies (Bill Buckner, Enzo Hernandez, Marty Perez)	4.00	
530	Carl Yastrzemski	30.00	
531	Mike Torrez	3.50	
532	Bill Rigney	3.50	
533	Mike Ryan	3.50	
534	Luke Walker	3.50	
535	Curt Flood	3.50	
536	Claude Raymond	3.50	
537	Tom Egan	3.50	
538	Angel Bravo	3.50	
539	Larry Brown	3.50	
540	Larry Dierker	3.50	
541	Bob Burda	3.50	
542	Bob Miller	3.50	
543	Yankees Team	7.50	
544	Vida Blue	3.50	
545	Dick Dietz	3.50	
546	John Matias	3.50	
547	Pat Dobson	3.50	
548	Don Mason	3.50	
549	Jim Brewer	3.50	
550	Harmon Killebrew	20.00	
551	Frank Linzy	3.50	
552	Buddy Bradford	3.50	
553	Kevin Collins	3.50	
554	Lowell Palmer	3.50	
555	Walt Williams	3.50	
556	Jim McGlothlin	3.50	
557	Tom Satriano	3.50	
558	Hector Torres	3.50	
559	A.L. Rookies (Terry Cox, Bill Gogolewski, Gary Jones)	3.50	
560	Rusty Staub	4.00	
561	Syd O'Brien	3.50	
562	Dave Giusti	3.50	
563	Giants Team	6.00	
564	Al Fitzmorris	3.50	
565	Jim Wynn	3.50	
566	Tim Cullen	3.50	
567	Walt Alston	4.00	
568	Sal Campisi	3.50	
569	Ivan Murrell	3.50	
570	Jim Palmer	24.00	
571	Ted Sizemore	3.50	
572	Jerry Kenney	3.50	
573	Ed Kranepool	3.50	
574	Jim Bunning	4.00	
575	Bill Freehan	3.50	
576	Cubs Rookies (Brock Davis, Adrian Garrett, Garry Jestadt)	3.50	
577	Jim Lonborg	4.00	
578	Ron Hunt	3.50	
579	Marty Pattin	3.50	
580	Tony Perez	6.00	
581	Roger Nelson	3.50	
582	Dave Cash	3.50	
583	Ron Cook	3.50	
584	Indians Team	6.00	
585	Willie Davis	3.50	
586	Dick Woodson	3.50	
587	Sonny Jackson	3.50	
588	Tom Bradley	3.50	
589	Bob Barton	3.50	
590	Alex Johnson	3.50	
591	Jackie Brown	3.50	
592	Randy Hundley	3.50	
593	Jack Aker	3.50	
594	Cards Rookies (Bob Chlupsa, Al Hrabosky, Bob Stinson)	3.50	
595	Dave Johnson	3.50	
596	Mike Jorgensen	3.50	
597	Ken Suarez	3.50	
598	Rick Wise	3.50	
599	Norm Cash	4.00	
600	Willie Mays	90.00	
601	Ken Tatum	3.50	
602	Marty Martinez	3.50	
603	Pirates Team	7.50	
604	John Gelnar	3.50	
605	Orlando Cepeda	6.00	
606	Chuck Taylor	3.50	
607	Paul Ratliff	3.50	
608	Mike Wegener	3.50	
609	Leo Durocher	3.50	
610	Amos Otis	3.50	
611	Tom Phoebus	3.50	
612	Indians Rookies (Lou Camilli, Ted Ford, Steve Mingori)	3.50	
613	Pedro Borbon	3.50	
614	Billy Cowan	3.50	
615	Mel Stottlemyre	3.50	
616	Larry Hisle	3.50	

617	Clay Dalrymple	3.50
618	Tug McGraw	3.50
619a	Checklist 644-752 (no copyright on back)	4.50
619b	Checklist 644-752 (with copyright, no wavy line on helmet brim)	3.50
619c	Checklist 644-752 (with copyright, wavy line on helmet brim)	3.50
620	Frank Howard	4.00
621	Ron Bryant	3.50
622	Joe Lahoud	3.50
623	Pat Jarvis	3.50
624	Athletics Team	6.00
625	Lou Brock	20.00
626	Freddie Patek	3.50
627	Steve Hamilton	3.50
628	John Bateman	3.50
629	John Hiller	3.50
630	Roberto Clemente	80.00
631	Eddie Fisher	3.50
632	Darrel Chaney	3.50
633	A.L. Rookies (Bobby Brooks, Pete Koegel, Scott Northey)	3.50
634	Phil Regan	3.50
635	Bobby Murcer	4.00
636	Denny Lemaster	3.50
637	Dave Bristol	3.50
638	Stan Williams	3.50
639	Tom Haller	3.50
640	Frank Robinson	35.00
641	Mets Team	8.00
642	Jim Roland	3.50
643	Rick Reichardt	3.50
644	Jim Stewart	6.00
645	Jim Maloney	6.00
646	Bobby Floyd	6.00
647	Juan Pizarro	4.50
648	Mets Rookies (Rich Folkers, Ted Martinez, Jon Matlack)	8.00
649	Sparky Lyle	8.00
650	Rich Allen	15.00
651	Jerry Robertson	6.00
652	Braves Team	5.00
653	Russ Snyder	6.00
654	Don Shaw	6.00
655	Mike Epstein	6.00
656	Gerry Nyman	6.00
657	Jose Azcue	4.50
658	Paul Lindblad	6.00
659	Byron Browne	6.00
660	Ray Culp	4.50
661	Chuck Tanner	6.00
662	Mike Hedlund	6.00
663	Marv Staehle	4.50
664	Major League Rookies (Archie Reynolds, Bob Reynolds, Ken Reynolds)	6.00
665	Ron Swoboda	8.00
666	Gene Brabender	6.00
667	Pete Ward	4.50
668	Gary Neibauer	4.50
669	Ike Brown	6.00
670	Bill Hands	4.50
671	Bill Voss	6.00
672	Ed Crosby	6.00
673	Gerry Janeski	6.00
674	Expos Team	5.00
675	Dave Boswell	4.50
676	Tommie Reynolds	4.50
677	Jack DiLauro	6.00
678	George Thomas	4.50
679	Don O'Riley	4.50
680	Don Mincher	6.00
681	Bill Butler	4.50
682	Terry Harmon	4.50
683	Bill Burbach	6.00
684	Curt Motton	4.50
685	Moe Drabowsky	4.50
686	Chico Ruiz	6.00
687	Ron Taylor	6.00
688	Sparky Anderson	20.00
689	Frank Baker	4.50
690	Bob Moose	4.50
691	Bob Heise	4.50
692	A.L. Rookies (Hal Haydel, Rogelio Moret, Wayne Twitchell)	6.00
693	Jose Pena	6.00
694	Rick Renick	6.00
695	Joe Niekro	5.00
696	Jerry Morales	4.50
697	Rickey Clark	6.00
698	Brewers Team	15.00
699	Jim Britton	4.50
700	Boog Powell	12.00
701	Bob Garibaldi	4.50
702	Milt Ramirez	4.50
703	Mike Kekich	4.50
704	J.C. Martin	6.00
705	Dick Selma	6.00
706	Joe Foy	6.00
707	Fred Lasher	4.50
708	Russ Nagelson	6.00
709	Major League Rookies (*Dusty Baker*, Don Baylor, Tom Paciorek)	90.00
710	Sonny Siebert	4.50
711	Larry Stahl	6.00
712	Jose Martinez	4.50
713	Mike Marshall	6.00
714	Dick Williams	7.00
715	Horace Clarke	6.00
716	Dave Leonhard	4.50
717	Tommie Aaron	6.00
718	Billy Wynne	4.50
719	Jerry May	6.00
720	Matty Alou	4.50
721	John Morris	4.50
722	Astros Team	9.00
723	Vicente Romo	6.00
724	Tom Tischinski	6.00
725	Gary Gentry	6.00
726	Paul Popovich	4.50
727	Ray Lamb	6.00
728	N.L. Rookies (Keith Lampard, Wayne Redmond, Bernie Williams)	4.50
729	Dick Billings	6.00
730	Jim Rooker	4.50
731	Jim Qualls	6.00
732	Bob Reed	4.50
733	Lee Maye	6.00
734	Rob Gardner	6.00
735	Mike Shannon	6.00
736	Mel Queen	6.00
737	Preston Gomez	6.00
738	Russ Gibson	6.00
739	Barry Lersch	6.00
740	Luis Aparicio	15.00
741	Skip Guinn	4.50
742	Royals Team	9.00
743	John O'Donoghue	6.00
744	Chuck Manuel	6.00
745	Sandy Alomar	6.00
746	Andy Kosco	4.50
747	N.L. Rookies (Balor Moore, Al Severinsen, Scipio Spinks)	4.50
748	John Purdin	6.00
749	Ken Szotkiewicz	4.50
750	Denny McLain	15.00
751	Al Weis	6.00
752	Dick Drago	6.00

1972 Topps

The largest Topps issue of its time appeared in 1972, with the set size reaching the 787 mark. The 2-1/2" by 3-1/2" cards are something special as well. Their fronts have a color photo which is shaped into an arch and surrounded by two different color borders, all of which is inside the overall white border. The player's name is in a white panel below the picture while the team name is above the picture in what might best be described as "superhero" type in a variety of colors. No mention of the player's position appears on the front. Cards backs are tame by comparison, featuring statistics and a trivia question. The set features a record number of specialty cards including more than six dozen "In Action" (shown as "IA" in checklists below) cards featuring action shots of popular players. There are the usual statistical leaders, playoff and World Series highlights. Other innovations are 16 "Boyhood Photo" cards which depict scrapbook black and white photos of 1972's top players, and a group of cards depicting the trophies which comprise baseball's major awards. Finally, a group of seven "Traded" cards was included which feature a large "Traded" across the front of the card.

JUAN PIZARRO

Mr. Mint Says - Psychedelic. I've probably had 500 near-mint to mint sets over the years, and lots of unopened. At one time Paul Lewicki and I had hundreds of boxes of

mid-numbers and the highs. A very popular and colorful set, with a nice, uncirculated vendor set home at about $2,500.

Quality control seemed to be getting better in these years. The superstars sell well, though the In-Action cards do not, but there is still interest because they are Hall of Famers and inexpensive.

The high numbers are becoming increasingly difficult to locate. With the high cost of table fees at shows, not many people feature commons on their tables, making completion of sets difficult.

		MT
Complete Set (787):		3000.
Common Player (1-394):		.75
Common Player (395-525):		1.00
Common Player (526-656):		2.00
Common Player (657-787):		6.00

1	World Champions (Pirates Team)	8.00
2	Ray Culp	.75
3	Bob Tolan	.75
4	Checklist 1-132	4.00
5	John Bateman	.75
6	Fred Scherman	.75
7	Enzo Hernandez	.75
8	Ron Swoboda	.75
9	Stan Williams	.75
10	Amos Otis	.75
11	Bobby Valentine	.75
12	Jose Cardenal	.75
13	Joe Grzenda	.75
14	Phillies Rookies (Mike Anderson, Pete Koegel, Wayne Twitchell)	.75
15	Walt Williams	.75
16	Mike Jorgensen	.75
17	Dave Duncan	.75
18a	Juan Pizarro (green under "C" and "S")	3.50
18b	Juan Pizarro (yellow under "C" and "S")	.75
19	Billy Cowan	.75
20	Don Wilson	.75
21	Braves Team	3.50
22	Rob Gardner	.75
23	Ted Kubiak	.75
24	Ted Ford	.75
25	Bill Singer	.75
26	Andy Etchebarren	.75
27	Bob Johnson	.75
28	Twins Rookies (Steve Brye, Bob Gebhard, Hal Haydel)	.75
29a	Bill Bonham (green under "C" and "S")	3.50
29b	Bill Bonham (yellow under "C" and "S")	.75
30	Rico Petrocelli	.90
31	Cleon Jones	.75
32	Cleon Jones (In Action)	.75
33	Billy Martin	4.50
34	Billy Martin (In Action)	1.50
35	Jerry Johnson	.75
36	Jerry Johnson (In Action)	.75
37	Carl Yastrzemski	10.00
38	Carl Yastrzemski (In Action)	6.00
39	Bob Barton	.75
40	Bob Barton (In Action)	.75

41	Tommy Davis	.80
42	Tommy Davis (In Action)	.75
43	Rick Wise	.75
44	Rick Wise (In Action)	.75
45a	Glenn Beckert (green under "C" and "S")	3.50
45b	Glenn Beckert (yellow under "C" and "S")	.75
46	Glenn Beckert (In Action)	.75
47	John Ellis	.75
48	John Ellis (In Action)	.75
49	Willie Mays	25.00
50	Willie Mays (In Action)	15.00
51	Harmon Killebrew	6.00
52	Harmon Killebrew (In Action)	4.00
53	Bud Harrelson	.75
54	Bud Harrelson (In Action)	.75
55	Clyde Wright	.75
56	Rich Chiles	.75
57	Bob Oliver	.75
58	Ernie McAnally	.75
59	*Fred Stanley*	.90
60	Manny Sanguillen	.75
61	Cubs Rookies (Gene Hiser, Burt Hooton, Earl Stephenson)	1.00
62	Angel Mangual	.75
63	Duke Sims	.75
64	Pete Broberg	.75
65	Cesar Cedeno	1.00
66	Ray Corbin	.75
67	Red Schoendienst	3.00
68	Jim York	.75
69	Roger Freed	.75
70	Mike Cuellar	.75
71	Angels Team	3.00
72	*Bruce Kison*	.75
73	Steve Huntz	.75
74	Cecil Upshaw	.75
75	Bert Campaneris	.90
76	Don Carrithers	.75
77	Ron Theobald	.75
78	Steve Arlin	.75
79	Red Sox Rookies (*Cecil Cooper*, Carlton Fisk, Mike Garman)	100.00
80	Tony Perez	4.00
81	Mike Hedlund	.75
82	Ron Woods	.75
83	Dalton Jones	.75
84	Vince Colbert	.75
85	N.L. Batting Leaders (Glenn Beckert, Ralph Garr, Joe Torre)	2.00
86	A.L. Batting Leaders (Bobby Murcer, Tony Oliva, Merv Rettenmund)	2.00
87	N.L. R.B.I. Leaders (Hank Aaron, Willie Stargell, Joe Torre)	4.50
88	A.L. R.B.I. Leaders (Harmon Killebrew, Frank Robinson, Reggie Smith)	3.50
89	N.L. Home Run Leaders (Hank Aaron, Lee May, Willie Stargell)	4.50
90	A.L. Home Run Leaders (Norm Cash, Reggie Jackson, Bill Melton)	3.50
91	N.L. E.R.A. Leaders (Dave Roberts, Tom Seaver, Don Wilson)	3.00
92	A.L. E.R.A. Leaders (Vida Blue, Jim Palmer, Wilbur Wood)	3.00
93	N.L. Pitching Leaders (Steve Carlton, Al Downing, Fergie Jenkins, Tom Seaver)	3.50
94	A.L. Pitching Leaders (Vida Blue, Mickey Lolich, Wilbur Wood)	2.00
95	N.L. Strikeout Leaders (Fergie Jenkins,Tom Seaver, Bill Stoneman)	3.00
96	A.L. Strikeout Leaders (Vida Blue, Joe Coleman, Mickey Lolich)	2.00
97	Tom Kelley	.75
98	Chuck Tanner	.70
99	*Ross Grimsley*	.80
100	Frank Robinson	6.00
101	Astros Rookies (Ray Busse, Bill Grief, J.R. Richard)	1.00
102	Lloyd Allen	.75
103	Checklist 133-263	3.00
104	*Toby Harrah*	1.50
105	Gary Gentry	.75
106	Brewers Team	3.00
107	*Jose Cruz*	2.50
108	Gary Waslewski	.75
109	Jerry May	.75
110	Ron Hunt	.75
111	Jim Grant	.75
112	Greg Luzinski	1.00
113	Rogelio Moret	.75
114	Bill Buckner	1.25
115	Jim Fregosi	.75
116	*Ed Farmer*	.75
117a	Cleo James (green under "C" and "S")	3.50
117b	Cleo James (yellow under "C" and "S")	.75
118	Skip Lockwood	.75
119	Marty Perez	.75
120	Bill Freehan	.75
121	Ed Sprague	.75
122	Larry Biittner	.75
123	Ed Acosta	.75
124	Yankees Rookies (Alan Closter, Roger Hambright, Rusty Torres)	.75
125	Dave Cash	.75
126	Bart Johnson	.75
127	Duffy Dyer	.75
128	Eddie Watt	.75
129	Charlie Fox	.75
130	Bob Gibson	6.00
131	Jim Nettles	.75
132	Joe Morgan	5.00
133	Joe Keough	.75
134	Carl Morton	.75
135	Vada Pinson	1.00
136	Darrel Chaney	.75
137	Dick Williams	.75
138	Mike Kekich	.75
139	Tim McCarver	1.00
140	Pat Dobson	.75
141	Mets Rookies (Buzz Capra, Jon Matlack, Leroy Stanton)	.75
142	*Chris Chambliss*	1.25
143	Garry Jestadt	.75
144	Marty Pattin	.75
145	Don Kessinger	.75
146	Steve Kealey	.75
147	*Dave Kingman*	4.00
148	Dick Billings	.75
149	Gary Neibauer	.75
150	Norm Cash	1.00
151	Jim Brewer	.75
152	Gene Clines	.75
153	Rick Auerbach	.75
154	Ted Simmons	1.00
155	Larry Dierker	.75
156	Twins Team	3.00
157	Don Gullett	.75
158	Jerry Kenney	.75
159	John Boccabella	.75
160	Andy Messersmith	.75
161	Brock Davis	.75
162	Brewers Rookies (Jerry Bell) (Bell & Porter photos transposed, Darrell Porter, Bob Reynolds)	.75
163	Tug McGraw	.75
164	Tug McGraw (In Action)	.75
165	*Chris Speier*	1.00
166	Chris Speier (In Action)	.75
167	Deron Johnson	.75
168	Deron Johnson (In Action)	.75
169	Vida Blue	1.00
170	Vida Blue (In Action)	.75
171	Darrell Evans	1.00
172	Darrell Evans (In Action)	.75

173	Clay Kirby	.75	246	Tom Burgmeier	.75
174	Clay Kirby (In Action)	.75	247	Milt May	.75
175	Tom Haller	.75	248	Tom Bradley	.75
176	Tom Haller (In Action)	.75	249	Harry Walker	.75
177	Paul Schaal	.75	250	Boog Powell	1.25
178	Paul Schaal (In Action)	.75	251a	Checklist 264-394 (small print on front)	3.00
179	Dock Ellis	.75	251b	Checklist 264-394 (large print on front)	3.00
180	Dock Ellis (In Action)	.75	252	Ken Reynolds	.75
181	Ed Kranepool	.75	253	Sandy Alomar	.75
182	Ed Kranepool (In Action)	.75	254	Boots Day	.75
183	Bill Melton	.75	255	Jim Lonborg	.90
184	Bill Melton (In Action)	.75	256	George Foster	1.00
185	Ron Bryant	.75	257	Tigers Rookies (Jim Foor, Tim Hosley, Paul Jata)	.75
186	Ron Bryant (In Action)	.75	258	Randy Hundley	.75
187	Gates Brown	.75	259	Sparky Lyle	1.00
188	Frank Lucchesi	.75	260	Ralph Garr	.75
189	Gene Tenace	.75	261	Steve Mingori	.75
190	Dave Giusti	.75	262	Padres Team	3.00
191	*Jeff Burroughs*	1.00	263	Felipe Alou	2.00
192	Cubs Team	3.00	264	Tommy John	2.00
193	*Kurt Bevacqua*	.75	265	Wes Parker	.75
194	Fred Norman	.75	266	Bobby Bolin	.75
195	Orlando Cepeda	2.00	267	Dave Concepcion	1.75
196	Mel Queen	.75	268	A's Rookies (Dwain Anderson, Chris Floethe)	.75
197	Johnny Briggs	.75	269	Don Hahn	.75
198	Dodgers Rookies (*Charlie Hough*, Bob O'Brien, Mike Strahler)	.75	270	Jim Palmer	10.00
199	Mike Fiore	.75	271	Ken Rudolph	.75
200	Lou Brock	6.00	272	*Mickey Rivers*	1.00
201	Phil Roof	.75	273	Bobby Floyd	.75
202	Scipio Spinks	.75	274	Al Severinsen	.75
203	*Ron Blomberg*	.75	275	Cesar Tovar	.75
204	Tommy Helms	.75	276	Gene Mauch	.75
205	Dick Drago	.75	277	Elliott Maddox	.75
206	Dal Maxvill	.75	278	Dennis Higgins	.75
207	Tom Egan	.75	279	Larry Brown	.75
208	Milt Pappas	.75	280	Willie McCovey	6.00
209	Joe Rudi	.75	281	Bill Parsons	.75
210	Denny McLain	1.00	282	Astros Team	3.00
211	Gary Sutherland	.75	283	Darrell Brandon	.75
212	Grant Jackson	.75	284	Ike Brown	.75
213	Angels Rookies (Art Kusnyer, Billy Parker, Tom Silverio)	.75	285	Gaylord Perry	6.00
214	Mike McQueen	.75	286	Gene Alley	.75
215	Alex Johnson	.75	287	Jim Hardin	.75
216	Joe Niekro	.75	288	Johnny Jeter	.75
217	Roger Metzger	.75	289	Syd O'Brien	.75
218	Eddie Kasko	.75	290	Sonny Siebert	.75
219	*Rennie Stennett*	.75	291	Hal McRae	1.00
220	Jim Perry	.75	292	Hal McRae (In Action)	.75
221	N.L. Playoffs (Bucs Champs!)	2.00	293	Danny Frisella	.75
222	A.L. Playoffs (Orioles Champs!)	2.00	294	Danny Frisella (In Action)	.75
223	World Series Game 1	2.00	295	Dick Dietz	.75
224	World Series Game 2	2.00	296	Dick Dietz (In Action)	.75
225	World Series Game 3	2.00	297	Claude Osteen	.75
226	World Series Game 4	2.00	298	Claude Osteen (In Action)	.75
227	World Series Game 5	2.00	299	Hank Aaron	25.00
228	World Series Game 6	2.00	300	Hank Aaron (In Action)	15.00
229	World Series Game 7	2.00	301	George Mitterwald	.75
230	World Series Summary (Series Celebration)	2.00	302	George Mitterwald (In Action)	.75
231	Casey Cox	.75	303	Joe Pepitone	.75
232	Giants Rookies (Chris Arnold, Jim Barr, Dave Rader)	.75	304	Joe Pepitone (In Action)	.75
233	Jay Johnstone	.75	305	Ken Boswell	.75
234	Ron Taylor	.75	306	Ken Boswell (In Action)	.75
235	Merv Rettenmund	.75	307	Steve Renko	.75
236	Jim McGlothlin	.75	308	Steve Renko (In Action)	.75
237	Yankees Team	4.50	309	Roberto Clemente	25.00
238	Leron Lee	.75	310	Roberto Clemente (In Action)	15.00
239	Tom Timmermann	.75	311	Clay Carroll	.75
240	Rich Allen	2.00	312	Clay Carroll (In Action)	.75
241	Rollie Fingers	6.00	313	Luis Aparicio	4.00
242	Don Mincher	.75	314	Luis Aparicio (In Action)	2.00
243	Frank Linzy	.75	315	Paul Splittorff	.75
244	Steve Braun	.75	316	Cardinals Rookies (*Jim Bibby*, Santiago Guzman, Jorge Roque)	.75
245	Tommie Agee	.75	317	Rich Hand	.75
			318	Sonny Jackson	.75

319	Aurelio Rodriguez	.75
320	Steve Blass	.75
321	Joe Lahoud	.75
322	Jose Pena	.75
323	Earl Weaver	1.00
324	Mike Ryan	.75
325	Mel Stottlemyre	.75
326	Pat Kelly	.75
327	*Steve Stone*	2.00
328	Red Sox Team	4.00
329	Roy Foster	.75
330	Catfish Hunter	3.50
331	Stan Swanson	.75
332	Buck Martinez	.75
333	Steve Barber	.75
334	Rangers Rookies (Bill Fahey, Jim Mason, Tom Ragland)	.75
335	Bill Hands	.75
336	Marty Martinez	.75
337	Mike Kilkenny	.75
338	Bob Grich	.75
339	Ron Cook	.75
340	Roy White	.75
341	Boyhood Photo (Joe Torre)	.75
342	Boyhood Photo (Wilbur Wood)	.75
343	Boyhood Photo (Willie Stargell)	1.50
344	Boyhood Photo (Dave McNally)	.75
345	Boyhood Photo (Rick Wise)	.75
346	Boyhood Photo (Jim Fregosi)	.75
347	Boyhood Photo (Tom Seaver)	4.00
348	Boyhood Photo (Sal Bando)	.75
349	Al Fitzmorris	.75
350	Frank Howard	1.00
351	Braves Rookies (Jimmy Britton, Tom House, Rick Kester)	.75
352	Dave LaRoche	.75
353	Art Shamsky	.75
354	Tom Murphy	.75
355	Bob Watson	.75
356	Gerry Moses	.75
357	Woodie Fryman	.75
358	Sparky Anderson	1.50
359	Don Pavletich	.75
360	Dave Roberts	.75
361	Mike Andrews	.75
362	Mets Team	4.00
363	Ron Klimkowski	.75
364	Johnny Callison	.75
365	Dick Bosman	.75
366	Jimmy Rosario	.75
367	Ron Perranoski	.75
368	Danny Thompson	.75
369	Jim Lefebvre	.75
370	Don Buford	.75
371	Denny Lemaster	.75
372	Royals Rookies (Lance Clemons, Monty Montgomery)	.75
373	John Mayberry	.75
374	Jack Heidemann	.75
375	Reggie Cleveland	.75
376	Andy Kosco	.75
377	Terry Harmon	.75
378	Checklist 395-525	3.00
379	Ken Berry	.75
380	Earl Williams	.75
381	White Sox Team	3.00
382	Joe Gibbon	.75
383	Brant Alyea	.75
384	Dave Campbell	.75
385	Mickey Stanley	.75
386	Jim Colborn	.75
387	Horace Clarke	.75
388	Charlie Williams	.75
389	Bill Rigney	.75
390	Willie Davis	.75
391	Ken Sanders	.75
392	Pirates Rookies (Fred Cambria, Richie Zisk)	.75
393	Curt Motton	.75
394	Ken Forsch	.75
395	Matty Alou	1.00
396	Paul Lindblad	1.00
397	Phillies Team	4.00
398	Larry Hisle	1.00
399	Milt Wilcox	1.00
400	Tony Oliva	1.50
401	Jim Nash	1.00
402	Bobby Heise	1.00
403	John Cumberland	1.00
404	Jeff Torborg	1.00
405	Ron Fairly	1.00
406	*George Hendrick*	1.50
407	Chuck Taylor	1.00
408	Jim Northrup	1.00
409	Frank Baker	1.00
410	Fergie Jenkins	6.00
411	Bob Montgomery	1.00
412	Dick Kelley	1.00
413	White Sox Rookies (Don Eddy, Dave Lemonds)	1.00
414	Bob Miller	1.00
415	Cookie Rojas	1.00
416	Johnny Edwards	1.00
417	Tom Hall	1.00
418	Tom Shopay	1.00
419	Jim Spencer	1.00
420	Steve Carlton	15.00
421	Ellie Rodriguez	1.00
422	Ray Lamb	1.00
423	Oscar Gamble	1.00
424	Bill Gogolewski	1.00
425	Ken Singleton	1.00
426	Ken Singleton (In Action)	1.00
427	Tito Fuentes	1.00
428	Tito Fuentes (In Action)	1.00
429	Bob Robertson	1.00
430	Bob Robertson (In Action)	1.00
431	Cito Gaston	2.50
432	Cito Gaston (In Action)	1.75
433	Johnny Bench	25.00
434	Johnny Bench (In Action)	15.00
435	Reggie Jackson	40.00
436	Reggie Jackson (In Action)	20.00
437	Maury Wills	1.50
438	Maury Wills (In Action)	1.00
439	Billy Williams	6.00
440	Billy Williams (In Action)	4.00
441	Thurman Munson	12.00
442	Thurman Munson (In Action)	7.00
443	Ken Henderson	1.00
444	Ken Henderson (In Action)	1.00
445	Tom Seaver	20.00
446	Tom Seaver (In Action)	12.00
447	Willie Stargell	6.00
448	Willie Stargell (In Action)	4.00
449	Bob Lemon	3.00
450	Mickey Lolich	1.25
451	Tony LaRussa	1.25
452	Ed Herrmann	1.00
453	Barry Lersch	1.00
454	A's Team	4.00
455	Tommy Harper	1.00
456	Mark Belanger	1.00
457	Padres Rookies (Darcy Fast, Mike Ivie, Derrel Thomas)	1.00
458	Aurelio Monteagudo	1.00
459	Rick Renick	1.00
460	Al Downing	1.00
461	Tim Cullen	1.00
462	Rickey Clark	1.00
463	Bernie Carbo	1.00
464	Jim Roland	1.00
465	Gil Hodges	3.00

466	Norm Miller	1.00
467	Steve Kline	1.00
468	Richie Scheinblum	1.00
469	Ron Herbel	1.00
470	Ray Fosse	1.00
471	Luke Walker	1.00
472	Phil Gagliano	1.00
473	Dan McGinn	1.00
474	Orioles Rookies (Don Baylor, Roric Harrison, Johnny Oates)	12.00
475	Gary Nolan	1.00
476	Lee Richard	1.00
477	Tom Phoebus	1.00
478a	Checklist 526-656 (small print on front)	3.00
478b	Checklist 526-656 (large printing on front)	3.00
479	Don Shaw	1.00
480	Lee May	1.00
481	Billy Conigliaro	1.00
482	Joe Hoerner	1.00
483	Ken Suarez	1.00
484	Lum Harris	1.00
485	Phil Regan	1.00
486	John Lowenstein	1.00
487	Tigers Team	4.00
488	Mike Nagy	1.00
489	Expos Rookies (Terry Humphrey, Keith Lampard)	1.00
490	Dave McNally	1.00
491	Boyhood Photo (Lou Piniella)	1.00
492	Boyhood Photo (Mel Stottlemyre)	1.00
493	Boyhood Photo (Bob Bailey)	1.00
494	Boyhood Photo (Willie Horton)	1.00
495	Boyhood Photo (Bill Melton)	1.00
496	Boyhood Photo (Bud Harrelson)	1.00
497	Boyhood Photo (Jim Perry)	1.00
498	Boyhood Photo (Brooks Robinson)	2.00
499	Vicente Romo	1.00
500	Joe Torre	1.00
501	Pete Hamm	1.00
502	Jackie Hernandez	1.00
503	Gary Peters	1.00
504	Ed Spiezio	1.00
505	Mike Marshall	1.00
506	Indians Rookies (Terry Ley, Jim Moyer, Dick Tidrow)	1.00
507	Fred Gladding	1.00
508	Ellie Hendricks	1.00
509	Don McMahon	1.00
510	Ted Williams	12.00
511	Tony Taylor	1.00
512	Paul Popovich	1.00
513	Lindy McDaniel	1.00
514	Ted Sizemore	1.00
515	Bert Blyleven	7.00
516	Oscar Brown	1.00
517	Ken Brett	1.00
518	Wayne Garrett	1.00
519	Ted Abernathy	1.00
520	Larry Bowa	1.25
521	Alan Foster	1.00
522	Dodgers Team	4.00
523	Chuck Dobson	1.00
524	Reds Rookies (Ed Armbrister, Mel Behney)	1.00
525	Carlos May	1.00
526	Bob Bailey	2.00
527	Dave Leonhard	2.00
528	Ron Stone	2.00
529	Dave Nelson	2.00
530	Don Sutton	4.00
531	Freddie Patek	2.00
532	Fred Kendall	2.00
533	Ralph Houk	2.00
534	Jim Hickman	2.00
535	Ed Brinkman	2.00
536	Doug Rader	2.00
537	Bob Locker	2.00
538	Charlie Sands	2.00

539	*Terry Forster*	2.00
540	Felix Millan	2.00
541	Roger Repoz	2.00
542	Jack Billingham	2.00
543	Duane Josephson	2.00
544	Ted Martinez	2.00
545	Wayne Granger	2.00
546	Joe Hague	2.00
547	Indians Team	6.00
548	Frank Reberger	2.00
549	Dave May	2.00
550	Brooks Robinson	20.00
551	Ollie Brown	2.00
552	Ollie Brown (In Action)	2.00
553	Wilbur Wood	2.00
554	Wilbur Wood (In Action)	2.00
555	Ron Santo	3.00
556	Ron Santo (In Action)	2.00
557	John Odom	2.00
558	John Odom (In Action)	2.00
559	Pete Rose	35.00
560	Pete Rose (In Action)	19.00
561	Leo Cardenas	2.00
562	Leo Cardenas (In Action)	2.00
563	Ray Sadecki	2.00
564	Ray Sadecki (In Action)	2.00
565	Reggie Smith	2.00
566	Reggie Smith (In Action)	2.00
567	Juan Marichal	6.00
568	Juan Marichal (In Action)	4.00
569	Ed Kirkpatrick	2.00
570	Ed Kirkpatrick (In Action)	2.00
571	Nate Colbert	2.00
572	Nate Colbert (In Action)	2.00
573	Fritz Peterson	2.00
574	Fritz Peterson (In Action)	2.00
575	Al Oliver	3.00
576	Leo Durocher	2.50
577	Mike Paul	2.00
578	Billy Grabarkewitz	2.00
579	*Doyle Alexander*	2.00
580	Lou Piniella	2.50
581	Wade Blasingame	2.00
582	Expos Team	5.00
583	Darold Knowles	2.00
584	Jerry McNertney	2.00
585	George Scott	2.00
586	Denis Menke	2.00
587	Billy Wilson	2.00
588	Jim Holt	2.00
589	Hal Lanier	2.00
590	Graig Nettles	3.00
591	Paul Casanova	2.00
592	Lew Krausse	2.00
593	Rich Morales	2.00
594	Jim Beauchamp	2.00
595	Nolan Ryan	250.00
596	Manny Mota	2.00
597	Jim Magnuson	2.00
598	Hal King	2.00
599	Billy Champion	2.00
600	Al Kaline	20.00
601	George Stone	2.00
602	Dave Bristol	2.00
603	Jim Ray	2.00
604a	Checklist 657-787 (copyright on right)	3.50
604b	Checklist 657-787 (copyright on left)	5.00
605	Nelson Briles	2.00
606	Luis Melendez	2.00
607	Frank Duffy	2.00
608	Mike Corkins	2.00
609	Tom Grieve	2.00
610	Bill Stoneman	2.00
611	Rich Reese	2.00

612	Joe Decker	2.00
613	Mike Ferraro	2.00
614	Ted Uhlaender	2.00
615	Steve Hargan	2.00
616	*Joe Ferguson*	2.00
617	Royals Team	5.00
618	Rich Robertson	2.00
619	Rich McKinney	2.00
620	Phil Niekro	4.50
621	Commissioners Award	2.00
622	MVP Award	2.00
623	Cy Young Award	2.00
624	Minor League Player Of The Year Award	2.00
625	Rookie Of The Year Award	2.00
626	Babe Ruth Award	2.00
627	Moe Drabowsky	2.00
628	Terry Crowley	2.00
629	Paul Doyle	2.00
630	Rich Hebner	2.00
631	John Strohmayer	2.00
632	Mike Hegan	2.00
633	Jack Hiatt	2.00
634	Dick Woodson	2.00
635	Don Money	2.00
636	Bill Lee	2.00
637	Preston Gomez	2.00
638	Ken Wright	2.00
639	J.C. Martin	2.00
640	Joe Coleman	2.00
641	Mike Lum	2.00
642	Denny Riddleberger	2.00
643	Russ Gibson	2.00
644	Bernie Allen	2.00
645	Jim Maloney	2.00
646	Chico Salmon	2.00
647	Bob Moose	2.00
648	Jim Lyttle	2.00
649	Pete Richert	2.00
650	Sal Bando	2.00
651	Reds Team	6.00
652	Marcelino Lopez	2.00
653	Jim Fairey	2.00
654	Horacio Pina	2.00
655	Jerry Grote	2.00
656	Rudy May	2.00
657	Bobby Wine	6.00
658	Steve Dunning	6.00
659	Bob Aspromonte	6.00
660	Paul Blair	6.00
661	Bill Virdon	6.00
662	Stan Bahnsen	6.00
663	Fran Healy	6.00
664	Bobby Knoop	6.00
665	Chris Short	6.00
666	Hector Torres	6.00
667	Ray Newman	6.00
668	Rangers Team	9.00
669	Willie Crawford	6.00
670	Ken Holtzman	6.00
671	Donn Clendenon	6.00
672	Archie Reynolds	6.00
673	Dave Marshall	6.00
674	John Kennedy	6.00
675	Pat Jarvis	6.00
676	Danny Cater	6.00
677	Ivan Murrell	6.00
678	Steve Luebber	6.00
679	Astros Rookies (Bob Fenwick, Bob Stinson)	6.00
680	Dave Johnson	6.00
681	Bobby Pfeil	6.00
682	Mike McCormick	6.00
683	Steve Hovley	6.00
684	Hal Breeden	6.00
685	Joe Horlen	6.00

686	Steve Garvey	45.00
687	Del Unser	6.00
688	Cardinals Team	12.00
689	Eddie Fisher	6.00
690	Willie Montanez	6.00
691	Curt Blefary	6.00
692	Curt Blefary (In Action)	6.00
693	Alan Gallagher	6.00
694	Alan Gallagher (In Action)	6.00
695	Rod Carew	75.00
696	Rod Carew (In Action)	35.00
697	Jerry Koosman	6.00
698	Jerry Koosman (In Action)	6.00
699	Bobby Murcer	6.00
700	Bobby Murcer (In Action)	6.00
701	Jose Pagan	6.00
702	Jose Pagan (In Action)	6.00
703	Doug Griffin	6.00
704	Doug Griffin (In Action)	6.00
705	Pat Corrales	6.00
706	Pat Corrales (In Action)	6.00
707	Tim Foli	6.00
708	Tim Foli (In Action)	6.00
709	Jim Kaat	9.00
710	Jim Kaat (In Action)	6.00
711	Bobby Bonds	12.00
712	Bobby Bonds (In Action)	7.00
713	Gene Michael	6.00
714	Gene Michael (In Action)	6.00
715	Mike Epstein	6.00
716	Jesus Alou	6.00
717	Bruce Dal Canton	6.00
718	Del Rice	6.00
719	Cesar Geronimo	6.00
720	Sam McDowell	6.00
721	Eddie Leon	6.00
722	Bill Sudakis	6.00
723	Al Santorini	6.00
724	A.L. Rookies (John Curtis, Rich Hinton, Mickey Scott)	6.00
725	Dick McAuliffe	6.00
726	Dick Selma	6.00
727	Jose Laboy	6.00
728	Gail Hopkins	6.00
729	Bob Veale	6.00
730	Rick Monday	6.00
731	Orioles Team	12.00
732	George Culver	6.00
733	Jim Hart	6.00
734	Bob Burda	6.00
735	Diego Segui	6.00
736	Bill Russell	6.00
737	*Lenny Randle*	6.00
738	Jim Merritt	6.00
739	Don Mason	6.00
740	Rico Carty	6.00
741	Major League Rookies (Tom Hutton, Rick Miller, John Milner)	6.00
742	Jim Rooker	6.00
743	Cesar Gutierrez	6.00
744	*Jim Slaton*	6.00
745	Julian Javier	6.00
746	Lowell Palmer	6.00
747	Jim Stewart	6.00
748	Phil Hennigan	6.00
749	Walter Alston	12.00
750	Willie Horton	6.00
751	Steve Carlton (Traded)	50.00
752	Joe Morgan (Traded)	30.00
753	Denny McLain (Traded)	10.00
754	Frank Robinson (Traded)	35.00
755	Jim Fregosi (Traded)	6.00
756	Rick Wise (Traded)	6.00
757	Jose Cardenal (Traded)	6.00
758	Gil Garrido	6.00
759	Chris Cannizzaro	6.00

760	Bill Mazeroski	12.00
761	A.L.-N.L. Rookies (*Ron Cey*, Ben Oglivie, Bernie Williams)	20.00
762	Wayne Simpson	6.00
763	Ron Hansen	6.00
764	Dusty Baker	9.00
765	Ken McMullen	6.00
766	Steve Hamilton	6.00
767	Tom McCraw	6.00
768	Denny Doyle	6.00
769	Jack Aker	6.00
770	Jim Wynn	6.00
771	Giants Team	9.00
772	Ken Tatum	6.00
773	Ron Brand	6.00
774	Luis Alvarado	6.00
775	Jerry Reuss	6.00
776	Bill Voss	6.00
777	Hoyt Wilhelm	16.00
778	Twins Rookies (Vic Albury, Rick Dempsey, Jim Strickland)	6.00
779	Tony Cloninger	6.00
780	Dick Green	6.00
781	Jim McAndrew	6.00
782	Larry Stahl	6.00
783	Les Cain	6.00
784	Ken Aspromonte	6.00
785	Vic Davalillo	6.00
786	Chuck Brinkman	6.00
787	Ron Reed	6.00

JIM HARDIN

BILL PARSONS

DON HAHN

CESAR TOVAR

FELIPE ALOU

GENE ALLEY

WILLIE McCOVEY

AL SEVERINSEN

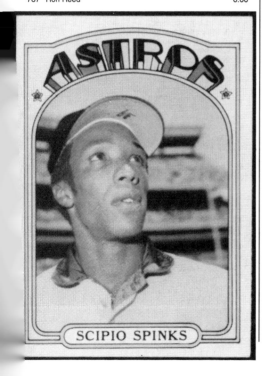

SCIPIO SPINKS

1973 Topps

Topps cut back to 660 cards in 1973. The set is interesting for it marks the last time cards were issued by series, a procedure which had produced many a scarce high number card over the years. These 2-1/2" x 3-1/2" cards have a color photo, accented by a silhouette of a player on the front, indicative of his position. Card backs are vertical for the first time since 1968, with the usual statistical and biographical information. Specialty cards begin with card number 1, which depicted Ruth, Mays and Aaron as the all-time home run leaders. It was followed by statistical leaders, although there also were additional all-time leader cards. Also present are playoff and World Series highlights. From the age-and-youth department, the 1973 Topps set has coaches and managers as well as more "Boyhood Photos."

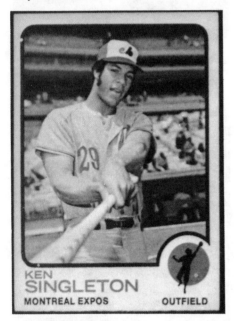

KEN SINGLETON
MONTREAL EXPOS　　　　OUTFIELD

Mr. Mint Says - Another boring set. The Schmidt card is very inactive currently, as is the rest of the set. This was the last year of cards being printed by series.

A nice, centered Schmidt should be worth $500, but most of the time they are off-center either way. The high numbers are not that much in demand and are relatively easy to get, and there were some centering problems in that series.

		MT
Complete Set (660):		1500.
Common Player (1-396):		.40
Common Player (397-528):		.70
Common Player (529-660):		2.00
1	All Time Home Run Leaders (Hank Aaron, Willie Mays, Babe Ruth)	30.00
2	Rich Hebner	.40
3	Jim Lonborg	.50
4	John Milner	.40
5	Ed Brinkman	.40
6	Mac Scarce	.40
7	Rangers Team	3.00
8	Tom Hall	.40
9	Johnny Oates	.40
10	Don Sutton	2.00
11	Chris Chambliss	.40
12a	Padres Mgr./Coaches (Dave Garcia) (Coaches background brown)	.75
12a	Padres Mgr./Coaches (Johnny Podres) (Coaches background brown)	.75
12a	Padres Mgr./Coaches (Bob Skinner) (Coaches background brown)	.75
12a	Padres Mgr./Coaches (Whitey Wietelmann) (Coaches background brown)	.75
12a	Padres Mgr./Coaches (Don Zimmer) (Coaches background brown)	.75
12b	Padres Mgr./Coaches (Dave Garcia) (Coaches background orange)	.75
12b	Padres Mgr./Coaches (Johnny Podres) (Coaches background orange)	.75
12b	Padres Mgr./Coaches (Bob Skinner) (Coaches background orange)	.75
12b	Padres Mgr./Coaches (Whitey Wietelmann) (Coaches background orange)	.75
12b	Padres Mgr./Coaches (Don Zimmer) (Coaches background orange)	.75
13	George Hendrick	.40
14	Sonny Siebert	.40
15	Ralph Garr	.40
16	Steve Braun	.40
17	Fred Gladding	.40
18	Leroy Stanton	.40
19	Tim Foli	.40
20a	Stan Bahnsen (small gap in left border)	.70
20b	Stan Bahnsen (no gap)	.40
21	Randy Hundley	.40
22	Ted Abernathy	.40
23	Dave Kingman	.75
24	Al Santorini	.40
25	Roy White	.50
26	Pirates Team	3.00
27	Bill Gogolewski	.40
28	Hal McRae	.75
29	Tony Taylor	.40
30	Tug McGraw	.40
31	*Buddy Bell*	4.00
32	Fred Norman	.40
33	Jim Breazeale	.40
34	Pat Dobson	.40
35	Willie Davis	.40
36	Steve Barber	.40
37	Bill Robinson	.40
38	Mike Epstein	.40
39	Dave Roberts	.40
40	Reggie Smith	.40
41	Tom Walker	.40
42	Mike Andrews	.40
43	*Randy Moffitt*	.40

44	Rick Monday	.40
45	Ellie Rodriguez (photo actually Paul Ratliff)	.40
46	Lindy McDaniel	.40
47	Luis Melendez	.40
48	Paul Splittorff	.40
49a	Twins Mgr./Coaches (Vern Morgan) (Coaches background brown)	.50
49a	Twins Mgr./Coaches (Frank Quilici) (Coaches background brown)	.50
49a	Twins Mgr./Coaches (Bob Rodgers) (Coaches background brown)	.50
49a	Twins Mgr./Coaches (Ralph Rowe) (Coaches background brown)	.50
49a	Twins Mgr./Coaches (Al Worthington) (Coaches background brown)	.50
49b	Twins Mgr./Coaches (Vern Morgan) (Coaches background orange)	.50
49b	Twins Mgr./Coaches (Frank Quilici) (Coaches background orange)	.50
49b	Twins Mgr./Coaches (Bob Rodgers) (Coaches background orange)	.50
49b	Twins Mgr./Coaches (Ralph Rowe) (Coaches background orange)	.50
49b	Twins Mgr./Coaches (Al Worthington) (Coaches background orange)	.50
50	Roberto Clemente	35.00
51	Chuck Seelbach	.40
52	Denis Menke	.40
53	Steve Dunning	.40
54	Checklist 1-132	2.00
55	Jon Matlack	.40
56	Merv Rettenmund	.40
57	Derrel Thomas	.40
58	Mike Paul	.40
59	*Steve Yeager*	.80
60	Ken Holtzman	.40
61	Batting Leaders (Rod Carew, Billy Williams)	2.25
62	Home Run Leaders (Dick Allen, Johnny Bench)	2.25
63	Runs Batted In Leaders (Dick Allen, Johnny Bench)	2.25
64	Stolen Base Leaders (Lou Brock, Bert Campaneris)	2.00
65	Earned Run Average Leaders (Steve Carlton, Luis Tiant)	2.00
66	Victory Leaders (Steve Carlton, Gaylord Perry, Wilbur Wood)	2.00
67	Strikeout Leaders (Steve Carlton, Nolan Ryan)	15.00
68	Leading Firemen (Clay Carroll, Sparky Lyle)	.75
69	Phil Gagliano	.40
70	Milt Pappas	.40
71	Johnny Briggs	.40
72	Ron Reed	.40
73	Ed Herrmann	.40
74	Billy Champion	.40
75	Vada Pinson	.75
76	Doug Rader	.40
77	Mike Torrez	.40
78	Richie Scheinblum	.40
79	Jim Willoughby	.40
80	Tony Oliva	.75
81a	Cubs Mgr./Coaches (Hank Aguirre) (trees in Coaches background)	.90
81a	Cubs Mgr./Coaches (Ernie Banks) (trees in Coaches background)	.90
81a	Cubs Mgr./Coaches (Larry Jansen) (trees in Coaches background)	.90
81a	Cubs Mgr./Coaches (Whitey Lockman) (trees in Coaches background)	.90
81a	Cubs Mgr./Coaches (Pete Reiser) (trees in Coaches background)	.90
81b	Cubs Mgr./Coaches (Hank Aguirre) (orange, solid background)	.70
81b	Cubs Mgr./Coaches (Ernie banks) (orange, solid background)	.70
81b	Cubs Mgr./Coaches (Larry Jansen) (orange, solid background)	.70
81b	Cubs Mgr./Coaches (Whitey Lockman) (orange, solid background)	.70
81b	Cubs Mgr./Coaches (Pete Reiser) (orange, solid background)	.70
82	Fritz Peterson	.40
83	Leron Lee	.40
84	Rollie Fingers	5.00
85	Ted Simmons	1.50
86	Tom McCraw	.40
87	Ken Boswell	.40
88	Mickey Stanley	.40
89	Jack Billingham	.40
90	Brooks Robinson	7.50
91	Dodgers Team	4.00
92	Jerry Bell	.40
93	Jesus Alou	.40
94	Dick Billings	.40
95	Steve Blass	.40
96	Doug Griffin	.40
97	Willie Montanez	.40
98	Dick Woodson	.40
99	Carl Taylor	.40
100	Hank Aaron	25.00
101	Ken Henderson	.40
102	Rudy May	.40
103	Celerino Sanchez	.40
104	Reggie Cleveland	.40
105	Carlos May	.40
106	Terry Humphrey	.40
107	Phil Hennigan	.40
108	Bill Russell	.60
109	Doyle Alexander	.40
110	Bob Watson	.40
111	Dave Nelson	.40
112	Gary Ross	.40
113	Jerry Grote	.40
114	Lynn McGlothen	.40
115	Ron Santo	.75
116a	Yankees Mgr./Coaches (Jim Hegan) (Coaches background brown)	2.25
116a	Yankees Mgr./Coaches (Ralph Houk) (Coaches background brown)	2.25
116a	Yankees Mgr./Coaches (Elston Howard) (Coaches background brown)	2.25
116a	Yankees Mgr./Coaches (Dick Howser) (Coaches background brown)	2.25
116a	Yankees Mgr./Coaches (Jim Turner) (Coaches background brown)	2.25
116b	Yankees Mgr./Coaches (Jim Hegan) (Coaches background orange)	.90
116b	Yankees Mgr./Coaches (Ralph Houk) (Coaches background orange)	.90
116b	Yankees Mgr./Coaches (Elston Howard) (Coaches background orange)	.90
116b	Yankees Mgr./Coaches (Dick Howser) (Coaches background orange)	.90
116b	Yankees Mgr./Coaches (Jim Turner) (Coaches background orange)	.90
117	Ramon Hernandez	.40
118	John Mayberry	.40
119	Larry Bowa	.75
120	Joe Coleman	.40
121	Dave Rader	.40
122	Jim Strickland	.40
123	Sandy Alomar	.40
124	Jim Hardin	.40
125	Ron Fairly	.40
126	Jim Brewer	.40
127	Brewers Team	3.00
128	Ted Sizemore	.40
129	Terry Forster	.40
130	Pete Rose	20.00
131a	Red Sox Mgr./Coaches (Doug Camilli) (Coaches background brown)	.70
131a	Red Sox Mgr./Coaches (Eddie Kasko) (Coaches background brown)	.70

131a Red Sox Mgr./Coaches (Don Lenhardt)		
(Coaches background brown)	.70	
131a Red Sox Mgr./Coaches (Eddie Popowski)		
(Coaches background brown)	.70	
131a Red Sox Mgr./Coaches (Lee Stange)		
(Coaches background brown)	.70	
131b Red Sox Mgr./Coaches (Doug Camilli)		
(Coaches background orange)	.50	
131b Red Sox Mgr./Coaches (Eddie Kasko)		
(Coaches background orange)	.50	
131b Red Sox Mgr./Coaches (Don Lenhardt)		
(Coaches background orange)	.50	
131b Red Sox Mgr./Coaches (Eddie Popowski)		
(Coaches background orange)	.50	
131b Red Sox Mgr./Coaches (Lee Stange)		
(Coaches background orange)	.50	
132 Matty Alou	.40	
133 Dave Roberts	.40	
134 Milt Wilcox	.40	
135 Lee May	.40	
136a Orioles Mgr./Coaches (George Bamberger)		
(Coaches background brown)	2.25	
136a Orioles Mgr./Coaches (Jim Frey)		
(Coaches background brown)	2.25	
136a Orioles Mgr./Coaches (Billy Hunter)		
(Coaches background brown)	2.25	
136a Orioles Mgr./Coaches (George Staller)		
Coaches background brown)	2.25	
136a Orioles Mgr./Coaches (Earl Weaver)		
(Coaches background brown)	2.25	
136b Orioles Mgr./Coaches (George Bamberger)		
(Coaches background orange)	.90	
136b Orioles Mgr./Coaches (Jim Frey)		
(Coaches background orange)	.90	
136b Orioles Mgr./Coaches (Billy Hunter)		
(Coaches background orange)	.90	
136b Orioles Mgr./Coaches (George Staller)		
(Coaches background orange)	.90	
136b Orioles Mgr./Coaches (Earl Weaver)		
(Coaches background orange)	.90	
137 Jim Beauchamp	.40	
138 Horacio Pina	.40	
139 Carmen Fanzone	.40	
140 Lou Piniella	.60	
141 Bruce Kison	.40	
142 Thurman Munson	10.00	
143 John Curtis	.40	
144 Marty Perez	.40	
145 Bobby Bonds	.90	
146 Woodie Fryman	.40	
147 Mike Anderson	.40	
148 *Dave Goltz*	.40	
149 Ron Hunt	.40	
150 Wilbur Wood	.40	
151 Wes Parker	.40	
152 Dave May	.40	
153 Al Hrabosky	.40	
154 Jeff Torborg	.40	
155 Sal Bando	.40	
156 Cesar Geronimo	.40	
157 Denny Riddleberger	.40	
158 Astros Team	3.00	
159 Cito Gaston	.75	
160 Jim Palmer	10.00	
161 Ted Martinez	.40	
162 Pete Broberg	.40	
163 Vic Davalillo	.40	
164 Monty Montgomery	.40	
165 Luis Aparicio	2.75	
166 Terry Harmon	.40	
167 Steve Stone	.40	
168 Jim Northrup	.40	
169 Ron Schueler	.40	
170 Harmon Killebrew	5.00	
171 Bernie Carbo	.40	
172 Steve Kline	.40	

173 Hal Breeden	.40	
174 *Rich Gossage*	15.00	
175 Frank Robinson	10.00	
176 Chuck Taylor	.40	
177 Bill Plummer	.40	
178 Don Rose	.40	
179a A's Mgr./Coaches (Jerry Adair)		
(Coaches background brown)	1.00	
179a A's Mgr./Coaches (Vern Hoscheit)		
(Coaches background brown)	1.00	
179a A's Mgr./Coaches (Irv Noren)		
(Coaches background brown)	1.00	
179a A's Mgr./Coaches (Wes Stock)		
(Coaches background brown)	1.00	
179a A's Mgr./Coaches (Dick Williams)		
(Coaches background brown)	1.00	
179b A's Mgr./Coaches (Jerry Adair)		
(Coaches background orange)	.70	
179b A's Mgr./Coaches (Vern Hoscheit)		
(Coaches background orange)	.70	
179b A's Mgr./Coaches (Irv Noren)		
(Coaches background orange)	.70	
179b A's Mgr./Coaches (Wes Stock)		
(Coaches background orange)	.70	
179b A's Mgr./Coaches (Dick Williams)		
(Coaches background orange)	.70	
180 Fergie Jenkins	4.00	
181 Jack Brohamer	.40	
182 *Mike Caldwell*	.40	
183 Don Buford	.40	
184 Jerry Koosman	.40	
185 Jim Wynn	.40	
186 Bill Fahey	.40	
187 Luke Walker	.40	
188 Cookie Rojas	.40	
189 Greg Luzinski	.90	
190 Bob Gibson	5.00	
191 Tigers Team	3.00	
192 Pat Jarvis	.40	
193 Carlton Fisk	30.00	
194 *Jorge Orta*	.40	
195 Clay Carroll	.40	
196 Ken McMullen	.40	
197 Ed Goodson	.40	
198 Horace Clarke	.40	
199 Bert Blyleven	3.00	
200 Billy Williams	4.00	
201 A.L. Playoffs (Hendrick Scores Winning Run.)	2.25	
202 N.L. Playoffs (Foster's Run Decides It.)	2.25	
203 World Series Game 1 (Tenace The Menace.)	2.25	
204 World Series Game 2 (A's Make It Two Straight.)	2.25	
205 World Series Game 3 (Reds Win Squeeker.)	2.25	
206 World Series Game 4 (Tenace Singles In Ninth.)	2.25	
207 World Series Game 5 (Odom Out At Plate.)	2.25	
208 World Series Game 6 (Reds' Slugging Ties Series.)	2.25	
209 World Series Game 7 (Campy Starts Winning Rally.)	2.25	
210 World Series Summary (World Champions.)	2.25	
211 Balor Moore	.40	
212 Joe Lahoud	.40	
213 Steve Garvey	7.50	
214 Dave Hamilton	.40	
215 Dusty Baker	.75	
216 Toby Harrah	.40	
217 Don Wilson	.40	
218 Aurelio Rodriguez	.40	
219 Cardinals Team	3.00	
220 Nolan Ryan	90.00	
221 Fred Kendall	.40	
222 Rob Gardner	.40	
223 Bud Harrelson	.40	
224 Bill Lee	.40	
225 Al Oliver	.75	
226 Ray Fosse	.40	
227 Wayne Twitchell	.40	
228 Bobby Darwin	.40	

229	Roric Harrison	.40
230	Joe Morgan	5.00
231	Bill Parsons	.40
232	Ken Singleton	.40
233	Ed Kirkpatrick	.40
234	*Bill North*	.40
235	Catfish Hunter	4.00
236	Tito Fuentes	.40
237a	Braves Mgr./Coaches (Lew Burdette) (Coaches background brown)	2.50
237a	Braves Mgr./Coaches (Jim Busby) (Coaches background brown)	2.50
237a	Braves Mgr./Coaches (Roy Hartsfield) (Coaches background brown)	2.50
237a	Braves Mgr./Coaches (Eddie Mathews) (Coaches background brown)	2.50
237a	Braves Mgr./Coaches (Ken Silvestri) (Coaches background brown)	2.50
237b	Braves Mgr./Coaches (Lew Burdette) (Coaches background orange)	2.25
237b	Braves Mgr./Coaches (Jim Busby) (Coaches background orange)	2.25
237b	Braves Mgr./Coaches (Roy Hartsfield) (Coaches background orange)	2.25
237b	Braves Mgr./Coaches (Eddie mathews) (Coaches background orange)	2.25
237b	Braves Mgr./Coaches (Ken Silvestri) (Coaches background orange)	2.25
238	Tony Muser	.40
239	Pete Richert	.40
240	Bobby Murcer	.60
241	Dwain Anderson	.40
242	George Culver	.40
243	Angels Team	3.00
244	Ed Acosta	.40
245	Carl Yastrzemski	15.00
246	Ken Sanders	.40
247	Del Unser	.40
248	Jerry Johnson	.40
249	Larry Biittner	.40
250	Manny Sanguillen	.40
251	Roger Nelson	.40
252a	Giants Mgr./Coaches (Joe Amalfitano) (Coaches background brown)	.70
252a	Giants Mgr./Coaches (Charlie Fox) (Coaches background brown)	.70
252a	Giants Mgr./Coaches (Andy Gilbert) (Coaches background brown)	.70
252a	Giants Mgr./Coaches (Don McMahon) (Coaches background brown)	.70
252a	Giants Mgr./Coaches (John McNamara) (Coaches background brown)	.70
252b	Giants Mgr./Coaches (Joe Amalfitano) (Coaches background orange)	.50
252b	Giants Mgr./Coaches (Charlie Fox) (Coaches background orange)	.50
252b	Giants Mgr./Coaches (Andy Gilbert) (Coaches background orange)	.50
252b	Giants Mgr./Coaches (Don McMahon) (Coaches background orange)	.50
252b	Giants Mgr./Coaches (John McNamara) (Coachesbackground orange)	.50
253	Mark Belanger	.40
254	Bill Stoneman	.40
255	Reggie Jackson	30.00
256	Chris Zachary	.40
257a	Mets Mgr./Coaches (Yogi Berra) (Coaches background brown)	3.00
257a	Mets Mgr./Coaches (Roy McMillan) (Coaches background brown)	3.00
257a	Mets Mgr./Coaches (Joe Pignatano) (Coaches background brown)	3.00
257a	Mets Mgr./Coaches (Rube Walker) (Coaches background brown)	3.00
257a	Mets Mgr./Coaches (Eddie Yost) (Coaches background brown)	3.00
257b	Mets Mgr./Coaches (Yogi berra) (Coaches background orange)	2.50

257b	Mets Mgr./Coaches (Roy McMillan) (Coaches background orange)	2.50
257b	Mets Mgr./Coaches (Joe Pignatano) (Coaches background orange)	2.50
257b	Mets Mgr./Coaches (Rube Walker) (Coaches background orange)	2.50
257b	Mets Mgr./Coaches (Eddie Yost) (Coaches background orange)	2.50
258	Tommy John	2.00
259	Jim Holt	.40
260	Gary Nolan	.40
261	Pat Kelly	.40
262	Jack Aker	.40
263	George Scott	.40
264	Checklist 133-264	2.00
265	Gene Michael	.40
266	Mike Lum	.40
267	Lloyd Allen	.40
268	Jerry Morales	.40
269	Tim McCarver	.75
270	Luis Tiant	.75
271	Tom Hutton	.40
272	Ed Farmer	.40
273	Chris Speier	.40
274	Darold Knowles	.40
275	Tony Perez	3.00
276	Joe Lovitto	.40
277	Bob Miller	.40
278	Orioles Team	3.00
279	Mike Strahler	.40
280	Al Kaline	8.00
281	Mike Jorgensen	.40
282	Steve Hovley	.40
283	Ray Sadecki	.40
284	Glenn Borgmann	.40
285	Don Kessinger	.40
286	Frank Linzy	.40
287	Eddie Leon	.40
288	Gary Gentry	.40
289	Bob Oliver	.40
290	Cesar Cedeno	.40
291	Rogelio Moret	.40
292	Jose Cruz	.60
293	Bernie Allen	.40
294	Steve Arlin	.40
295	Bert Campaneris	.75
296	Reds Mgr./Coaches (Sparky Anderson, Alex Grammas, Ted Kluszewski, George Scherger, Larry Shepard)	2.00
297	Walt Williams	.40
298	Ron Bryant	.40
299	Ted Ford	.40
300	Steve Carlton	15.00
301	Billy Grabarkewitz	.40
302	Terry Crowley	.40
303	Nelson Briles	.40
304	Duke Sims	.40
305	Willie Mays	35.00
306	Tom Burgmeier	.40
307	Boots Day	.40
308	Skip Lockwood	.40
309	Paul Popovich	.40
310	Dick Allen	.75
311	Joe Decker	.40
312	Oscar Brown	.40
313	Jim Ray	.40
314	Ron Swoboda	.40
315	John Odom	.40
316	Padres Team	3.00
317	Danny Cater	.40
318	Jim McGlothlin	.40
319	Jim Spencer	.40
320	Lou Brock	6.00
321	Rich Hinton	.40

No.	Name	Price
322	*Garry Maddox*	1.00
323	Tigers Mgr./Coaches (Art Fowler, Billy Martin, Joe Schultz, Charlie Silvera, Dick Tracewski)	1.50
324	Al Downing	.40
325	Boog Powell	.75
326	Darrell Brandon	.40
327	John Lowenstein	.40
328	Bill Bonham	.40
329	Ed Kranepool	.40
330	Rod Carew	15.00
331	Carl Morton	.40
332	*John Felske*	.40
333	Gene Clines	.40
334	Freddie Patek	.40
335	Bob Tolan	.40
336	Tom Bradley	.40
337	Dave Duncan	.40
338	Checklist 265-396	2.00
339	Dick Tidrow	.40
340	Nate Colbert	.40
341	Boyhood Photo (Jim Palmer)	2.00
342	Boyhood Photo (Sam McDowell)	.40
343	Boyhood Photo (Bobby Murcer)	.40
344	Boyhood Photo (Catfish Hunter)	1.50
345	Boyhood Photo (Chris Speier)	.40
346	Boyhood Photo (Gaylord Perry)	1.50
347	Royals Team	3.00
348	Rennie Stennett	.40
349	Dick McAuliffe	.40
350	Tom Seaver	20.00
351	Jimmy Stewart	.40
352	*Don Stanhouse*	.40
353	Steve Brye	.40
354	Billy Parker	.40
355	Mike Marshall	.40
356	White Sox Mgr./Coaches (Joe Lonnett, Jim Mahoney, Al Monchak, Johnny Sain, Chuck Tanner)	.60
357	Ross Grimsley	.40
358	Jim Nettles	.40
359	Cecil Upshaw	.40
360	Joe Rudi (photo actually Gene Tenace)	.40
361	Fran Healy	.40
362	Eddie Watt	.40
363	Jackie Hernandez	.40
364	Rick Wise	.40
365	Rico Petrocelli	.40
366	Brock Davis	.40
367	Burt Hooton	.40
368	Bill Buckner	.60
369	Lerrin LaGrow	.40
370	Willie Stargell	6.00
371	Mike Kekich	.40
372	Oscar Gamble	.40
373	Clyde Wright	.40
374	Darrell Evans	.40
375	Larry Dierker	.40
376	Frank Duffy	.40
377	Expos Mgr./Coaches (Dave Bristol, Larry Doby, Gene Mauch, Cal McLish, Jerry Zimmerman)	.60
378	Lenny Randle	.40
379	Cy Acosta	.40
380	Johnny Bench	20.00
381	Vicente Romo	.40
382	Mike Hegan	.40
383	Diego Segui	.40
384	Don Baylor	2.00
385	Jim Perry	.40
386	Don Money	.40
387	Jim Barr	.40
388	Ben Oglivie	.40
389	Mets Team	3.00
390	Mickey Lolich	.75
391	*Lee Lacy*	.40
392	Dick Drago	.40
393	Jose Cardenal	.40
394	Sparky Lyle	.40
395	Roger Metzger	.40
396	Grant Jackson	.40
397	Dave Cash	.70
398	Rich Hand	.70
399	George Foster	1.50
400	Gaylord Perry	6.00
401	Clyde Mashore	.70
402	Jack Hiatt	.70
403	Sonny Jackson	.70
404	Chuck Brinkman	.70
405	Cesar Tovar	.70
406	Paul Lindblad	.70
407	Felix Millan	.70
408	Jim Colborn	.70
409	Ivan Murrell	.70
410	Willie McCovey	6.00
411	Ray Corbin	.70
412	Manny Mota	.70
413	Tom Timmermann	.70
414	Ken Rudolph	.70
415	Marty Pattin	.70
416	Paul Schaal	.70
417	Scipio Spinks	.70
418	Bobby Grich	.70
419	Casey Cox	.70
420	Tommie Agee	.70
421	Angels Mgr./Coaches (Tom Morgan, Salty Parker, Jimmie Reese, John Roseboro, Bobby Winkles)	.70
422	Bob Robertson	.70
423	Johnny Jeter	.70
424	Denny Doyle	.70
425	Alex Johnson	.70
426	Dave LaRoche	.70
427	Rick Auerbach	.70
428	Wayne Simpson	.70
429	Jim Fairey	.70
430	Vida Blue	1.00
431	Gerry Moses	.70
432	Dan Frisella	.70
433	Willie Horton	.70
434	Giants Team	4.00
435	Rico Carty	.70
436	Jim McAndrew	.70
437	John Kennedy	.70
438	Enzo Hernandez	.70
439	Eddie Fisher	.70
440	Glenn Beckert	.70
441	Gail Hopkins	.70
442	Dick Dietz	.70
443	Danny Thompson	.70
444	Ken Brett	.70
445	Ken Berry	.70
446	Jerry Reuss	.70
447	Joe Hague	.70
448	John Hiller	.70
449a	Indians Mgr./Coaches (Ken Aspromonte) (Spahn's ear pointed)	1.50
449a	Indians Mgr./Coaches (Rocky Colavito) (Spahn's ear pointed)	1.50
449a	Indians Mgr./Coaches (Joe Lutz) (Spahn's ear pointed)	1.50
449a	Indians Mgr./Coaches (Warren Spahn) (Spahn's ear pointed)	1.50
449b	Indians Mgr./Coaches (Ken Aspromonte) (Spahn's ear round)	2.00
449b	Indians Mgr./Coaches (Rocky Colavito) (Spahn's ear round)	2.00
449b	Indians Mgr./Coaches (Joe Lutz) (Spahn's ear round)	2.00
449b	Indians Mgr./Coaches (Warren Spahn) (Spahn's ear round)	2.00
450	Joe Torre	.70
451	John Vukovich	.70

#	Player	Price
452	Paul Casanova	.70
453	Checklist 397-528	2.25
454	Tom Haller	.70
455	Bill Melton	.70
456	Dick Green	.70
457	John Strohmayer	.70
458	Jim Mason	.70
459	Jimmy Howarth	.70
460	Bill Freehan	.70
461	Mike Corkins	.70
462	Ron Blomberg	.70
463	Ken Tatum	.70
464	Cubs Team	4.00
465	Dave Giusti	.70
466	Jose Arcia	.70
467	Mike Ryan	.70
468	Tom Griffin	.70
469	Dan Monzon	.70
470	Mike Cuellar	.70
471	All-Time Hit Leader (Ty Cobb)	5.00
472	All-Time Grand Slam Leader (Lou Gehrig)	7.50
473	All-Time Total Base Leader (Hank Aaron)	5.00
474	All-Time RBI Leader (Babe Ruth)	12.00
475	All-Time Batting Leader (Ty Cobb)	5.00
476	All-Time Shutout Leader (Walter Johnson)	2.00
477	All-Time Victory Leader (Cy Young)	2.00
478	All-Time Strikeout Leader (Walter Johnson)	2.00
479	Hal Lanier	.70
480	Juan Marichal	6.00
481	White Sox Team	4.00
482	*Rick Reuschel*	1.50
483	Dal Maxvill	.70
484	Ernie McAnally	.70
485	Norm Cash	1.00
486a	Phillies Mgr./Coaches (Carroll Berringer) (Coaches background brown-red)	.90
486a	Phillies Mgr./Coaches (Billy DeMars) (Coaches background brown-red)	.90
486a	Phillies Mgr./Coaches (Danny Ozark) (Coaches background brown-red)	.90
486a	Phillies Mgr./Coaches (Ray Rippelmeyer) (Coaches background brown-red)	.90
486a	Phillies Mgr./Coaches (Bobby Wine) (Coaches background brown-red)	.90
486b	Phillies Mgr./Coaches (Carroll Beringer) (Coaches background orange)	.70
486b	Phillies Mgr./Coaches (Billy DeMars) (Coaches background orange)	.70
486b	Phillies Mgr./Coaches (Danny Ozark) (Coaches background orange)	.70
486b	Phillies Mgr./Coaches (Ray Rippelmeyer) (Coaches background orange)	.70
486b	Phillies Mgr./Coaches (Bobby Wine) (Coaches background orange)	.70
487	Bruce Dal Canton	.70
488	Dave Campbell	.70
489	Jeff Burroughs	.70
490	Claude Osteen	.70
491	Bob Montgomery	.70
492	Pedro Borbon	.70
493	Duffy Dyer	.70
494	Rich Morales	.70
495	Tommy Helms	.70
496	Ray Lamb	.70
497	Cardinals Mgr./Coaches (Vern Benson, George Kissell, Red Schoendienst, Barney Schultz)	1.25
498	Graig Nettles	1.00
499	Bob Moose	.70
500	A's Team	4.00
501	Larry Gura	.70
502	Bobby Valentine	.70
503	Phil Niekro	5.00
504	Earl Williams	.70
505	Bob Bailey	.70
506	Bart Johnson	.70
507	Darrel Chaney	.70
508	Gates Brown	.70
509	Jim Nash	.70
510	Amos Otis	.70
511	Sam McDowell	.70
512	Dalton Jones	.70
513	Dave Marshall	.70
514	Jerry Kenney	.70
515	Andy Messersmith	.70
516	Danny Walton	.70
517a	Pirates Mgr./Coaches (Don Leppert) (Coaches background brown)	2.00
517a	Pirates Mgr./Coaches (Bill Mazeroski) (Coaches background brown)	2.00
517a	Pirates Mgr./Coaches (Dave Ricketts) (Coaches background brown)	2.00
517a	Pirates Mgr./Coaches (Bill Virdon) (Coaches background brown)	2.00
517a	Pirates Mgr./Coaches (Mel Wright) (Coaches background brown)	2.00
517b	Pirates Mgr./Coaches (Don Leppert) (Coaches background orange)	.70
517b	Pirates Mgr./Coaches (Bill Mazeroski) (Coaches background orange)	.70
517b	Pirates Mgr./Coaches (Dave Ricketts) (Coaches background orange)	.70
517b	Pirates Mgr./Coaches (Bill Virdon) (Coaches background orange)	.70
517b	Pirates Mgr./Coaches (Mel Wright) (Coaches background orange)	.70
518	Bob Veale	.70
519	John Edwards	.70
520	Mel Stottlemyre	.70
521	Braves Team	4.00
522	Leo Cardenas	.70
523	Wayne Granger	.70
524	Gene Tenace	.70
525	Jim Fregosi	.70
526	Ollie Brown	.70
527	Dan McGinn	.70
528	Paul Blair	.70
529	Milt May	2.00
530	Jim Kaat	4.00
531	Ron Woods	2.00
532	Steve Mingori	2.00
533	Larry Stahl	2.00
534	Dave Lemonds	2.00
535	John Callison	2.00
536	Phillies Team	6.00
537	Bill Slayback	2.00
538	Jim Hart	2.00
539	Tom Murphy	2.00
540	Cleon Jones	2.00
541	Bob Bolin	2.00
542	Pat Corrales	2.00
543	Alan Foster	2.00
544	Von Joshua	2.00
545	Orlando Cepeda	4.00
546	Jim York	2.00
547	Bobby Heise	2.00
548	Don Durham	2.00
549	Rangers Mgr./Coaches (Chuck Estrada, Whitey Herzog, Chuck Hiller, Jackie Moore)	2.50
550	Dave Johnson	2.00
551	Mike Kilkenny	2.00
552	J.C. Martin	2.00
553	Mickey Scott	2.00
554	Dave Concepcion	2.50
555	Bill Hands	2.00
556	Yankees Team	7.50
557	Bernie Williams	2.00
558	Jerry May	2.00
559	Barry Lersch	2.00
560	Frank Howard	2.00

561	Jim Geddes	2.00
562	Wayne Garrett	2.00
563	Larry Haney	2.00
564	Mike Thompson	2.00
565	Jim Hickman	2.00
566	Lew Krausse	2.00
567	Bob Fenwick	2.00
568	Ray Newman	2.00
569	Dodgers Mgr./Coaches (Red Adams, Walt Alston, Monty Basgall, Jim Gilliam, Tom Lasorda)	4.00
570	Bill Singer	2.00
571	Rusty Torres	2.00
572	Gary Sutherland	2.00
573	Fred Beene	2.00
574	Bob Didier	2.00
575	Dock Ellis	2.00
576	Expos Team	5.00
577	*Eric Soderholm*	2.00
578	Ken Wright	2.00
579	Tom Grieve	2.00
580	Joe Pepitone	2.00
581	Steve Kealey	2.00
582	Darrell Porter	2.00
583	Bill Greif	2.00
584	Chris Arnold	2.00
585	Joe Niekro	2.00
586	Bill Sudakis	2.00
587	Rich McKinney	2.00
588	Checklist 529-660	2.00
589	Ken Forsch	2.00
590	Deron Johnson	2.00
591	Mike Hedlund	2.00
592	John Boccabella	2.00
593	Royals Mgr./Coaches (Galen Cisco, Harry Dunlop, Charlie Lau, Jack McKeon)	2.25
594	Vic Harris	2.00
595	Don Gullett	2.00
596	Red Sox Team	6.00
597	Mickey Rivers	2.00
598	Phil Roof	2.00
599	Ed Crosby	2.00
600	Dave McNally	2.00
601	Rookie Catchers (George Pena, Sergio Robles, Rick Stelmaszek)	2.00
602	Rookie Pitchers (Mel Behney, Ralph Garcia, Doug Rau)	2.00
603	Rookie Third Basemen (Terry Hughes, Bill McNulty, Ken Reitz)	2.00
604	Rookie Pitchers (Jesse Jefferson, Dennis O'Toole, Bob Strampe)	2.00
605	Rookie First Basemen (Pat Bourque, Enos Cabell, Gonzalo Marquez)	2.00
606	Rookie Outfielders (*Gary Matthews*, Tom Paciorek, Jorge Roque)	2.25
607	Rookie Shortstops (Ray Busse, Pepe Frias, Mario Guerrero)	2.00
608	Rookie Pitchers (*Steve Busby*, Dick Colpaert, George Medich)	2.25
609	Rookie Second Basemen (Larvell Blanks, Pedro Garcia, Dave Lopes)	4.00
610	Rookie Pitchers (Jimmy Freeman, Charlie Hough, Hank Webb)	2.25
611	Rookie Outfielders (Rich Coggins, Jim Wohlford, Richie Zisk)	2.25
612	Rookie Pitchers (Steve Lawson, Bob Reynolds, Brent Strom)	2.00
613	Rookie Catchers (*Bob Boone*, Mike Ivie, Skip Jutze)	30.00
614	Rookie Outfielders (*Alonza Bumbry*, Dwight Evans, Charlie Spikes)	30.00
615	Rookie Third Basemen (Ron Cey, John Hilton, Mike Schmidt)	450.00
616	Rookie Pitchers (Norm Angelini, Steve Blateric, Mike Garman)	2.00
617	Rich Chiles	2.00

618	Andy Etchebarren	2.00
619	Billy Wilson	2.00
620	Tommy Harper	2.00
621	Joe Ferguson	2.00
622	Larry Hisle	2.00
623	Steve Renko	2.00
624	Astros Mgr./Coaches (Leo Durocher, Preston Gomez, Grady Hatton, Hub Kittle, Jim Owens)	2.25
625	Angel Mangual	2.00
626	Bob Barton	2.00
627	Luis Alvarado	2.00
628	Jim Slaton	2.00
629	Indians Team	5.00
630	Denny McLain	3.00
631	Tom Matchick	2.00
632	Dick Selma	2.00
633	Ike Brown	2.00
634	Alan Closter	2.00
635	Gene Alley	2.00
636	Rick Clark	2.00
637	Norm Niller	2.00
638	Ken Reynolds	2.00
639	Willie Crawford	2.00
640	Dick Bosman	2.00
641	Reds Team	6.00
642	Jose Laboy	2.00
643	Al Fitzmorris	2.00
644	Jack Heidemann	2.00
645	Bob Locker	2.00
646	Brewers Mgr./Coaches (Del Crandall, Harvey Kuenn, Joe Nossek, Bob Shaw, Jim Walton)	2.25
647	George Stone	2.00
648	Tom Egan	2.00
649	Rich Folkers	2.00
650	Felipe Alou	3.00
651	Don Carrithers	2.00
652	Ted Kubiak	2.00
653	Joe Hoerner	2.00
654	Twins Team	6.00
655	Clay Kirby	2.00
656	John Ellis	2.00
657	Bob Johnson	2.00
658	Elliott Maddox	2.00
659	Jose Pagan	2.00
660	Fred Scherman	2.00

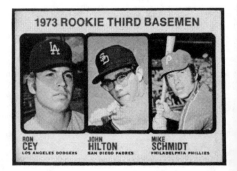

1973 ROOKIE THIRD BASEMEN

RON CEY — LOS ANGELES DODGERS　JOHN HILTON — SAN DIEGO PADRES　MIKE SCHMIDT — PHILADELPHIA PHILLIES

1974 Topps

Issued all at once at the beginning of the year, rather than by series throughout the baseball season as had been done since 1952, this 660-card '74 Topps set features a famous group of error cards. At the time the cards were printed, it was uncertain whether the San Diego Padres would move to Washington, D.C., and by the time a decision was made some Padres cards had appeared with a "Washington, Nat'l League" designation on the front. A total of 15 cards were affected, and those with the Washington designation bring prices well in excess of regular cards of the same players (the Washington variations are not included in the complete set prices quoted below). The 2-1/2" by 3-1/2" cards feature color photos (frequently game-action shots) along with the player's name, team and position. Specialty cards abound, starting with a Hank Aaron tribute and running through the usual managers, statistical leaders, playoff and World Series highlights, multi-player rookie cards and All-Stars.

absence of major rookies. There were fancy factory sets that were in a colorful box with the team checklists and sold at Sears, and these always bring $800 or $900 at auction when totally mint.

The #1 card (Aaron Home Run King) is a toughie. The Washington National League variations are interesting and they sell well at current prices.

I've had hundreds of boxes of this year in the last decade, and unopened material is still available.

		MT
Complete Set (660):		850.00
Common Player:		.30
1	Hank Aaron (All-Time Home Run King)	24.00
2	Aaron Special 1954-57	3.00
3	Aaron Special 1958-61	3.00
4	Aaron Special 1962-65	3.00
5	Aaron Special 1966-69	3.00
6	Aaron Special 1970-73	3.00
7	Catfish Hunter	4.00
8	George Theodore	.30
9	Mickey Lolich	.60
10	Johnny Bench	15.00
11	Jim Bibby	.30
12	Dave May	.30
13	Tom Hilgendorf	.30
14	Paul Popovich	.30
15	Joe Torre	.30
16	Orioles Team	2.00
17	Doug Bird	.30
18	Gary Thomasson	.30
19	Gerry Moses	.30
20	Nolan Ryan	80.00
21	Bob Gallagher	.30
22	Cy Acosta	.30
23	Craig Robinson	.30
24	John Hiller	.30
25	Ken Singleton	.30
26	*Bill Campbell*	.30
27	George Scott	.30
28	Manny Sanguillen	.30
29	Phil Niekro	2.00
30	Bobby Bonds	.50
31	Astros Mgr./Coaches (Roger Craig, Preston Gomez, Grady Hatton, Hub Kittle, Bob Lillis)	.75
32a	John Grubb (Washington)	3.50
32b	John Grubb (San Diego)	.30
33	Don Newhauser	.30
34	Andy Kosco	.30
35	Gaylord Perry	4.00
36	Cardinals Team	2.00
37	Dave Sells	.30
38	Don Kessinger	.30
39	Ken Suarez	.30
40	Jim Palmer	9.00
41	Bobby Floyd	.30
42	Claude Osteen	.30
43	Jim Wynn	.30
44	Mel Stottlemyre	.30
45	Dave Johnson	.30
46	Pat Kelly	.30

OAKLAND ◀ PITCHER

ROLLIE FINGERS   A's

Mr. Mint Says - Behold, another uninteresting bunch. The Ryan card and the Winfield rookie hold up the set right now. Otherwise, it is very slow moving because of the

No.	Player	Price
47	*Dick Ruthven*	.30
48	Dick Sharon	.30
49	Steve Renko	.30
50	Rod Carew	10.00
51	Bobby Heise	.30
52	Al Oliver	.75
53a	Fred Kendall (Washington)	3.50
53b	Fred Kendall (San Diego)	.30
54	*Elias Sosa*	.30
55	Frank Robinson	9.00
56	Mets Team	2.00
57	Darold Knowles	.30
58	Charlie Spikes	.30
59	Ross Grimsley	.30
60	Lou Brock	5.00
61	Luis Aparicio	2.50
62	Bob Locker	.30
63	Bill Sudakis	.30
64	Doug Rau	.30
65	Amos Otis	.30
66	Sparky Lyle	.30
67	Tommy Helms	.30
68	Grant Jackson	.30
69	Del Unser	.30
70	Dick Allen	.50
71	Danny Frisella	.30
72	Aurleio Rodriguez	.30
73	Mike Marshall	.30
74	Twins Team	2.00
75	Jim Colborn	.30
76	Mickey Rivers	.30
77a	Rich Troedson (Washington)	3.50
77b	Rich Troedson (San Diego)	.30
78	Giants Mgr./Coaches (Joe Amalfitano, Charlie Fox, Andy Gilbert, Don McMahon, John McNamara)	.30
79	Gene Tenace	.30
80	Tom Seaver	15.00
81	Frank Duffy	.30
82	Dave Giusti	.30
83	Orlando Cepeda	2.00
84	Rick Wise	.30
85	Joe Morgan	6.00
86	Joe Ferguson	.30
87	Fergie Jenkins	4.00
88	Freddie Patek	.30
89	Jackie Brown	.30
90	Bobby Murcer	.40
91	Ken Forsch	.30
92	Paul Blair	.30
93	Rod Gilbreath	.30
94	Tigers Team	2.00
95	Steve Carlton	9.00
96	*Jerry Hairston*	.30
97	Bob Bailey	.30
98	Bert Blyleven	1.00
99	Brewers Mgr./Coaches (Del Crandall, Harvey Kuenn, Joe Nossek, Jim Walton, Al Widmar)	.30
100	Willie Stargell	6.00
101	Bobby Valentine	.30
102a	Bill Greif (Washington)	3.50
102b	Bill Greif (San Diego)	.30
103	Sal Bando	.30
104	Ron Bryant	.30
105	Carlton Fisk	15.00
106	Harry Parker	.30
107	Alex Johnson	.30
108	Al Hrabosky	.30
109	Bob Grich	.40
110	Billy Williams	6.00
111	Clay Carroll	.30
112	Dave Lopes	.40
113	Dick Drago	.30
114	Angels Team	2.00
115	Willie Horton	.30
116	Jerry Reuss	.30
117	Ron Blomberg	.30
118	Bill Lee	.30
119	Phillies Mgr./Coaches (Carroll Beringer, Bill DeMars, Danny Ozark, Ray Ripplemeyer, Bobby Wine)	.30
120	Wilbur Wood	.30
121	Larry Lintz	.30
122	Jim Holt	.30
123	Nelson Briles	.30
124	Bob Coluccio	.30
125a	Nate Colbert (Washington)	3.50
125b	Nate Colbert (San Diego)	.30
126	Checklist 1-132	1.50
127	Tom Paciorek	.30
128	John Ellis	.30
129	Chris Speier	.30
130	Reggie Jackson	25.00
131	Bob Boone	2.50
132	Felix Millan	.30
133	*David Clyde*	.30
134	Denis Menke	.30
135	Roy White	.40
136	Rick Reuschel	.30
137	Al Bumbry	.30
138	Ed Brinkman	.30
139	Aurelio Monteagudo	.30
140	Darrell Evans	.60
141	Pat Bourque	.30
142	Pedro Garcia	.30
143	Dick Woodson	.30
144	Dodgers Mgr./Coaches (Red Adams, Walter Alston, Monty Basgall, Jim Gilliam, Tom Lasorda)	1.50
145	Dock Ellis	.30
146	Ron Fairly	.30
147	Bart Johnson	.30
148a	Dave Hilton (Washington)	3.50
148b	Dave Hilton (San Diego)	.30
149	Mac Scarce	.30
150	John Mayberry	.30
151	Diego Segui	.30
152	Oscar Gamble	.30
153	Jon Matlack	.30
154	Astros Team	2.00
155	Bert Campaneris	.30
156	Randy Moffitt	.30
157	Vic Harris	.30
158	Jack Billingham	.30
159	Jim Ray Hart	.30
160	Brooks Robinson	9.00
161	*Ray Burris*	.30
162	Bill Freehan	.30
163	Ken Berry	.30
164	Tom House	.30
165	Willie Davis	.30
166	Royals Mgr./Coaches (Galen Cisco, Harry Dunlop, Charlie Lau, Jack McKeon)	.45
167	Luis Tiant	.50
168	Danny Thompson	.30
169	*Steve Rogers*	.30
170	Bill Melton	.30
171	Eduardo Rodriguez	.30
172	Gene Clines	.30
173a	*Randy Jones* (Washington)	3.50
173b	*Randy Jones* (San Diego)	.30
174	Bill Robinson	.30
175	Reggie Cleveland	.30
176	John Lowenstein	.30
177	Dave Roberts	.30
178	Garry Maddox	.30
179	Mets Mgr./Coaches (Yogi Berra, Roy McMillan, Joe Pignatano, Rube Walker, Eddie Yost)	2.00
180	Ken Holtzman	.30
181	Cesar Geronimo	.30
182	Lindy McDaniel	.30

183	Johnny Oates	.30	250b	Willie McCovey (San Diego)	5.00
184	Rangers Team	2.00	251	Graig Nettles	.30
185	Jose Cardenal	.30	252	*Dave Parker*	20.00
186	Fred Scherman	.30	253	John Boccabella	.30
187	Don Baylor	.50	254	Stan Bahnsen	.30
188	Rudy Meoli	.30	255	Larry Bowa	.40
189	Jim Brewer	.30	256	Tom Griffin	.30
190	Tony Oliva	.50	257	Buddy Bell	.40
191	Al Fitzmorris	.30	258	Jerry Morales	.30
192	Mario Guerrero	.30	259	Bob Reynolds	.30
193	Tom Walker	.30	260	Ted Simmons	.50
194	Darrell Porter	.30	261	Jerry Bell	.30
195	Carlos May	.30	262	Ed Kirkpatrick	.30
196	Jim Fregosi	.30	263	Checklist 133-264	1.50
197a	Vicente Romo (Washington)	3.50	264	Joe Rudi	.30
197b	Vicente Romo (San Diego)	.30	265	Tug McGraw	.30
198	Dave Cash	.30	266	Jim Northrup	.30
199	Mike Kekich	.30	267	Andy Messersmith	.30
200	Cesar Cedeno	.30	268	Tom Grieve	.30
201	Batting Leaders (Rod Carew, Pete Rose)	4.00	269	Bob Johnson	.30
202	Home Run Leaders (Reggie Jackson, Willie Stargell)	5.00	270	Ron Santo	.50
203	RBI Leaders (Reggie Jackson, Willie Stargell)	5.00	271	Bill Hands	.30
204	Stolen Base Leaders (Lou Brock, Tommy Harper)	1.50	272	Paul Casanova	.30
205	Victory Leaders (Ron Bryant, Wilbur Wood)	.50	273	Checklist 265-396	1.50
206	Earned Run Average Leaders (Jim Palmer, Tom Seaver)	2.00	274	Fred Beene	.30
			275	Ron Hunt	.30
207	Strikeout Leaders (Nolan Ryan, Tom Seaver)	15.00	276	Angels Mgr./Coaches (Tom Morgan, Salty Parker, Jimmie Reese, John Roseboro, Bobby Winkles)	.30
208	Leading Firemen (John Hiller, Mike Marshall)	.50			
209	Ted Sizemore	.30	277	Gary Nolan	.30
210	Bill Singer	.30	278	Cookie Rojas	.30
211	Cubs Team	2.00	279	Jim Crawford	.30
212	Rollie Fingers	5.00	280	Carl Yastrzemski	10.00
213	Dave Rader	.30	281	Giants Team	2.00
214	Billy Grabarkewitz	.30	282	Doyle Alexander	.30
215	Al Kaline	8.00	283	Mike Schmidt	75.00
216	Ray Sadecki	.30	284	Dave Duncan	.30
217	Tim Foli	.30	285	Reggie Smith	.30
218	Johnny Briggs	.30	286	Tony Muser	.30
219	Doug Griffin	.30	287	Clay Kirby	.30
220	Don Sutton	2.00	288	*Gorman Thomas*	.50
221	White Sox Mgr./Coaches (Joe Lonnett, Jim Mahoney, Alex Monchak, Johnny Sain, Chuck Tanner)	.45	289	Rick Auerbach	.30
			290	Vida Blue	.40
222	Ramon Hernandez	.30	291	Don Hahn	.30
223	Jeff Burroughs	.30	292	Chuck Seelbach	.30
224	Roger Metzger	.30	293	Milt May	.30
225	Paul Splittorff	.30	294	Steve Foucault	.30
226a	Washington Nat'l. Team	6.00	295	Rick Monday	.30
226b	Padres Team	2.00	296	Ray Corbin	.30
227	Mike Lum	.30	297	Hal Breeden	.30
228	Ted Kubiak	.30	298	Roric Harrison	.30
229	Fritz Peterson	.30	299	Gene Michael	.30
230	Tony Perez	1.25	300	Pete Rose	15.00
231	Dick Tidrow	.30	301	Bob Montgomery	.30
232	Steve Brye	.30	302	Rudy May	.30
233	Jim Barr	.30	303	George Hendrick	.30
234	John Milner	.30	304	Don Wilson	.30
235	Dave McNally	.30	305	Tito Fuentes	.30
236	Cardinals Mgr./Coaches (Vern Benson, George Kissell, Johnny Lewis, Red Schoendienst, Barney Schultz)	.75	306	Orioles Mgr./Coaches (George Bamberger, Jim Frey, Billy Hunter, George Staller, Earl Weaver)	1.50
			307	Luis Melendez	.30
237	Ken Brett	.30	308	Bruce Dal Canton	.30
238	Fran Healy	.30	309a	Dave Roberts (Washington)	3.50
239	Bill Russell	.30	309b	Dave Roberts (San Diego)	.30
240	Joe Coleman	.30	310	Terry Forster	.30
241a	Glenn Beckert (Washington)	3.50	311	Jerry Grote	.30
241b	Glenn Beckert (San Diego)	3.50	312	Deron Johnson	.30
242	Bill Gogolewski	.30	313	Berry Lersch	.30
243	Bob Oliver	.30	314	Brewers Team	2.00
244	Carl Morton	.30	315	Ron Cey	.60
245	Cleon Jones	.30	316	Jim Perry	.30
246	A's Team	2.00	317	Richie Zisk	.30
247	Rick Miller	.30	318	Jim Merritt	.30
248	Tom Hall	.30	319	Randy Hundley	.30
249	George Mitterwald	.30	320	Dusty Baker	.40
250a	Willie McCovey (Washington)	25.00			

321	Steve Braun	.30
322	Ernie McAnally	.30
323	Richie Scheinblum	.30
324	Steve Kline	.30
325	Tommy Harper	.30
326	Reds Mgr./Coaches (Sparky Anderson, Alex Grammas, Ted Kluszewski, George Scherger, Larry Shepard)	1.50
327	Tom Timmermann	.30
328	Skip Jutze	.30
329	Mark Belanger	.30
330	Juan Marichal	4.00
331	All-Star Catchers (Johnny Bench, Carlton Fisk)	5.00
332	All-Star First Basemen (Hank Aaron, Dick Allen)	5.00
333	All-Star Second Basemen (Rod Carew, Joe Morgan)	3.00
334	All-Star Third Basemen (Brooks Robinson, Ron Santo)	3.00
335	All-Star Shortstops (Bert Campaneris, Chris Speier)	.40
336	All-Star Left Fielders (Bobby Murcer, Pete Rose)	2.50
337	All-Star Center Fielders (Cesar Cedeno, Amos Otis)	.40
338	All-Star Right Fielders (Reggie Jackson, Billy Williams)	5.00
339	All-Star Pitchers (Catfish Hunter, Rick Wise)	.80
340	Thurman Munson	5.00
341	*Dan Driessen*	.30
342	Jim Lonborg	.30
343	Royals Team	2.00
344	Mike Caldwell	.30
345	Bill North	.30
346	Ron Reed	.30
347	Sandy Alomar	.30
348	Pete Richert	.30
349	John Vukovich	.30
350	Bob Gibson	6.00
351	Dwight Evans	5.00
352	Bill Stoneman	.30
353	Rich Coggins	.30
354	Cubs Mgr./Coaches (Hank Aguirre, Whitey Lockman, Jim Marshall, J.C. Martin, Al Spangler)	.30
355	Dave Nelson	.30
356	Jerry Koosman	.30
357	Buddy Bradford	.30
358	Dal Maxvill	.30
359	Brent Strom	.30
360	Greg Luzinski	.50
361	Don Carrithers	.30
362	Hal King	.30
363	Yankees Team	3.00
364a	Cito Gaston (Washington)	4.50
364b	Cito Gaston (San Diego)	.75
365	Steve Busby	.30
366	Larry Hisle	.30
367	Norm Cash	.50
368	Manny Mota	.30
369	Paul Lindblad	.30
370	Bob Watson	.30
371	Jim Slaton	.30
372	Ken Reitz	.30
373	John Curtis	.30
374	Marty Perez	.30
375	Earl Williams	.30
376	Jorge Orta	.30
377	Ron Woods	.30
378	Burt Hooton	.30
379	Rangers Mgr./Coaches (Art Fowler, Frank Lucchesi, Billy Martin, Jackie Moore, Charlie Silvera)	1.00
380	Bud Harrelson	.30
381	Charlie Sands	.30
382	Bob Moose	.30
383	Phillies Team	2.00
384	Chris Chambliss	.30
385	Don Gullett	.30
386	Gary Matthews	.30
387a	Rich Morales (Washington)	3.50
387b	Rich Morales (San Diego)	.30
388	Phil Roof	.30
389	Gates Brown	.30
390	Lou Piniella	.30
391	Billy Champion	.30
392	Dick Green	.30
393	Orlando Pena	.30
394	Ken Henderson	.30
395	Doug Rader	.30
396	Tommy Davis	.30
397	George Stone	.30
398	Duke Sims	.30
399	Mike Paul	.30
400	Harmon Killebrew	5.00
401	Elliott Maddox	.30
402	Jim Rooker	.30
403	Red Sox Mgr./Coaches (Don Bryant, Darrell Johnson, Eddie Popowski, Lee Stange, Don Zimmer)	.45
404	Jim Howarth	.30
405	Ellie Rodriguez	.30
406	Steve Arlin	.30
407	Jim Wohlford	.30
408	Charlie Hough	.40
409	Ike Brown	.30
410	Pedro Borbon	.30
411	Frank Baker	.30
412	Chuck Taylor	.30
413	Don Money	.30
414	Checklist 397-528	1.50
415	Gary Gentry	.30
416	White Sox Team	2.00
417	Rich Folkers	.30
418	Walt Williams	.30
419	Wayne Twitchell	.30
420	Ray Fosse	.30
421	Dan Fife	.30
422	Gonzalo Marquez	.30
423	Fred Stanley	.30
424	Jim Beauchamp	.30
425	Pete Broberg	.30
426	Rennie Stennett	.30
427	Bobby Bolin	.30
428	Gary Sutherland	.30
429	Dick Lange	.30
430	Matty Alou	.30
431	*Gene Garber*	.30
432	Chris Arnold	.30
433	Lerrin LaGrow	.30
434	Ken McMullen	.30
435	Dave Concepcion	.50
436	Don Hood	.30
437	Jim Lyttle	.30
438	Ed Herrmann	.30
439	Norm Miller	.30
440	Jim Kaat	1.25
441	Tom Ragland	.30
442	Alan Foster	.30
443	Tom Hutton	.30
444	Vic Davalillo	.30
445	George Medich	.30
446	Len Randle	.30
447	Twins Mgr./Coaches (Vern Morgan, Frank Quilici, Bob Rodgers, Ralph Rowe)	.30
448	Ron Hodges	.30
449	Tom McCraw	.30
450	Rich Hebner	.30
451	Tommy John	1.00
452	Gene Hiser	.30
453	Balor Moore	.30
454	Kurt Bevacqua	.30
455	Tom Bradley	.30
456	*Dave Winfield*	225.00
457	Chuck Goggin	.30
458	Jim Ray	.30
459	Reds Team	.90

460	Boog Powell	.75
461	John Odom	.30
462	Luis Alvarado	.30
463	Pat Dobson	.30
464	Jose Cruz	.60
465	Dick Bosman	.30
466	Dick Billings	.30
467	Winston Llenas	.30
468	Pepe Frias	.30
469	Joe Decker	.30
470	A.L. Playoffs (Reggie Jackson)	6.00
471	N.L. Playoffs	.80
472	World Series Game 1	.80
473	World Series Game 2 (Willie Mays)	5.00
474	World Series Game 3	.80
475	World Series Game 4	.80
476	World Series Game 5	.80
477	World Series Game 6 (Reggie Jackson)	8.00
478	World Series Game 7	.80
479	World Series Summary (A's Celebrate)	.80
480	Willie Crawford	.30
481	Jerry Terrell	.30
482	Bob Didier	.30
483	Braves Team	2.00
484	Carmen Fanzone	.30
485	Felipe Alou	.90
486	Steve Stone	.30
487	Ted Martinez	.30
488	Andy Etchebarren	.30
489	Pirates Mgr./Coaches (Don Leppert, Bill Mazeroski, Danny Murtaugh, Don Osborn, Bob Skinner)	.75
490	Vada Pinson	.60
491	Roger Nelson	.30
492	Mike Rogodzinski	.30
493	Joe Hoerner	.30
494	Ed Goodson	.30
495	Dick McAuliffe	.30
496	Tom Murphy	.30
497	Bobby Mitchell	.30
498	Pat Corrales	.30
499	Rusty Torres	.30
500	Lee May	.30
501	Eddie Leon	.30
502	Dave LaRoche	.30
503	Eric Soderholm	.30
504	Joe Niekro	.30
505	Bill Buckner	.30
506	Ed Farmer	.30
507	Larry Stahl	.30
508	Expos Team	2.00
509	Jesse Jefferson	.30
510	Wayne Garrett	.30
511	Toby Harrah	.30
512	Joe Lahoud	.30
513	Jim Campanis	.30
514	Paul Schaal	.30
515	Willie Montanez	.30
516	Horacio Pina	.30
517	Mike Hegan	.30
518	Derrel Thomas	.30
519	Bill Sharp	.30
520	Tim McCarver	.45
521	Indians Mgr./Coaches (Ken Aspromonte, Clay Bryant, Tony Pacheco)	.30
522	J.R. Richard	.30
523	Cecil Cooper	.50
524	Bill Plummer	.30
525	Clyde Wright	.30
526	Frank Tepedino	.30
527	Bobby Darwin	.30
528	Bill Bonham	.30
529	Horace Clarke	.30
530	Mickey Stanley	.30

531	Expos Mgr./Coaches (Dave Bristol, Larry Doby, Gene Mauch, Cal McLish, Jerry Zimmerman)	.40
532	Skip Lockwood	.30
533	Mike Phillips	.30
534	Eddie Watt	.30
535	Bob Tolan	.30
536	Duffy Dyer	.30
537	Steve Mingori	.30
538	Cesar Tovar	.30
539	Lloyd Allen	.30
540	Bob Robertson	.30
541	Indians Team	2.00
542	Rich Gossage	2.00
543	Danny Cater	.30
544	Ron Schueler	.30
545	Billy Conigliaro	.30
546	Mike Corkins	.30
547	Glenn Borgmann	.30
548	Sonny Siebert	.30
549	Mike Jorgensen	.30
550	Sam McDowell	.30
551	Von Joshua	.30
552	Denny Doyle	.30
553	Jim Willoughby	.30
554	Tim Johnson	.30
555	Woodie Fryman	.30
556	Dave Campbell	.30
557	Jim McGlothlin	.30
558	Bill Fahey	.30
559	Darrel Chaney	.30
560	Mike Cuellar	.30
561	Ed Kranepool	.30
562	Jack Aker	.30
563	Hal McRae	.40
564	Mike Ryan	.30
565	Milt Wilcox	.30
566	Jackie Hernandez	.30
567	Red Sox Team	3.00
568	Mike Torrez	.30
569	Rick Dempsey	.30
570	Ralph Garr	.30
571	Rich Hand	.30
572	Enzo Hernandez	.30
573	Mike Adams	.30
574	Bill Parsons	.30
575	Steve Garvey	8.00
576	Scipio Spinks	.30
577	Mike Sadek	.30
578	Ralph Houk	.30
579	Cecil Upshaw	.30
580	Jim Spencer	.30
581	Fred Norman	.30
582	*Bucky Dent*	.50
583	Marty Pattin	.30
584	Ken Rudolph	.30
585	Merv Rettenmund	.30
586	Jack Brohamer	.30
587	*Larry Christenson*	.30
588	Hal Lanier	.30
589	Boots Day	.30
590	Rogelio Moret	.30
591	Sonny Jackson	.30
592	Ed Bane	.30
593	Steve Yeager	.30
594	Leroy Stanton	.30
595	Steve Blass	.30
596	Rookie Pitchers (*Wayne Garland*, Fred Holdsworth, Mark Littell, Dick Pole)	.30
597	Rookie Shortstops (Dave Chalk, John Gamble, Pete Mackanin, Manny Trillo)	.80
598	Rookie Outfielders (Dave Augustine, Ken Griffey, Steve Ontiveros, Jim Tyrone)	15.00
599a	Rookie Pitchers (Ron Diorio) (Freisleben-Washington)	.80

599a	Rookie Pitchers (Dave Freisleben) (Freisleben-Washington)	.80
599a	Rookie Pitchers (Frank Riccelli) (Freisleben-Washington)	.80
599a	Rookie Pitchers (Greg Shanahan) (Freisleben-Washington)	.80
599b	Rookie Pitchers (Ron Diorio) (Freisleben-San Diego large print)	3.50
599b	Rookie Pitchers (Dave Freisleben) (Freisleben-San Diego large print)	3.50
599b	Rookie Pitchers (Frank Riccelli) (Freisleben-San Diego large print)	3.50
599b	Rookie Pitchers (Greg Shanahan) (Freisleben-San Diego large print)	3.50
599c	Rookie Pitchers (Ron Diorio) (Freisleben-San Diego small print)	6.00
599c	Rookie Pitchers (Dave Freisleben) (Freisleben-San Diego small print)	6.00
599c	Rookie Pitchers (Frank Riccelli) (Freisleben-San Diego small print)	6.00
599c	Rookie Pitchers (Greg Shanahan) (Freisleben-San Diego small print)	6.00
600	Rookie Infielders (Ron Cash, Jim Cox, Bill Madlock, Reggie J. Sanders)	2.50
601	Rookie Outfielders (Ed Armbrister, Rich Bladt, BrianDowning, Bake McBride)	3.00
602	Rookie Pitchers (Glenn Abbott, Rick Henninger, Craig Swan, Dan Vossler)	.30
603	Rookie Catchers (Barry Foote, Tom Lundstedt, Charlie Moore, Sergio Robles)	.30
604	Rookie Infielders (Terry Hughes, John Knox, Andy Thornton, Frank White)	4.00
605	Rookie Pitchers (Vic Albury, Ken Frailing, Kevin Kobel, Frank Tanana)	4.00
606	Rookie Outfielders (Jim Fuller, Wilbur Howard, Tommy Smith, Otto Velez)	.30
607	Rookie Shortstops (Leo Foster, Tom Heintzelman, Dave Rosello, Frank Taveras)	.30
608a	Rookie Pitchers (Bob Apodaco)	2.00
608a	Rookie Pitchers (Dick Baney)	2.00
608a	Rookie Pitchers (John D'Acquisto)	2.00
608a	Rookie Pitchers (Mike Wallace)	2.00
608b	Rookie Pitchers (Bob Apodaca)	.30
608b	Rookie Pitchers (Dick Baney)	.30
608b	Rookie Pitchers (John D'Acquisto)	.30
608b	Rookie Pitchers (Mike Wallace)	.30
609	Rico Petrocelli	.30
610	Dave Kingman	.45
611	Rick Stelmaszek	.30
612	Luke Walker	.30
613	Dan Monzon	.30
614	Adrian Devine	.30
615	Johnny Jeter	.30
616	Larry Gura	.30
617	Ted Ford	.30
618	Jim Mason	.30
619	Mike Anderson	.30
620	Al Downing	.30
621	Bernie Carbo	.30
622	Phil Gagliano	.30
623	Celerino Sanchez	.30
624	Bob Miller	.30
625	Ollie Brown	.30
626	Pirates Team	2.00
627	Carl Taylor	.30
628	Ivan Murrell	.30
629	Rusty Staub	.60
630	Tommie Agee	.30
631	Steve Barber	.30
632	George Culver	.30
633	Dave Hamilton	.30
634	Braves Mgr./Coaches (Jim Busby, Eddie Mathews, Connie Ryan, Ken Silvestri, Herm Starrette)	1.50
635	John Edwards	.30
636	Dave Goltz	.30
637	Checklist 529-660	1.50

638	Ken Sanders	.30
639	Joe Lovitto	.30
640	Milt Pappas	.30
641	Chuck Brinkman	.30
642	Terry Harmon	.30
643	Dodgers Team	3.00
644	Wayne Granger	.30
645	Ken Boswell	.30
646	George Foster	.75
647	*Juan Beniquez*	.30
648	Terry Crowley	.30
649	Fernando Gonzalez	.30
650	Mike Epstein	.30
651	Leron Lee	.30
652	Gail Hopkins	.30
653	Bob Stinson	.30
654a	Jesus Alou (no position)	5.00
654b	Jesus Alou ("Outfield")	.30
655	Mike Tyson	.30
656	Adrian Garrett	.30
657	Jim Shellenback	.30
658	Lee Lacy	.30
659	Joe Lis	.30
660	Larry Dierker	.30

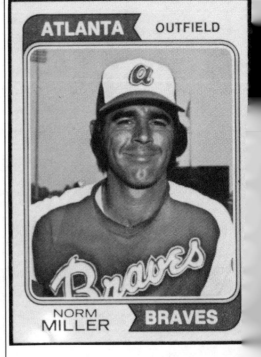

1975 Topps

This year Topps produced another 660-card set, one which collectors either seem to like or despise. The 2-1/2" by 3-1/2" cards have a color photo which is framed by a round-cornered white frame. Around that is an eye-catching two-color border in bright colors. The team name appears at the top in bright letters while the player name is at the bottom and his position a baseball at the lower right. A facsimile autograph runs across the picture. The card backs are vertical, and feature normal statistical and biographical information along with a trivia quiz. Specialty cards include a new 24-card series on MVP winners going back to 1951. Other specialty cards include statistical leaders and post-season highlights. The real highlight of the set, however, are the rookie cards which include their numbers such names as George Brett, Gary Carter, Robin Yount, Jim Rice, Keith Hernandez and Fred Lynn. While the set was released at one time, card numbers 1-132 were printed in somewhat shorter supply than the remainder of the issue.

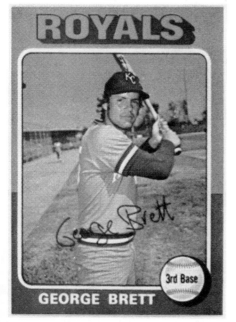

Mr. Mint Says - Probably the most popular set from the 1970s. Very colorful, and it looks nice when it's mint, and it is always a good seller. Brett and Yount rookie cards are joined by several other strong rookies, and the last Aaron card (#660) is always a very good seller. I have had unopened cases over the years, and there are still unopened boxes around.

When you get to 1975 and forward, the print lines seem to disappear, but there are still some print dots even after that.

		MT
Complete Set (660):		1100.
Common Player (1-132):		.35
Common Player (133-660):		.30
Complete Mini Set:		1000.
Common Mini Player:		.40

1	'74 Highlights (Hank Aaron)	25.00
2	'74 Highlights (Lou Brock)	2.00
3	'74 Highlights (Bob Gibson)	1.75
4	'74 Highlights (Al Kaline)	2.00
5	'74 Highlights (Nolan Ryan)	30.00
6	'74 Highlights (Mike Marshall)	.40
7	'74 Highlights (Dick Bosman, Steve Busby, Nolan Ryan)	1.00
8	Rogelio Moret	.35
9	Frank Tepedino	.35
10	Willie Davis	.35
11	Bill Melton	.35
12	David Clyde	.35
13	Gene Locklear	.35
14	Milt Wilcox	.35
15	Jose Cardenal	.35
16	Frank Tanana	.35
17	Dave Concepcion	.45
18	Tigers Team (Ralph Houk)	2.00
19	Jerry Koosman	.35
20	Thurman Munson	7.00
21	Rollie Fingers	5.00
22	Dave Cash	.35
23	Bill Russell	.35
24	Al Fitzmorris	.35
25	Lee May	.35
26	Dave McNally	.35
27	Ken Reitz	.35
28	Tom Murphy	.35
29	Dave Parker	8.00
30	Bert Blyleven	1.00
31	Dave Rader	.35
32	Reggie Cleveland	.35
33	Dusty Baker	.40
34	Steve Renko	.35
35	Ron Santo	.50
36	Joe Lovitto	.35
37	Dave Freisleben	.35
38	Buddy Bell	.35
39	Andy Thornton	.40
40	Bill Singer	.35
41	Cesar Geronimo	.35
42	Joe Coleman	.35
43	Cleon Jones	.35
44	Pat Dobson	.35
45	Joe Rudi	.40
46	Phillies Team (Danny Ozark)	2.00
47	Tommy John	1.25
48	Freddie Patek	.35
49	Larry Dierker	.35
50	Brooks Robinson	6.00
51	*Bob Forsch*	.80
52	Darrell Porter	.35

53	Dave Giusti	.35	126	Checklist 1-132	1.50
54	Eric Soderholm	.35	127	Glen Borgmann	.35
55	Bobby Bonds	.35	128	Bill Lee	.35
56	Rick Wise	.35	129	Rick Monday	.35
57	Dave Johnson	.35	130	Phil Niekro	1.50
58	Chuck Taylor	.35	131	Toby Harrah	.35
59	Ken Henderson	.35	132	Randy Moffitt	.35
60	Fergie Jenkins	4.00	133	Dan Driessen	.35
61	Dave Winfield	70.00	134	Ron Hodges	.30
62	Fritz Peterson	.35	135	Charlie Spikes	.30
63	Steve Swisher	.35	136	Jim Mason	.30
64	Dave Chalk	.35	137	Terry Forster	.30
65	Don Gullett	.35	138	Del Unser	.30
66	Willie Horton	.35	139	Horacio Pina	.30
67	Tug McGraw	.35	140	Steve Garvey	5.00
68	Ron Blomberg	.35	141	Mickey Stanley	.30
69	John Odom	.35	142	Bob Reynolds	.30
70	Mike Schmidt	70.00	143	*Cliff Johnson*	.30
71	Charlie Hough	.35	144	Jim Wohlford	.30
72	Royals Team (Jack McKeon)	2.00	145	Ken Holtzman	.30
73	J.R. Richard	.35	146	Padres Team (John McNamara)	2.00
74	Mark Belanger	.35	147	Pedro Garcia	.30
75	Ted Simmons	.35	148	Jim Rooker	.30
76	Ed Sprague	.35	149	Tim Foli	.30
77	Richie Zisk	.35	150	Bob Gibson	5.00
78	Ray Corbin	.35	151	Steve Brye	.30
79	Gary Matthews	.35	152	Mario Guerrero	.30
80	Carlton Fisk	15.00	153	Rick Reuschel	.30
81	Ron Reed	.35	154	Mike Lum	.30
82	Pat Kelly	.35	155	Jim Bibby	.30
83	Jim Merritt	.35	156	Dave Kingman	.45
84	Enzo Hernandez	.35	157	Pedro Borbon	.30
85	Bill Bonham	.35	158	Jerry Grote	.30
86	Joe Lis	.35	159	Steve Arlin	.30
87	George Foster	.75	160	Graig Nettles	.45
88	Tom Egan	.35	161	Stan Bahnsen	.30
89	Jim Ray	.35	162	Willie Montanez	.30
90	Rusty Staub	.60	163	Jim Brewer	.30
91	Dick Green	.35	164	Mickey Rivers	.30
92	Cecil Upshaw	.35	165	Doug Rader	.30
93	Dave Lopes	.40	166	Woodie Fryman	.30
94	Jim Lonborg	.35	167	Rich Coggins	.30
95	John Mayberry	.35	168	Bill Greif	.30
96	Mike Cosgrove	.35	169	Cookie Rojas	.30
97	Earl Williams	.35	170	Bert Campaneris	.40
98	Rich Folkers	.35	171	Ed Kirkpatrick	.30
99	Mike Hegan	.35	172	Red Sox Team (Darrell Johnson)	2.00
100	Willie Stargell	6.00	173	Steve Rogers	.30
101	Expos Team (Gene Mauch)	2.00	174	Bake McBride	.30
102	Joe Decker	.35	175	Don Money	.30
103	Rick Miller	.35	176	Burt Hooton	.30
104	Bill Madlock	1.25	177	Vic Correll	.30
105	Buzz Capra	.35	178	Cesar Tovar	.30
106	*Mike Hargrove*	.35	179	Tom Bradley	.30
107	Jim Barr	.35	180	Joe Morgan	5.00
108	Tom Hall	.35	181	Fred Beene	.30
109	George Hendrick	.35	182	Don Hahn	.30
110	Wilbur Wood	.35	183	Mel Stottlemyre	.30
111	Wayne Garrett	.35	184	Jorge Orta	.30
112	Larry Hardy	.35	185	Steve Carlton	10.00
113	Elliott Maddox	.35	186	Willie Crawford	.30
114	Dick Lange	.35	187	Denny Doyle	.30
115	Joe Ferguson	.35	188	Tom Griffin	.30
116	Lerrin LaGrow	.35	189	1951-MVPs (Yogi Berra, Roy Campanella)	3.00
117	Orioles Team (Earl Weaver)	2.50	190	1952-MVPs (Hank Sauer, Bobby Shantz)	.40
118	Mike Anderson	.35	191	1953-MVPs (Roy Campanella, Al Rosen)	.90
119	Tommy Helms	.35	192	1954-MVPs (Yogi Berra, Willie Mays)	2.00
120	Steve Busby (photo actually Fran Healy)	.35	193	1955-MVPs (Yogi Berra, Roy Campanella)	2.00
121	Bill North	.35	194	1956-MVPs (Mickey Mantle, Don Newcombe)	6.00
122	Al Hrabosky	.35	195	1957-MVPs (Hank Aaron, Mickey Mantle)	10.00
123	Johnny Briggs	.35	196	1958-MVPs (Ernie Banks, Jackie Jensen)	.90
124	Jerry Reuss	.35	197	1959-MVPs (Ernie Banks, Nellie Fox)	.90
125	Ken Singleton	.35	198	1960-MVPs (Dick Groat, Roger Maris)	1.25

199	1961-MVPs (Roger Maris, Frank Robinson)	1.50
200	1962-MVPs (Mickey Mantle, Maury Wills)	6.00
201	1963-MVPs (Elston Howard, Sandy Koufax)	1.50
202	1964-MVPs (Ken Boyer, Brooks Robinson)	1.25
203	1965-MVPs (Willie Mays, Zoilo Versalles)	1.25
204	1966-MVPs (Roberto Clemente, Frank Robinson)	1.50
205	1967-MVPs (Orlando Cepeda, Carl Yastrzemski)	1.25
206	1968-MVPs (Bob Gibson, Denny McLain)	1.25
207	1969-MVPs (Harmon Killebrew, Willie McCovey)	1.50
208	1970-MVPs (Johnny Bench, Boog Powell)	1.25
209	1971-MVPs (Vida Blue, Joe Torre)	.50
210	1972-MVPs (Rich Allen, Johnny Bench)	1.25
211	1973-MVPs (Reggie Jackson, Pete Rose)	6.00
212	1974-MVPs (Jeff Burroughs, Steve Garvey)	.75
213	Oscar Gamble	.30
214	Harry Parker	.30
215	Bobby Valentine	.30
216	Giants Team (Wes Westrum)	2.00
217	Lou Piniella	.30
218	Jerry Johnson	.30
219	Ed Herrmann	.30
220	Don Sutton	1.50
221	Aurelio Rodriquez (Rodriguez)	.30
222	Dan Spillner	.30
223	*Robin Yount*	185.00
224	Ramon Hernandez	.30
225	Bob Grich	.30
226	Bill Campbell	.30
227	Bob Watson	.30
228	*George Brett*	220.00
229	Barry Foote	.30
230	Catfish Hunter	2.00
231	Mike Tyson	.30
232	Diego Segui	.30
233	Billy Grabarkewitz	.30
234	Tom Grieve	.30
235	Jack Billingham	.30
236	Angels Team (Dick Williams)	2.00
237	Carl Morton	.30
238	Dave Duncan	.30
239	George Stone	.30
240	Garry Maddox	.30
241	Dick Tidrow	.30
242	Jay Johnstone	.30
243	Jim Kaat	1.25
244	Bill Buckner	.30
245	Mickey Lolich	.40
246	Cardinals Team (Red Schoendienst)	2.00
247	Enos Cabell	.30
248	Randy Jones	.30
249	Danny Thompson	.30
250	Ken Brett	.30
251	Fran Healy	.30
252	Fred Scherman	.30
253	Jesus Alou	.30
254	Mike Torrez	.30
255	Dwight Evans	4.00
256	Billy Champion	.30
257	Checklist 133-264	1.50
258	Dave LaRoche	.30
259	Len Randle	.30
260	Johnny Bench	12.00
261	Andy Hassler	.30
262	Rowland Office	.30
263	Jim Perry	.30
264	John Milner	.30
265	Ron Bryant	.30
266	Sandy Alomar	.30
267	Dick Ruthven	.30
268	Hal McRae	.40
269	Doug Rau	.30
270	Ron Fairly	.30
271	Jerry Moses	.30

272	Lynn McGlothen	.30
273	Steve Braun	.30
274	Vicente Romo	.30
275	Paul Blair	.30
276	White Sox Team (Chuck Tanner)	2.00
277	Frank Taveras	.30
278	Paul Lindblad	.30
279	Milt May	.30
280	Carl Yastrzemski	12.00
281	Jim Slaton	.30
282	Jerry Morales	.30
283	Steve Foucault	.30
284	Ken Griffey	.70
285	Ellie Rodriguez	.30
286	Mike Jorgensen	.30
287	Roric Harrison	.30
288	Bruce Ellingsen	.30
289	Ken Rudolph	.30
290	Jon Matlack	.30
291	Bill Sudakis	.30
292	Ron Schueler	.30
293	Dick Sharon	.30
294	*Geoff Zahn*	.30
295	Vada Pinson	.45
296	Alan Foster	.30
297	Craig Kusick	.30
298	Johnny Grubb	.30
299	Bucky Dent	.40
300	Reggie Jackson	30.00
301	Dave Roberts	.30
302	*Rick Burleson*	.30
303	Grant Jackson	.30
304	Pirates Team (Danny Murtaugh)	2.00
305	Jim Colborn	.30
306	Batting Leaders (Rod Carew, Ralph Garr)	.80
307	Home Run Leaders (Dick Allen, Mike Schmidt)	.90
308	Runs Batted In Leaders (Johnny Bench, Jeff Burroughs)	.80
309	Stolen Base Leaders (Lou Brock, Bill North)	.75
310	Victory Leaders (Jim Hunter, Fergie Jenkins, Andy Messersmith, Phil Niekro)	.80
311	Earned Run Average Leaders (Buzz Capra, Catfish Hunter)	.50
312	Strikeout Leaders (Steve Carlton, Nolan Ryan)	9.00
313	Leading Firemen (Terry Forster, Mike Marshall)	.50
314	Buck Martinez	.30
315	Don Kessinger	.30
316	Jackie Brown	.30
317	Joe Lahoud	.30
318	Ernie McAnally	.30
319	Johnny Oates	.30
320	Pete Rose	20.00
321	Rudy May	.30
322	Ed Goodson	.30
323	Fred Holdsworth	.30
324	Ed Kranepool	.35
325	Tony Oliva	.45
326	Wayne Twitchell	.30
327	Jerry Hairston	.30
328	Sonny Siebert	.30
329	Ted Kubiak	.30
330	Mike Marshall	.30
331	Indians Team (Frank Robinson)	2.00
332	Fred Kendall	.30
333	Dick Drago	.30
334	*Greg Gross*	.30
335	Jim Palmer	8.00
336	Rennie Stennett	.30
337	Kevin Kobel	.30
338	Rick Stelmaszek	.30
339	Jim Fregosi	.30
340	Paul Splittorff	.30
341	Hal Breeden	.30
342	Leroy Stanton	.30

343	Danny Frisella	.30
344	Ben Oglivie	.30
345	Clay Carroll	.30
346	Bobby Darwin	.30
347	Mike Caldwell	.30
348	Tony Muser	.30
349	Ray Sadecki	.30
350	Bobby Murcer	.30
351	Bob Boone	.40
352	Darold Knowles	.30
353	Luis Melendez	.30
354	Dick Bosman	.30
355	Chris Cannizzaro	.30
356	Rico Petrocelli	.30
357	Ken Forsch	.30
358	Al Bumbry	.30
359	Paul Popovich	.30
360	George Scott	.30
361	Dodgers Team (Walter Alston)	3.00
362	Steve Hargan	.30
363	Carmen Fanzone	.30
364	Doug Bird	.30
365	Bob Bailey	.30
366	Ken Sanders	.30
367	Craig Robinson	.30
368	Vic Albury	.30
369	Merv Rettenmund	.30
370	Tom Seaver	15.00
371	Gates Brown	.30
372	John D'Acquisto	.30
373	Bill Sharp	.30
374	Eddie Watt	.30
375	Roy White	.30
376	Steve Yeager	.30
377	Tom Hilgendorf	.30
378	Derrel Thomas	.30
379	Bernie Carbo	.30
380	Sal Bando	.30
381	John Curtis	.30
382	Don Baylor	.45
383	Jim York	.30
384	Brewers Team (Del Crandall)	2.00
385	Dock Ellis	.30
386	Checklist 265-396	1.50
387	Jim Spencer	.30
388	Steve Stone	.30
389	Tony Solaita	.30
390	Ron Cey	.30
391	Don DeMola	.30
392	Bruce Bochte	.30
393	Gary Gentry	.30
394	Larvell Blanks	.30
395	Bud Harrelson	.30
396	Fred Norman	.30
397	Bill Freehan	.30
398	Elias Sosa	.30
399	Terry Harmon	.30
400	Dick Allen	.80
401	Mike Wallace	.30
402	Bob Tolan	.30
403	Tom Buskey	.30
404	Ted Sizemore	.30
405	John Montague	.30
406	Bob Gallagher	.30
407	*Herb Washington*	.35
408	Clyde Wright	.30
409	Bob Robertson	.30
410	Mike Cueller (Cuellar)	.30
411	George Mitterwald	.30
412	Bill Hands	.30
413	Marty Pattin	.30
414	Manny Mota	.30
415	John Hiller	.30

416	Larry Lintz	.30
417	Skip Lockwood	.30
418	Leo Foster	.30
419	Dave Goltz	.30
420	Larry Bowa	.40
421	Mets Team (Yogi Berra)	2.50
422	Brian Downing	.30
423	Clay Kirby	.30
424	John Lowenstein	.30
425	Tito Fuentes	.30
426	George Medich	.30
427	Clarence Gaston	.30
428	Dave Hamilton	.30
429	*Jim Dwyer*	.30
430	Luis Tiant	.40
431	Rod Gilbreath	.30
432	Ken Berry	.30
433	Larry Demery	.30
434	Bob Locker	.30
435	Dave Nelson	.30
436	Ken Frailing	.30
437	*Al Cowens*	.30
438	Don Carrithers	.30
439	Ed Brinkman	.30
440	Andy Messersmith	.30
441	Bobby Heise	.30
442	Maximino Leon	.30
443	Twins Team (Frank Quilici)	2.00
444	Gene Garber	.30
445	Felix Millan	.30
446	Bart Johnson	.30
447	Terry Crowley	.30
448	Frank Duffy	.30
449	Charlie Williams	.30
450	Willie McCovey	4.00
451	Rick Dempsey	.30
452	Angel Mangual	.30
453	Claude Osteen	.30
454	Doug Griffin	.30
455	Don Wilson	.30
456	Bob Coluccio	.30
457	Mario Mendoza	.30
458	Ross Grimsley	.30
459	A.L. Championships	.80
460	N.L. Championships (Steve Garvey)	.80
461	World Series Game 1 (Reggie Jackson)	2.00
462	World Series Game 2	.80
463	World Series Game 3 (Rollie Fingers)	1.00
464	World Series Game 4	.80
465	World Series Game 5	.80
466	World Series SummaryA's Do It Again	.80
467	Ed Halicki	.30
468	Bobby Mitchell	.30
469	Tom Dettore	.30
470	Jeff Burroughs	.30
471	Bob Stinson	.30
472	Bruce Dal Canton	.30
473	Ken McMullen	.30
474	Luke Walker	.30
475	Darrell Evans	.45
476	*Ed Figueroa*	.30
477	Tom Hutton	.30
478	Tom Burgmeier	.30
479	Ken Boswell	.30
480	Carlos May	.30
481	*Will McEnaney*	.30
482	Tom McCraw	.30
483	Steve Ontiveros	.30
484	Glenn Beckert	.30
485	Sparky Lyle	.30
486	Ray Fosse	.30
487	Astros Team (Preston Gomez)	2.00
488	Bill Travers	.30

489	Cecil Cooper	.45
490	Reggie Smith	.30
491	Doyle Alexander	.30
492	Rich Hebner	.30
493	Don Stanhouse	.30
494	*Pete LaCock*	.30
495	Nelson Briles	.30
496	Pepe Frias	.30
497	Jim Nettles	.30
498	Al Downing	.30
499	Marty Perez	.30
500	Nolan Ryan	80.00
501	Bill Robinson	.30
502	Pat Bourque	.30
503	Fred Stanley	.30
504	Buddy Bradford	.30
505	Chris Speier	.30
506	Leron Lee	.30
507	Tom Carroll	.30
508	Bob Hansen	.30
509	Dave Hilton	.30
510	Vida Blue	.50
511	Rangers Team (Billy Martin)	2.00
512	Larry Milbourne	.30
513	Dick Pole	.30
514	Jose Cruz	.30
515	Manny Sanguillen	.30
516	Don Hood	.30
517	Checklist 397-528	1.25
518	Leo Cardenas	.30
519	Jim Todd	.30
520	Amos Otis	.30
521	Dennis Blair	.30
522	Gary Sutherland	.30
523	Tom Paciorek	.30
524	John Doherty	.30
525	Tom House	.30
526	Larry Hisle	.30
527	Mac Scarce	.30
528	Eddie Leon	.30
529	Gary Thomasson	.30
530	Gaylord Perry	3.00
531	Reds Team (Sparky Anderson)	3.00
532	Gorman Thomas	.30
533	Rudy Meoli	.30
534	Alex Johnson	.30
535	Gene Tenace	.30
536	Bob Moose	.30
537	Tommy Harper	.30
538	Duffy Dyer	.30
539	Jesse Jefferson	.30
540	Lou Brock	4.00
541	Roger Metzger	.30
542	Pete Broberg	.30
543	Larry Biittner	.30
544	Steve Mingori	.30
545	Billy Williams	3.00
546	John Knox	.30
547	Von Joshua	.30
548	Charlie Sands	.30
549	Bill Butler	.30
550	Ralph Garr	.30
551	Larry Christenson	.30
552	Jack Brohamer	.30
553	John Boccabella	.30
554	Rich Gossage	.45
555	Al Oliver	.60
556	Tim Johnson	.30
557	Larry Gura	.30
558	Dave Roberts	.30
559	Bob Montgomery	.30
560	Tony Perez	2.00
561	A's Team (Alvin Dark)	2.00

562	Gary Nolan	.30
563	Wilbur Howard	.30
564	Tommy Davis	.30
565	Joe Torre	.70
566	Ray Burris	.30
567	*Jim Sundberg*	.30
568	Dale Murray	.30
569	Frank White	.40
570	Jim Wynn	.35
571	Dave Lemanczyk	.30
572	Roger Nelson	.30
573	Orlando Pena	.30
574	Tony Taylor	.30
575	Gene Clines	.30
576	Phil Roof	.30
577	John Morris	.30
578	Dave Tomlin	.30
579	Skip Pitlock	.30
580	Frank Robinson	6.00
581	Darrel Chaney	.30
582	Eduardo Rodriguez	.30
583	Andy Etchebarren	.30
584	Mike Garman	.30
585	Chris Chambliss	.30
586	Tim McCarver	.45
587	Chris Ward	.30
588	Rick Auerbach	.30
589	Braves Team (Clyde King)	2.00
590	Cesar Cedeno	.30
591	Glenn Abbott	.30
592	Balor Moore	.30
593	Gene Lamont	.30
594	Jim Fuller	.30
595	Joe Niekro	.30
596	Ollie Brown	.30
597	Winston Llenas	.30
598	Bruce Kison	.30
599	Nate Colbert	.30
600	Rod Carew	9.00
601	Juan Beniquez	.30
602	John Vukovich	.30
603	Lew Krausse	.30
604	Oscar Zamora	.30
605	John Ellis	.30
606	Bruce Miller	.30
607	Jim Holt	.30
608	Gene Michael	.30
609	Ellie Hendricks	.30
610	Ron Hunt	.30
611	Yankees Team (Bill Virdon)	3.00
612	Terry Hughes	.30
613	Bill Parsons	.30
614	Rookie Pitchers (Jack Kucek, Dyar Miller, Vern Ruhle, Paul Siebert)	.30
615	Rookie Pitchers (Pat Darcy, Dennis Leonard, Tom Underwood, Hank Webb)	.30
616	Rookie Outfielders (Dave Augustine, Pepe Mangual, Jim Rice, John Scott)	15.00
617	Rookie Infielders (Mike Cubbage, Doug DeCinces, Reggie J. Sanders, Manny Trillo)	1.25
618	Rookie Pitchers (*Jamie Easterly*, Tom Johnson, Scott McGregor, Rick Rhoden)	2.25
619	Rookie Outfielders (Benny Ayala, Nyls Nyman, Tommy Smith, Jerry Turner)	.30
620	Rookie Catchers-Outfielders (*Gary Carter*, Marc Hill, Danny Meyer, Leon Roberts)	32.00
621	Rookie Pitchers (*John Denny*, Rawly Eastwick, Jim Kern, Juan Veintidos)	.60
622	Rookie Outfielders (Ed Armbrister, Fred Lynn, Tom Poquette, Terry Whitfield)	10.00
623	Rookie Infielders (*Phil Garner*, Keith Hernandez, Bob Sheldon, Tom Veryzer)	10.00
624	Rookie Pitchers (Doug Konieczny, Gary Lavelle, Jim Otten, Eddie Solomon)	.30
625	Boog Powell	.45

626	Larry Haney	.30
627	Tom Walker	.30
628	*Ron LeFlore*	.80
629	Joe Hoerner	.30
630	Greg Luzinski	.45
631	Lee Lacy	.30
632	Morris Nettles	.30
633	Paul Casanova	.30
634	Cy Acosta	.30
635	Chuck Dobson	.30
636	Charlie Moore	.30
637	Ted Martinez	.30
638	Cubs Team (Jim Marshall)	2.00
639	Steve Kline	.30
640	Harmon Killebrew	5.00
641	Jim Northrup	.30
642	Mike Phillips	.30
643	Brent Strom	.30
644	Bill Fahey	.30
645	Danny Cater	.30
646	Checklist 529-660	1.50
647	*Claudell Washington*	1.00
648	Dave Pagan	.30
649	Jack Heidemann	.30
650	Dave May	.30
651	John Morlan	.30
652	Lindy McDaniel	.30
653	Lee Richards	.30
654	Jerry Terrell	.30
655	Rico Carty	.30
656	Bill Plummer	.30
657	Bob Oliver	.30
658	Vic Harris	.30
659	Bob Apodaca	.30
660	Hank Aaron	30.00

MANNY MOTA

THURMAN MUNSON

KEN GRIFFEY

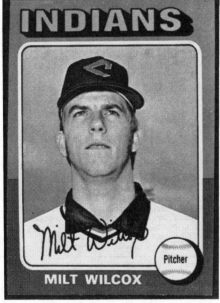

MILT WILCOX

Win 3rd Straight World Series!

NOLAN RYAN

1975 Topps Mini

One of the most popular Topps sets of the 1970s is really a test issue. The Topps Minis measure 2-1/4" by 3-1/8," exactly 20 percent smaller than the regular card size. Other than their size, the Minis are in every way the same as the regular cards. The experiment primarily took place in parts of Michigan and the West Coast, where the Minis were snapped up quickly by collectors.

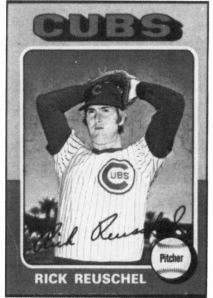

RICK REUSCHEL

Mr. Mint Says - People have always said that the Minis are worth double, but I think the figure should be closer to $400 or $500 more than the traditional size. I have had unopened cases over the years, and there are still boxes around. They were more popular several years ago than they are now, and only the superstars sell well individually.

Not many side to side centering problems with the Minis, but there are some from top to bottom and there also is a slight problem with the minis in terms of size. There were a lot of cards that were cut short. Even when you buy an uncirculated set from an old-time collector, you find little size differences.

		MT
Complete Set:		1500.
Common Player:		.40
1	'74 Highlights (Hank Aaron)	25.00
2	'74 Highlights (Lou Brock)	3.50
3	'74 Highlights (Bob Gibson)	3.25
4	'74 Highlights (Al Kaline)	3.25
5	'74 Highlights (Nolan Ryan)	15.00
6	'74 Highlights (Mike Marshall)	.60
7	'74 Highlights (Dick Bosman, Steve Busby, Nolan Ryan)	3.00
8	Rogelio Moret	.40
9	Frank Tepedino	.40
10	Willie Davis	.60
11	Bill Melton	.40
12	David Clyde	.40
13	Gene Locklear	.40
14	Milt Wilcox	.40
15	Jose Cardenal	.40
16	Frank Tanana	.60
17	Dave Concepcion	.90
18	Tigers Team (Ralph Houk)	1.25
19	Jerry Koosman	.40
20	Thurman Munson	10.00
21	Rollie Fingers	6.00
22	Dave Cash	.40
23	Bill Russell	.60
24	Al Fitzmorris	.40
25	Lee May	.60
26	Dave McNally	.60
27	Ken Reitz	.40
28	Tom Murphy	.40
29	Dave Parker	10.00
30	Bert Blyleven	2.00
31	Dave Rader	.40
32	Reggie Cleveland	.40
33	Dusty Baker	.90
34	Steve Renko	.40
35	Ron Santo	.80
36	Joe Lovitto	.40
37	Dave Freisleben	.40
38	Buddy Bell	.75
39	Andy Thornton	.60
40	Bill Singer	.40
41	Cesar Geronimo	.40
42	Joe Coleman	.40
43	Cleon Jones	.40
44	Pat Dobson	.40
45	Joe Rudi	.60
46	Phillies Team (Danny Ozark)	1.25
47	Tommy John	2.50
48	Freddie Patek	.40
49	Larry Dierker	.40
50	Brooks Robinson	10.00
51	Bob Forsch	1.25
52	Darrell Porter	.60
53	Dave Giusti	.40
54	Eric Soderholm	.40
55	Bobby Bonds	.80
56	Rick Wise	.60
57	Dave Johnson	1.25
58	Chuck Taylor	.40
59	Ken Henderson	.40
60	Fergie Jenkins	3.00
61	Dave Winfield	60.00
62	Fritz Peterson	.40
63	Steve Swisher	.40
64	Dave Chalk	.40
65	Don Gullett	.40
66	Willie Horton	.60
67	Tug McGraw	.60
68	Ron Blomberg	.40
69	John Odom	.40
70	Mike Schmidt	60.00
71	Charlie Hough	.60
72	Royals Team (Jack McKeon)	1.25

#	Name	Price		#	Name	Price
73	J.R. Richard	.60		146	Padres Team (John McNamara)	1.25
74	Mark Belanger	.60		147	Pedro Garcia	.40
75	Ted Simmons	.60		148	Jim Rooker	.40
76	Ed Sprague	.40		149	Tim Foli	.40
77	Richie Zisk	.40		150	Bob Gibson	7.00
78	Ray Corbin	.40		151	Steve Brye	.40
79	Gary Matthews	.60		152	Mario Guerrero	.40
80	Carlton Fisk	12.00		153	Rick Reuschel	.60
81	Ron Reed	.40		154	Mike Lum	.40
82	Pat Kelly	.40		155	Jim Bibby	.40
83	Jim Merritt	.40		156	Dave Kingman	.90
84	Enzo Hernandez	.40		157	Pedro Borbon	.40
85	Bill Bonham	.40		158	Jerry Grote	.40
86	Joe Lis	.40		159	Steve Arlin	.40
87	George Foster	1.75		160	Graig Nettles	2.00
88	Tom Egan	.40		161	Stan Bahnsen	.40
89	Jim Ray	.40		162	Willie Montanez	.40
90	Rusty Staub	.90		163	Jim Brewer	.40
91	Dick Green	.40		164	Mickey Rivers	.60
92	Cecil Upshaw	.40		165	Doug Rader	.60
93	Dave Lopes	.60		166	Woodie Fryman	.40
94	Jim Lonborg	.75		167	Rich Coggins	.40
95	John Mayberry	.40		168	Bill Greif	.40
96	Mike Cosgrove	.40		169	Cookie Rojas	.40
97	Earl Williams	.40		170	Bert Campaneris	.60
98	Rich Folkers	.40		171	Ed Kirkpatrick	.40
99	Mike Hegan	.40		172	Red Sox Team (Darrell Johnson)	1.25
100	Willie Stargell	7.00		173	Steve Rogers	.40
101	Expos Team (Gene Mauch)	1.25		174	Bake McBride	.40
102	Joe Decker	.40		175	Don Money	.40
103	Rick Miller	.40		176	Burt Hooton	.40
104	Bill Madlock	1.00		177	Vic Correll	.40
105	Buzz Capra	.40		178	Cesar Tovar	.40
106	Mike Hargrove	.60		179	Tom Bradley	.40
107	Jim Barr	.40		180	Joe Morgan	10.00
108	Tom Hall	.40		181	Fred Beene	.40
109	George Hendrick	.40		182	Don Hahn	.40
110	Wilbur Wood	.40		183	Mel Stottlemyre	.60
111	Wayne Garrett	.40		184	Jorge Orta	.40
112	Larry Hardy	.40		185	Steve Carlton	15.00
113	Elliott Maddox	.40		186	Willie Crawford	.40
114	Dick Lange	.40		187	Denny Doyle	.40
115	Joe Ferguson	.40		188	Tom Griffin	.40
116	Lerrin LaGrow	.40		189	1951-MVPs (Larry (Yogi) Berra, Roy Campanella)	4.00
117	Orioles Team (Earl Weaver)	1.25		190	1952-MVPs (Hank Sauer, Bobby Shantz)	.60
118	Mike Anderson	.40		191	1953-MVPs (Roy Campanella, Al Rosen)	2.00
119	Tommy Helms	.40		192	1954-MVPs (Yogi Berra, Willie Mays)	7.00
120	Steve Busby (photo actually Fran Healy)	.40		193	1955-MVPs (Yogi Berra, Roy Campanella)	4.00
121	Bill North	.40		194	1956-MVPs (Mickey Mantle, Don Newcombe)	9.00
122	Al Hrabosky	.40		195	1957-MVPs (Hank Aaron, Mickey Mantle)	15.00
123	Johnny Briggs	.40		196	1958-MVPs (Ernie Banks, Jackie Jensen)	4.00
124	Jerry Reuss	.60		197	1959-MVPs (Ernie Banks, Nellie Fox)	6.00
125	Ken Singleton	.60		198	1960-MVPs (Dick Groat, Roger Maris)	6.00
126	Checklist 1-132	2.25		199	1961-MVPs (Roger Maris, Frank Robinson)	6.00
127	Glen Borgmann	.40		200	1962-MVPs (Mickey Mantle, Maury Wills)	9.00
128	Bill Lee	.60		201	1963-MVPs (Elston Howard, Sandy Koufax)	4.00
129	Rick Monday	.60		202	1964-MVPs (Ken Boyer, Brooks Robinson)	3.50
130	Phil Niekro	4.00		203	1965-MVPs (Willie Mays, Zoilo Versalles)	3.00
131	Toby Harrah	.40		204	1966-MVPs (Roberto Clemente, Frank Robinson)	7.00
132	Randy Moffitt	.40		205	1967-MVPs (Orlando Cepeda, Carl Yastrzemski)	5.00
133	Dan Driessen	.60		206	1968-MVPs (Bob Gibson, Denny McLain)	3.00
134	Ron Hodges	.40		207	1969-MVPs (Harmon Killebrew, Willie McCovey)	3.00
135	Charlie Spikes	.40		208	1970-MVPs (Johnny Bench, Boog Powell)	2.50
136	Jim Mason	.40		209	1971-MVPs (Vida Blue, Joe Torre)	.80
137	Terry Forster	.40		210	1972-MVPs (Rich Allen, Johnny Bench)	1.75
138	Del Unser	.40		211	1973-MVPs (Reggie Jackson, Pete Rose)	7.00
139	Horacio Pina	.40		212	1974-MVPs (Jeff Burroughs, Steve Garvey)	1.25
140	Steve Garvey	9.00		213	Oscar Gamble	.40
141	Mickey Stanley	.40		214	Harry Parker	.40
142	Bob Reynolds	.40		215	Bobby Valentine	.40
143	Cliff Johnson	.40		216	Giants Team (Wes Westrum)	1.25
144	Jim Wohlford	.40		217	Lou Piniella	.80
145	Ken Holtzman	.60		218	Jerry Johnson	.40

219	Ed Herrmann	.40
220	Don Sutton	3.00
221	Aurelio Rodriquez (Rodriguez)	.40
222	Dan Spillner	.40
223	Robin Yount	200.00
224	Ramon Hernandez	.40
225	Bob Grich	.60
226	Bill Campbell	.40
227	Bob Watson	.40
228	George Brett	250.00
229	Barry Foote	.40
230	Catfish Hunter	4.00
231	Mike Tyson	.40
232	Diego Segui	.40
233	Billy Grabarkewitz	.40
234	Tom Grieve	.40
235	Jack Billingham	.40
236	Angels Team (Dick Williams)	1.25
237	Carl Morton	.40
238	Dave Duncan	.40
239	George Stone	.40
240	Garry Maddox	.60
241	Dick Tidrow	.40
242	Jay Johnstone	.60
243	Jim Kaat	2.00
244	Bill Buckner	.80
245	Mickey Lolich	.80
246	Cardinals Team (Red Schoendienst)	1.25
247	Enos Cabell	.40
248	Randy Jones	.40
249	Danny Thompson	.40
250	Ken Brett	.40
251	Fran Healy	.40
252	Fred Scherman	.40
253	Jesus Alou	.40
254	Mike Torrez	.40
255	Dwight Evans	1.50
256	Billy Champion	.40
257	Checklist 133-264	2.25
258	Dave LaRoche	.40
259	Len Randle	.40
260	Johnny Bench	15.00
261	Andy Hassler	.40
262	Rowland Office	.40
263	Jim Perry	.60
264	John Milner	.40
265	Ron Bryant	.40
266	Sandy Alomar	.40
267	Dick Ruthven	.40
268	Hal McRae	.60
269	Doug Rau	.40
270	Ron Fairly	.60
271	Jerry Moses	.40
272	Lynn McGlothen	.40
273	Steve Braun	.40
274	Vicente Romo	.40
275	Paul Blair	.60
276	White Sox Team (Chuck Tanner)	1.25
277	Frank Taveras	.40
278	Paul Lindblad	.40
279	Milt May	.40
280	Carl Yastrzemski	10.00
281	Jim Slaton	.40
282	Jerry Morales	.40
283	Steve Foucault	.40
284	Ken Griffey	3.00
285	Ellie Rodriguez	.40
286	Mike Jorgensen	.40
287	Roric Harrison	.40
288	Bruce Ellingsen	.40
289	Ken Rudolph	.40
290	Jon Matlack	.40
291	Bill Sudakis	.40
292	Ron Schueler	.40
293	Dick Sharon	.40
294	Geoff Zahn	.40
295	Vada Pinson	1.50
296	Alan Foster	.40
297	Craig Kusick	.40
298	Johnny Grubb	.40
299	Bucky Dent	.60
300	Reggie Jackson	30.00
301	Dave Roberts	.40
302	Rick Burleson	.80
303	Grant Jackson	.40
304	Pirates Team (Danny Murtaugh)	1.25
305	Jim Colborn	.40
306	Batting Leaders (Rod Carew, Ralph Garr)	1.25
307	Home Run Leaders (Dick Allen, Mike Schmidt)	1.25
308	Runs Batted In Leaders (Johnny Bench, Johnny Burroughs)	1.25
309	Stole Base Leaders (Lou Brock, Bill North)	1.25
310	Victory Leaders (Catfish Hunter, Fergie Jenkins, Andy Messersmith, Phil Niekro)	1.25
311	Earned Run Average Leaders (Buzz Capra, Catfish Hunter)	.80
312	Strikeout Leaders (Steve Carlton, Nolan Ryan)	15.00
313	Leading Firemen (Terry Forster, Mike Marshall)	.80
314	Buck Martinez	.40
315	Don Kessinger	.40
316	Jackie Brown	.40
317	Joe Lahoud	.40
318	Ernie McAnally	.40
319	Johnny Oates	.40
320	Pete Rose	25.00
321	Rudy May	.40
322	Ed Goodson	.40
323	Fred Holdsworth	.40
324	Ed Kranepool	.40
325	Tony Oliva	2.50
326	Wayne Twitchell	.40
327	Jerry Hairston	.40
328	Sonny Siebert	.40
329	Ted Kubiak	.40
330	Mike Marshall	.60
331	Indians Team (Frank Robinson)	1.25
332	Fred Kendall	.40
333	Dick Drago	.40
334	Greg Gross	.40
335	Jim Palmer	10.00
336	Rennie Stennett	.40
337	Kevin Kobel	.40
338	Rick Stelmaszek	.40
339	Jim Fregosi	.60
340	Paul Splittorff	.40
341	Hal Breeden	.40
342	Leroy Stanton	.40
343	Danny Frisella	.40
344	Ben Oglivie	.60
345	Clay Carroll	.40
346	Bobby Darwin	.40
347	Mike Caldwell	.40
348	Tony Muser	.40
349	Ray Sadecki	.40
350	Bobby Murcer	.60
351	Bob Boone	2.00
352	Darold Knowles	.40
353	Luis Melendez	.40
354	Dick Bosman	.40
355	Chris Cannizzaro	.40
356	Rico Petrocelli	.40
357	Ken Forsch	.40
358	Al Bumbry	.40
359	Paul Popovich	.40
360	George Scott	.40
361	Dodgers Team (Walter Alston)	1.50
362	Steve Hargan	.40

No.	Player	Price
363	Carmen Fanzone	.40
364	Doug Bird	.40
365	Bob Bailey	.40
366	Ken Sanders	.40
367	Craig Robinson	.40
368	Vic Albury	.40
369	Merv Rettenmund	.40
370	Tom Seaver	20.00
371	Gates Brown	.40
372	John D'Acquisto	.40
373	Bill Sharp	.40
374	Eddie Watt	.40
375	Roy White	.60
376	Steve Yeager	.40
377	Tom Hilgendorf	.40
378	Derrel Thomas	.40
379	Bernie Carbo	.40
380	Sal Bando	.60
381	John Curtis	.40
382	Don Baylor	.90
383	Jim York	.40
384	Brewers Team (Del Crandall)	1.25
385	Dock Ellis	.40
386	Checklist 265-396	2.25
387	Jim Spencer	.40
388	Steve Stone	.60
389	Tony Solaita	.40
390	Ron Cey	.60
391	Don DeMola	.40
392	Bruce Bochte	.40
393	Gary Gentry	.40
394	Larvell Blanks	.40
395	Bud Harrelson	.40
396	Fred Norman	.40
397	Bill Freehan	.60
398	Elias Sosa	.40
399	Terry Harmon	.40
400	Dick Allen	1.25
401	Mike Wallace	.40
402	Bob Tolan	.40
403	Tom Buskey	.40
404	Ted Sizemore	.40
405	John Montague	.40
406	Bob Gallagher	.40
407	Herb Washington	.80
408	Clyde Wright	.40
409	Bob Robertson	.40
410	Mike Cueller (Cuellar)	.60
411	George Mitterwald	.40
412	Bill Hands	.40
413	Marty Pattin	.40
414	Manny Mota	.60
415	John Hiller	.40
416	Larry Lintz	.40
417	Skip Lockwood	.40
418	Leo Foster	.40
419	Dave Goltz	.40
420	Larry Bowa	.60
421	Mets Team (Yogi Berra)	1.50
422	Brian Downing	.60
423	Clay Kirby	.40
424	John Lowenstein	.40
425	Tito Fuentes	.40
426	George Medich	.40
427	Cito Gaston	.75
428	Dave Hamilton	.40
429	Jim Dwyer	.40
430	Luis Tiant	.80
431	Rod Gilbreath	.40
432	Ken Berry	.40
433	Larry Demery	.40
434	Bob Locker	.40
435	Dave Nelson	.40
436	Ken Frailing	.40
437	Al Cowens	.40
438	Don Carrithers	.40
439	Ed Brinkman	.40
440	Andy Messersmith	.60
441	Bobby Heise	.40
442	Maximino Leon	.40
443	Twins Team (Frank Quilici)	1.25
444	Gene Garber	.40
445	Felix Millan	.40
446	Bart Johnson	.40
447	Terry Crowley	.40
448	Frank Duffy	.40
449	Charlie Williams	.40
450	Willie McCovey	7.00
451	Rick Dempsey	.60
452	Angel Mangual	.40
453	Claude Osteen	.40
454	Doug Griffin	.40
455	Don Wilson	.40
456	Bob Coluccio	.40
457	Mario Mendoza	.40
458	Ross Grimsley	.40
459	A.L. Championships	1.25
460	N.L. Championships	1.25
461	World Series Game 1	2.25
462	World Series Game 2	1.50
463	World Series Game 3	1.50
464	World Series Game 4	1.25
465	World Series Game 5	1.25
466	World Series Summary	1.25
467	Ed Halicki	.40
468	Bobby Mitchell	.40
469	Tom Dettore	.40
470	Jeff Burroughs	.40
471	Bob Stinson	.40
472	Bruce Dal Canton	.40
473	Ken McMullen	.40
474	Luke Walker	.40
475	Darrell Evans	.90
476	Ed Figueroa	.40
477	Tom Hutton	.40
478	Tom Burgmeier	.40
479	Ken Boswell	.40
480	Carlos May	.40
481	Will McEnaney	.40
482	Tom McCraw	.40
483	Steve Ontiveros	.40
484	Glenn Beckert	.40
485	Sparky Lyle	.60
486	Ray Fosse	.40
487	Astros Team (Preston Gomez)	1.25
488	Bill Travers	.40
489	Cecil Cooper	.75
490	Reggie Smith	.60
491	Doyle Alexander	.60
492	Rich Hebner	.40
493	Doug Stanhouse	.40
494	Pete LaCock	.40
495	Nelson Briles	.40
496	Pepe Frias	.40
497	Jim Nettles	.40
498	Al Downing	.40
499	Marty Perez	.40
500	Nolan Ryan	90.00
501	Bill Robinson	.40
502	Pat Bourque	.40
503	Fred Stanley	.40
504	Buddy Bradford	.40
505	Chris Speier	.40
506	Leron Lee	.40
507	Tom Carroll	.40
508	Bob Hansen	.40

No.	Player	Value
509	Dave Hilton	.40
510	Vida Blue	.80
511	Rangers Team (Billy Martin)	1.25
512	Larry Milbourne	.40
513	Dick Pole	.40
514	Jose Cruz	.80
515	Manny Sanguillen	.40
516	Don Hood	.40
517	Checklist 397-528	2.25
518	Leo Cardenas	.40
519	Jim Todd	.40
520	Amos Otis	.40
521	Dennis Blair	.40
522	Gary Sutherland	.40
523	Tom Paciorek	.40
524	John Doherty	.40
525	Tom House	.40
526	Larry Hisle	.40
527	Mac Scarce	.40
528	Eddie Leon	.40
529	Gary Thomasson	.40
530	Gaylord Perry	6.00
531	Reds Team (Sparky Anderson)	1.50
532	Gorman Thomas	.40
533	Rudy Meoli	.40
534	Alex Johnson	.40
535	Gene Tenace	.40
536	Bob Moose	.40
537	Tommy Harper	.40
538	Duffy Dyer	.40
539	Jesse Jefferson	.40
540	Lou Brock	7.00
541	Roger Metzger	.40
542	Pete Broberg	.40
543	Larry Biittner	.40
544	Steve Mingori	.40
545	Billy Williams	6.00
546	John Knox	.40
547	Von Joshua	.40
548	Charlie Sands	.40
549	Bill Butler	.40
550	Ralph Garr	.40
551	Larry Christenson	.40
552	Jack Brohamer	.40
553	John Boccabella	.40
554	Rich Gossage	1.75
555	Al Oliver	1.25
556	Tim Johnson	.40
557	Larry Gura	.40
558	Dave Roberts	.40
559	Bob Montgomery	.40
560	Tony Perez	4.00
561	A's Team (Alvin Dark)	1.25
562	Gary Nolan	.40
563	Wilbur Howard	.40
564	Tommy Davis	.60
565	Joe Torre	1.00
566	Ray Burris	.40
567	Jim Sundberg	.60
568	Dale Murray	.40
569	Frank White	.60
570	Jim Wynn	.60
571	Dave Lemanczyk	.40
572	Roger Nelson	.40
573	Orlando Pena	.40
574	Tony Taylor	.40
575	Gene Clines	.40
576	Phil Roof	.40
577	John Morris	.40
578	Dave Tomlin	.40
579	Skip Pitlock	.40
580	Frank Robinson	7.00
581	Darrel Chaney	.40
582	Eduardo Rodriguez	.40
583	Andy Etchebarren	.40
584	Mike Garman	.40
585	Chris Chambliss	.60
586	Tim McCarver	1.25
587	Chris Ward	.40
588	Rick Auerbach	.40
589	Braves Team (Clyde King)	1.25
590	Cesar Cedeno	.60
591	Glenn Abbott	.40
592	Balor Moore	.40
593	Gene Lamont	.40
594	Jim Fuller	.40
595	Joe Niekro	.60
596	Ollie Brown	.40
597	Winston Llenas	.40
598	Bruce Kison	.40
599	Nate Colbert	.40
600	Rod Carew	12.00
601	Juan Beniquez	.40
602	John Vukovich	.40
603	Lew Krausse	.40
604	Oscar Zamora	.40
605	John Ellis	.40
606	Bruce Miller	.40
607	Jim Holt	.40
608	Gene Michael	.40
609	Ellie Hendricks	.40
610	Ron Hunt	.40
611	Yankees Team (Bill Virdon)	1.75
612	Terry Hughes	.40
613	Bill Parsons	.40
614	Rookie Pitchers (Jack Kucek, Dyar Miller, Vern Ruhle, Paul Siebert)	.40
615	Rookie Pitchers (Pat Darcy, Dennis Leonard, Tom Underwood, Hank Webb)	.90
616	Rookie Outfielders (Dave Augustine, Pepe Mangual, Jim Rice, John Scott)	15.00
617	Rookie Infielders (Mike Cubbage, Manny Trillo, Doug DeCinces, Reggie Sanders)	2.50
618	Rookie Pitchers (Jamie Easterly, Tom Johnson, Scott McGregor, Rick Rhoden)	5.00
619	Rookie Outfielders (Benny Ayala, Nyls Nyman, Tommy Smith, Jerry Turner)	.40
620	Rookie Catchers-Outfielders (Gary Carter, Marc Hill, Danny Meyer, Leon Roberts)	40.00
621	Rookie Pitchers (John Denny, Rawly Eastwick, Jim Kern, Juan Veintidos)	.90
622	Rookie Outfielders (Ed Armbrister, Fred Lynn, Tom Poquette, Terry Whitfield)	15.00
623	Rookie Infielders (Phil Garner, Keith Hernandez, Bob Sheldon, Tom Veryzer)	20.00
624	Rookie Pitchers (Doug Konieczny, Gary Lavelle, Jim Otten, Eddie Solomon)	.40
625	Boog Powell	2.00
626	Larry Haney	.40
627	Tom Walker	.40
628	Ron LeFlore	1.25
629	Joe Hoerner	.40
630	Greg Luzinski	2.00
631	Lee Lacy	.40
632	Morris Nettles	.40
633	Paul Casanova	.40
634	Cy Acosta	.40
635	Chuck Dobson	.40
636	Charlie Moore	.40
637	Ted Martinez	.40
638	Cubs Team (Jim Marshall)	1.25
639	Steve Kline	.40
640	Harmon Killebrew	6.00
641	Jim Northrup	.40
642	Mike Phillips	.40
643	Brent Strom	.40
644	Bill Fahey	.40
645	Danny Cater	.40

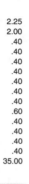

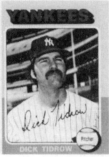

1954 Wilson Franks

The 2-5/8" by 3-3/4" cards are among the most popular and difficult to find baseball card sets issued with hot dogs during the 1950s. The cards feature color-added photos on the front where the player's name, team and position appear at the top. The front also has a facsimile autograph and a color picture of a package of Wilson's frankfurters. The card backs feature personal information, a short career summary and 1953 and career statistics. The 20-card set includes players from a number of teams and was distributed nationally in the frankfurter packages. The problem with such distribution is that the cards are very tough to find without grease stains from the hot dogs.

are in above average condition, but mint ones are scarce.

In 1990 at a Chicago show a major find walked in with almost 300 gem mint assorted cards, but not even one Williams card. With all of those, the only printing problem I noticed was the centering.

		MT
Complete Set:		7500.
Common Player:		200.00
(1)	Roy Campanella	850.00
(2)	Del Ennis	200.00
(3)	Carl Erskine	300.00
(4)	Ferris Fain	175.00
(5)	Bob Feller	700.00
(6)	Nelson Fox	300.00
(7)	Johnny Groth	200.00
(8)	Stan Hack	200.00
(9)	Gil Hodges	500.00
(10)	Ray Jablonski	200.00
(11)	Harvey Kuenn	300.00
(12)	Roy McMillan	200.00
(13)	Andy Pafko	200.00
(14)	Paul Richards	200.00
(15)	Hank Sauer	200.00
(16)	Red Schoendienst	300.00
(17)	Enos Slaughter	450.00
(18)	Vern Stephens	200.00
(19)	Sammy White	200.00
(20)	Ted Williams	3500.00

Mr. Mint Says - Possibly the most popular and scarce regional set ever made due to its design, color and the players included. It seems to have been patterned after the 1954 Topps cards, but what I like is the little package of weiners that appears to float in the background. The Williams card is the key, but there are lots of Hall of Famers.

I think that the interest has gone down in this set a bit. Most of the cards that you see

1933 World Wide Gum

(Canadian Goudey, V353)

Also known as "Canadian Goudeys," this 94-card set drew heavily on its U.S. contemporary. Card fronts are identical to the '33 Goudeys and the backs are nearly so. The first 52 cards in the set carry the same card numbers as their American counterparts, while cards #53-94 have different numbers than the U.S. version. Card backs can be found printed entirely in English, or in English and French; the former being somewhat scarcer. Cards measure approximately 2-3/8" x 2-7/8".

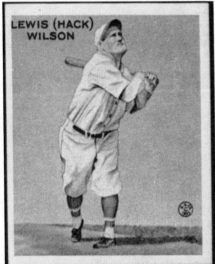

LEWIS (HACK) WILSON

Mr. Mint Says - I don't know of anyone piecing these sets together now. A nicely matched set of these "North of the Border" cards would bring 35 to 50 percent more than the near-mint price. Ruth and Gehrig sell very quickly if they are nice, but most of the singles seem dead as a doornail.

		MT
Complete Set (94):		27500.
Common Player:		75.00
1	Benny Bengough	300.00
2	Arthur (Dazzy) Vance	250.00
3	Hugh Critz	75.00
4	Henry (Heinie) Schuble	75.00
5	Floyd (Babe) Herman	175.00
6	Jimmy Dykes	175.00
7	Ted Lyons	200.00
8	Roy Johnson	75.00

9	Dave Harris	75.00
10	Glenn Myatt	75.00
11	Billy Rogell	75.00
12	George Pipgras	75.00
13	Lafayette Thompson	75.00
14	Henry Johnson	75.00
15	Victor Sorrell	75.00
16	George Blaeholder	75.00
17	Watson Clark	75.00
18	Herold (Muddy) Ruel	75.00
19	Bill Dickey	300.00
20	Bill Terry	250.00
21	Phil Collins	75.00
22	Harold (Pie) Traynor	175.00
23	Hazen (Ki-Ki) Cuyler	175.00
24	Horace Ford	75.00
25	Paul Waner	200.00
26	Chalmer Cissell	75.00
27	George Connally	75.00
28	Dick Bartell	75.00
29	Jimmy Foxx	375.00
30	Frank Hogan	75.00
31	Tony Lazzeri	175.00
32	John (Bud) Clancy	75.00
33	Relph Kress	75.00
34	Bob O'Farrell	75.00
35	Al Simmons	175.00
36	Tommy Thevenow	75.00
37	Jimmy Wilson	75.00
38	Fred Brickell	75.00
39	Mark Koenig	75.00
40	Taylor Douthit	75.00
41	Gus Mancuso	75.00
42	Eddie Collins	225.00
43	Lew Fonseca	75.00
44	Jim Bottomley	225.00
45	Larry Benton	75.00
46	Ethan Allen	75.00
47	Henry "Heinie" Manush	175.00
48	Marty McManus	75.00
49	Frank Frisch	350.00
50	Ed Brandt	75.00
51	Charlie Grimm	100.00
52	Andy Cohen	75.00
53	Jack Quinn	75.00
54	Urban (Red) Faber	200.00
55	Lou Gehrig	4000.00
56	John Welch	75.00
57	Bill Walker	75.00
58	Frank (Lefty) O'Doul	150.00
59	Edmund (Bing) Miller	75.00
60	Waite Hoyt	300.00
61	Max Bishop	75.00
62	"Pepper" Martin	150.00
63	Joe Cronin	300.00
64	Burleigh Grimes	200.00
65	Milton Gaston	75.00
66	George Grantham	75.00
67	Guy Bush	75.00
68	Willie Kamm	75.00
69	Gordon (Mickey) Cochrane	300.00
70	Adam Comorosky	75.00
71	Alvin Crowder	75.00
72	Willis Hudlin	75.00
73	Eddie Farrell	75.00
74	Leo Durocher	225.00
75	Walter Stewart	75.00
76	George Walberg	75.00
77	Glenn Wright	90.00

78	Charles (Buddy) Myer	75.00
79	James (Zack) Taylor	75.00
80	George Herman (Babe) Ruth	6000.00
81	D'Arcy (Jake) Flowers	75.00
82	Ray Kolp	75.00
83	Oswald Bluege	75.00
84	Morris (Moe) Berg	150.00
85	Jimmy Foxx	375.00
86	Sam Byrd	75.00
87	Danny Mcfayden (McFayden)	75.00
88	Joe Judge	75.00
89	Joe Sewell	200.00
90	Lloyd Waner	200.00
91	Luke Sewell	75.00
92	Leo Mangum	75.00
93	George Herman (Babe) Ruth	6000.00
94	Al Spohrer	75.00

1934 World Wide Gum

(Canadian Goudey, V354)

Again a near-clone of the American issue, the '34 "Canadian Goudeys" feature the same number (96) and size (2-3/8" x 2-7/8") of cards. Player selection is considerably different, however. Cards #1-48 feature the same front design as the '33 World Wide/Goudey sets. Cards #49-96 have the "Lou Gehrig says..." graphic on the front. Backs can be found in either all-English or English and French.

Mr. Mint Says - These sure look pretty when they are new and bright. A nicely matched set would easily bring $20,000 to $25,000, but once again, the only major interest in singles would be Ruth and Gehrig.

		MT
Complete Set (96):		20000.
Common Player:		75.00

1	Rogers Hornsby	400.00
2	Eddie Morgan	75.00
3	Valentine J. (Val) Picinich	75.00
4	Rabbit Maranville	175.00
5	Flint Rhem	75.00
6	Jim Elliott	75.00
7	Fred (Red) Lucas	75.00
8	Fred Marberry	75.00
9	Clifton Heathcote	75.00
10	Bernie Friberg	75.00
11	Elwood (Woody) English	75.00
12	Carl Reynolds	75.00
13	Ray Benge	75.00
14	Ben Cantwell	75.00
15	Irvin (Bump) Hadley	75.00
16	Herb Pennock	175.00
17	Fred Lindstrom	175.00
18	Edgar (Sam) Rice	200.00
19	Fred Frankhouse	75.00
20	Fred Fitzsimmons	75.00
21	Earl Combs (Earle)	175.00
22	George Uhle	75.00
23	Richard Coffman	75.00
24	Travis C. Jackson	200.00
25	Robert J. Burke	75.00
26	Randy Moore	75.00
27	John Henry (Heinie) Sand	75.00
28	George Herman (Babe) Ruth	6000.00
29	Tris Speaker	300.00
30	Perce (Pat) Malone	75.00
31	Sam Jones	75.00
32	Eppa Rixey	175.00
33	Floyd (Pete) Scott	75.00
34	Pete Jablonowski	75.00
35	Clyde Manion	75.00
36	Dibrell Williams	75.00
37	Glenn Spencer	75.00
38	Ray Kremer	75.00
39	Phil Todt	75.00
40	Russell Rollings	75.00
41	Earl Clark	75.00
42	Jess Petty	75.00
43	Frank O'Rourke	75.00
44	Jesse Haines	75.00
45	Horace Lisenbee	75.00
46	Owen Carroll	75.00
47	Tom Zachary	75.00
48	Charlie Ruffing	200.00
49	Ray Benge	75.00
50	Elwood (Woody) English	75.00
51	Ben Chapman	75.00
52	Joe Kuhel	75.00
53	Bill Terry	250.00
54	Robert (Lefty) Grove	300.00
55	Jerome (Dizzy) Dean	350.00
56	Charles (Chuck) Klein	200.00
57	Charley Gehringer	300.00
58	Jimmy Foxx	375.00
59	Gordon (Mickey) Cochrane	300.00
60	Willie Kamm	75.00
61	Charlie Grimm	100.00
62	Ed Brandt	75.00
63	Tony Piet	75.00
64	Frank Frisch	350.00
65	Alvin Crowder	75.00
66	Frank Hogan	75.00
67	Paul Waner	200.00
68	Henry (Heinie) Manush	175.00
69	Leo Durocher	225.00
70	Floyd Vaughan	175.00
71	Carl Hubbell	250.00
72	Hugh Critz	75.00
73	John (Blondy) Ryan	75.00
74	Roger Cramer	100.00
75	Baxter Jordan	75.00
76	Ed Coleman	75.00
77	Julius Solters	75.00
78	Charles (Chick) Hafey	175.00
79	Larry French	75.00
80	Frank (Don) Hurst	75.00
81	Gerald Walker	75.00
82	Ernie Lombardi	175.00

83	Walter (Huck) Betts	75.00
84	Luke Appling	200.00
85	John Frederick	75.00
86	Fred Walker	75.00
87	Tom Bridges	75.00
88	Dick Porter	75.00
89	John Stone	75.00
90	James (Tex) Carleton	75.00
91	Joe Stripp	75.00
92	Lou Gehrig	4000.00
93	George Earnshaw	75.00
94	Oscar Melillo	75.00
95	Oral Hildebrand	75.00
96	John Allen	75.00

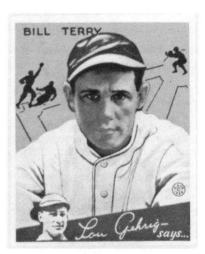

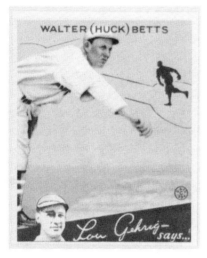

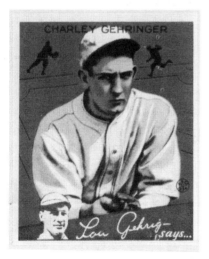

1936 World Wide Gum

(Canadian Goudey, V355)

This black and white Canadian set was issued by World Wide Gum in 1936. The cards measure approximately 2-1/2" by 2-7/8", and the set includes both portrait and action photos. The card number and player's name (appearing in all capital letters) are printed inside a white box below the photo.

No. 96 LOU GEHRIG

Mr. Mint Says - Gotta be tough, I've never owned one. DiMaggio and Gehrig are quick sellers. These cards are rarely seen in top condition.

		MT
Complete Set (134):		23000.
Common Player:		110.00

1	Jimmy Dykes	125.00
2	Paul Waner	250.00
3	Cy Blanton	110.00
4	Sam Leslie	110.00
5	Johnny Louis Vergez	110.00
6	Arky Vaughan	250.00
7	Bill Terry	300.00
8	Joe Moore	110.00
9	Gus Mancuso	110.00
10	Fred Marberry	110.00
11	George Selkirk	110.00
12	Spud Davis	110.00
13	Chuck Klein	250.00
14	Fred Fitzsimmons	110.00
15	Bill Delancey	110.00
16	Billy Herman	
17	George Davis	110.00
18	Rip Collins	

19	Dizzy Dean	
20	Roy Parmelee	110.00
21	Vic Sorrell	110.00
22	Harry Danning	110.00
23	Hal Schumacher	110.00
24	Cy Perkins	110.00
25	Speedy Durocher	300.00
26	Glenn Myatt	110.00
27	Bob Seeds	110.00
28	Jimmy Ripple	110.00
29	Al Schacht	110.00
30	Pete Fox	
31	Del Baker	110.00
32	Flea Clifton	110.00
33	Tommy Bridges	110.00
34	Bill Dickey	400.00
35	Wally Berger	110.00
36	Slick Castleman	110.00
37	Dick Bartell	110.00
38	Red Rolfe	110.00
39	Waite Hoyt	250.00
40	Wes Ferrell	110.00
41	Hank Greenberg	400.00
42	Charlie Gehringer	250.00
43	Goose Goslin	250.00
44	Schoolboy Rowe	110.00
45	Mickey Cochrane	300.00
46	Joe Cronin	300.00
47	Jimmie Foxx	
48	Jerry Walker	110.00
49	Charlie Gelbert	110.00
50	Roy Hayworth (Ray)	110.00
51	Joe DiMaggio	2500.00
52	Billy Rogell	110.00
53	Joe McCarthy	300.00
54	Phil Cavaretta (Cavarretta)	110.00
55	Kiki Cuyler	250.00
56	Lefty Gomez	300.00
57	Gabby Hartnett	250.00
58	Johnny Marcum	
59	Burgess Whitehead	110.00
60	Whitey Whitehill	110.00
61	Buckey Walters	110.00
62	Luke Sewell	110.00
63	Joey Kuhel	110.00
64	Lou Finney	110.00
65	Fred Lindstrom	250.00
66	Paul Derringer	110.00
67	Steve O'Neil (O'Neill)	110.00
68	Mule Haas	110.00
69	Freck Owen	110.00
70	Wild Bill Hallahan	110.00
71	Bill Urbanski	
72	Dan Taylor	110.00
73	Heinie Manush	
74	Jo-Jo White	110.00
75	Mickey Medwick (Ducky)	250.00
76	Joe Vosmik	110.00
77	Al Simmons	250.00
78	Shag Shaughnessy	110.00
79	Harry Smythe	110.00
80	Benny Tate	110.00
81	Billy Rhiel	110.00
82	Lauri Myllykangas	110.00
83	Ben Sankey	110.00
84	Crip Polli	
85	Jim Bottomley	250.00
86	William Clark	
87	Ossie Bluege	110.00

88	Lefty Grove	300.00
89	Charlie Grimm	110.00
90	Ben Chapman	110.00
91	Frank Crosetti	200.00
92	John Pomorski	110.00
93	Jesse Haines	250.00
94	Chick Hafey	250.00
95	Tony Piet	110.00
96	Lou Gehrig	3500.00
97	Bill Jurges	110.00
98	Smead Jolley	110.00
99	Jimmy Wilson	110.00
100	Lonnie Warneke	110.00
101	Lefty Tamulis	110.00
102	Charlie Ruffing	
103	Earl Grace	110.00
104	Rox Lawson	110.00
105	Stan Hack	110.00
106	August Galan	110.00
107	Frank Frisch	250.00
108	Bill McKechnie	250.00
109	Bill Lee	110.00
110	Connie Mack	300.00
111	Frank Reiber	110.00
112	Zeke Bonura	110.00
113	Luke Appling	250.00
114	Monte Pearson	110.00
115	Bob O'Farrell	110.00
116	Marvin Duke	110.00
117	Paul Florence	110.00
118	John Berley	110.00
119	Tom Oliver	110.00
120	Norman Kies	110.00
121	Hal King	110.00
122	Tom Abernathy	110.00
123	Phil Hensick	110.00
124	Roy Schalk (Ray)	250.00
125	Paul Dunlap	110.00
126	Benny Bates	110.00
127	George Puccinelli	110.00
128	Stevie Stevenson	110.00
129	Rabbit Maranville	250.00
130	Bucky Harris	250.00
131	Al Lopez	
132	Buddy Myer	110.00
133	Cliff Bolton	110.00
134	Estel Crabtree	110.00

No. 34 BILL DICKEY

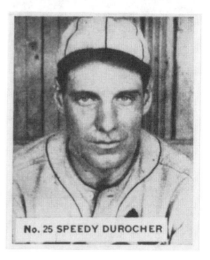

No. 25 SPEEDY DUROCHER

No. 51 JOE DI MAGGIO

303